GEOMETRY

Ray C. Jurgensen

Alfred J. Donnelly

John E. Maier

Gerald R. Rising

EDITORIAL ADVISER
Albert E. Meder, Jr.

HOUGHTON MIFFLIN COMPANY / BOSTON

ATLANTA   DALLAS   GENEVA, ILL.   HOPEWELL, N.J.   PALO ALTO

THE AUTHORS

Ray C. Jurgensen, Chairman of the Mathematics Department and holder of the Eppley Chair of Mathematics, Culver Military Academy and Culver Academy for Girls, Culver, Indiana.

Alfred J. Donnelly, Master Instructor and holder of the William Pitt Oakes Chair of Mathematics, Culver Military Academy and Culver Academy for Girls.

John E. Maier, formerly Master Instructor in Mathematics at Culver Military Academy and Culver Academy for Girls.

Gerald R. Rising, Professor and Chairman, Department of Instruction, State University of New York at Buffalo.

EDITORIAL ADVISER

Albert E. Meder, Jr., Dean and Vice Provost and Professor of Mathematics, Emeritus, Rutgers University, The State University of New Jersey.

The authors wish to express their appreciation to **Miriam M. Schaefer** for the work she did in preparing the optional computer sections for this text.

CONTENTS

Chapter 6 Similar Polygons 189

Chapter 7 Right Triangles 233

SYMBOLS

adj. ∡	adjacent angles (p. 38)		side of a square (p. 313; p. 319; p. 311)
∠, ∡	angle, angles (p. 37)		
alt. ext. ∡	alternate exterior angles (p. 78)	l	length of slant height (p. 333)
alt. int. ∡	alternate interior angles (p. 78)	$\overleftrightarrow{RS}$	line containing points R and S (p. 1)
a	apothem (p. 319)		
$\overarc{AB}$	arc with endpoints A and B (p. 280)	$\rightarrow$	mapping, is mapped into (p. 428)
A	area (p. 311)	$m\angle AOB$	measure of $\angle AOB$ (p. 41)
B	area of base (p. 330)	$m\,\overarc{AB}$	measure of $\overarc{AB}$ (p. 280)
$\overline{XZY}$	point Z lies between points X and Y (p. 11)	m	meters (p. 325)
		n-gon	polygon with n sides (p. 103)
cm	centimeter (p. 23)	(x, y)	ordered pair (p. 391)
⊙ O	circle with center O (p. 271)	∥	parallel, is parallel to (p. 77)
C	circumference (p. 322)	▱	parallelogram (p. 155)
comp. ∡	complementary angles (p. 46)	p	perimeter (p. 198)
°	composition of mappings (p. 448)	⊥	perpendicular, is perpendicular to (p. 54)
≅	congruent, is congruent to (p. 10)	π	pi (p. 323)
		quad.	quadrilateral (p. 159)
≇	not congruent, is not congruent to (p. 10)	r	radius (p. 323)
		$\dfrac{a}{b}$, $a:b$	ratio of a to b (p. 189)
corr. ∡	corresponding angles (p. 78, p. 118)	$\overrightarrow{AB}$	ray with endpoint A, passing through point B (p. 10)
↔	corresponds to (p. 117)		
cos	cosine (p. 254)	rect.	rectangle (p. 163)
cm³	cubic centimeters (p. 331)	M_j	reflection in line j (p. 433)
°	degrees (p. 41)	rt. ∠	right angle (p. 46)
d	diameter; distance; length of diagonal (p. 323; p. 14; p. 313)	rt. △	right triangle (p. 127)
		$R_{O,\alpha}$	rotation about point O through $\alpha°$ (p. 452)
$D_{O,k}$	dilation with center O and scale factor k (p. 460)	$\overline{RS}$	segment joining points R and S (p. 10)
H_O	half-turn about point O (p. 438)	~	similar, is similar to (p. 196)
≐	is approximately equal to (p. 251)	sin	sine (p. 254)
		m	slope (p. 401)
isos. △	isosceles triangle (p. 97)	cm²	square centimeters (p. 310)
km	kilometers (p. 274)	$\sqrt{x}$	positive square root of x (p. 233)
L.A.	lateral area (p. 330)		
h	length of altitude, height (p. 311)	supp. ∡	supplementary angles (p. 46)
		tan	tangent (p. 250)
b	length of base (p. 311)	T.A.	total area (p. 330)
RS	length of $\overline{RS}$, distance between points R and S (p. 9)	$T_{XX'}$	translation that maps X into X' (p. 456)
s	length of a side of an equilateral triangle; length of a side of a regular polygon; length of a	trans.	transversal (p. 78)
		△, ▲	triangle, triangles (p. 96)
		vert. ∡	vertical angles (p. 38)
		V	volume (p. 331)

ELEMENTS OF GEOMETRY

Points, Lines, and Planes

Objectives

1. Recognize the terms *point, line,* and *plane* as being undefined.
2. Draw representations of points, lines, and planes.
3. Use the terms: lies on, lies in, contains, intersects, intersection.
4. Define collinear points and coplanar points.
5. Distinguish between postulates and theorems.
6. Select the appropriate postulate, from the first five, to support assertions.
7. State and apply the first three theorems.

1-1 *Undefined Terms and Basic Definitions*

Points, *lines*, and *planes* are basic to geometry. The following paragraphs explain how the terms are used.

   A point is pictured by a dot. A dot must have some size, but the point it represents does not have any size. Points are named by capital letters. The pictured points, *C* and *D*, are distinct, or different, points. In this book *two points* will mean two different points, *three points* will mean three different points, and so on. A similar policy will be followed with regard to other geometric objects.

D •

C •

   A line extends indefinitely, as the arrowheads in the picture of a line suggest. A line, containing infinitely many points, is considered to be a set of points. Because the line shown below contains points *R* and *S*, it can be designated by $\overleftrightarrow{RS}$ (read "line *R, S*"). The line can also be called *line j*. Notice that a lowercase letter is used in this case.

A plane is a flat surface. Such things as windowpanes and desk tops suggest planes. However, a windowpane has thickness, whereas a plane does not. Also, a windowpane is limited in size, whereas a plane extends indefinitely. Since it is not possible to draw a picture that extends indefinitely, a plane is usually represented by a four-sided figure.

Because a plane is a set of points, the intersection of two planes is the set of points shared by the planes. When the intersection of two planes actually contains points, we say that the planes *intersect*. When the intersection is the empty set, we say that the planes are *parallel*.

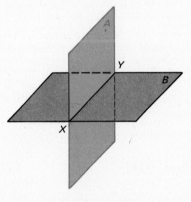

$A \cap B = \overleftrightarrow{XY}$

Planes A and B intersect.

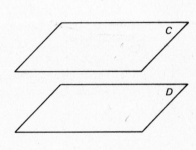

$C \cap D = \emptyset$

Planes C and D are parallel.

The terms point, line, and plane are called *undefined* terms. Other terms of geometry are defined. Notice that the definitions below are based on the undefined terms.

Space: The set of all points.

Collinear (ko-**lin**-ee-er) points: A set of points that lie on one line.

Coplanar (ko-**plain**-er) points: A set of points that lie on one plane.

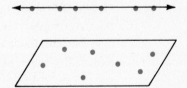

Alongside the figures shown below are expressions used to describe relationships between points, lines, and planes.

A lies in j.
A lies on j.
A is contained in j.
j contains A.
j is drawn through A.

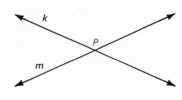

k and m intersect in P.
k and m intersect at P.
$k \cap m = P$
P is the intersection of k and m.

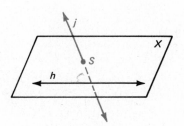

S and h lie in X.
X contains S and h.
X intersects, or cuts, j at S.
j intersects X at S.
j and h do not intersect.
$j \cap h = \emptyset$

Oral Exercises

1. Suppose there is a line, $\overleftrightarrow{RS}$. Does $\overleftrightarrow{RS}$ end at point S?
2. Does a plane have edges?
3. Suppose there is a line g. Can there be a rectangle so large that all of g lies inside the rectangle?
4. Suppose point P lies in plane X. Are there some points in X that are a million miles from P?
5. How many points does a plane contain?
6. How many lines does a plane contain?
7. How many points does a line contain?
8. Can two lines contain a given point?
9. How many lines can contain a given point?
10. Can two planes contain a given line?
11. Can three planes contain a given line?
12. Suppose that the intersection of two planes is the empty set. Do we say that the planes intersect?

Written
Exercises

Classify each statement as true or false.

A

1. $j \cap \overleftrightarrow{AC} = B$
2. $j \cap \overleftrightarrow{DC} = \emptyset$
3. $j \cap P = \overrightarrow{AC}$
4. P contains $\overleftrightarrow{DC}$.
5. P contains X.
6. $\overleftrightarrow{AC}$ lies in P.
7. A lies in both P and j.
8. Another name for $\overleftrightarrow{AC}$ is $\overleftrightarrow{BC}$.
9. Points A, B, and C are collinear.
10. Points A, B, C, and D are coplanar.
11. It is possible to draw a line that contains points D and X.
12. It is possible to draw a line that contains points A, C, and X.
13. It is possible for a plane to contain points A, C, and X.
14. It is possible for a plane to contain points A, D, and X.
15. It is possible for a plane to contain points X, A, B, and C.
16. Any line that lies in plane P must intersect $\overleftrightarrow{AC}$.

Exs. 1–24

B

17. A line containing points A and D must lie in plane P.
18. Any line that intersects line j at point B must lie in plane P.
19. Any plane, other than P, that contains point B must intersect plane P.
20. Any plane that contains point X must intersect plane P.
21. Every plane that contains point X also contains line j.
22. Every plane that contains both points A and B also contains point C.
23. Every plane that contains both points A and D must also contain point B.
24. Every plane that contains line j intersects $\overleftrightarrow{DC}$.

Draw and label a figure that meets the conditions stated. Use a straight-edge.

25. Line k intersects plane M in point P.
26. Point A lies outside plane X. Three lines j, k, and m all contain A and inter-sect X.
27. Plane B and line n not contained in B both intersect line s at point C.
28. Planes Y and Z intersect.

C

29. Two nonintersecting planes R and S are both intersected by a line j.
30. Lines c and d intersect. Plane X contains c but does not contain d.
31. Three planes X, Y, and Z all contain line j.
32. Planes X and Y intersect in line b, planes X and Z intersect in line c, and planes Y and Z intersect in line d.

4 *GEOMETRY*

1-2 *First Postulates and Theorems*

Recall, from algebra, two statements that are true for all real numbers *a* and *b*.

$$a + b = b + a \qquad a(-b) = -ab$$

The first statement, assumed without proof, is a *postulate* of algebra. The second, which can be proved, is a *theorem*. In mathematics, basic assumptions are called axioms, or postulates. Statements that are proved are called theorems.

Five postulates about points, lines, and planes are listed below. Additional postulates of geometry will be introduced from time to time.

POSTULATE 1 A line contains at least two points; a plane contains at least three points not all in one line; space contains at least four points not all in one plane.

POSTULATE 2 Through any two points there is exactly one line.

POSTULATE 3 Through any three points not on one line there is exactly one plane.

POSTULATE 4 If two points lie in a plane, then the line joining the points lies in that plane.

POSTULATE 5 If two planes intersect, then their intersection is a line.

It is possible to prove some theorems about points, lines, and planes on the basis of the first five postulates. The theorems stated below will be used in proofs that come later. You will not, however, be asked to study proofs of these theorems.

THEOREM 1-1 If two lines intersect, they intersect in exactly one point.

Given: Lines *j* and *k* intersect.

Prove: Lines *j* and *k* intersect in exactly one point (point *P* in the diagram).

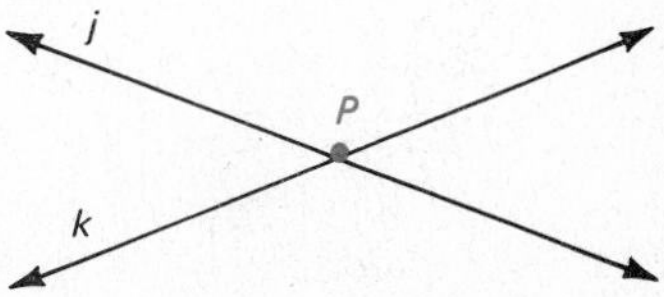

THEOREM 1-2   If a point lies outside a line, exactly one plane contains the line and the point.

Given: Point *A* outside line *l*.

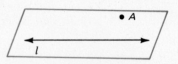

Prove: Exactly one plane contains both *A* and *l*.

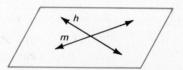

THEOREM 1-3   If two lines intersect, exactly one plane contains both lines.

Given: Lines *h* and *m* intersect.

Prove: Exactly one plane contains both *h* and *m*.

The phrase *exactly one* appears several times in the postulates and theorems. You can use the phrase *one and only one* instead. For example, two correct forms of Postulate 2 are:

Through any two points there is exactly one line.
Through any two points there is one and only one line.

Oral Exercises   Restate the postulate or theorem, using the phrase *one and only one*.

1. Postulate 3   3. Theorem 1-2
2. Theorem 1-1   4. Theorem 1-3

5. How do theorems differ from postulates?
6. Which word means the same thing as the word *axiom*—the word *postulate* or the word *theorem?*
7. A line *j* and two points *A* and *B* are given. Do points *A* and *B* have to lie on *j*? How many lines contain both *A* and *B*?
8. Three noncollinear points *C*, *D*, and *E* are given. Is there some line that both *C* and *D* lie on? Is there some line that all three points lie on?
9. Three points *G*, *H*, and *K* are given. Does it follow from Postulate 3 that exactly one plane contains points *G*, *H*, and *K*?
10. Would it seem wise to take two contradictory statements as postulates?

In the figure, point *X* lies in both planes *P* and *S*.

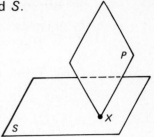

11. Does the diagram show all of plane *P*? All of plane *S*?
12. Do planes *P* and *S* intersect?
13. Is it correct to say that the intersection of planes *P* and *S* is point *X*?
14. State the postulate that tells what the intersection of planes *P* and *S* must be.

Written Exercises

Write in full the postulate that justifies the statement.

A

1. Points *A* and *B* lie in one and only one line.
2. Noncollinear points *R*, *S*, and *T* lie in one and only one plane.
3. When plane *Z* contains line *j*, plane *Z* also contains some point not on *j*.
4. When points *A* and *B* lie in plane *Y*, $\overleftrightarrow{AB}$ lies in *Y*.

Draw a figure to represent the situation described.

5. Three points on a line.
6. Three points not on any line.
7. Four points on a plane.
8. Four points not on any one plane.

Classify each statement as true or false.

9. An undefined term can be used in a postulate.
10. Postulates are proved.
11. Two planes can intersect in exactly one point.
12. When a line lies in a plane, every point in the line lies in the plane.
13. If point *A* and line *j* both lie in plane *P*, then point *A* must lie on line *j*.
14. Two intersecting lines can have two points in common.
15. A set of points must be collinear if there is a plane that contains all points of the set.
16. Given any two lines, exactly one plane contains both lines.

In the figure, *XYZW* is a *square*. Point *A* lies outside the plane of that square. State whether the set of points is collinear; noncollinear but coplanar; or noncoplanar.

17. {*X, B, Z*}
18. {*A, B, X*}
19. {*A, W, B, Y*}
20. {*A, X, Z, Y*}

State whether the lines are coplanar.

21. $\overleftrightarrow{AW}$, $\overleftrightarrow{AY}$
22. $\overleftrightarrow{AW}$, $\overleftrightarrow{AY}$, $\overleftrightarrow{AX}$
23. $\overleftrightarrow{ZW}$, $\overleftrightarrow{ZB}$, $\overleftrightarrow{ZY}$
24. $\overleftrightarrow{AX}$, $\overleftrightarrow{AZ}$, $\overleftrightarrow{XZ}$

B 25. Given: Points R and S both lie in plane X.

     a. What can you conclude about $\overleftrightarrow{RS}$?

     b. State the postulate that justifies your conclusion.

26. Given: Planes Y and Z both contain point P.

     a. What can you conclude about the intersection of Y and Z?

     b. State the postulate that justifies your conclusion.

27. Given: Line m contains both points X and Y.

             Line n contains both points X and Y.

     a. What can you conclude about m and n?

     b. State the postulate that justifies your conclusion.

28. Given: The vertices of square $ABCD$ lie in plane Z.

     a. What can you conclude, with respect to Z, about each side of the square?

     b. State the postulate that justifies your conclusion.

29. When two lines intersect and one of them lies in a plane Z, must the other line also lie in Z?

30. When three lines intersect in one point, must all three lines lie in one plane?

C 31. Draw figures showing four points A, B, C, D in such positions that $\overleftrightarrow{AB}$, $\overleftrightarrow{AC}$, $\overleftrightarrow{AD}$, $\overleftrightarrow{BC}$, $\overleftrightarrow{BD}$, $\overleftrightarrow{CD}$

     a. are six different lines;

     b. are only four lines;

     c. are all the same line.

32. Draw figures showing two essentially different ways in which three noncoplanar lines can be coplanar in pairs.

33. Think of the five statements formed by replacing the word "line" with the word "circle" in Postulates 1–5. Classify the five statements as true or false.

34. Explain why a line k cannot intersect a plane Z in two different points P and Q. *Hint:* Use Postulate 4 in your explanation.

Self-Test Using points, lines, or planes shown in the diagram, complete each sentence in any one correct way.

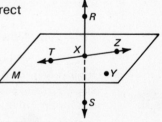

1. __?__ lies on __?__ .
2. __?__ lies in __?__ .
3. __?__ contains __?__ .
4. __?__ intersects __?__ .
5. The intersection of plane M and $\overleftrightarrow{RS}$ is __?__ .
6. Four points that are coplanar but not collinear are points __?__ .

                                       Exs. 1–6

7. Suppose Sally talks about line j and John talks about line k. Can you be sure that lines j and k are different lines?

8. Suppose this text uses the phrase "two planes." Can you be sure that the planes are different planes?

In Exercises 9–12, three noncollinear points *A*, *B*, *C* are given. State the postulate that justifies the assertion.

9. There is a line containing both *A* and *B*.
10. There is a plane containing points *A*, *B*, and *C*.
11. $\overleftrightarrow{AB}$ lies in the plane referred to in Exercise 10.
12. If two planes *X* and *Y* both contain point *B*, then *X* ∩ *Y* is a line.

Complete the statements.

13. If a point lies outside a line, exactly one __?__ .
14. If two lines intersect, exactly one __?__ .

Check your answers with those printed at the back of the book.

Subsets of a Line

Objectives

1. Identify lines, segments, and rays.
2. Use symbols to name lines, segments, rays, and distances.
3. Define congruent segments, midpoint of a segment, and bisector of a segment.
4. Interpret the symbol $\overline{NTJ}$.
5. Use the words coordinate and graph.
6. Apply the Ruler Postulate.
7. State and apply the theorem about the existence of a point that is on a given ray and is at a given distance from the endpoint of the ray.
8. State and apply the midpoint theorem.

1-3 *Segments and Rays*

Suppose different people measure to determine how far apart two given points are. The measurements should be approximately equal and should be close to a *measure* you think of as the true distance.

POSTULATE 6	For any two points there is a unique positive number called the **distance** between the points.

The distance between points *R* and *S* is expressed by *RS* or by *SR*.

A point between two other points: Point *B*, on $\overleftrightarrow{AC}$, is said to lie between points *A* and *C* if and only if $AB + BC = AC$.

Segment: Given any two points *R* and *S*, segment *RS* is the set of points consisting of *R* and *S* and all points that lie between *R* and *S*. Segment *RS* is denoted by $\overline{RS}$. Points *R* and *S* are the *endpoints* of $\overline{RS}$.

Ray: Ray *AB*, denoted by $\overrightarrow{AB}$, is the union of $\overline{AB}$ and the set of points *X* for which it is true that *B* lies between *A* and *X*. Notice that the *endpoint* of $\overrightarrow{AB}$ is point *A*, the point named first.

Opposite Rays: $\overrightarrow{SR}$ and $\overrightarrow{ST}$ are called opposite rays if *S* lies on $\overleftrightarrow{RT}$ between *R* and *T*.

Congruent Segments: Segments with equal lengths.
Here $AB = XY$, so $\overline{AB}$ and $\overline{XY}$ are *congruent*.
$\overline{AB}$ is congruent to $\overline{XY}$. ($\overline{AB} \cong \overline{XY}$)
$\overline{XY}$ is congruent to $\overline{AB}$. ($\overline{XY} \cong \overline{AB}$)
The symbol $\ncong$ is read, "is not congruent to."

Midpoint of a Segment: Point *M* is the midpoint of $\overline{RS}$ if *M* lies on $\overline{RS}$ and $RM = MS$.

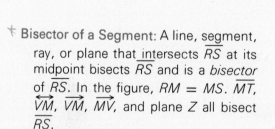

Bisector of a Segment: A line, segment, ray, or plane that intersects $\overline{RS}$ at its midpoint bisects $\overline{RS}$ and is a *bisector* of $\overline{RS}$. In the figure, $RM = MS$. $\overline{MT}$, $\overleftrightarrow{VM}$, $\overrightarrow{VM}$, $\overrightarrow{MV}$, and plane *Z* all bisect $\overline{RS}$.

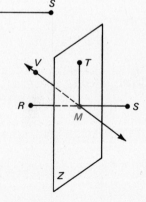

A symbol for Between: To abbreviate the statement: "Point Z lies between points X and Y" we shall write $\overline{XZY}$. A bar can also be used to indicate that four or more collinear points are listed in order.

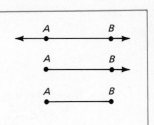

$\overleftrightarrow{AB}$ line containing A and B

$\overrightarrow{AB}$ ray with endpoint A, through B

$\overline{AB}$ segment joining A and B

AB length of $\overline{AB}$; distance between A and B

Oral Exercises

1. How many endpoints does a segment have?
   How many endpoints does a line have?
   How many endpoints does a ray have?
2. Which point is the endpoint of $\overrightarrow{JK}$, point J or point K?
3. Read each of the names: $\overleftrightarrow{HT}$ $\overline{HT}$ HT $\overrightarrow{HT}$
4. Which of the following symbols does not denote a set of points?
   $\overleftrightarrow{AB}$ CD $\overrightarrow{EF}$ $\overline{GH}$
5. Two rays have the same endpoint. Must they be opposite rays?
6. Given: $JX = KX$. Can you conclude that X is the midpoint of $\overline{JK}$?

Given $\overline{EZF}$.

7. Do $\overrightarrow{ZE}$ and $\overrightarrow{EZ}$ name the same ray?
8. Do $\overrightarrow{EZ}$ and $\overrightarrow{EF}$ name the same ray?
9. Name a pair of opposite rays. Name three segments.
10. Give a simpler name for $\overrightarrow{EZ} \cap \overline{ZF}$; for $\overrightarrow{EZ} \cup \overrightarrow{ZF}$; for $\overrightarrow{ZE} \cup \overrightarrow{ZF}$.

Written Exercises

Classify each statement as true or false.
Given: Point Y is the midpoint of $\overline{RS}$.

A

1. S lies between R and Y.
2. $\overrightarrow{YS}$ contains R.
3. $RY = YS$
4. $\overline{RY} \cong \overline{YS}$
5. $RY = \frac{1}{2}RS$
6. $\overline{RY} \cap \overline{YS} = \overline{RS}$
7. $\overrightarrow{RY} \cup \overline{RS} = \overrightarrow{RY}$
8. $\overrightarrow{RY} \cup \overrightarrow{YS} = \overline{RS}$

Given: B is the midpoint of $\overline{AC}$; C is the midpoint of $\overline{AD}$.

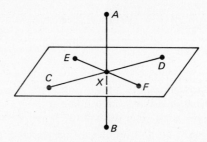

9. If $AD = 20$, $AB = \underline{\ ?\ }$.

10. If $BC = 13$, $CD = \underline{\ ?\ }$.

11. If $AB = 3\frac{1}{7}$, $AD = \underline{\ ?\ }$.

12. If $AD = 21$, $AB = \underline{\ ?\ }$.

13. If $AD = 4.4$, $BD = \underline{\ ?\ }$.

14. If $AB = 5.1$, $CD = \underline{\ ?\ }$.

15. If $AD = 18$, $AB + CD = \underline{\ ?\ }$.

✦16. If $CD = 11$, $BD = \underline{\ ?\ }$.

Given: $\overline{AB}$, $\overline{CD}$, and $\overline{EF}$ bisect each other at X.
Complete the statements.

17. $CX = \underline{\ ?\ }$; $\underline{\ ?\ } = XF$; $AX = \underline{\ ?\ }$

18. $\overline{CX} \cong \underline{\ ?\ }$; $\underline{\ ?\ } \cong \overline{XF}$; $\overline{AX} \cong \underline{\ ?\ }$

19. If $AX = EX$, then $AB = \underline{\ ?\ }$ and $\overline{AB} \cong \underline{\ ?\ }$.

20. If $XD = XF$, then $CD = \underline{\ ?\ }$ and $\overline{CD} \cong \underline{\ ?\ }$.

In Exercises 21–32, draw two segments, $\overline{RS}$ and $\overline{TW}$, so that the conditions are satisfied.

B 21. $\overline{RS}$ and $\overline{TW}$ lie on one line.

22. $\overline{RS}$ and $\overline{TW}$ intersect, but neither segment bisects the other.

23. $\overline{RS}$ and $\overline{TW}$ bisect each other.

24. $\overline{RS}$ bisects $\overline{TW}$, but $\overline{TW}$ does not bisect $\overline{RS}$.

25. $\overline{RS}$ and $\overline{TW}$ do not intersect, but $\overrightarrow{RS}$ and $\overrightarrow{TW}$ do intersect.

26. $\overline{RS}$ and $\overline{TW}$ do not intersect, but $\overrightarrow{RS}$ and $\overrightarrow{WT}$ do intersect.

27. $\overline{RS}$ and $\overline{TW}$ are coplanar, but $\overleftrightarrow{RS}$ and $\overleftrightarrow{TW}$ do not intersect.

28. $\overline{RS}$ and $\overline{TW}$ are clearly not coplanar.

29. $\overline{RS} \cup \overline{TW} = \overline{RS}$

30. $\overline{RS} \cup \overline{TW} = \overline{RW}$

31. $\overline{RS} \cap \overline{TW} = \overline{TW}$

32. $\overline{RS} \cap \overline{TW} = \overline{RS}$

C Given: *C* is the midpoint of $\overline{AB}$; *D* is the midpoint of $\overline{AC}$;
$\quad\quad\quad$ *E* is the midpoint of $\overline{AD}$; *F* is the midpoint of $\overline{AE}$;
$\quad\quad\quad$ *G* is the midpoint of $\overline{AF}$; *H* is the midpoint of $\overline{AG}$.

33. If *AB* = 28, *AH* = ___?___ .
34. If *AB* = 3.6, *CE* = ___?___ .
35. If *HF* = 12, *FC* = ___?___ .

36. If *GC* = 1, *HB* = ___?___ .
37. If *AH* + *DC* = 34, *AB* = ___?___ .
38. If *GH* + *BC* = 66, *EC* = ___?___ .

1-4 *The Ruler Postulate*

Recall the number lines you used in algebra.

In the diagram:
$\quad$ The *coordinate* of point *J* is −2.
$\quad$ The *graph* of the number −2 is point *J*.
$\quad$ The *origin* is point *K*. (The origin has coordinate 0.)
$\quad$ *MR* = 5 − 3 = 2; $\quad$ *JK* = 0 − (−2) = 2; $\quad$ *JM* = 3 − (−2) = 5;
$\quad$ *KR* = 5 − 0 = 5

$\quad$ Suppose there is a number line on which points *C* and *D* have coordinates *u* and *v*. You cannot say "*CD* = *u* − *v*" unless you know that *u* − *v* is a positive number, and you cannot say "*CD* = *v* − *u*" unless you know that *v* − *u* is a positive number. However, you can say "*CD* = |*u* − *v*|."
$\quad$ The use of a number line involves the following basic assumption.

POSTULATE 7 (THE RULER POSTULATE)
$\quad$ The points on a line can be paired with the real numbers in such a way that:
1. Any desired point is paired with zero;
2. The distance between any two points is equal to the absolute value of the difference of the numbers paired with the points.

$$AB = |x - y| \quad\quad AB = |y - x|$$

The Ruler Postulate leads to the following theorems.

THEOREM 1-4 On a ray there is exactly one point at a given distance d from the endpoint of the ray.

Given: $\overrightarrow{RS}$; a distance d.

Prove: There is exactly one point X on $\overrightarrow{RS}$ such that $RX = d$.

Outline of Proof:

Using the Ruler Postulate, pair point R with zero and other points on $\overrightarrow{RS}$ with positive numbers. Exactly one point (call it X) is paired with the number d. $RX = |d - 0| = d$.

THEOREM 1-5 A segment has exactly one midpoint.

Given: $\overline{AB}$

Prove: $\overline{AB}$ has exactly one midpoint.

Outline of Proof:

Using the Ruler Postulate, pair point A with zero and points on $\overline{AB}$ with positive numbers. B is paired with some positive number (call it j). Exactly one point (call it M) is paired with the number $\frac{1}{2}j$.

$$AM = |\tfrac{1}{2}j - 0| = \tfrac{1}{2}j \qquad MB = |j - \tfrac{1}{2}j| = \tfrac{1}{2}j$$

Since $AM = MB$, point M is the midpoint of $\overline{AB}$.

Oral Exercises

Express the number in a simpler way.

EXAMPLE. $|2 - 5|$

SOLUTION: $|2 - 5| = |-3| = 3$

1. $|8|$
2. $|-8|$
3. $|0|$
4. $|-3.5|$

5. $|13 - 0|$
6. $|0 - 13|$
7. $|-5|$
8. $-|5|$

9. $|8 - 2|$
10. $|2 - 8|$
11. $|3 - (-2)|$
12. $|-9 + (+1)|$

In Exercises 13–26, name the point, or state the number, described.

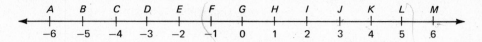

13. The graph of the number 4
14. The coordinate of point D
15. The origin
16. The coordinate of the origin
17. The endpoint of $\overrightarrow{EJ}$ −2 or E
18. The endpoint of $\overrightarrow{JE}$ 3 on J
19. The midpoint of $\overline{HL}$ J+3

20. The midpoint of $\overline{CK}$ J
21. The point on $\overrightarrow{DM}$ two units from D F
22. The point on $\overrightarrow{MD}$ two units from M K
23. The distance between points B and F 4
24. The length of $\overline{LF}$ 6
25. Two points three units from point G J D
26. Two points four units from point E A I

Written Exercises

The numbers given are the coordinates of two points on the number line. State the distance between the points.

A
1. 4 and 11
2. −6 and 0
3. −13 and −21 8
4. −9 and 4 13
5. 8.6 and 3.4 5.2
6. −5.1 and −3.7

7. Is there a greatest real number? No
8. Is there an endpoint on the number line? No
9. Does 0 represent a real number? Yes
10. Does $\frac{1}{0}$ represent a real number? No
11. Refer to Theorem 1-4. Can the distance d be such that:
    a. Point X does not lie on $\overline{RS}$?
    b. Point X is the same point as point S?
12. Refer to Theorem 1-4. Suppose $d = \frac{1}{2}RS$. Describe the position of point X.

In Exercises 13–16, use the sets $A = \{-4, -3, 0, 1, 5\}$ and $B = \{-3, -2, 0, 2\}$. For each exercise draw a new number line. On it graph the points whose coordinates are the elements of the indicated sets.

13. A
14. B
15. $A \cap B$
16. $A \cup B$

In Exercises 17–22, the coordinates of the endpoints of a segment are given. State: (a) the length of the segment, (b) the coordinate of the midpoint of the segment.

B
17. 9 and 1
18. −2 and 6
19. −3 and −7$\frac{1}{2}$

20. 2 and $\square\frac{1}{3}$
21. 0 and −2$\frac{1}{7}$
22. −2$\frac{1}{4}$ and −2$\frac{1}{5}$

In Exercises 23–34, state whether the sentence becomes a true statement when x is replaced by 5.

23. $3x > 12$

24. $x^2 = 25$

25. $-2x < -11$

26. $12 - x > x$

27. $x(x - 5) = 0$

28. $(x - 4)(x - 6) > 0$

29. $|-x| = 5$

30. $|1 - x| = 4$

31. $x - |x| = 10$

32. $|x| = |-x|$

33. $\dfrac{1}{x} < \dfrac{1}{x^2}$

34. $x^4 > 500$

In Exercises 35–40, state the solution set.

EXAMPLE. $|2x + 3| = 17$

SOLUTION: $\begin{array}{llll} 2x + 3 = 17 & \text{or} & 2x + 3 = -17 \\ 2x = 14 & & 2x = -20 \\ x = 7 & & x = -10 \end{array}$

The solution set is $\{7, -10\}$.

C 35. $|x + 5| = 9$

36. $|x - 4| = 9$

37. $|3x| = 15$

38. $\left|\dfrac{x}{-4}\right| = 2$

39. $|3x - 5| = 26$

40. $|4x + 2| = 26$

41. On a number line, point R has coordinate 2 and point S has coordinate 6. A is the midpoint of $\overline{RS}$, B is the midpoint of $\overline{RA}$, C is the midpoint of $\overline{RB}$, and D is the midpoint of $\overline{RC}$. Find the coordinate of point D.

42. Repeat Exercise 41, but let the coordinate of R be 3 and the coordinate of S be -2.

Self-Test Match the entries in the two columns.

1. A line

2. A distance

3. A segment

4. A ray

a. $\overline{AB}$

b. RS

c. $\overrightarrow{CD}$

d. $\overleftrightarrow{PQ}$

On a number line, point A has coordinate 6, point B coordinate -2.

5. The length of $\overline{AB}$ is ___?___ .

6. The midpoint of $\overline{AB}$ has coordinate ___?___ .

7. The point that lies on $\overrightarrow{AB}$ and is 5 units from A has coordinate ___?___ .

8. It is given that the graph of the number -4 is point K. State which of the three expressions is correct: $\overline{ABK}$, $\overline{AKB}$, $\overline{KAB}$.

9. Complete the definition. Congruent segments are segments ___?___ .

10. Complete the theorem. Every segment has exactly ___?___ .

Check your answers with those printed at the back of the book.

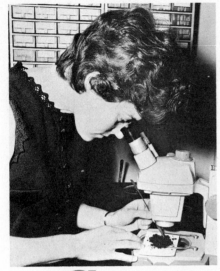

Careers

Geology

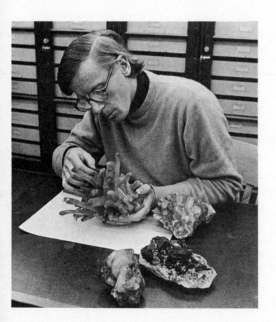

A geologist is an environmental scientist who specializes in studying the structure, composition, and history of the earth's crust. Geologists often spend a large amount of time in the field, examining rocks, minerals, and fossils. By drilling deep into the earth, they can discover the nature of rock layers under the earth's surface. This information helps locate deposits of oil, coal, and water.

Other geologists spend considerable time in laboratories analyzing mineral samples obtained in the field. Geologic research into the structure and properties of minerals is aided by x-ray techniques and complex instruments such as the petrographic microscope, which permits close study of rock formations.

In geology, as in all the sciences, a working knowledge of mathematics is an essential tool. Some of the basic geometric solids you will study in this book are commonly found in crystalline structures, such as those in the photograph on the left.

Proofs in Geometry

Objectives

1. Distinguish between deductive and inductive thinking.
2. Use each type of thinking appropriately.
3. Recognize the hypothesis and conclusion of a conditional.
4. State the converse of an if-then statement.
5. List four kinds of reasons that can be used in proofs.
6. Write simple proofs in two-column form.

1-5 Deductive Reasoning

Suppose you know that the following two statements are true.

1. Every convention delegate sings well.
2. Mrs. Lang is a convention delegate.

You can conclude:

3. Mrs. Lang sings well.

Once any reasonable person accepts the truth of Statements 1 and 2, he knows that Statement 3 is also true. Statement 3 is a *conclusion* that follows from the other statements.

The kind of reasoning illustrated above is called deductive reasoning. When, having accepted some statements, you reason from them to a conclusion, you reason *deductively* (dee-**duck**-tiv-ly). You *deduce*. The process is called *deduction*, and sometimes the conclusion itself is called a deduction.

In contrast to deductive reasoning, there is *inductive* thinking. Consider a baseball player who tries a new way of gripping a bat. In his next five times at bat he gets five hits. He decides: "The new grip is better." His decision, which may be incorrect, is based upon inductive thinking. Induction is the process of observing individual cases and then stating a general principle suggested by them.

Some of the discoveries that mathematicians make are made by inductive thinking. Of course mathematicians don't stop with guesses; they strive for conclusions that are certain. When they prove that statements are true, they use deductive reasoning.

In our deductive work in geometry, we shall permit ourselves to use postulates and theorems of algebra. We shall often use properties such as the commutative property without particular mention. The properties we shall use most often, and refer to by name, are listed below. In these statements, *a*, *b*, *c*, and *d* denote any real numbers.

Postulates and Theorems of Equality

Reflexive Property	$a = a$
Symmetric Property	If $a = b$, then $b = a$.
Transitive Property	If $a = b$ and $b = c$, then $a = c$.
Addition Property	If $a = b$ and $c = d$, then $a + c = b + d$.
Subtraction Property	If $a = b$ and $c = d$, then $a - c = b - d$.
Multiplication Property	If $a = b$ and $c = d$, then $ac = bd$.
Division Property	If $a = b$ and $c = d$, and $c \neq 0$, then $\dfrac{a}{c} = \dfrac{b}{d}$.

Postulates and Theorems of Inequality

Transitive Property	If $a < b$ and $b < c$, then $a < c$.
Addition Property	If $a < b$, then $a + c < b + c$.
Subtraction Property	If $a < b$, then $a - c < b - c$.
Multiplication Property	If $a < b$ and $c > 0$, then $ac < bc$.
	If $a < b$ and $c < 0$, then $ac > bc$.
Division Property	If $a < b$ and $c > 0$, then $\dfrac{a}{c} < \dfrac{b}{c}$.
	If $a < b$ and $c < 0$, then $\dfrac{a}{c} > \dfrac{b}{c}$.

The Substitution Principle

If $a = b$, then "a" may be replaced by "b" in any equation or inequality.

Oral Exercises

Tell whether the thinking process is deductive or inductive.

1. The first four times Susan ate peanuts she became ill. Her mother decided: Peanuts are bad for Susan.

2. On each of his first days in a new town, a man saw messy streets. He said: "This is a dirty town."

3. A girl is fifteen years old. She points out: "Three years from now I'll be eighteen."

4. A boy remarks: "If a number is greater than ten, then twice that number is greater than twenty."

5. Knowing that, for all real numbers c and d, $c - d = c + (-d)$, you decide $3 - 7 = 3 + (-7)$.

6. Tom notices: $2^2 = 4$ and $4 > 2$; $3^2 = 9$ and $9 > 3$; $4^2 = 16$ and $16 > 4$; $(6.5)^2 = 42.25$ and $42.25 > 6.5$. He states: "The square of any number is greater than the number itself."

7. On March 1, a family went bowling. Again on April 1, May 1, and June 1, the family went bowling. The youngest child announced: "We always go bowling on the first of the month."

8. The music director announced: "Anybody who misses two or more rehearsals will not be permitted to sing in our concert." After being out of town during three rehearsals Herb said: "Well, I can't sing in the concert."

9. The teacher noticed that Nancy had a well-prepared geometry assignment on each of the first several Mondays of the school year. The teacher said: "Nancy studies hard on weekends."

10. A student learning about absolute value examined the statements: $|6| = 6$; $|-6| = 6$; $|-\frac{1}{4}| = \frac{1}{4}$; $|.35| = .35$. He decided: Every absolute value is a positive number.

11. Knowing that $x^2 - y^2 = (x + y)(x - y)$ for all algebraic expressions x and y, Jeannie decided: $[a + b]^2 - 25 = ([a + b] + 5)([a + b] - 5)$.

12. Jim knows that he is older than John. When he finds out that John is older than Rick, Jim says: "I'm older than Rick."

Identify the property of equality that supports each statement.

13. If $3n - 5 = 25$, then $3n = 30$.
14. If $\frac{1}{3}y = 12$, then $y = 36$.
15. Where j is a number, $j = j$.
16. Name the principle that supports the statement: If $b > c + 2d$ and $j = c$, then $b > j + 2d$.

Written Exercises

A teacher announces that she has two different members of the set $\{2, 4, 6, 8\}$ in mind. Which of the following deductions can you correctly make about the two numbers?

A

1. Both numbers are divisible by 2.
2. One of the two numbers is divisible by 4.
3. The sum of the numbers is greater than 5.
4. The product of the numbers is less than 50.
5. The product of the numbers is divisible by 4.
6. The product of the numbers is divisible by 8.
7. Each of the numbers is a factor of 264.
8. The square of at least one of the numbers is greater than 16.
9. Exactly one of the numbers satisfies the inequality $x^2 > 3x$.
10. At least one of the numbers satisfies the inequality $-3x < -10$.
11. At least one of the numbers satisfies the compound sentence $4 < x - 1 < 6$.
12. Both numbers satisfy the inequality $\dfrac{x^2}{x - 1} > 5$.

Use inductive thinking to discover a pattern. Then state the next two numbers that fit the pattern.

13. 2, 4, 6, 8, _?_ , _?_
14. 2, 4, 8, 16, _?_ , _?_
15. $1, \frac{1}{2}, \frac{1}{3}, \frac{1}{4},$ _?_ , _?_
16. $\frac{1}{2}, \frac{2}{3}, \frac{3}{4}, \frac{4}{5},$ _?_ , _?_
17. 1, −3, 9, −27, _?_ , _?_
18. 64, 32, 16, 8, _?_ , _?_

19. 1, 4, 9, 16, _?_ , _?_
20. 3, −3, 6, −6, 9, −9, _?_ , _?_
21. $x, x^2, x^3, x^4,$ _?_ , _?_
22. $y, y^3, y^5, y^7,$ _?_ , _?_
23. $\frac{c}{d^2}, \frac{c^2}{d^4}, \frac{c^3}{d^6}, \frac{c^4}{d^8},$ _?_ , _?_
24. $ab^2, a^3b^3, a^5b^4, a^7b^5,$ _?_ , _?_

Some facts about three collinear points *A, B, C* are given. Deduce which point lies between the other two.

EXAMPLE. $AB = 1; BC = 2; AC = 3$
SOLUTION: Because $AB + BC = AC$, $\overline{ABC}$. ($\overline{CBA}$ is also correct.)

25. $AB = 5; BC = 2; AC = 7$
26. $AB = 5; BC = 2; AC = 3$
27. $AB = 4; AC = 4; BC = 8$
28. $BC = j; AB = j − k; AC = k$

B　29. C lies on $\overrightarrow{AB}$ but not on $\overline{AB}$.
30. C lies on $\overrightarrow{BA}$ but not on $\overline{AB}$.
31. C lies on both $\overrightarrow{AB}$ and $\overrightarrow{BA}$.
32. B does not lie on $\overline{AC}$, and C does not lie on $\overline{AB}$.
33. $AB > AC > BC$
34. $AC > AB$ and $AB = BC$

Some facts are given. State a conclusion that follows from the facts.

EXAMPLE. N is a root of the equation $x^2 − 2x − 15 = 0$
SOLUTION:
$$x^2 − 2x − 15 = 0$$
$$(x − 5)(x + 3) = 0$$
$$x − 5 = 0 \text{ or } x + 3 = 0$$
$$x = 5 \text{ or } x = −3 \qquad \text{Conclusion: } N \in \{5, −3\}$$

35. N is a root of the equation $5x − 1 = 34$.
36. N is a root of the equation $x^2 − 6x + 8 = 0$.
37. N is the greater of the two roots of the equation $x^2 − x − 6 = 0$.
38. N is the greater of the two roots of the equation $x^2 + 8x + 15 = 0$.
39. N is an integer and $2.7 < N < 3.6$.
40. N is an even integer and $3 < N < 9$.

C　41. N is a root of each of the equations:
$$x^2 = 25; \quad x^2 − x − 30 = 0; \quad x^3 + 6x^2 − 25 = 0$$

42. N is a root of each of the equations:
$$\frac{2}{x} = \frac{x}{8}; \quad x^3 = 16x; \quad x^3 = x^2 + 48$$

Explain where the reasoning is faulty.

43. The square of every positive even integer is greater than 3. If $x > 0$ and $x^2 > 3$, then x must be a positive even integer.

44. Let a and b represent the same number.

1. $a = b$

2. $a \cdot a = a \cdot b$

3. $a^2 = ab$

4. $a^2 - b^2 = ab - b^2$

5. $(a + b)(a - b) = b(a - b)$

6. $\dfrac{(a + b)(a - b)}{a - b} = \dfrac{b(a - b)}{a - b}$

7. $a + b = b$

8. $b + b = b$

9. $2b = b$

10. $2 = 1$

1-6 *If-Then Statements*

Such statements as "*If* I get the answer to that problem, *then* I will phone you" can be described as if-then statements. For examples in geometry, see Postulates 4 and 5 and Theorems 1-1, 1-2, and 1-3. In these theorems the word *then* is not printed, but it can be understood.

If-then statements are called *conditionals*. When p and q represent statements, the compound statement "If p, then q" is a conditional. In the conditional, p is the hypothesis; it states what is *given*. The statement q is the conclusion; it states what we are to *prove*.

Some statements can be easily recognized as conditionals after they are expressed in if-then form.

EXAMPLE

a. Express in if-then form the statement:
   The sum of any two odd integers j and k is an even integer.
b. State the hypothesis of the conditional.
c. State the conclusion of the conditional.

SOLUTION:

a. If j and k are odd integers, then $j + k$ is an even integer.
b. Hypothesis: j and k are odd integers.
c. Conclusion: $j + k$ is an even integer.

Consider the following pair of statements.

If $x = 5$, then $2x = 10$.
If $2x = 10$, then $x = 5$.

Notice that you can form one conditional from the other by interchanging the hypothesis and conclusion. The statements are *converses* of each other. The converse of the conditional *If p, then q* is the conditional *If q, then p.*

It is a common mistake to believe that the converse of a true conditional must itself be true. A simple example shows that this is not always the case.

A conditional: If $x > 10$, then $x > 4$. *True*
The converse: If $x > 4$, then $x > 10$. *False*

Once a conditional has been proved, however, it is natural to investigate the converse. Sometimes the converse can also be proved by deductive reasoning.

Oral Exercises

State the hypothesis and conclusion of each conditional.

1. If it rains hard, then the ground gets wet.
2. If I work that hard problem, then I will phone you.
3. If a lion is very hungry, it acts restless.
4. If a lion acts hungry, it is restless.
5. A person succeeds if he tries.
6. An apple is soft if it is too ripe.
7. Seven points are collinear if the seven points lie on line j.
8. A number is positive if it is greater than its opposite.

Express each statement in *if-then* form.

9. When a square has a side 3 cm long, the perimeter of the square is 12 cm.
10. When $5x - 2 = 33$, $x = 7$.
11. Two planes intersect, provided that the planes are not parallel.
12. $7x > 14$, provided that $x > 2$.
13. When y is a negative number, $-y$ is a positive number.
14. When $a = b$, $a - b = 0$.
15. The product of any two odd integers p and q is an odd integer.
16. The difference of any two odd integers c and d is an even integer.

State the converse of the conditional.

17. If r, then s.
18. If $a + b = c$, then $a = c - b$.
19. If Ann works hard, she gets a lot done.
20. If George eats potato chips, he drinks ice water.

Written Exercises

State the hypothesis and conclusion of each conditional.

A 1. If John hurries, he arrives on time.
2. If Jim works hard, he feels good.
3. Two segments with unequal lengths are not congruent.
4. Two planes that intersect have many points in common.

State the hypothesis and conclusion of each conditional.

5. Mary can be president if she campaigns.
6. Sally plays well when the weather is warm.
7. The picnic will be canceled in the event of heavy rainfall.
8. The vice president takes charge when the president is indisposed.

Express each statement in *if-then* form.

9. Every positive number has two square roots.
10. Every Virginian is a Southerner.
11. An apple that grew too fast has inferior flavor.
12. A car with poor brakes is a menace on the highway.
13. A person who respects democracy hates tyranny.
14. A person who lives in a glass house should not throw stones.
15. Squares with equal areas have equal perimeters.
16. Squares with equal perimeters have equal areas.

State the converse of the conditional.

17. If a, then b.
18. If a figure is a square, then it is a rectangle.
19. If $3x + 5 = 25$, then $x = \frac{20}{3}$.
20. If $x > 20$, then $-x < 20$.
21. If this year is 1981, then next year will be 1982.
22. If the Bensons live north of the Richmonds, then the Richmonds live south of the Bensons.
23. If a figure is a square, then the figure has four congruent sides.
24. If a rectangle has four congruent sides, then the rectangle is a square.

In each exercise: a. Classify the statement as true or false.
b. State the converse.
c. Classify the converse as true or false.

B 25. If a number is positive, then the square of the number is positive.
26. If a number is negative, then the square of the number is positive.
27. If a figure has more than four sides, the figure has six sides.
28. If a line and a plane intersect, they have exactly one point in common.
29. If M is the midpoint of $\overline{AB}$, then $AM = MB$.
30. If $\overline{RX} \cong \overline{XT}$, then X is the midpoint of $\overline{RT}$.
31. If today is Friday, then tomorrow will be Saturday.
32. If a girl was born in 1961, then the year 2000 will mark the 39th anniversary of her birth.
33. If $x = -2$, then $(x - 5)(x + 2) = 0$.
34. If $2j$ is an even integer, then j is an even integer.

C 35. If k is an odd integer, then $13k$ is an odd integer.

36. If an integer is divisible by both 4 and 15, then the integer is divisible by 20.

37. If $(x - 3)(x + 7) = 0$, then $x = 3$ or $x = -7$.

38. If $x^2 = 5x$, then $x = 5$.

39. If $|2x - 10| = 0$, then $x = 5$ or -5.

40. If $x = 10$ or $x = 6$, then $|x - 3| = 0$.

1-7 *Proofs in Two-Column Form*

You prove a statement in geometry by using deductive reasoning to show that the statement follows from the hypothesis and other accepted material. Often the assertions made in a proof are listed in one column, and reasons which support the assertions are listed in an adjacent column.

EXAMPLE. A proof in two-column form.

Given: $\overline{AKD}$; $AD = AB$

Prove: $AK + KD = AB$

Proof:

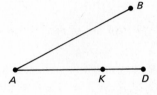

STATEMENTS	REASONS
1. $\overline{AKD}$	1. Given
2. $AK + KD = AD$	2. Definition of between
3. $AD = AB$	3. Given
4. $AK + KD = AB$	4. Transitive property of equality

Some people prefer to support Statement 4, above, with the reason *The Substitution Principle*. Both reasons are correct.

The reasons used in the example are of three types: *Given* (Steps 1 and 3), *Definition* (Step 2), and *Postulate* (Step 4). Just one other kind of reason, *Theorem,* can be used in a mathematical proof. Postulates and theorems from both algebra and geometry can be used.

> ### Reasons Used in Proofs
>
> Given (Facts provided for a particular problem)
> Definitions
> Postulates
> Theorems that have already been proved.

Accept the statement in the first column. State the reason that supports
the conclusion.

Accepted Statement	Conclusion
1. $AB + 7 = 9$	1. $AB = 2$ sub^t
2. $AB + BC = AC$	2. $AB = AC - BC$ subt.
3. $RS = 10$	3. $2RS = 20$ mult
4. $TQ = 14$	4. $\dfrac{TQ}{2} = 7$ division
5. $XY = UV$	5. $XY + 8 = UV + 8$
6. $XY = UV$	6. $XY + YU = YU + UV$ Add
7. $\overline{JNK}$	7. $JN + NK = JK$ Between
8. $CP + PD = CD$	8. $\overline{CPD}$ Between
9. W is the midpoint of $\overline{GH}$.	9. $GW = WH$ def. of midpoint
10. M lies on $\overline{ST}$; $SM = MT$.	10. M is the midpoint of $\overline{ST}$. def of mid
11. $AB + CD = JK$; $CD = 5$	11. $AB + 5 = JK$
12. $RS - TQ = UV$; $RS = 14$	12. $14 - TQ = UV$
13. $a < b$	13. $a + 7 < b + 7$ inequal
14. $a < b$	14. $\dfrac{a}{2} < \dfrac{b}{2}$ division
15. $c > d$	15. $2c > 2d$
16. $a + b < c$; $c = 10$	16. $a + b < 10$ sub

Copy everything shown. Complete the proof by writing reasons.

Given: $\overline{RONY}$; $\overline{RO} \cong \overline{NY}$

Prove: $RN = OY$

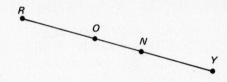

Proof:

	STATEMENTS		REASONS
A	1. $\overline{RO} \cong \overline{NY}$		1. _?_
	2. $RO = NY$		2. _?_
	3. $ON = ON$		3. _?_
	4. $RO + ON = ON + NY$		4. _?_
	5. $\overline{RONY}$		5. _?_
	6. $RO + ON = RN$		6. _?_
	7. $ON + NY = OY$		7. _?_
	8. $RN = OY$		8. _?_

Given: $\overline{XAB}$; $\overline{XCD}$
$XA = XC$; $AB = CD$

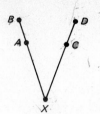

Prove: $XB = XD$

Proof:

STATEMENTS	REASONS
9. $XA = XC$	9. _?_
10. $AB = CD$	10. _?_
11. $XA + AB = XC + CD$	11. _?_
12. $\overline{XAB}$	12. _?_
13. $XA + AB = XB$	13. _?_
14. $\overline{XCD}$	14. _?_
15. $XC + CD = XD$	15. _?_
16. $XB = XD$	16. _?_

Copy the figure, what is given, and what is to be proved. Write a proof in two-column form.

B 17. Given: $\overline{XKY}$
Prove: $XK = XY - KY$
(*Hint:* Only three steps are needed.)

18. Given: $\overline{OTE}$
Prove: $TE = OE - OT$

19. Given: $\overline{ABCD}$; $AB > CD$
Prove: $AC > BD$
(*Hint:* See Exercises 1–8.)

20. Given: $\overline{RSTV}$; $RT = SV$
Prove: $RS = TV$

C 21. Given: $\overline{NGK}$; $\overline{NHJ}$;
$KG = JH$; $GN = HN$
Prove: $KN = JN$

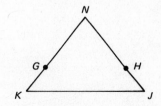

22. Given: $\overline{NGK}$; $\overline{NHJ}$;
$KN < JN$; $GN = HN$
Prove: $KG < JH$

Self-Test State whether the thinking is deductive or inductive.

1. It is known that $5n = 20$. It is decided that $n = 4$.
2. A chemical is spread on grass in four places. In each place the grass dies. It is decided that the chemical is a grass-killer.

In Exercises 3–6, use the conditional: If X is the midpoint of $\overline{JK}$, then $\overline{JX} \cong \overline{XK}$.

3. State the hypothesis.
4. State the conclusion.
5. State the converse of the conditional.
6. Is the original statement true? Is the converse true?
7. List the four kinds of reasons that can be used in proofs.

State the reasons needed to complete the proof.

Given: $\overline{ABC}$; $AB = 2$;
$\qquad BC = 3$; $XY = 5$

Prove: $\overline{XY} \cong \overline{AC}$

Proof:

STATEMENTS	REASONS
8. $\overline{ABC}$	8. _?_
9. $AB + BC = AC$	9. _?_
10. $AB = 2$; $BC = 3$	10. _?_
11. $2 + 3 = AC$, or $AC = 5$	11. _?_
12. $XY = 5$	12. _?_
13. $XY = AC$	13. _?_
14. $\overline{XY} \cong \overline{AC}$	14. _?_

CHAPTER SUMMARY

1. The terms "point," "line," and "plane" are undefined terms.
2. Basic assumptions are called axioms or postulates. Statements that are proved are called theorems.
3. $\overleftrightarrow{AB}$ denotes a line, $\overline{AB}$ a segment, and $\overrightarrow{AB}$ a ray. They are sets of points. AB is a positive number, the distance between A and B.
4. The symbol $\overline{AMB}$ means that point M lies between points A and B.
5. Induction is the process of observing individual cases and then guessing a general law suggested by them.
6. Deduction is the process of reasoning from some accepted statements to a conclusion.

CHAPTER TEST

In Exercises 1–15, classify each statement as true or false.

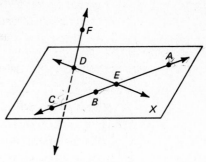

Exs. 1–15

1. B lies on $\overleftrightarrow{AC}$. T
2. $\overleftrightarrow{CB}$ contains point A. T
3. $\overleftrightarrow{AC}$ and $\overleftrightarrow{DE}$ intersect at D. F
4. $\overleftrightarrow{FD} \cap X = D$ T
5. X contains $\overleftrightarrow{FD}$. F
6. A, B, and C are collinear points. T
7. A, E, D, and F are coplanar points. F
8. A line containing points D and C must lie in plane X. F
9. Every plane that contains point E must contain point B. F
10. Exactly one plane contains both $\overleftrightarrow{AC}$ and point F. T
11. $\overleftrightarrow{EC}$ contains point A. F
12. $\overrightarrow{BC}$ and $\overrightarrow{BA}$ are opposite rays. T
13. If $AB = BC$, then $\overline{AB} = \overline{BC}$. F
14. $\overleftrightarrow{EC}$ contains point A. T
15. If $AB = BC$, then B is the midpoint of $\overline{AC}$. T

16. The coordinates of points R and S on a number line are -5 and 12. $RS = $ __?17__

17. Points T and W lie on a number line. $TW = 9$ and the coordinate of T is 5. The coordinate of W is __-4__ or __?14__

18. Points P, Q, and R lie on a number line, and $\overline{PQR}$. If $PR = 15$ and $PQ = 9$, then $QR = $ __?6__.

19. If D, E, and F are collinear points such that $EF = 12$, $DF = 7$, and $ED = 5$, then point __D__ lies between points __?__ and __?E__.

20. Use inductive thinking to discover the next two terms of 2, 5, 10, 17, __?26__ __?37__

21. Is the converse of "If an integer is even, then the square of the integer is even" a true statement? yes

22. To prove a statement in geometry, we use __deduction ?__ reasoning to show that the statement follows from the hypotheses and other accepted statements.

Write proofs in two-column form.

23. Given: $\overline{RSTW}$; $RS = TW$
    Prove: $\overline{RT} \cong \overline{SW}$

24. Given: $\overline{RSTW}$; $\overline{RS} \cong \overline{TW}$;
    $\overline{PT}$ bisects $\overline{SW}$.
    Prove: $RS = ST$

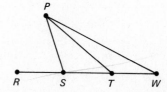

CHAPTER REVIEW

1-1 *Undefined Terms and Definitions*

Draw and label the figure described.

1. Line t contains point A.
2. Point R is the intersection of lines k and l.
3. Line k lies in plane X.
4. Line l intersects plane M at point A.

1-2 *First Postulates and Theorems*

5. How do theorems differ from postulates?
6. Can two planes intersect in exactly one point?
7. If point R and line t both lie in plane X, must R lie on t?
8. If two lines intersect, how many planes contain both lines?

1-3 *Segments and Rays*

Classify each statement as true or false.

9. Point X lies on $\overline{AB}$.
10. Point B lies between points A and X.
11. $\overrightarrow{AM}$ and $\overrightarrow{MX}$ are opposite rays.
12. If M is the midpoint of $\overline{AB}$, then $\overline{AM} \cong \overline{MB}$.

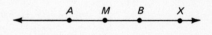

1-4 *The Ruler Postulate*

State the number described.

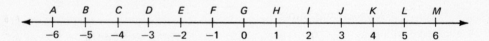

13. The coordinate of point K.
14. The coordinate of the endpoint of $\overrightarrow{CM}$.
15. The coordinate of the midpoint of $\overline{BH}$.
16. The length of $\overline{JB}$.

1-5 *Deductive Reasoning*

17. Use inductive thinking to discover the next two terms of 1, 4, 16, 64, $\underline{}$, $\underline{}$.

Make a deduction based on the given information.

18. $x + y = 21$ and $y = 13$
19. $x < y$ and $y < z$
20. The sum of two particular integers is an odd integer.

1-6 *If-Then Statements*

21. Express "The sum of two even integers is an even integer" in if-then form.
22. Write the converse of "If $x = 0$, then $xy = 0$." Is the converse true?
23. State the hypothesis and the conclusion of the statement, "One can grow good tomatoes if he keeps the tomatoes off the ground."

1-7 *Proof in Two-Column Form*

Copy what is shown. Complete the proof by filling in the reasons.

Given: $\overline{RST}$; $RS = AB$

Prove: $AB + ST = RT$

Proof:

STATEMENTS	REASONS
24. $\overline{RST}$	24. __?__ Given
25. $RS + ST = RT$	25. __?__
26. $RS = AB$	26. __?__
27. $AB + ST = RT$	27. __?__

REVIEWING ALGEBRAIC SKILLS

Solve each equation.

1. $t + 7 = 19$
2. $8 + h = 12$
3. $e - 5 = 13$
4. $17 = g - 4$
5. $2e + 1 = 15$
6. $3s + 4 = 9$
7. $4a - 2 = 22$
8. $7x - 5 = 15$
9. $12 - j = 2j$
10. $14 + u = 4u$
11. $3l + 16 = 4l$
12. $2e + 15 = 6e$
13. $5z + 1 = 2z + 19$
14. $7q + 5 = 2q + 11$
15. $7 - 3y = 4y - 14$

16. $5 - 6l = 3l - 11$
17. $2(w + 7) = 4w$
18. $6(m + \frac{1}{2}) = 8m$
19. $12 = 3(a - 5)$
20. $5(2x - 4) = 4x + 8$
21. $3(3g + 2) = 5g + 17$
22. $6(2e - 1) = 3e + 4$
23. $4(3n + \frac{3}{4}) = 5n + 19$
24. $8(e + \frac{1}{4}) = 2e + 14$
25. $4(\frac{3}{4}q + 2) = q + 16$
26. $6(\frac{2}{3}b - 4) = 2b + 1$
27. $3(3e + 4) + 1 = 2e + 34$
28. $5(2m + 1) - 2 = 3m + 10$
29. $4 + 3(y + 6) = 6(y - 1)$
30. $7(4z - 1) + 6 = 3(2z + 5)$

programming in BASIC

These optional sections appear at the end of several chapters. They may be used with any computer that accepts the language BASIC.

The modern computer has been referred to as a "brain." It can do many complex calculations quickly and accurately. However, it cannot think or plan for itself. It is really an extension of the human mind. It must be programmed in order to operate.

The following computer program was written to find the length and midpoint of a segment on the number line.

```
10   PRINT "TYPE THE COORDINATE OF ONE ENDPOINT:"
20   INPUT A
30   PRINT "TYPE THE COORDINATE OF THE OTHER ENDPOINT:"
40   INPUT B
50   LET D=ABS(A-B)
60   PRINT "LENGTH OF SEGMENT AB IS ";D
70   LET M=(A+B)/2
80   PRINT "MIDPOINT OF SEGMENT AB IS ";M
90   END
```

In running this program, the computer will follow the order of the line numbers.

Line Number	Instruction to the Computer
10,30	Print the information between the quotation marks.
20,40	Print a question mark. After the user types a number, let A (or B) take that value.
50	Calculate $|A - B|$ and let D take that value.
70	Calculate $\dfrac{A + B}{2}$ and let M take that value.
60,80	Print the information inside the quotation marks followed by the value of the length (or midpoint). (The space following the word "is" allows for a space before the number in the print-out.)
90	Stop running the program. (Every program must have this END statement.)

Type this program at your terminal. Then type LIST. The computer will print the complete program. If a line is not correct, simply retype that line. When the list of the program is correct, type RUN. Use 9 for the first endpoint and 5 for the second. The computer print-out will look like this:

```
RUN

TYPE THE COORDINATE OF ONE ENDPOINT:
?9
TYPE THE COORDINATE OF THE OTHER ENDPOINT:
?5
LENGTH OF SEGMENT AB IS  4
MIDPOINT OF SEGMENT AB IS  7

END
```

Run the program with the following numbers also:

5	9	Ans.	4	7
23.85	−4.915	Ans.	28.765	9.4675
−5	−5	Ans.	0	−5

The last numbers suggested above for the endpoints were the same. The computer was able to calculate a value for length and midpoint. However, we know that a line segment has a positive length and different endpoints.

We can change our program so that no one can put in the same number for both endpoints. To do this, we type the following lines as an addition to our program.

```
42   IF A <> B THEN 50
44   PRINT "ENDPOINTS MUST BE DIFFERENT."
46   GOTO 10
```

Lines 42 and 46 instruct the computer to "branch" to a place in the program other than the next line. In running the program, the computer will go to line 50 if A and B are not equal (<>). What do you think the computer will do if A and B are equal?

After you have typed these new lines, have the computer LIST the program. Notice that the computer has inserted the lines in the proper order. RUN the program using −5 and −5; notice the branching that the computer did. RUN it also with −5 and 5.

In our program we can provide for input of both endpoints on the same line. Again modifying our program, we type:

```
10   PRINT   "TYPE THE COORDINATES OF THE ENDPOINTS:"
20   INPUT A,B
30
40
```

Here lines 10 and 20 replace the original lines with those numbers. By typing just the line numbers 30 and 40, we delete those lines. LIST the program again to show this. The following is a RUN of the program.

```
RUN


TYPE THE COORDINATES OF THE ENDPOINTS:
?17,95
LENGTH OF SEGMENT AB IS   78
MIDPOINT OF SEGMENT AB IS   56
```

Notice when the computer prints the question mark for input, we type the two numbers separated by a comma. The computer gives the value of 17 to A and 95 to B.

Before you start to type in another program at the terminal, type SCR (for scratch). This clears your work area in the computer, and you start work with a clean slate.

Exercises

1. Using the above program, find the length and midpoint of a segment, on the number line, whose endpoints have coordinates:
   (a) 1.17386 and 2.17394
   (b) −978.3 and 804
   (c) −56.2 and 56.2
2. Write a program to find the second endpoint of a segment when you know one endpoint and the length. (Note: Provide for the two possible answers.)
3. Write a program to find the second endpoint of a segment if you know one endpoint and the midpoint of the segment.

Möbius Bands

The United States Patent Office has actually granted patents for objects that involve a *Möbius band*. Such a band is described below.

Label the corners of a long, narrow strip of paper. (Think of the concealed side as being colored red.)

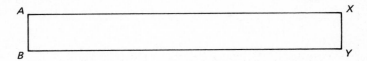

Give the strip a half-twist.

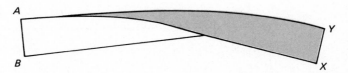

Paste the ends together, *A* falling on *Y*, and *B* falling on *X*. A *Möbius band* results.

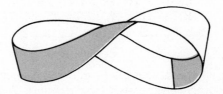

If you slit the band lengthwise down the middle you do not get two bands. You get one band that is twice as long.

extra for xperts

Exercises

1. Make a Möbius band and slit it, lengthwise, down the middle.
2. Slit the band made in Exercise 1 a second time down the middle. Write a sentence or two describing what happens.
3. Make a Möbius band and color one side. How much of the band is left uncolored? How many sides does a Möbius band have?
4. Give a full twist to a rectangular strip *ABYX* (similar to the one shown above). Paste the ends together, *A* falling on *X*, *B* falling on *Y*. How many sides does the band have?
5. Slit the strip made in Exercise 4 down the middle. Write a brief description of what is formed.
6. Make a Möbius band. Let the band be k cm wide. Make a lengthwise cut, staying $\frac{1}{3}k$ cm from the right-hand edge. Describe the result.

2

ANGLES;
PERPENDICULAR LINES

Angles and Their Measure

Objectives

1. Use three letters to name an angle.
2. Recognize a half-plane and the interior and exterior of an angle.
3. Illustrate adjacent angles and vertical angles.
4. Use the Protractor Postulate.
5. State and apply the Angle Addition Postulate and the theorem about adjacent angles with exterior sides in a line.
6. Define congruent angles and the special angles named in Section 2-3.

2-1 *Angles and Half-Planes*

An **angle** ($\angle$) is the union of two noncollinear rays that have the same endpoint. The two rays are the **sides** of the angle; the common endpoint is the **vertex** (plural: *vertices*).

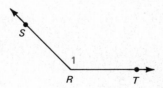 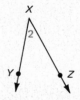

The sides of the angle at the left, above, are $\overrightarrow{RS}$ and $\overrightarrow{RT}$. The vertex is point R. The angle can be designated by $\angle 1$, $\angle R$, $\angle SRT$, or $\angle TRS$. When three letters are used to name an angle, the letter that names the vertex is placed between the other two letters. Correct three-letter names for $\angle 2$ are $\angle YXZ$ and $\angle ZXY$.

For some work with angles, the idea of *half-plane* is needed. In the diagram, line *j* separates plane *M* into three subsets. One subset is line *j*. Another subset, shown in gray, contains point *A*. That subset is called a half-plane. The third subset, shown in color, is also a half-plane. Points *A* and *B* lie on opposite sides of line *j* and lie in opposite half-planes. Line *j* is the edge of each half-plane, but does not lie in either half-plane.

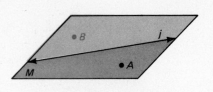

The next figure shows ∠*S* lying in plane *Z*. Points *R*, *S*, and *T* lie *on* the angle. Point *N* lies in the *interior* of the angle. The interior of ∠*RST* is the intersection of the half-plane that contains *R* and has edge $\overleftrightarrow{ST}$ with the half-plane that contains *T* and has edge $\overleftrightarrow{SR}$. Points *P* and *V*, which lie neither on the angle nor in the interior, lie in the exterior of the ∠*RST*.

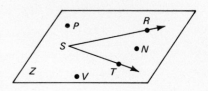

Adjacent angles (adj. ∠s) are two angles in a plane that have a common side but have no interior points in common. With respect to adjacent angles 1 and 2, $\overrightarrow{OA}$ and $\overrightarrow{OC}$ are called the exterior sides. The exterior sides of adjacent angles 3 and 4 are $\overrightarrow{XU}$ and $\overrightarrow{XW}$.

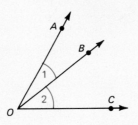

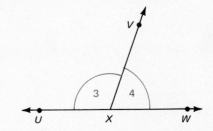

Notice, above, that point *O* is the vertex of three angles. Hence "∠*O*" does not clearly identify any one of the angles and is not a satisfactory name for ∠*AOC*, ∠1, or ∠2.

Vertical angles (vert. ∠s) are two angles whose sides form two pairs of opposite rays.

∠5 and ∠6 are vertical angles.
∠7 and ∠8 are vertical angles.

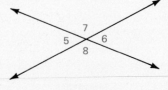

Oral Exercises

1. Name the angle in four ways.
2. Name the vertex of the angle.
3. Name the sides of the angle.
4. Is it correct to say that point *A* lies in the interior of the angle?
5. Name three points that lie on the angle.
6. Name a point that lies in the interior of the angle; name a point in the exterior of the angle.

7. Name two pairs of vertical angles.
8. Name four pairs of adjacent angles.

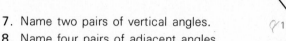

State whether ∠1 and ∠2 are adjacent angles.

9.

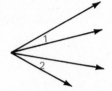

11.

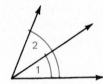

10.

12.

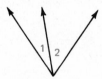

Written Exercises

A

1. Name ∠1 in two different ways.
2. Name ∠2 in four different ways.

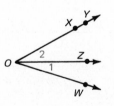

3. Name six different angles.

4. Name five different angles. ($\overrightarrow{UK}$ and $\overrightarrow{UG}$ are opposite rays.)

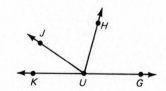

Line *g* separates a plane into two half-planes. Points *R* and *S* lie in one of the half-planes, and point *T* lies in the other. Complete each sentence by writing *must, might,* or *cannot.*

5. $\overline{RS}$ __?__ intersect *g*. *cannot*
6. $\overline{RT}$ __?__ intersect *g*. *must*
7. $\overline{ST}$ __?__ intersect *g*.
8. $\overrightarrow{RS}$ __?__ intersect *g*.
9. $\overleftrightarrow{RS}$ __?__ intersect *g*. *must*
10. The ray that lies opposite to $\overrightarrow{RT}$ __?__ intersect *g*. *cannot*

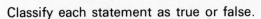

Classify each statement as true or false.

11. *E* lies in the interior of ∠*AXB*.
12. *B* lies in the interior of ∠*AXB*.
13. *F* lies in the exterior of ∠*AXC*.
14. *D* lies in the exterior of ∠*BXC*.
15. ∠*AXB* and ∠*AXC* are adjacent angles.
16. ∠*AXD* and ∠*BXC* are vertical angles.
17. $\overrightarrow{XB}$ is the common side of ∠*AXB* and ∠*BXC*.
18. $\overrightarrow{XD}$ and $\overrightarrow{XB}$ are the exterior sides of adjacent angles *DXA* and *AXB*.

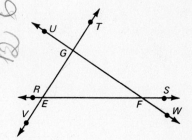

The figure shown is made up of three lines.

B 19. How many angles are shown? 12
20. How many pairs of vertical angles are shown?
21. How many pairs of adjacent angles are shown?
22. Name the angle whose interior contains point *U*.
23. Point *U* lies on four different angles. Name the four.
24. Point *V* lies in the exterior of seven different angles. Name the seven.

A hexagon with three diagonals that intersect in a point is shown.

C 25. How many angles are shown? 30
26. Point *P* lies in the interior of how many of the angles shown? 6
27. How many pairs of vertical angles are shown? 6
28. How many pairs of adjacent angles are shown? 24

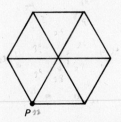

2-2 *The Protractor*

A protractor has been placed over ∠*AOB* in the diagram. The *degree measure* of ∠*AOB* is 65. More simply, the *measure* of ∠*AOB* is 65 (*m*∠*AOB* = 65). We also say: ∠*AOB* is a 65° angle.

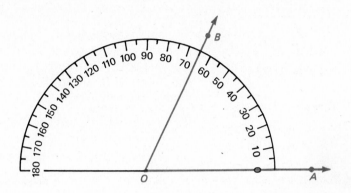

You can find the measures of many angles with just one placement of a protractor.

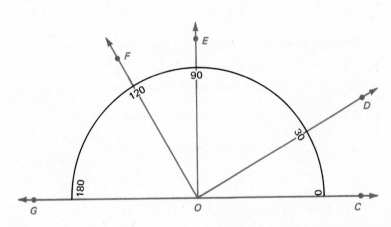

$m\angle COD = 30 - 0 = 30$ $m\angle DOG = 180 - 30 = 150$
$m\angle COE = 90 - 0 = 90$ $m\angle EOF = 120 - 90 = 30$
$m\angle COF = 120 - 0 = 120$ $m\angle EOG = 180 - 90 = 90$
$m\angle DOE = 90 - 30 = 60$ $m\angle FOG = 180 - 120 = 60$
$m\angle DOF = 120 - 30 = 90$

In the figure above, ∠*DOE* is *congruent* to ∠*FOG* (∠*DOE* ≅ ∠*FOG*). **Congruent angles** are angles that have equal measures.

Our work with angles will be based on the following three postulates.

<table>
<tr><td>**POSTULATE 8**</td><td>For every angle there is a unique number between 0 and 180 called the **measure** of the angle.</td></tr>
</table>

POSTULATE 9 (PROTRACTOR POSTULATE)	The set of rays which have a common endpoint O in the edge of a half-plane, and which lie in the half-plane or its edge, can be paired with the numbers between 0 and 180, inclusive, in such a way that: 1. One of the rays in the edge is paired with 0, and the other is paired with 180; 2. If $\overrightarrow{OA}$ is paired with x and $\overrightarrow{OB}$ with y, then $m\angle AOB = \|x - y\|$.

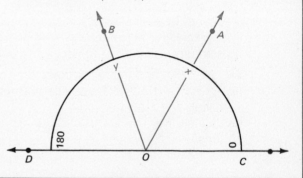

POSTULATE 10 (ANGLE ADDITION POSTULATE)	If point B lies in the interior of $\angle AOC$, then $m\angle AOB + m\angle BOC = m\angle AOC$.

B lies in the interior of $\angle AOC$.

$m\angle 1 + m\angle 2 = m\angle 3$

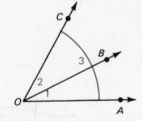

When you use Postulate 9 or 10 in proofs, you may write *Protractor Postulate* or *Angle Addition Postulate*, respectively, as your reason.

Oral
Exercises

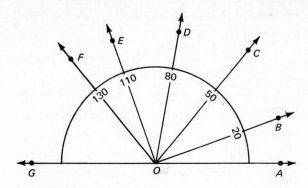

1. Name five angles that have $\overrightarrow{OA}$ as a side.
2. Name six angles that have $\overrightarrow{OD}$ as a side.
3. State the measures of $\angle AOB$, $\angle BOC$, $\angle COE$, and $\angle DOG$.
4. State the measures of $\angle GOF$, $\angle GOC$, and $\angle COB$.
5. Name an angle that has measure 90.
6. $\angle AOB \cong \angle$? FOE
7. $m\angle COD = m\angle$? AOE
8. $\angle COD \cong \angle$? BOC
9. Why would it be incorrect to say $\angle AOB \cong \angle DOE$? BOE
10. Which angle, of those pictured, has the greatest measure? AOB
11. $\angle BOC$ and $\angle COD$ are adjacent angles. The exterior sides of those adjacent angles are ? and ? .
12. $\angle AOB$ and $\angle BOG$ are adjacent angles. The exterior sides of those adjacent angles are ? and ? .

Written
Exercises

A

In Exercises 1–16, refer to the plane figure shown.

1. Name the six angles in the figure.
2. Which angle, of those pictured, has the greatest measure?
3. Name two angles adjacent to $\angle CUD$.
4. Name two angles adjacent to $\angle EUD$.
5. $m\angle BUC + m\angle CUD = m\angle$? DUE
6. $m\angle CUD + m\angle DUE = m\angle$? CUD
7. $m\angle EUD + m\angle DUB = m\angle$? BUE
8. $m\angle EUC + m\angle CUB = m\angle$? EUD
9. If $m\angle CUD = 35$ and $m\angle DUE = 25$, then $m\angle CUE =$? .
10. If $m\angle BUE = 70$ and $m\angle CUE = 55$, then $m\angle BUC =$? .
11. If $m\angle DUC = j$ and $m\angle CUB = k$, then $m\angle DUB =$? .
12. If $m\angle BUC = k$ and $m\angle CUE = h$, then $m\angle BUE =$? .

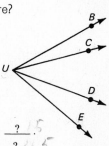

13. In a proof, what reason would you write to support the following assertion?
$m \angle BUC + m \angle CUD = m \angle BUD$

14. In a proof, what reason would you write to support the following assertion?
$m \angle EUC + m \angle CUB = m \angle EUB$

15. Suppose it is known that $m \angle BUC = 20$ and $m \angle DUE = 20$. What reason supports the statement $\angle BUC \cong \angle DUE$?

16. Suppose it is known that $\angle BUC \cong \angle DUE$. What reason supports the statement $m \angle BUC = m \angle DUE$?

Copy everything shown. Write the reasons needed to complete the proof.

Given: A plane figure;
$\quad\quad m \angle WKX = m \angle YKZ$

Prove: $m \angle WKY = m \angle XKZ$

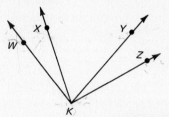

Proof:

STATEMENTS	REASONS
17. $m \angle WKX = m \angle YKZ$	17. _?_ Given
18. $m \angle XKY = m \angle XKY$	18. _?_ reflexive
19. $m \angle WKX + m \angle XKY = m \angle XKY + m \angle YKZ$	19. _?_ addition
20. $m \angle WKX + m \angle XKY = m \angle WKY$	20. _?_
21. $m \angle XKY + m \angle YKZ = m \angle XKZ$	21. _?_
22. $m \angle WKY = m \angle XKZ$	22. _?_

Given: A plane figure;
$\quad\quad m \angle WKY > m \angle XKZ$

Prove: $m \angle WKX > m \angle YKZ$

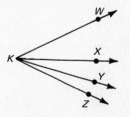

Proof:

STATEMENTS	REASONS
B 23. $m \angle WKY > m \angle XKZ$	23. _?_ given
24. $m \angle WKX + m \angle XKY = m \angle WKY$	24. _?_
25. $m \angle XKY + m \angle YKZ = m \angle XKZ$	25. _?_
26. $m \angle WKX + m \angle XKY > m \angle XKY + m \angle YKZ$	26. _?_
27. $m \angle XKY = m \angle XKY$	27. _?_
28. $m \angle WKX > m \angle YKZ$	28. _?_

44 *GEOMETRY*

The measures of the angles in the plane figure are given in terms of *x*.
Find the numerical value of *x*.

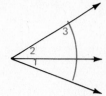

29. $m\angle 1 = 2x$, $m\angle 2 = 3x$, $m\angle 3 = 4x + 7$
30. $m\angle 1 = 30$, $m\angle 2 = 4x$, $m\angle 3 = 6x$
31. $m\angle 1 = 60 - x$, $m\angle 2 = x$, $m\angle 3 = 3x$
32. $m\angle 1 = x$, $m\angle 2 = 2x - 10$, $m\angle 3 = 2x + 10$

Write proofs in two-column form. The figures shown are plane figures.

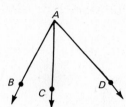

C 33. Given: $m\angle BAC = r$;
$\qquad m\angle CAD = s$
$\quad$ Prove: $m\angle BAD = r + s$

34. Given: $m\angle BAD = k$;
$\qquad m\angle BAC = j$
$\quad$ Prove: $m\angle CAD = k - j$

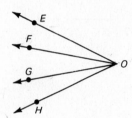

35. Given: $m\angle EOF = s$;
$\qquad m\angle FOG = t$;
$\qquad m\angle FOH = s + t$
$\quad$ Prove: $\angle EOG \cong \angle FOH$

36. Given: The plane figure
$\quad$ Prove: $m\angle EOF + m\angle FOG +$
$\qquad m\angle GOH = m\angle EOH$

2-3 *Special Angles*

Perhaps you are already familiar with the kinds of angles defined below.

Acute angle: An angle whose measure is less than 90.

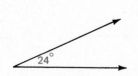

Right angle (rt. ∠): An angle whose measure is 90.

Obtuse angle: An angle whose measure is greater than 90.

Complementary angles (comp. ⩘): Two angles whose measures have the sum 90.

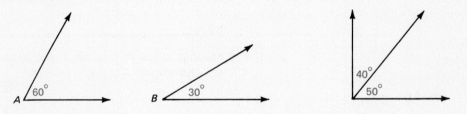

∠A is said to be a *complement* of ∠B.

Supplementary angles (supp. ⩘): Two angles whose measures have the sum 180.

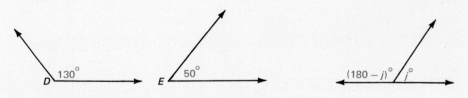

∠D is said to be a *supplement* of ∠E.

Bisector of an angle: $\overrightarrow{AX}$ is said to be the bisector of $\angle BAC$ if X lies in the interior of $\angle BAC$ and $\angle BAX \cong \angle XAC$. We say that $\overrightarrow{AX}$ bisects $\angle BAC$. $\overleftrightarrow{AX}$ also bisects $\angle BAC$. $\overline{AX}$ determines the bisector of $\angle BAC$.

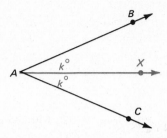

Dihedral (dy-**hee**-dral) angle: The union of a line and two noncoplanar half-planes that have the line as edge. Each of the half-planes is a *face* of the dihedral angle.

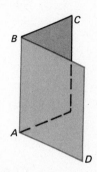

Dihedral angle C-BA-D

Notice that the Angle Addition Postulate does not apply to adjacent angles whose exterior sides lie in a line. The following theorem applies to such angles.

THEOREM 2-1   If the exterior sides of two adjacent angles lie in a line, then the angles are supplementary.

Given: $\angle RXS$ and $\angle SXT$ are adj. $\measuredangle$;
$\overrightarrow{XR}$ and $\overrightarrow{XT}$ lie in $\overleftrightarrow{TR}$.

Prove: $\angle RXS$ and $\angle SXT$ are supp. $\measuredangle$.

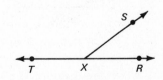

Proof:

STATEMENTS	REASONS
1. $\overrightarrow{XR}$ can be paired with 0, $\overrightarrow{XT}$ with 180, and $\overrightarrow{XS}$ with some number j, where $0 < j < 180$.	1. Protractor Postulate
2. $m\angle RXS = |j - 0| = j$ $m\angle SXT = |180 - j| = 180 - j$	2. Protractor Postulate
3. $m\angle RXS + m\angle SXT = 180$	3. Addition property of equality
4. $\angle RXS$ and $\angle SXT$ are supp. $\measuredangle$	4. Def. of supp. $\measuredangle$

Given: $\overleftrightarrow{AB}$ and $\overleftrightarrow{CD}$ intersect at X.
Name the figures described.

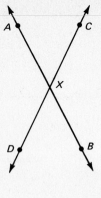

1. Two acute angles
2. Two obtuse angles
3. Two pairs of vertical angles
4. Four pairs of adjacent angles
5. Four pairs of supplementary angles
6. Two pairs of opposite rays
7. Two supplements of $\angle AXC$ ∠4,2
8. Two supplements of $\angle AXD$ ∠L
9. Two angles that appear to have equal measures
10. If the angles named in Exercise 9 do have equal measures, the angles are called ___?___ angles.

11. Is it correct to describe three angles as complementary?
12. Is it correct to describe four angles as supplementary?
13. Suppose $\angle 1$ and $\angle 2$ are known to be complementary. If $m\angle 1 = 20$, then $m\angle 2 = $ ___?___.
14. Suppose $\angle 3$ and $\angle 4$ are known to be supplementary. If $m\angle 3 = 40$, then $m\angle 4 = $ ___?___.

A plane figure is shown.

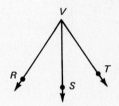

15. If $m\angle RVS = m\angle SVT$, then $\angle RVS$ and $\angle SVT$ are ___?___ angles. $\overrightarrow{VS}$ is said to ___?___ $\angle RVT$.
16. If $m\angle RVS = \frac{1}{2}m\angle RVT$, then $m\angle RVS = m\angle$ ___?___ and $\angle SVT \cong \angle$ ___?___. $\overrightarrow{VS}$ is a ___?___ of $\angle RVT$.

A A plane figure is shown. $m\angle 9 = 90$.

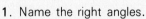

1. Name the right angles.
2. Name the acute angles.
3. Name the obtuse angles.
4. Name two pairs of vertical angles.
5. Name six pairs of supplementary angles.
6. Write the postulate or theorem that supports the statement that $\angle 5$ and $\angle 10$ are supplementary angles.
7. If $m\angle 7$ is represented by j, then $m\angle 1$ is represented by ___?___.
8. If $m\angle 5$ is represented by $180 - k$, then $m\angle 10$ is represented by ___?___.

Write the reasons that support the steps in the following proof.

Given: $m\angle BAC < 4j + 6k$;

$\overrightarrow{AX}$ bisects $\angle BAC$.

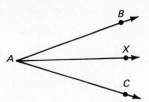

Prove: $m\angle BAX < 2j + 3k$

Proof:

STATEMENTS	REASONS
9. $m\angle BAC < 4j + 6k$	9. __?__
10. $m\angle BAX + m\angle XAC = m\angle BAC$	10. __?__
11. $m\angle BAX + m\angle XAC < 4j + 6k$	11. __?__
12. $\overrightarrow{AX}$ bisects $\angle BAC$.	12. __?__
13. $\angle XAC \cong \angle BAX$	13. __?__
14. $m\angle XAC = m\angle BAX$	14. __?__
15. $m\angle BAX + m\angle BAX < 4j + 6k$, or $2m\angle BAX < 4j + 6k$	15. __?__
16. $m\angle BAX < 2j + 3k$	16. __?__

In Exercises 17–20, $\angle 1$ and $\angle 2$ are complementary angles. State the numerical value of x.

B 17. $m\angle 1 = 2x$, $m\angle 2 = 3x$

18. $m\angle 1 = x$, $m\angle 2 = x + 20$

19. $m\angle 1 = 2m\angle 2$, $m\angle 2 = x$

20. $m\angle 1 = 30 + x$, $m\angle 2 = 40 + x$

In Exercises 21–24, $\angle 3$ and $\angle 4$ are supplementary angles. State the numerical value of y.

21. $m\angle 3 = 2y$, $m\angle 4 = 3y - 15$

22. $m\angle 3 = y + 10$, $m\angle 4 = 3y - 10$

23. $m\angle 3 = 5m\angle 4$, $m\angle 4 = y$

24. $m\angle 3 = 160 - y$, $m\angle 4 = 170 - y$

25. Two angles are complementary. The measure of one is five times the measure of the other. Find the measure of each angle.

26. Two angles are supplementary. The measure of one is four-fifths the measure of the other. Find the measure of each angle.

C 27. The measure of a supplement of $\angle C$ is four times the measure of a complement of $\angle C$. Find $m\angle C$.

28. For any angle D, the difference of the measures of a supplement of $\angle D$ and a complement of $\angle D$ is a certain number. Find that number.

In the plane figure, $\overrightarrow{OC}$ bisects $\angle BOA$, $\overrightarrow{OD}$ bisects $\angle BOC$, $\overrightarrow{OE}$ bisects $\angle BOD$, and $\overrightarrow{OF}$ bisects $\angle BOE$.

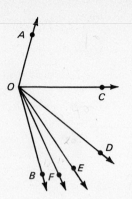

29. If $m\angle AOB = 160$, $m\angle COF = $ _?_ .
30. If $m\angle FOC = 77$, $m\angle EOB = $ _?_ .
31. If $m\angle BOD = m\angle DOE + 19$, $m\angle COE = $ _?_ .
32. If $\overrightarrow{OT}$ (not shown) and $\overrightarrow{OB}$ are opposite rays, and $m\angle TOA = m\angle COD$, then $m\angle DOF = $ _?_ .

Write proofs in two-column form.

33. Given: $\overleftrightarrow{XTY}$; $\overrightarrow{TZ}$;
    $\angle 1 \cong \angle ZTY$
    Prove: $\angle 1$ is supp. to $\angle ZTX$.

34. Given: $\overleftrightarrow{XTY}$; $\overrightarrow{TZ}$;
    $\angle 1$ and $\angle 2$ are supp. $\&$;
    $\angle 1 \cong \angle ZTY$

    Prove: $\angle 2 \cong \angle ZTX$

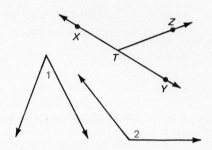

Self-Test Draw two rays, $\overrightarrow{OP}$ and $\overrightarrow{OR}$, in such a way that $\overrightarrow{OP} \cup \overrightarrow{OR}$ is:

1. a line
2. a right angle
3. an acute angle
4. an obtuse angle

5. Use three letters to name the angle drawn in Exercise 4.
6. In your drawing for Exercise 3, place a point in the interior of the angle. Label the point K.
7. If $\angle A \cong \angle B$, $m\angle A = 5x$, and $m\angle B = 3x + 40$, then $x = $ _?_ .
8. $\angle C$ and $\angle D$ are complementary angles. $\angle C$ and $\angle E$ are supplementary angles. If $m\angle C = j$, then $m\angle D = $ _?_ and $m\angle E = $ _?_ .

$\overleftrightarrow{AB}$, $\overleftrightarrow{CD}$, and $\overleftrightarrow{XE}$ lie in a plane and intersect at X.

9. How many pairs of vertical angles does the figure show?
10. How many pairs of adjacent angles does the figure show?
11. State the theorem that supports the assertion that $\angle CXB$ and $\angle BXD$ are supplementary angles.
12. Name the postulate that supports the assertion that $m\angle AXE + m\angle EXC = m\angle AXC$.

Check your answers with those printed at the back of the book.

Theorems

Objectives

1. State and apply the theorem about the existence of a ray that, together with a given ray, forms an angle of given measure.
2. State and apply the angle bisector theorem.
3. Recognize the information conveyed by a diagram.
4. Define perpendicular lines and a line perpendicular to a plane.
5. State and apply the theorems that deal with perpendicular lines and right angles (Theorems 2-4 through 2-8).
6. State and apply the theorems about two angles complementary or supplementary to the same angle or to congruent angles.
7. List the five parts of a demonstration of a theorem.
8. Apply the reflexive, symmetric, and transitive properties of congruence of segments and of angles.
9. Write simple proofs in two-column form.

2-4 *Forming Certain Angles*

Compare the theorems below with Theorems 1-4 and 1-5.

THEOREM 2-2 In a half-plane, through the endpoint of a ray that lies in the edge of the half-plane, there is exactly one other ray such that the angle formed by the two rays has a given measure.

Given: Half-plane H with edge $\overleftrightarrow{OA}$; measure j

Prove: In H there is exactly one ray, $\overrightarrow{OB}$, such that $m \angle BOA = j$.

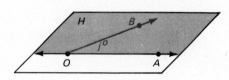

Outline of Proof:

Using the Protractor Postulate, pair $\overrightarrow{OA}$ with 0, and those rays in H that have endpoint O with numbers between 0 and 180. Just one of those rays, $\overrightarrow{OB}$ in the figure, is paired with the number j. That ray is such that $m \angle BOA = |j - 0| = j$.

THEOREM 2-3 An angle has exactly one bisector.

Given: $\angle COD$

Prove: There is exactly one ray, $\overrightarrow{OY}$, that bisects $\angle COD$.

The proof is left as Exercise 32.

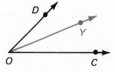

In the plane figure, it is clear that ∠RES and ∠SET are adjacent angles. It is not clear whether the angles are congruent. That kind of information is not conveyed by a diagram.

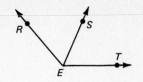

In this book:

1. When a diagram pictures one point between two other points, you may use the betweenness property in proofs.
2. When a diagram pictures two adjacent angles in a half-plane, you may use the Angle Addition Postulate in proofs.
3. No specific conclusions about segment length or angle measure are to be reached from diagrams.

For example, you can conclude from this diagram that X lies between A and D, and that ∠BAC and ∠CAD are adjacent angles. The diagram does not tell you that ∠BAD is a right angle, that $\overrightarrow{AC}$ bisects ∠BAD, or that $\overline{AX} \cong \overline{XD}$.

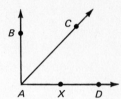

Oral Exercises

1. Name two rays that form a 40° angle with $\overrightarrow{JY}$.
2. Name two rays that form a 40° angle with $\overrightarrow{JX}$.
3. m∠RJT = ___?___
4. m∠TJY = ___?___
5. Name a ray that forms an 80° angle with $\overrightarrow{JS}$.
6. Because ∠ZJY and ∠SJY are congruent angles, $\overrightarrow{JY}$ is said to ___?___ ∠ZJS, and $\overrightarrow{JY}$ is called the ___?___ of ∠ZJS.
7. State the theorem that supports the statement that ∠XJT and ∠TJY are supplementary angles.
8. m∠YJS + m∠SJT = m∠ ___?___

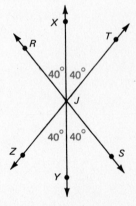

State whether you may assert, from using the diagram, that the statement is correct.

9. Point X lies between points D and B.
10. ∠DBC is a right angle.
11. ∠ABD and ∠DBC are adjacent angles.
12. X is the midpoint of $\overrightarrow{BD}$.
13. Point B lies between points A and C.
14. $\overline{AB} \cong \overline{CB}$

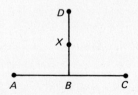

Written Exercises

Copy the figure on your paper and use it for Exercises 1–8. Restrict yourself to one half-plane.

A
1. Draw $\overrightarrow{OC}$ such that $m\angle COB = 80$.
2. $m\angle COB + m\angle COA = \underline{\ ?\ }$
3. Draw $\overrightarrow{OD}$ such that $m\angle DOB = 40$.
4. $m\angle BOD + m\angle COD = m\angle\underline{\ ?\ }$
5. $m\angle COD = \underline{\ ?\ }$ (numerical value)
6. Because $\angle COD \cong \angle BOD$ in the plane figure, $\overrightarrow{OD}$ is said to $\underline{\ ?\ }\ \angle COB$.
7. Draw the bisector of $\angle COA$. Label it $\overrightarrow{OE}$.
8. $m\angle EOA = \underline{\ ?\ }$

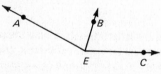

Draw a figure for Exercise 9. Use that figure for Exercises 9–14.

9. Draw a line, $\overleftrightarrow{YZ}$. Choose some point on $\overline{YZ}$ and label that point X. Draw $\overrightarrow{XR}$ so that $m\angle RXZ = 50$.
10. $m\angle RXY = \underline{\ ?\ }$
11. Draw the bisector of $\angle RXZ$. Call it $\overrightarrow{XS}$. $m\angle RXS = m\angle SXZ = \underline{\ ?\ }$
12. Draw the bisector of $\angle RXY$. Call it $\overrightarrow{XT}$. $m\angle RXT = m\angle TXY = \underline{\ ?\ }$
13. $m\angle RXS + m\angle RXT = m\angle\underline{\ ?\ }$
14. $m\angle SXT = \underline{\ ?\ }$ (numerical value)

Write the reasons needed to complete the proof of the statement: When an angle is bisected, two acute angles are formed.

Given: $\angle AEC$; $\overrightarrow{EB}$ bisects $\angle AEC$.

Prove: $\angle AEB$ and $\angle BEC$ are acute angles.

Proof:

STATEMENTS	REASONS
B 15. $\angle AEC$ has a measure, and $m\angle AEC < 180$.	15. $\underline{\ ?\ }$
16. $m\angle AEB + m\angle BEC = m\angle AEC$	16. $\underline{\ ?\ }$
17. $\overrightarrow{EB}$ bisects $\angle AEC$.	17. $\underline{\ ?\ }$
18. $\angle AEB \cong \angle BEC$	18. $\underline{\ ?\ }$
19. $m\angle AEB = m\angle BEC$	19. $\underline{\ ?\ }$
20. $m\angle AEB + m\angle AEB = m\angle AEC$, or $2m\angle AEB = m\angle AEC$	20. $\underline{\ ?\ }$
21. $2m\angle AEB < 180$	21. $\underline{\ ?\ }$
22. $m\angle AEB < 90$	22. $\underline{\ ?\ }$
23. $m\angle BEC < 90$	23. $\underline{\ ?\ }$
24. $\angle AEB$ and $\angle BEC$ are acute $\angle$s.	24. $\underline{\ ?\ }$

25. Draw a line, $\overleftrightarrow{XY}$. Take a point P on $\overleftrightarrow{XY}$. Complete a figure that suggests that there are infinitely many rays $\overrightarrow{PQ}$ such that $m\angle QPX = 90$.

26. Repeat Exercise 25, but use $m\angle QPX = 30$.

Draw a figure for Exercise 27. Use that figure for Exercises 27–30.

27. Draw a line, $\overleftrightarrow{AB}$. Choose some point P on $\overleftrightarrow{AB}$. In a half-plane that has $\overleftrightarrow{AB}$ as its edge, draw $\overrightarrow{PQ}$ so that $m\angle QPA = 90$.

28. In the half-plane opposite the half-plane chosen in Exercise 27, draw $\overrightarrow{PR}$ so that $m\angle RPA = 90$.

29. $\angle QPA$ and $\angle RPA$ are congruent, adjacent angles. As a pair, they are also __?__ angles.

30. Consider $\overrightarrow{PQ} \cup \overrightarrow{PR}$. Is the union a line or is it an angle?

C 31. A rectangular solid is shown. $\overline{AB}$ is one edge, and $\overline{ACB}$. State whether it is possible to have a point P on the face shown in color and a point G on the gray face in such positions that the statement is true.

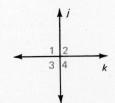

   a. $m\angle PCG = 20$

   b. $m\angle PCG = 175$

   c. $\overrightarrow{CA}$ bisects $\angle PCG$.

   d. $\angle PCA$ is supp. to $\angle GCB$.

32. Outline a proof of Theorem 2-3. (*Hint:* See Theorem 2-2, page 51, for guidance.)

2-5 *Right Angles and Perpendicular Lines*

Perpendicular lines ($\perp$ lines) are two lines that form right angles. When j and k are perpendicular lines, we say that j is *perpendicular* to k ($j \perp k$) and that k is perpendicular to j. From the definition of perpendicular lines we can conclude that:

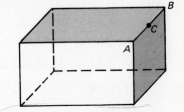

If $j \perp k$, then each numbered angle is a rt. $\angle$.

If any one of the angles is a rt. $\angle$, then $j \perp k$. (See Exercises 1–8.)

The word *perpendicular* is also used for segments and rays. Diagrams sometimes have marks ($\sqsupset$) to show perpendicularity. This diagram indicates: $t \perp j$; $\overrightarrow{AB} \perp j$; $\overline{AB} \perp j$.

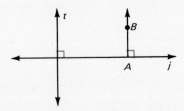

The proofs of the next four theorems are left as exercises (Exercises 23–31).

THEOREM 2-4   All right angles are congruent.

Given: ∠1 and ∠2 are rt. ∠s.

Prove: ∠1 ≅ ∠2

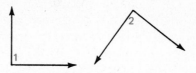

THEOREM 2-5   If two lines are perpendicular, they form congruent adjacent angles.

Given: $j \perp k$

Prove: ∠3 ≅ ∠4

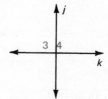

THEOREM 2-6   If two lines form congruent adjacent angles, the lines are perpendicular.

Given: ∠5 ≅ ∠6

Prove: $r \perp s$

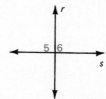

THEOREM 2-7   If the exterior sides of two adjacent acute angles lie in perpendicular lines, the angles are complementary.

Given: ∠1 and ∠2 are adj. acute ∠s;
$\overleftrightarrow{XY} \perp \overleftrightarrow{ZW}$

Prove: ∠1 and ∠2 are comp. ∠s.

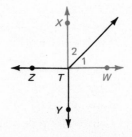

THEOREM 2-8 In a plane, through a given point on a line, there is exactly one perpendicular to the line.

Given: $\overleftrightarrow{AB}$ in plane M;
Point P on $\overleftrightarrow{AB}$.

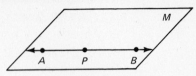

Prove: In M there is exactly one line perpendicular to $\overleftrightarrow{AB}$ at P.

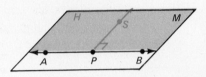

Outline of Proof:

From Theorem 2-2 we see that in half-plane H there is exactly one ray, $\overrightarrow{PS}$ in the figure, such that $m \angle SPB = 90$. Then $\overleftrightarrow{PS}$ is the one line, in M, that is perpendicular to $\overleftrightarrow{AB}$ at P.

Notice, in Theorem 2-8, the phrase *In a plane*. The figure below suggests that there are, at a point in a line, infinitely many perpendiculars to the line.

A line is said to be **perpendicular to a plane** if it is perpendicular to every line that lies in the plane and intersects the line. If $\overleftrightarrow{RS} \perp M$, then $\overleftrightarrow{RS} \perp h$, $\overleftrightarrow{RS} \perp j$, and $\overleftrightarrow{RS} \perp k$.

Suppose that lines h, j, and k are not only perpendicular to $\overline{RS}$, but also bisect $\overline{RS}$. Then each of them is a **perpendicular bisector** of $\overline{RS}$.

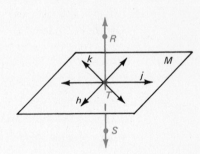

Oral Exercises In Exercises 1–10 you are given $\overleftrightarrow{AB} \perp \overleftrightarrow{CD}$. State whether you can conclude:

1. $\overleftrightarrow{AX} \perp \overleftrightarrow{CD}$
2. $\overleftrightarrow{AB} \perp \overleftrightarrow{CD}$ T
3. $\overrightarrow{AX} \perp \overleftrightarrow{CD}$ T
4. $\overrightarrow{XA} \perp \overline{CD}$ F
5. $\overline{AX} \cong \overline{BX}$ F
6. $\overleftrightarrow{AB}$ bisects $\overline{CD}$ F
7. $\angle AXC$ is a rt. $\angle$ T
8. $\angle AXD \cong \angle BXD$ T

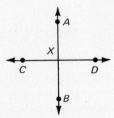

9. $\overleftrightarrow{CD}$ is the only line perpendicular to $\overleftrightarrow{AB}$ at X. F
10. $\overleftrightarrow{AB}$ is the only line perpendicular to $\overleftrightarrow{CD}$ at X.

In the plane figure you are given $\overleftrightarrow{RS} \perp \overleftrightarrow{TZ}$. Classify each statement as true or false.

11. $\overleftrightarrow{RS} \perp \overleftrightarrow{UV}$ _F_
12. $\angle RKT$ is a rt. $\angle$. _T_
13. $m\angle SKV = 90$ _F_
14. $m\angle TKU + m\angle UKR = 90$ _T_
15. $\angle RKU$ and $\angle SKV$ are comp. $\triangle$. _F_
16. $\angle ZKV$ and $\angle TKS$ are supp. $\triangle$. _F_
17. $\angle ZKV$ is supp. to $\angle VKT$. _F_
18. $\angle ZKV$ is comp. to $\angle VKS$. _T_
19. $m\angle TKU + m\angle UKZ = 180$ _T_
20. $m\angle UKZ < 90$ _F_
21. $m\angle VKS > 90$
22. $\angle UKT$ and $\angle VKS$ are vert. $\triangle$.

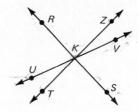

Written Exercises

In Exercises 1–8 it is given that $\angle 1$ is a right angle. Complete the statements, expressing measures by numerical values whenever possible.

A

1. $m\angle 1 + m\angle 2 = \underline{\ ?\ }$
2. $m\angle 1 = \underline{\ ?\ }$
3. From Exercises 1 and 2 we deduce: $m\angle 2 = \underline{\ ?\ }$ _90_
4. $m\angle 1 + m\angle 3 = \underline{\ ?\ }$
5. From Exercises 2 and 4 we deduce: $m\angle 3 = \underline{\ ?\ }$.
6. $m\angle 3 + m\angle 4 = \underline{\ ?\ }$
7. From Exercises 5 and 6 we deduce: $m\angle 4 = \underline{\ ?\ }$.
8. Exercises 1–7 show that when one angle formed by two lines is a right angle, all four angles are $\underline{\ ?\ }$ angles and the lines are $\underline{\ ?\ }$.

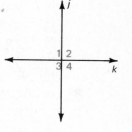

State the definition, postulate, or theorem that supports the statement about the plane figure.

9. If $\angle AXD$ is a rt. $\angle$, then $\overleftrightarrow{AB} \perp \overleftrightarrow{CD}$.
10. If $\overleftrightarrow{AB} \perp \overleftrightarrow{CD}$, then $\angle CXB$ and $\angle DXB$ are rt. $\triangle$.
11. If $m\angle CXB = 90$, then $\angle CXB$ is a rt. $\angle$.
12. If $\overleftrightarrow{AB} \perp \overleftrightarrow{CD}$, then $\angle CXB \cong \angle DXB$.
13. If $\overleftrightarrow{AB} \perp \overleftrightarrow{CD}$, then $\angle 1$ and $\angle 2$ are comp. $\triangle$.
14. If $\angle 1$ and $\angle 2$ are comp. $\triangle$, then $m\angle 1 + m\angle 2 = 90$.
15. $\angle 1$ and $\angle CXE$ are supp. $\triangle$.
16. If $\angle CXB \cong \angle DXB$, then $\overleftrightarrow{AB} \perp \overleftrightarrow{CD}$.

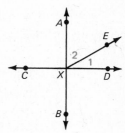

You are given: $\overleftrightarrow{YZ} \perp$ plane R; plane P contains $\overleftrightarrow{YZ}$. State how many lines can be drawn that satisfy the conditions.

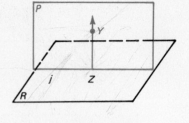

B 17. Lines that lie in P and intersect R at point Z.

18. Lines that lie in P and are perpendicular to line j at Z.

19. Lines that lie in R and are perpendicular to j at Z.

20. Lines in neither P nor R but perpendicular to j at Z.

21. Lines in P and perpendicular to $\overleftrightarrow{ZY}$ at Y.

22. Lines in R and perpendicular to $\overleftrightarrow{ZY}$ at Y.

Copy everything shown. Supply the reasons needed to complete the proof of Theorem 2-7.

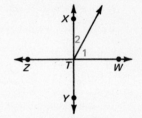

Given: $\angle 1$ and $\angle 2$ are adj. acute $\underline{\hspace{-2mm}\measuredangle}$;
$\overleftrightarrow{XY} \perp \overleftrightarrow{ZW}$

Prove: $\angle 1$ and $\angle 2$ are comp. $\underline{\hspace{-2mm}\measuredangle}$.

Proof:

STATEMENTS	REASONS
23. $\overleftrightarrow{XY} \perp \overleftrightarrow{ZW}$	23. ?
24. $\angle XTW$ is a rt. $\angle$.	24. ?
25. $m\angle XTW = 90$	25. ?
26. $m\angle 1 + m\angle 2 = m\angle XTW$	26. ?
27. $m\angle 1 + m\angle 2 = 90$	27. ?
28. $\angle 1$ and $\angle 2$ are comp. $\underline{\hspace{-2mm}\measuredangle}$.	28. ?

29. Copy what is shown for Theorem 2-4 on page 55; then write a proof in two-column form. (*Hint:* Show that $\angle 1$ and $\angle 2$ have equal measures.)

30. Copy what is shown for Theorem 2-5 on page 55; then write a proof in two-column form. (*Hint:* Show that $\angle 3$ and $\angle 4$ are right angles. Then apply Theorem 2-4.)

C 31. Copy what is shown for Theorem 2-6 on page 55; then write a proof in two-column form. (*Hint:* Use the facts that $m\angle 5 + m\angle 6 = 180$ and $m\angle 5 = m\angle 6$ to show that $m\angle 5 = 90$ and $\angle 5$ is a rt. $\angle$.)

32. Write a proof in two-column form.

Given: A plane figure;
$m\angle 3 = m\angle 4$;
$m\angle 2 = m\angle 5$

Prove: $\angle 5$ and $\angle 1$ are comp. $\underline{\hspace{-2mm}\measuredangle}$.

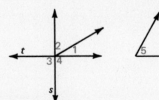

2-6 *Complementary and Supplementary Angles*

Notice in the following proof of Theorem 2-9 how some statements can be written in pairs supported by the same reason.

THEOREM 2-9 **If two angles are complementary to the same angle, they are congruent to each other.**

Given: $\angle 1$ is comp. to $\angle 3$;
$\qquad \angle 2$ is comp. to $\angle 3$.

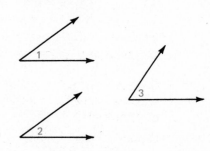

Prove: $\angle 1 \cong \angle 2$

Proof:

STATEMENTS	REASONS
1. $\angle 1$ is comp. to $\angle 3$; $\angle 2$ is comp. to $\angle 3$.	1. Given
2. $m\angle 1 + m\angle 3 = 90$; $m\angle 2 + m\angle 3 = 90$	2. Definition of comp. $\angle$s.
3. $m\angle 1 + m\angle 3 = m\angle 2 + m\angle 3$	3. Substitution principle
4. $\qquad m\angle 3 = \qquad m\angle 3$	4. Reflexive prop. of equality
5. $m\angle 1 \qquad = m\angle 2$	5. Subtraction prop. of equality
6. $\angle 1 \cong \angle 2$	6. Definition of $\cong$ $\angle$s.

THEOREM 2-10 **If two angles are complementary to two congruent angles, they are congruent to each other.**

Given: $\angle 1$ is comp. to $\angle 3$;
$\qquad \angle 2$ is comp. to $\angle 4$;
$\qquad \angle 3 \cong \angle 4$

Prove: $\angle 1 \cong \angle 2$

The proof is left as Exercise 27.

THEOREM 2-11 If two angles are supplementary to the same angle, they are congruent to each other.

Given: ∠5 is supp. to ∠7;
       ∠6 is supp. to ∠7.

Prove: ∠5 ≅ ∠6

The proof is left as Exercise 28.

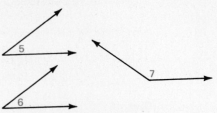

THEOREM 2-12 If two angles are supplementary to two congruent angles, they are congruent to each other.

Given: ∠5 is supp. to ∠7;
       ∠6 is supp. to ∠8;
       ∠7 ≅ ∠8

Prove: ∠5 ≅ ∠6

Proof:

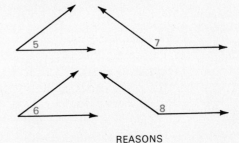

STATEMENTS	REASONS
1. ∠5 is supp. to ∠7; ∠6 is supp. to ∠8.	1. Given
2. $m\angle 5 + m\angle 7 = 180$; $m\angle 6 + m\angle 8 = 180$	2. Definition of supp. ∆.
3. $m\angle 5 + m\angle 7 = m\angle 6 + m\angle 8$	3. Substitution principle
4. $\angle 7 \cong$ $\angle 8$	4. Given
5. $m\angle 7 =$ $m\angle 8$	5. Definition of ≅ ∆.
6. $m\angle 5$ $= m\angle 6$	6. Subtraction prop. of equality
7. ∠5 ≅ ∠6	7. Definition of ≅ ∆.

Oral Exercises

In the plane figure, $\overrightarrow{RS} \perp \overleftrightarrow{TV}$. Name the figures described.

1. Two right angles ⊤
2. An obtuse angle
3. A pair of complementary angles TRS,
4. Two angles that are supplementary but not congruent TVS BVS
5. Two congruent supplementary angles TrS, SrT
6. Two angles that are adjacent to ∠XRS

      SrT

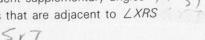

Given the plane figure with angles having the measures shown, name the figures described.

7. Two complementary adjacent angles $90° - 40° - 50°$
8. Two complementary nonadjacent angles
9. Two right angles
10. An angle that is supplementary to $\angle BCD$
11. Two segments perpendicular to $\overline{AD}$
12. An angle, with vertex C, that is not adjacent to $\angle BCA$
$D A C$

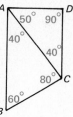

Written Exercises

A

Write the definition, postulate, or theorem that supports the statement.

1. $\angle 2$ is supplementary to $\angle 1$, and $\angle 3$ is supplementary to $\angle 1$.
2. If $\angle 3$ and $\angle 2$ are both supplementary to $\angle 1$, then $\angle 3 \cong \angle 2$.
3. If $m\angle 3 = m\angle 6$, then $\angle 3 \cong \angle 6$.
4. Since $\angle 1$ is supplementary to $\angle 2$, and $\angle 5$ is supplementary to $\angle 6$, then, if $\angle 2 \cong \angle 6$, $\angle 1 \cong \angle 5$.

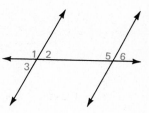

In Exercises 5–8, draw the figure described.

5. Two adjacent complementary angles
6. Two complementary angles that are not adjacent angles
7. Two adjacent supplementary angles
8. Two supplementary angles that are not adjacent angles

Complete the proofs by supplying reasons.

Given: $\angle 3$ is supp. to $\angle 2$.

Prove: $m\angle 1 = m\angle 3$

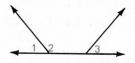

Proof:

STATEMENTS	REASONS
9. $\angle 3$ is supp. to $\angle 2$.	9. ?
10. $\angle 1$ is supp. to $\angle 2$.	10. ?
11. $\angle 1 \cong \angle 3$	11. ?
12. $m\angle 1 = m\angle 3$	12. ?

Given: The plane figure;
      ∠AXC and ∠BXD are rt. ⓢ.

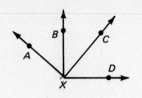

Prove: ∠AXB ≅ ∠CXD

Proof:

STATEMENTS	REASONS
13. ∠AXC and ∠BXD are rt. ⓢ.	13. ?
14. $\overrightarrow{XA} \perp \overrightarrow{XC}$; $\overrightarrow{XB} \perp \overrightarrow{XD}$	14. ?
15. ∠AXB is comp. to ∠BXC; ∠CXD is comp. to ∠BXC.	15. ?
16. ∠AXB ≅ ∠CXD	16. ?

Given: $\overleftrightarrow{EF} \perp$ plane M;
      $\overleftrightarrow{EF}$, $\overleftrightarrow{JK}$, and $\overrightarrow{TR}$ are coplanar;
      $\overleftrightarrow{EF}$, $\overleftrightarrow{GH}$, and $\overrightarrow{TS}$ are coplanar;
      ∠ETS ≅ ∠ETR

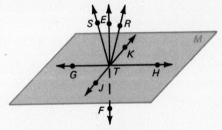

Prove: m∠STG = m∠RTK

Proof:

	STATEMENTS	REASONS
B	17. $\overleftrightarrow{EF} \perp$ plane M	17. ?
	18. $\overleftrightarrow{EF} \perp \overleftrightarrow{GH}$; $\overleftrightarrow{EF} \perp \overleftrightarrow{JK}$	18. ?
	19. ∠STG is comp. to ∠ETS; ∠RTK is comp. to ∠ETR	19. ?
	20. ∠ETS ≅ ∠ETR	20. ?
	21. ∠STG ≅ ∠RTK	21. ?
	22. m∠STG = m∠RTK	22. ?

Copy what is shown. Write proofs in two-column form.

23. Given: $\overline{AC} \perp \overline{BC}$;
       ∠3 is comp. to ∠1.

    Prove: ∠3 ≅ ∠2

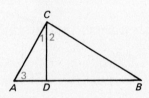

24. Given: The plane figure; ∠RXS and
       ∠RYS are rt. ⓢ; ∠5 ≅ ∠6

    Prove: ∠7 ≅ ∠8

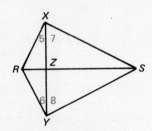

25. Given: $m\angle CBD = 40$;
$m\angle CDF = 40$

Prove: $\angle ABD \cong \angle CDE$

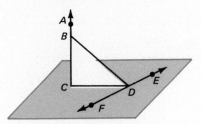

26. Given: $m\angle 2 = 120$;
$m\angle 8 = 60$

Prove: $\angle 4$ and $\angle 7$ are supp. ∠s.

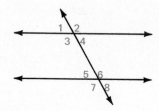

C **27.** Copy what is shown for Theorem 2-10 on page 59. Then write a proof in two-column form.

28. Copy what is shown for Theorem 2-11 on page 60. Write a proof in two-column form.

2-7 *Demonstration of a Theorem*

A demonstration of a theorem consists of five parts:

1. Statement
2. Figure
3. Given or Hypothesis: A list, in terms of the figure, of the conditions assumed in the theorem.
4. Prove or Conclusion: A list, in terms of the figure, of what is to be deduced.
5. Proof: A series of statements, supported by reasons, that lead to the desired conclusion.

Some demonstrations include an *Analysis,* written between the Conclusion and the Proof. See the paragraph immediately following the proof of Theorem 2-13.

The following suggestions may help you to develop ability to prove theorems.

1. Draw a reasonably accurate figure, avoiding special cases that might mislead. When a theorem refers to *an* angle, for instance, you should not draw a *right* angle.
2. When a theorem is not stated in if-then form, try to state it in that form.
3. Unless you discover a method of proof at once, try reasoning back from the conclusion. Think: "The conclusion will be true if __?__ is true. This, in turn, will be true if __?__ is true. . . ." Sometimes this procedure leads back to a given statement. If so, you have found a method of proof.
4. When Suggestion 3 does not work, studying the proofs of previous theorems may suggest methods to try.

Suggestion 2 sometimes helps a person identify what is given and what is to be proved. Thus, Theorem 2-13 may be simpler to demonstrate in the form: "If two lines intersect, the vertical angles formed are congruent."

THEOREM 2-13 Vertical angles are congruent.

Given: $\angle 1$ and $\angle 2$ are vert. $\angle$s.

Prove: $\angle 1 \cong \angle 2$

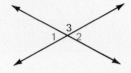

Proof:

STATEMENTS	REASONS
1. $\angle 1$ is supp. to $\angle 3$.	1. If the ext. sides of two adj. $\angle$s lie in a line, the $\angle$s are supp.
2. $\angle 2$ is supp. to $\angle 3$.	2. Same as Reason 1.
3. $\angle 1 \cong \angle 2$	3. Supplements of the same $\angle$ are $\cong$.

If you had proved the theorem yourself, you would have needed to reason as follows: "To prove that $\angle 1$ and $\angle 2$ are congruent angles, you can use the fact that each angle is a supplement of $\angle 3$." This statement could, as a guide to readers, be labeled *Analysis*. If included in the demonstration, it would be placed between the Conclusion and the Proof.

The following two theorems are particularly awkward to state in if-then form. Before looking at the theorems you should review the reflexive, symmetric, and transitive properties of equality, page 19. Proofs of the following congruence properties depend upon those properties of equality.

THEOREM 2-14 Congruence of segments is reflexive, symmetric, and transitive.

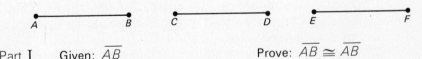

Part I   Given: $\overline{AB}$ Prove: $\overline{AB} \cong \overline{AB}$

Part II   Given: $\overline{AB} \cong \overline{CD}$ Prove: $\overline{CD} \cong \overline{AB}$

Part III   Given: $\overline{AB} \cong \overline{CD}$; $\overline{CD} \cong \overline{EF}$ Prove: $\overline{AB} \cong \overline{EF}$

THEOREM 2-15 Congruence of angles is reflexive, symmetric, and transitive.

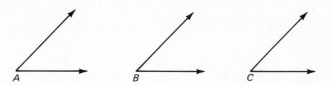

Part I Given: $\angle A$ Prove: $\angle A \cong \angle A$

Part II Given: $\angle A \cong \angle B$ Prove: $\angle B \cong \angle A$

Part III Given: $\angle A \cong \angle B$; $\angle B \cong \angle C$ Prove: $\angle A \cong \angle C$

Oral Exercises

State the property of equality that is illustrated.

1. If $j = k$, then $k = j$.
2. $13 = 13$
3. If $b = c$ and $c = d$, then $b = d$. ~~Sub~~

State the part of the theorem on segment congruence that applies.

4. $\overline{RS} \cong \overline{RS}$
5. If $\overline{RS} \cong \overline{TW}$, then $\overline{TW} \cong \overline{RS}$. *symetric*
6. If $\overline{RS} \cong \overline{TW}$ and $\overline{TW} \cong \overline{XY}$, then $\overline{RS} \cong \overline{XY}$. *Transitive*

State the part of the theorem on angle congruence that applies.

7. If $\angle X \cong \angle Y$ and $\angle Y \cong \angle Z$, then $\angle X \cong \angle Z$. *transitive*
8. If $\angle 1 \cong \angle 2$, then $\angle 2 \cong \angle 1$. *symetric*
9. $\angle PDE \cong \angle PDE$ *reflexive*

10. Suppose you begin a proof by stating: "$\angle ACB \cong \angle YCX$." What reason can you give to support the assertion? *Vertical are ≅*

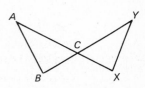

Written Exercises

A 1–5. List, in order, the five essential parts of a demonstration of a theorem.

Complete the proof by supplying reasons.

Given: $\angle 2 \cong \angle 3$

Prove: $\angle 1 \cong \angle 4$

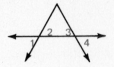

Proof:

STATEMENTS	REASONS
6. $\angle 1 \cong \angle 2$	6. ?
7. $\angle 2 \cong \angle 3$	7. ?
8. $\angle 1 \cong \angle 3$	8. ?
9. $\angle 3 \cong \angle 4$	9. ?
10. $\angle 1 \cong \angle 4$	10. ?

Each figure shows two intersecting lines. The measures of two angles are represented. Find the numerical value of x.

11.

2x   80

13.

$\frac{2}{3}$x

90

15.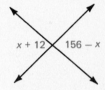

$x + 12$ $156 - x$

12.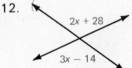

$2x + 28$

$3x - 14$

14.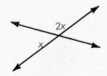

$2x$

x

16.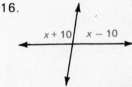

$x + 10$ $x - 10$

In Exercises 17–19, use the statement: If two angles are supplementary and one of them is a right angle, then the other is a right angle.

B 17. Draw a figure.   18. List the Given.   19. State the Conclusion.

In Exercises 20–22, use the statement: If two angles are complementary and the measure of one of them is less than 30, then the measure of the other one is greater than 60.

20. Draw a figure.   21. List the Given.   22. State the Conclusion.

In Exercises 23–25, use the statement: If two vertical angles are supplementary, then each of the angles is a right angle.

23. Draw a figure.   24. List the Given.   25. State the Conclusion.

In Exercises 26–28, use the statement: If three noncoplanar rays have the same endpoint, the sum of the measures of two of the angles formed is greater than the measure of the third angle.

26. Draw a figure.   27. List the Given.   28. State the Conclusion.

Write proofs in two-column form.

29. Given: $\angle 1 \cong \angle 3$
    Prove: $\angle 2 \cong \angle 3$ *transitive*

    Transitive

30. Given: $\angle 4 \cong \angle 1$?
    Prove: $\angle 4 \cong \angle 2$

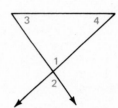

31. Given: $\overleftrightarrow{AB}, \overleftrightarrow{CD}, \overleftrightarrow{EF}$ intersect at X;
    $\angle EXB \cong \angle EXD$

    Prove: $\angle AXF \cong \angle CXF$

32. Given: $\overleftrightarrow{AB}, \overleftrightarrow{CD}, \overleftrightarrow{EF}$ intersect at X;
    $\angle EXB \cong \angle BXD$; $m\angle AXC = j$

    Prove: $m\angle EXB = j$

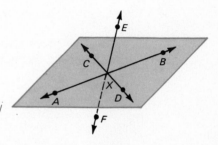

C 33. Write a complete demonstration of the statement, *Congruence of segments is transitive.*

34. Herb tried to make up a difficult problem by drawing two intersecting lines and assigning the angle measures shown. Explain why Herb's problem didn't make sense.

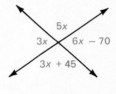

Ex. 34

Challenge

A block in the shape of a cube is made of white plastic. The exterior is painted red. The block is separated, by cuts parallel to the faces, into twenty-seven cubical blocks. How many of the small blocks have three red faces? Two red faces? One red face? No red face?

Self-Test State the theorem or postulate that supports the assertion.

1. There is a ray, $\overrightarrow{AX}$, in a half-plane with edge $\overleftrightarrow{AC}$ such that $m\angle XAC = 30$.
2. $\angle C$ can be bisected.
3. $\angle 2 \cong \angle 3$
4. If $\angle 1 \cong \angle 2$, then $j \perp k$.
5. If $j \perp k$, then $\angle 5$ and $\angle 6$ are comp. $\angle$.
6. If $\angle 5$ is supp. to $\angle 7$, and $\angle 6$ is supp. to $\angle 7$, then $\angle 5 \cong \angle 6$.
7. Complete the definition. Perpendicular lines are two ___?___ .
8. List the five parts of a demonstration of a theorem.
9. If $\overline{AB}$ is any segment, $\overline{AB} \cong \overline{AB}$, because congruence of segments is ___?___ .
10. If $\angle C \cong \angle D$ and $\angle D \cong \angle E$, then $\angle C \cong \angle E$, because congruence of angles is ___?___ .

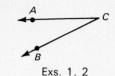

Exs. 1, 2

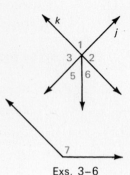

Exs. 3-6

Check your answers with those printed at the back of the book.

CHAPTER SUMMARY

1. *Angles*
   Congruent angles are angles that have equal measures.
   The measure of an angle is a real number between 0 and 180.
   An angle may be acute, right, or obtuse.
   Two angles may be complementary, supplementary, or neither.
   The Angle Addition Postulate is used to add the measures of two adjacent angles that lie in a half plane.
   If the exterior sides of two adjacent angles lie in a line, then the angles are supplementary.
   An angle has exactly one bisector.

2. *Perpendicular lines and right angles*.
   Perpendicular lines form right angles.
   All right angles are congruent.
   Perpendicular lines form congruent adjacent angles.
   If the exterior sides of two adjacent acute angles lie in perpendicular lines, the angles are complementary.
   In a plane, through a given point on a line, there is exactly one perpendicular to the line.

3. Two angles are congruent if the two angles are:
   a. Complementary to the same angle or to congruent angles.
   b. Supplementary to the same angle or to congruent angles.
   c. Vertical angles.

4. A demonstration of a theorem consists of five parts.
   Statement   Figure   Given   Conclusion   Proof

CHAPTER TEST

Exercises 1–14 refer to the plane figure with $\overleftrightarrow{ER} \perp \overleftrightarrow{AC}$.

1. $\angle DRC$ is the union of __?__ and __?__ .
2. Name a pair of vertical angles. _ARC_
3. Name an acute angle that is adjacent to $\angle DRC$.
4. $m\angle ARE + m\angle ERD = m\angle$ _ARD_
5. $m\angle ERC =$ _DRC_
6. Is $\angle ERD$ complementary to $\angle DRC$?
7. Is $\angle ERD$ complementary to $\angle ARB$? _No_
8. Is $\angle ARD$ supplementary to $\angle DRC$?
9. If $m\angle ARB = 28$, then $m\angle ARD =$ _152_
10. If $m\angle ARD = 10x + 30$ and $m\angle DRC = 3x + 7$, then $x =$ _12_ .
11. In a plane, how many lines can be drawn perpendicular to $\overleftrightarrow{BR}$ at point D?
12. Name a point that is in the interior of $\angle ERC$ but in the exterior of $\angle DRC$. _58_
13. If $m\angle BRC = 148$, then $m\angle ERD =$ __?__ .
14. State the theorem that supports the fact that $\angle ARD$ is supplementary to $\angle DRC$.

15. $\overrightarrow{OH}$ bisects $\angle JOK$. If $m\angle HOK = 5x - 1$ and $m\angle JOK = 9x + 5$, then $x =$ __?__ .

In Exercises 16–20, supply the missing reasons.

Given: $l \perp t$;
      $\angle 1$ is comp. to $\angle 3$

Prove: $m\angle 2 = m\angle 3$

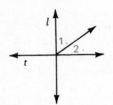

Proof:

STATEMENTS	REASONS
16. $l \perp t$	16. __?__ Given
17. $\angle 1$ is comp. to $\angle 2$	17. __?__ Given
18. $\angle 1$ is comp. to $\angle 3$	18. __?__
19. $\angle 2 \cong \angle 3$	19. __?__
20. $m\angle 2 = m\angle 3$	20. __?__

21. Write a proof in two-column form.
    Given: $\overleftrightarrow{AB}$, $\overleftrightarrow{CD}$, and $\overleftrightarrow{EF}$ intersect at X; $\angle 1 \cong \angle 2$
    Prove: $\overleftrightarrow{XC}$ bisects $\angle AXE$.

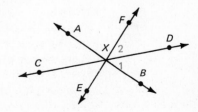

2-1 *Angles and Half-planes*

1. An angle is the union of two __?__ rays that have the same __?__ .

2. A line separates a plane into two ~~half~~

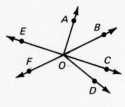

Exercises 3–5 refer to the plane figure.

3. Name a pair of vertical angles.

4. Is ∠AOC adjacent to ∠BOC? *~~∠E∠OF~~*

5. Name a point that lies in the interior of ∠FOC. *~~∠~~*   Exs. 3–5

2-2 *The Protractor*

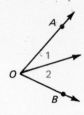

6. Congruent angles are angles that have equal __?__ .

7. If *b* is the measure of an angle, then __?__ > *b* > __?__ .

8. If $m\angle 1 = 5x$, $m\angle 2 = 7x - 2$,   and $m\angle AOB = 11x + 4$, then $x = $ __?__ .

Ex. 8

2-3 *Special Angles*

9. The measure of an acute angle is ____?____ 90.
   $$(<, =, >)$$

10. If ∠A is complementary to ∠B, then $m\angle A + m\angle B = $ __?__ .

11. $\overrightarrow{YP}$ bisects ∠XYZ if P lies in the interior of ∠XYZ and $\angle X\underline{~?~} \cong \angle \underline{P~?~}$.

12. If the exterior sides of two adjacent angles lie in a line, then the angles are __?__ .

2-4 *Forming Certain Angles*

Classify each statement as true or false.

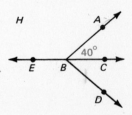

13. In half-plane *H*, there is exactly one ray, $\overrightarrow{BA}$, such that $m\angle ABC = 40$. T

14. If $m\angle DBA = 82$, then $m\angle ABC < m\angle DBC$. T

15. If $m\angle EBD = 140$, then $\overrightarrow{BC}$ bisects ∠DBA. T

2-5 *Right Angles and Perpendicular Lines*

16. All right angles are __?~~93~~__

17. If two lines form congruent adjacent angles, the lines are __?__ .

18. If the exterior sides of two adjacent acute angles lie in perpendicular lines, the angles are __?__ .

19. In a plane, how many lines can be drawn that are perpendicular to a given line at a point on the line? *1*

2-6 Complementary and Supplementary Angles

20. If $\angle R$ is a supplement of $\angle T$, then $m\angle R + m\angle T = \underline{180}$.
21. If $m\angle A + m\angle B = 180$ and $m\angle B + m\angle C = 180$, then $\angle A \cong \underline{?C}$.
22. If two angles are congruent and complementary, then each has measure $\underline{?45}$
23. If $\angle 1$ is supplementary to $\angle 2$ and $m\angle 1 < 70$, then $m\angle 2 > \underline{20}$.

2-7 Demonstration of a Theorem

In Exercises 24–26, use the statement: If two angles are supplementary and the measure of one of them is less than 90, then the measure of the other one is greater than 90.

24. Draw a figure.
25. List, in terms of the figure, what is given.
26. List, in terms of the figure, what is to be proved.

REVIEWING ALGEBRAIC SKILLS

Solve each equation.

1. $\dfrac{x}{2} = 4$

2. $\dfrac{2x}{5} = 4$

3. $\dfrac{3y}{4} - 3 = 0$

4. $\dfrac{z}{3} + 2 = 5$

5. $\dfrac{j}{7} - 1 = 3$

6. $\dfrac{u}{10} - \dfrac{1}{5} = 3$

7. $\dfrac{x}{4} + \dfrac{1}{2} = 3$

8. $e = \dfrac{e}{5} + 2$

9. $\dfrac{4}{m} + \dfrac{2}{m} = 1$

10. $\dfrac{6}{w} + 2 = 4$

11. $\dfrac{e}{5} = \dfrac{4}{15}$

12. $\dfrac{x}{7} = \dfrac{5}{2}$

13. $\dfrac{8}{y} = \dfrac{2}{7}$

14. $\dfrac{8}{3} = \dfrac{10}{k}$

15. $\dfrac{3}{8} = \dfrac{e}{8}$

16. $\dfrac{2}{12} = \dfrac{3}{m}$

17. $\dfrac{g}{9} + \dfrac{2}{3}g = 7$

18. $\dfrac{9}{2} + \dfrac{3}{5}e = \dfrac{3}{4}$

19. $\dfrac{n}{8} - \dfrac{n}{12} = \dfrac{1}{8}$

20. $\dfrac{7}{2e} - \dfrac{5}{3e} = 2$

21. $\dfrac{2}{7b} - \dfrac{1}{4} = 3$

22. $\dfrac{x-1}{5} + \dfrac{x-2}{2} = 3$

23. $\dfrac{y-2}{3} + \dfrac{3y-5}{6} = \dfrac{8}{3}$

24. $\dfrac{3z-1}{2} - \dfrac{z+2}{5} = z + \dfrac{1}{10}$

Express the value of x correct to two decimal places.

25. $1.5x + 6 = 7$
26. $4.2x - 1 = 5$
27. $0.6x + 4 = 19$

28. $0.7x - 2 = 17$
29. $1.8x + 4 = 0.4x + 7$
30. $3.9x - 2 = 1.7x + 10$

programming in BASIC

In the computer programs we used in Chapter 1, data was secured for calculations by means of an *input statement*. In this unit we will consider another means for providing the computer with data. Study this program.

```
10    DATA 30,131,65,118,90,75
20    LET N=1
30    PRINT "MEASURE","MEASURE"
40    PRINT "OF THE","OF THE"
50    PRINT "ANGLE","SUPPLEMENT"
60    PRINT
70    READ A
80    LET S=180-A
90    PRINT A,S
100   IF N=6 THEN 130
110   LET N=N+1
120   GOTO 70
130   END
```

Line Number	Instruction to the Computer
10	Store this set of numbers to be used by the program.
20	Set N equal to 1.
30,40,50	Print a heading for a table. (By placing the words in separate quotes and separated by a comma, you instruct the computer to print the first word at the beginning of the line and the second word starting in print-space 16.)
60	Line space (nothing printed)
70	Give A the value of the next item on the data line.
80	Calculate 180-A and let S take that value.
90	Print the new values of A and S.
100	When the value of N is 6 (the number of items in data), branch to the END statement.
110	Add 1 to N. Let N equal this new value.
120	Branch to line 70 where another item of data will be read.
130	Stop.

This program illustrates the repeated reading of data by the computer. N is used as a *counter*. Type, LIST, and RUN this program. This is the RUN of the program.

MEASURE OF THE ANGLE	MEASURE OF THE SUPPLEMENT
30	150
131	49
65	115
118	62
90	90
75	105

In this program the computer had to run through lines 70, 80, 90, and 100 six times. We call this process *looping*. There is another way to instruct the computer to do this same looping.

The program has been modified as shown below to contain a pair of statements, one beginning with FOR and the other beginning with NEXT. The first time the computer reaches line 65, it gives I the value 1. The instruction "NEXT I" adds 1 to the value of I, and the computer branches back to line 65. After all of the values of I have been used, the computer goes to the line following the NEXT statement, which in this case is END.

```
10   DATA 30,131,65,118,90,75
30   PRINT "MEASURE","MEASURE"
40   PRINT "OF THE","OF THE"
50   PRINT "ANGLE","SUPPLEMENT"
60   PRINT
65   FOR I=1 TO 6
70   READ A
80   LET S=180-A
90   PRINT A,S
100  NEXT I
130  END
```

Modify the program which is in the computer to this form. Then LIST and RUN the program. Your print-out should be exactly the same as for the original program.

1. Modify the program in this unit to print out the measure of the complement of a given angle. Some of the measures are greater than or equal to 90. Therefore your program should plan to skip over those measures. Your print-out should be:

```
MEASURE          MEASURE
OF THE           OF THE
ANGLE            COMPLEMENT

  30               60
  65               25
  75               15
THE OTHER ANGLES HAVE NO COMPLEMENT.
```

2. Write a program that has the following measures as data:

   157, 30, 65, 90, 72, 117, 6, 89

   The program is to print the measure of the angle, state whether the angle is acute, obtuse, or right, print the measure of its supplement, and the measure of its complement (if a complement exists). The following could be a possible print-out for the first two items.

```
THE MEASURE OF THE ANGLE IS 157
THE ANGLE IS OBTUSE
THE MEASURE OF THE SUPPLEMENT IS 23

THE MEASURE OF THE ANGLE IS 30
THE ANGLE IS ACUTE
THE MEASURE OF THE SUPPLEMENT IS 150
THE MEASURE OF THE COMPLEMENT IS 60
```

extra for experts

Paradoxes

Sometimes a seemingly sound analysis of a situation leads to a conclusion that contradicts fact. Twenty-four hundred years ago, Zeno stated examples that some of the world's best thinkers have had trouble explaining away. One of Zeno's paradoxes follows.

Achilles and the tortoise
Because Achilles can run several times as fast as the tortoise, the tortoise is given a head start when they race. Achilles starts at *A*, the tortoise at *B*. By the time Achilles reaches *B*, the tortoise has gone to *C*. By the time Achilles reaches *C*, the tortoise has gone to *D*. And so on. How *can* Achilles overtake the tortoise?

Sometimes statements that sound logical have built-in contradictions. Consider the predicament of the barber in the village described below.

The Barber
All men in a certain village are clean-shaven. Each man shaves himself if and only if he is not shaved by the village's only barber, a man. Who shaves the barber? Not another man, for only one villager is a barber. Not the barber himself, for no man shaved by the barber shaves himself.

Some other examples follow. Regard them not as problems to be solved, but as situations worth your careful thinking.

1. Consider the truth or falsehood of: This statement is a falsehood.
2. The array below shows that the number of even positive integers is as great as the number of positive integers.

   1   2   3   4   .   .   . n .   .   .
   2   4   6   8   .   .   . $2n$.   .   .

3. An egg dropped from a point one meter above the floor cannot reach the floor. For it must fall the first half-meter; then it must fall half of the remaining half-meter; then it must fall half of the remaining quarter meter; then half of the remaining eighth meter. And so on.
4. $\overline{AB}$ is as long as $\overline{CD}$, below, because $\overline{AB}$ contains as many points as $\overline{CD}$.

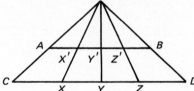

5. The cruel ruler of a certain land has a policy that enables him to imprison innocent people. Each citizen who answers questions truthfully goes free, whereas a person who responds falsely is thrown into prison. The ruler simply asks each opponent the question: "Where are you going?" Whatever the answer is, the unfortunate person is thrown into prison with the explanation: "You spoke falsely. As you must admit, you were going to prison."

What answer can one give to confound the ruler?

3

PARALLEL LINES
AND PLANES

When Lines and Planes Are Parallel

Objectives

1. Distinguish between parallel lines and skew lines.
2. Identify the angles that are formed when two lines are cut by a transversal.
3. Recognize the angle relationships that exist when two parallel lines are cut by a transversal.
4. Write indirect proofs.

3-1 *Definitions*

Lines that lie in the same plane and have no point in common are called **parallel lines** (∥ lines). Consider lines l and m in the figure shown. Note that lines l and m lie in one plane, the plane that contains points E, F, G, and H. Since l and m have no common point, l is parallel to m ($l \parallel m$).

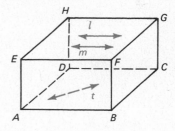

Lines that have no point in common are not necessarily parallel. Note that the definition of parallel lines requires that the lines be coplanar. Lines l and t have no point in common, but these lines are non-coplanar. Lines such as these that have no point in common and do not lie in any one plane are said to be **skew lines**.

In the figure, do you think that the lines containing $\overline{AB}$ and $\overline{HG}$ are parallel? Would your answer be the same for the lines containing $\overline{BF}$ and $\overline{HG}$?

We also speak of planes being parallel. **Parallel planes** are planes that have no point in common. The plane containing points A, B, C and D and the one containing points E, F, G, and H are parallel planes.

If a line and a plane have no point in common, we say the line is *parallel* to the plane. For example, in the figure on the preceding page, line *t* is parallel to the plane containing points *E*, *F*, *G*, and *H*.

Remember that two distinct lines intersect, are parallel, or are skew. Two distinct planes either intersect or are parallel.

You may already be familiar with the terms explained below.

A line such as line *t* is called a *transversal*. A transversal (trans.) is a line that intersects two or more coplanar lines in different points. Note that the transversal lies in the same plane as the two lines it intersects.

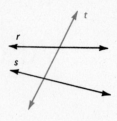

When a transversal is drawn, some of the angles are given special names according to their location in the figure. We name the angles as follows.

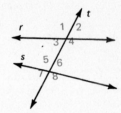

Interior angles: Angles 3, 4, 5 and 6
Exterior angles: Angles 1, 2, 7 and 8

Corresponding angles (corr. ∠): A pair of angles such as ∠2 and ∠6 are called corresponding angles. Note that the two angles are on the same side of the transversal, they have different vertices, and one is an exterior angle while the other is an interior angle. The other pairs of corresponding angles are ∠1 and ∠5; ∠3 and ∠7; ∠4 and ∠8.

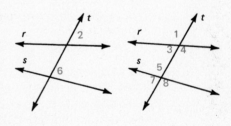

Alternate interior angles (alt. int. ∠): Two interior angles, such as ∠4 and ∠5, that have different vertices and are on opposite sides of the transversal are called alternate interior angles. The other pair of alternate interior angles is ∠3 and ∠6.

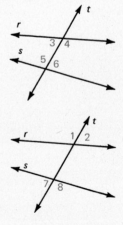

Alternate exterior angles (alt. ext. ∠). Two exterior angles, such as ∠1 and ∠8, that have different vertices and are on opposite sides of the transversal are called alternate exterior angles. The other pair of alternate exterior angles is ∠2 and ∠7.

Oral Exercises

In Exercises 1–6, name the figures described.

1. The transversal 2

2. Four pairs of corresponding angles 5, 6, 10, 12 7, 11, 9, 13

3. Two pairs of alternate interior angles

4. Two pairs of alternate exterior angles

5. Two pairs of interior angles on the same side of the transversal

6. Two pairs of exterior angles on the same side of the transversal 7 and 11

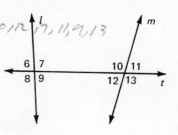

Classify each statement as true or false.

7. Two skew lines may be coplanar. F

8. If two lines are parallel, the lines are coplanar. T

9. Two skew lines may intersect. F

10. If two planes are parallel, any line in one of the planes is parallel to the other plane. T

11. If a line is parallel to a plane, every plane containing the line is parallel to the given plane. F

12. It is possible for each of two intersecting lines to be parallel to the same plane. T

13. When a transversal intersects two lines, four pairs of corresponding angles are formed. T

14. The angles that make up one pair of corresponding angles lie on opposite sides of the transversal. F

Written Exercises

Complete each of the following with one of the words *Always*, *Sometimes*, or *Never*.

A

1. Two skew lines are __?__ parallel.

2. Two parallel lines are __?__ coplanar.

3. A line in the plane of the ceiling and a line in the plane of the floor are __?__ parallel.

4. Two lines in the plane of the floor are __?__ skew.

5. If a line is parallel to a plane, a plane containing that line is __?__ parallel to the given plane.

6. Two lines parallel to the same plane are __?__ parallel to each other.

7. Two lines parallel to a third line are __?__ parallel to each other.

8. Two planes parallel to the same line are __?__ parallel to each other.

9. When there is a transversal of two lines, the three lines are __?__ coplanar.

10. Skew lines __?__ intersect.

11. Two planes parallel to the same plane are __?__ parallel to each other.

12. Two lines skew to a third line are __?__ skew to each other.
13. Two lines perpendicular to a third line are __?__ parallel to each other.
14. Through a point outside a plane there is __?__ more than one line parallel to the plane.

B 15. If a line intersects one of two parallel lines, then it __?__ intersects the other line also.
16. If a line is skew to the edge of a dihedral angle, then the line __?__ lies in one of the faces of the angle.
17. If each of three intersecting lines is skew to a fourth line, the three lines are __?__ coplanar.
18. If a line is parallel to the edge of a dihedral angle, the line is __?__ parallel to each face of the angle.
19. A plane containing point A is __?__ parallel to $\overleftrightarrow{BC}$.
20. A plane containing $\overleftrightarrow{AC}$ is __?__ parallel to $\overleftrightarrow{AB}$.

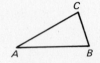

Exs. 19, 20

C 21. If the sides of two angles lie in parallel lines, the angles are __?__ congruent.
22. If line t is skew to line m, there __?__ exists a plane that contains line t and is parallel to line m.
23. If line m is skew to line k, there __?__ exists a line that is perpendicular to both m and k.
24. If line r is skew to line s, there __?__ exist many planes parallel to both r and s.
25. Planes R and S are cut by plane T in lines a and b. There __?__ exists a line skew to line a and parallel to line b.
26. Prove: If two parallel planes are cut by a third plane, the lines of intersection are parallel. (*Hint:* Show that the lines are coplanar and do not intersect.)

3-2 *When Lines are Parallel*

On a sheet of paper, draw a large figure similar to the one shown, with parallel lines l and m cut by transversal t. Use a protractor to measure ∠2 and ∠6. Did you find that the measures of the two angles are approximately equal? Select another pair of corresponding angles and compare their measures. Your findings should be consistent with the following postulate.

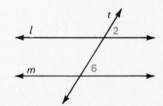

> **POSTULATE 11** If two parallel lines are cut by a transversal, corresponding angles are congruent.

We can use this postulate to prove the following two theorems.

THEOREM 3-1 If two parallel lines are cut by a transversal, alternate interior angles are congruent.

Given: $l \parallel m$; transversal t cuts l and m.

Prove: $\angle 1 \cong \angle 2$

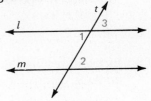

Proof:

STATEMENTS	REASONS
1. $l \parallel m$; t is a transversal	1. Given
2. $\angle 3 \cong \angle 2$	2. If two $\parallel$ lines are __?__ .
3. $\angle 1 \cong \angle 3$	3. Vert. $\angle$s are $\cong$.
4. $\angle 1 \cong \angle 2$	4. Congruence of $\angle$s is transitive.

In the same way the other pair of alternate interior angles can be proved congruent.

THEOREM 3-2 If a transversal is perpendicular to one of two parallel lines, it is perpendicular to the other one also.

Given: Transversal t cuts l and n;
$t \perp l$; $l \parallel n$

Prove: $t \perp n$

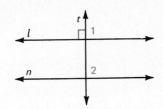

Proof:

STATEMENTS	REASONS
1. $t \perp l$	1. Given
2. $\angle 1$ is a rt. $\angle$.	2. If two lines are $\perp$, they form rt. $\angle$s.
3. $m\angle 1 = 90$	3. Definition of a rt. $\angle$
4. $l \parallel n$	4. Given
5. $\angle 1 \cong \angle 2$	5. If two parallel lines __?__ .
6. $m\angle 1 = m\angle 2$	6. Definition of congruent $\angle$s
7. $m\angle 2 = 90$	7. Substitution principle
8. $\angle 2$ is a rt. $\angle$.	8. Definition of a rt. $\angle$
9. $t \perp n$	9. If two lines meet to __?__ .

Given $r \parallel s$, classify each statement as true or false.

1. $m\angle 8 = m\angle 12$ 5. $m\angle 7 = m\angle 13$
2. $m\angle 6 = m\angle 11$ 6. $m\angle 6 = m\angle 8$
3. $m\angle 8 = m\angle 10$ 7. $m\angle 6 = m\angle 12$
4. $m\angle 9 = m\angle 10$ 8. $m\angle 10 = m\angle 11$

In Exercises 9–16, $s \parallel t$. The measure of one
angle is given. Find the measure of $\angle 8$.

9. $m\angle 2 = 110$ 13. $m\angle 3 = 2m\angle 4$
10. $m\angle 3 = 112$ 14. $m\angle 3 = 2m\angle 5$
11. $m\angle 4 = 80$ 15. $m\angle 1 = m\angle 2 - 20$
12. $m\angle 5 = 76$ 16. $m\angle 6 = m\angle 7 + 20$

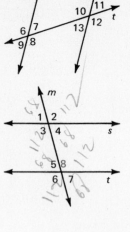

In Exercises 1–12, $l \parallel m$ and $t \parallel s$. Find the measure of the indicated
angle.

1. $m\angle 2 = 80$; $m\angle 12 = \underline{\ ?\ }$ 80°
2. $m\angle 15 = 78$; $m\angle 2 = \underline{\ ?\ }$ 78
3. $m\angle 8 = 110$; $m\angle 1 = \underline{\ ?\ }$ 110
4. $m\angle 13 = 84$; $m\angle 12 = \underline{\ ?\ }$ 84
5. $m\angle 5 = 86$; $m\angle 16 = \underline{\ ?\ }$ 86
6. $m\angle 3 = 108$; $m\angle 13 = \underline{\ ?\ }$ 72
7. $m\angle 1 = 102.5$; $m\angle 12 = \underline{\ ?\ }$ 45
8. $m\angle 7 = 81.7$; $m\angle 9 = \underline{\ ?\ }$ 99
9. $m\angle 5 + m\angle 7 = 158$; $m\angle 12 = \underline{\ ?\ }$ 79
10. $m\angle 6 + m\angle 14 = 198$; $m\angle 3 = \underline{\ ?\ }$ 99
11. $m\angle 12 + m\angle 15 = 156$; $m\angle 6 = \underline{\ ?\ }$ 162
12. $m\angle 9 + m\angle 14 = 188$; $m\angle 4 = \underline{\ ?\ }$ 86

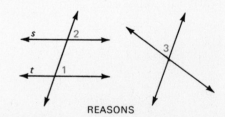

EXAMPLE

Given: $s \parallel t$; $\angle 1 \cong \angle 3$

Prove: $\angle 2 \cong \angle 3$

Proof:

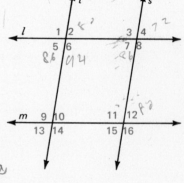

STATEMENTS	REASONS
1. $s \parallel t$	1. Given
2. $\angle 2 \cong \angle 1$	2. If two $\parallel$ lines are cut by a transversal, corr. $\angle$s are $\cong$.
3. $\angle 1 \cong \angle 3$	3. Given
4. $\angle 2 \cong \angle 3$	4. Congruence of $\angle$s is transitive.

13. Given: $l \parallel m$; $\angle 1 \cong \angle 4$
    Prove: $\angle 3 \cong \angle 4$
14. Given: $l \parallel m$; $\angle 2 \cong \angle 4$
    Prove: $\angle 3 \cong \angle 4$

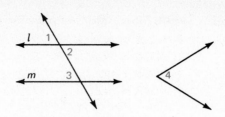

15. Given: The plane figure;
    $j \parallel k$; $k \parallel l$
    Prove: $\angle 1 \cong \angle 3$
16. Given: The plane figure;
    $j \parallel k$; $k \parallel l$
    Prove: $\angle 1 \cong \angle 6$

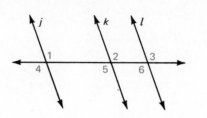

17. Given: The plane figure;
    $\overleftrightarrow{AB} \parallel \overleftrightarrow{EC}$; $\overleftrightarrow{BC} \parallel \overleftrightarrow{EF}$
    Prove: $\angle 1 \cong \angle 3$
18. Given: The plane figure;
    $\overleftrightarrow{AB} \parallel \overleftrightarrow{EC}$; $\overleftrightarrow{BC} \parallel \overleftrightarrow{EF}$
    Prove: $\angle 4 \cong \angle 6$
19. Given: The plane figure;
    $\overleftrightarrow{AB} \parallel \overleftrightarrow{EC}$; $\overleftrightarrow{BC} \parallel \overleftrightarrow{EF}$
    Prove: $\angle 3 \cong \angle 8$
20. Given: The plane figure;
    $\overleftrightarrow{AB} \parallel \overleftrightarrow{EC}$; $\overleftrightarrow{BC} \parallel \overleftrightarrow{EF}$
    Prove: $\angle 7 \cong \angle 4$

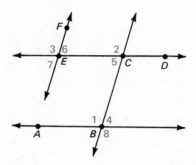

B 21. Given: $l \parallel n$
    Prove: $m\angle 3 + m\angle 6 = 180$
22. Given: $l \parallel n$
    Prove: $m\angle 2 + m\angle 7 = 180$
23. Given: $l \parallel n$
    Prove: $m\angle 5 + m\angle 2 = 180$
24. Given: $l \parallel n$
    Prove: $m\angle 8 + m\angle 3 = 180$

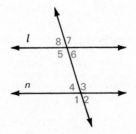

25. Prove: If two parallel lines are cut by a transversal, alternate exterior angles are congruent.
26. Prove: If two parallel lines are cut by a transversal, interior angles on the same side of the transversal are supplementary.

In the plane figure shown for Exercises 27–30, $a \parallel b$ and $c \parallel d$.

27. $m\angle 1 = 20(x - 2)$
    $m\angle 3 = 10(x + 3)$
    Find x.

28. $m\angle 1 = 11(x - 1)$
    $m\angle 6 = 2(4x + 11)$
    Find x.

29. $m\angle 9 = x^2 - x$
    $m\angle 2 = 2x + 108$
    Find x.

30. $m\angle 4 = 5x + 82$
    $m\angle 10 = x^2 - 3x + 18$
    Find x.

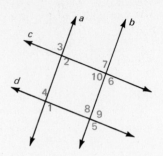

C 31. Given: The plane figure;
    $\overline{AE} \parallel \overline{BD}; \angle 3 \cong \angle 4$
    Prove: $\overline{BD}$ bisects $\angle EBC$.

32. Given: The plane figure;
    $\overline{AE} \parallel \overline{BD}; \overline{BD}$ bisects $\angle EBC$.
    Prove: $m\angle 5 = m\angle 6 + m\angle 2$

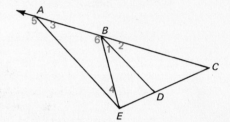

3-3 *Indirect Proof*

Indirect proof is a form of proof that is frequently used in everyday reasoning as well as in the study of mathematics. It is of particular value when a direct proof is difficult or impossible. The following is a simple example of the reasoning used in an indirect proof.

John and Leslie were looking at an American-made automobile and John said, "That is a 1969 model." Leslie disagreed and used the indirect method of reasoning.

Leslie: Suppose that the car is a 1969 model. Then it will have mountings for seat belts, since all American-made 1969 models had such mountings.

John: I accept that fact.

Leslie: Inspect the car and tell me if it has the mountings.

John: There are no such mountings in the car.

Leslie: Then the car was not made in 1969.

John: You are correct.

Although we write direct proofs in the two-column form, it seems more natural to write indirect proofs in paragraph form, and we shall use this form in this book.

EXAMPLE 1

Given: $\angle A \not\cong \angle B$

Prove: $\angle A$ and $\angle B$ are not both right angles.

To begin an indirect proof, you suppose that the negation of what you wish to prove is true.

Proof: Suppose $\angle A$ and $\angle B$ are right angles.

You then reason logically until you encounter a contradiction of a known fact.

Then by a theorem that says all right angles are congruent, we have $\angle A \cong \angle B$. But this contradicts our given fact that $\angle A \not\cong \angle B$.

You then point out that your assumption in your opening statement is false and that it follows that the desired conclusion is true.

Hence our assumption that $\angle A$ and $\angle B$ are both right angles is false, and it follows that $\angle A$ and $\angle B$ are not both right angles.

EXAMPLE 2

Given: Lines m and s cut by transversal t; $\angle 1 \not\cong \angle 2$

Prove: m and s are not parallel.

Proof: Suppose that m is parallel to s. Then, since $\angle 1$ and $\angle 2$ are corresponding angles, we have $\angle 1 \cong \angle 2$. But this contradicts the given fact that $\angle 1 \not\cong \angle 2$. Hence our supposition that m is parallel to s is false, and it follows that m is not parallel to s.

The success of an indirect proof depends on your finding a contradiction of a known fact. The known fact may be the hypothesis of the statement being proved, a postulate, or a theorem. Indirect proof is sometimes called "proof by contradiction."

1. To start an indirect proof, you suppose the __?__ of what you want to prove is __?__. Then you proceed to reason logically until you encounter a __?__ of a known fact. You can now conclude that your supposition is __?__. You can then state that the conclusion of the statement is __?__.

In Exercises 2–10, assume that you are to use the indirect method to prove the given statement. State the first sentence of your proof.

2. $AB = 17$
3. t is not equal to y.
4. l is not parallel to m.
5. $\angle 5 \cong \angle 6$
6. $AB + BC = AC$

7. $\angle D$ and $\angle E$ are right angles.
8. Mike is not the same age as Jane.
9. $\angle K$ is supplementary to $\angle M$.
10. $x > y$

Written
Exercises

Write an indirect proof of each of the following.

A
1. Given: $\angle D \not\cong \angle E$
   Prove: $\angle D$ and $\angle E$ are not both right angles.

2. Given: The plane figure;
   $\angle 1 \not\cong \angle 2$
   Prove: r is not parallel to s.

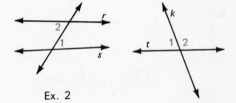

Ex. 2

3. Given: t is not perpendicular to k.
   Prove: $\angle 1 \not\cong \angle 2$
4. Given: $\angle 1 \not\cong \angle 2$
   Prove: t is not perpendicular to k.

Exs. 3, 4

B
5. Given: The plane figure;
   $m\angle 2 + m\angle 3 \neq 180$
   Prove: a is not parallel to b.
6. Given: The plane figure;
   $\angle 1 \not\cong \angle 4$
   Prove: a is not parallel to b.

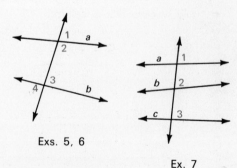

C
7. Given: The plane figure;
   $a \parallel c$; $\angle 2 \not\cong \angle 3$
   Prove: b is not parallel to a.

Exs. 5, 6

Ex. 7

8. Given: The plane figure;
$m\angle 2 \neq m\angle 3$
Prove: $m\angle 1 + m\angle 2 \neq m\angle 3 + m\angle 4$

Self-Test

1. Name the relative positions there are for two distinct lines in space.
2. Name the relative positions there are for two distinct planes in space.
3. If two coplanar lines do not intersect, they must be __?__ lines.

In the plane figure shown, lines *a*, *b*, and *c* are parallel to each other. Classify each statement as true or false.

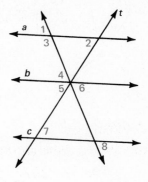

4. $\angle 3$ and $\angle 7$ are a pair of corresponding angles.
5. $\angle 2 \cong \angle 7$
6. $\angle 2$ and $\angle 5$ are a pair of corresponding angles.
7. $m\angle 1 = m\angle 6$
8. $\angle 4$ and $\angle 8$ are a pair of alternate exterior angles.
9. If *t* is perpendicular to line *a*, then *t* is also perpendicular to line *c*.
10. To begin an indirect proof, you suppose that the __?__ of what you wish to prove is true.
11. In an indirect proof you reason logically until you meet a __?__ of a known fact.

Challenge

A piece of wood contains a square hole, a circular hole, and a triangular hole as illustrated. Explain how one block of wood in the shape of a cube with a 2-cm edge can be cut down so that it will pass through, but will plug, each of the holes in turn.

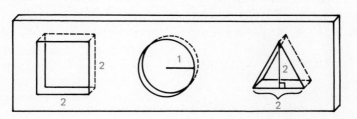

Careers

Construction

We come into contact with the products of the construction industry in almost every aspect of our daily lives, from the houses we live in, to the roads we travel upon. The building trades encompass a wide range of occupations: surveyors, carpenters, electricians, plumbers, bricklayers, and masons, to name a few.

Mathematics is important in the construction process from the planning stage to the finishing touches. Successful planning of any construction project involves applying mathematical principles to problems of structure and design. Precision in carrying out the architect's plans is needed to guarantee the quality of the finished structure.

A careful look at a building under construction will reveal applications of geometric principles, particularly those involving parallel and perpendicular lines and planes. The photograph above of Canadian Indians erecting a geodesic dome in Montreal shows an interesting application of triangles.

Proving that Lines Are Parallel

Objectives

1. Write the converse of a statement.
2. State and apply the postulate and theorems that can be used to prove that two lines are parallel.
3. State and use the theorems about the existence of exactly one parallel and exactly one perpendicular to a given line through a point outside the line.

3-4 *Converses of Theorems*

The converse of a statement was explained in Section 1-6. In this section we shall consider several converses of statements relating to parallel lines.

To form the converse of some statements, it is necessary to reword the hypothesis and the conclusion. This is true in forming the converse of Postulate 11. Postulate 11 states, as you recall, "If two parallel lines are cut by a transversal, corresponding angles are congruent."

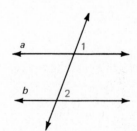

Postulate 11

Hypothesis: $a \parallel b$
Conclusion: $\angle 1 \cong \angle 2$

Converse

Hypothesis: $\angle 1 \cong \angle 2$
Conclusion: $a \parallel b$

The converse of Postulate 11 will be our Postulate 12.

POSTULATE 12 If two lines are cut by a transversal so that corresponding angles are congruent, the lines are parallel.

We can use Postulate 12 to prove the converses of two theorems that were covered earlier in this chapter.

THEOREM 3-3 If two lines are cut by a transversal so that the alternate interior angles are congruent, the lines are parallel.

Given: Lines k and l cut by transversal t;
      $\angle 1 \cong \angle 2$

Prove: $k \parallel l$

Proof:

STATEMENTS	REASONS
1. k and l cut by transversal t	1. Given
2. $\angle 1 \cong \angle 2$	2. Given
3. $\angle 2 \cong \angle 3$	3. Vert. ∠ are ≅.
4. $\angle 1 \cong \angle 3$	4. __?__
5. $k \parallel l$	5. If two lines are cut by a transversal so that corr. ∠ are ≅, the lines are ∥.

THEOREM 3-4 In a plane, if two lines are perpendicular to a third line, they are parallel to each other.

Given: Plane figure; $t \perp l$; $t \perp m$

Prove: $l \parallel m$

The proof is left as Exercise 17.

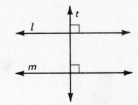

Oral Exercises

In Exercises 1–6, (a) classify the statement as true or false; (b) state the converse of the statement; (c) classify the converse as true or false.

1. If $x + 4 = 18$, then $x = 14$.
2. If $x > 19$, then $x = 22$.
3. If two lines do not intersect, then the lines are parallel.
4. If two parallel lines are cut by a transversal, corresponding angles are congruent.
5. If $ab = 0$, then $a = 0$.
6. If I live in Texas, then I live in the United States.

In Exercises 7–10, the figure is a plane figure. State the theorem or postulate that supports the indicated conclusion.

7. Given: $\angle 1 \cong \angle 2$
   Conclusion: $l \parallel m$

8. Given: $l \parallel m$
   Conclusion: $\angle 1 \cong \angle 2$

9. Given: $\angle 1 \cong \angle 3$
   Conclusion: $l \parallel m$

10. Given: $l \perp t$; $m \perp t$
    Conclusion: $l \parallel m$

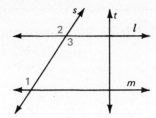

Written Exercises

In Exercises 1–10, use the information given and then identify the lines, if any, that must be parallel in the plane figure. If there are not any lines that have to be parallel, write *none*.

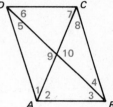

A

1. $\angle 1 \cong \angle 8$
2. $\angle 4 \cong \angle 5$
3. $\angle 2 \cong \angle 6$
4. $\angle 3 \cong \angle 7$

5. $\angle 6 \cong \angle 3$
6. $\angle 2 \cong \angle 7$
7. $\angle 9 \cong \angle 10$
8. $\angle 4 \cong \angle 8$

9. $m\angle 9 = m\angle 1 + m\angle 8$
10. $m\angle 5 = 20$; $m\angle 3 = 50$; $m\angle ABC = 70$

11. Given: The plane figure;
    $m\angle 1 = 101$; $m\angle 2 = 101$
    Prove: $f \parallel g$

12. Given: The plane figure;
    $m\angle 2 = 105$; $m\angle 3 = 105$
    Prove: $f \parallel g$

13. Given: The plane figure;
    $\angle 1 \cong \angle 4$
    Prove: $f \parallel g$

14. Given: The plane figure;
    $m\angle 5 = 80$; $m\angle 6 = 80$
    Prove: $f \parallel g$

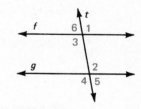

Exs. 11–14

B

15. Given: The plane figure;
    $m\angle 3 + m\angle 6 = 180$;
    $m\angle 2 + m\angle 3 = 180$
    Prove: $\overline{BC} \parallel \overline{EF}$

16. Given: The plane figure;
    $\overline{BC} \parallel \overline{EF}$; $\angle 6 \cong \angle 7$
    Prove: $\overline{AB} \parallel \overline{DC}$

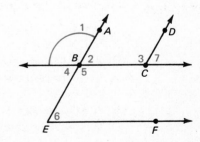

17. Prove: In a plane, if two lines are perpendicular to a third line, they are parallel to each other.

18. Prove: If two lines are cut by a transversal so that alternate exterior angles are congruent, the lines are parallel.

19. Prove: If two lines are cut by a transversal so that interior angles on the same side of the transversal are supplementary, the lines are parallel.

20. Given: The plane figure;
    $m\angle ABD = 90$;
    $m\angle FDB = 90$
    Prove: $\overline{AB} \parallel \overline{DF}$

21. Given: The plane figure;
    $m\angle 1 = m\angle 4$;
    $\overline{BC} \parallel \overline{ED}$
    Prove: $\overline{AB} \parallel \overline{DF}$

22. Given: The plane figure; $m\angle ABD = m\angle FDB$;
    $m\angle 1 = m\angle 4$
    Prove: $\overline{BC} \parallel \overline{ED}$

Exs. 20–23

C 23. Given: The plane figure; $\angle 3$ is supp. to $\angle ABR$; $\angle ABR \cong \angle DBR$
    Prove: $\overline{BC} \parallel \overline{ED}$

24. Prove: If two parallel lines are cut by a transversal, then bisectors of corresponding angles are parallel.

25. Prove: If two parallel lines are cut by a transversal, then bisectors of alternate interior angles are parallel.

26. Prove: If two lines are cut by a transversal so that the bisectors of a pair of corresponding angles are parallel, then the two lines are parallel.

3-5 *A Parallel and a Perpendicular to a Line*

At times the proof of a theorem is dependent upon the use of a line that is not mentioned in the theorem. Such a line is called an *auxiliary line*, and it is normally shown in the figure as a dashed line. We shall use an auxiliary line in proving the following theorem.

THEOREM 3-5 **Through a point outside a line, exactly one parallel can be drawn to the line.**

Given: Line l and point R, not on l

Prove: I. There exists a line through R that is parallel to line l. (A direct proof is used.)

   II. Not more than one line through R is parallel to line l. (An indirect proof is used.)

Proof of Part I

Prove: There exists a line through R that is parallel to line l.

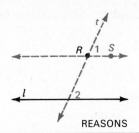

Proof:

STATEMENTS	REASONS
1. Through point R and some point on l draw a line, say t.	1. Through any two points there is exactly one line.
2. In the plane determined by t and l, draw a ray, $\vec{RS}$, such that $\angle 1$ and $\angle 2$ are congruent corresponding angles.	2. In a half plane, through the endpoint of a ray lying in the edge of the half-plane, there is exactly one other ray such that the angle formed by the two rays has a given measure.
3. $\overleftrightarrow{RS}$ is parallel to l.	3. If two lines are cut by a transversal so that corr. $\angle s$ are $\cong$, the lines are $\parallel$.

Proof of Part II

Prove: $\overleftrightarrow{RS}$ is the only line through R that is parallel to line l.

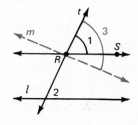

Proof: Suppose that there is another line through R that is parallel to line l. Call the line m. Then $\angle 3 \cong \angle 2$ because when two parallel lines are cut by a transversal, corresponding angles are congruent. But we also have $\angle 1 \cong \angle 2$. Then, by the transitive property of congruence, $\angle 1 \cong \angle 3$. But $\angle 1$ cannot be congruent to $\angle 3$, for in a half-plane, through the endpoint of a ray lying in the edge of the half-plane, there is exactly one ray such that the angle formed by the two rays has a given measure. Therefore our supposition must be false and it follows that there is not more than one line through R that is parallel to line l.

If we substitute the word *perpendicular* for the word *parallel* in Theorem 3-5, we have the following statement whose proof is left as Exercise 20.

THEOREM 3-6 **Through a point outside a line, exactly one perpendicular can be drawn to that line.**

Classify each statement as true or as false.

1. Through a point outside a line there is exactly one line parallel to the given line. F
2. Through a point outside a plane there is exactly one line parallel to the given plane. F
3. Through a point outside a line there is exactly one line perpendicular to the given line. T
4. Through a point outside a line there is exactly one line skew to the given line. F
5. Through a point on a line there is exactly one line perpendicular to the given line. F
6. Through a point outside a plane there is exactly one line perpendicular to the given plane. T

Exercises 7–10 refer to the figure shown.

7. How many lines can be drawn through A that are perpendicular to $\overleftrightarrow{BC}$? T
8. How many lines can be drawn through B that are parallel to $\overleftrightarrow{AC}$? T
9. How many lines, in the plane, can be drawn through X that are perpendicular to $\overleftrightarrow{AB}$? F
10. How many lines can be drawn through C that are parallel to $\overleftrightarrow{AB}$?

In Exercises 1–4, a plane figure is given.

A

1. Must at least one of the lines, a or b, intersect line l? yes
2. Is it possible that both line a and line b intersect line l? yes
3. Is it possible that both line a and line b are parallel to line l? no
4. Is it possible that either line a or line b is skew to line l? no

In Exercises 5–8, lines c, d, and m do not all lie in one plane.

5. Is it possible that neither line c nor line d intersect m? yes
6. Is it possible that both line c and line d intersect line m? no
7. Is it possible that both line c and line d are parallel to line m? yes
8. Is it possible that both line c and line d are skew to line m? yes

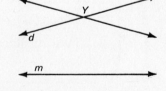

Using intuition, inductive thinking, or deductive reasoning, classify each of the statements as true or false.

B

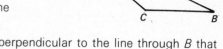

9. Through point C there is exactly one line perpendicular to $\overline{AB}$. T

10. Through point B there exists a line perpendicular to $\overleftrightarrow{AC}$. T

11. Through point A there is exactly one line perpendicular to $\overleftrightarrow{BC}$. T

12. The line through A parallel to $\overleftrightarrow{BC}$ is perpendicular to the line through B that is parallel to $\overleftrightarrow{AC}$. F

13. The line through C perpendicular to $\overleftrightarrow{AB}$ forms a right angle with the line through C parallel to $\overleftrightarrow{AB}$. T

14. The line through A perpendicular to $\overleftrightarrow{BC}$ and the line through B perpendicular to $\overleftrightarrow{AC}$ will intersect in the interior of $\angle ACB$.

15. The line through A parallel to $\overleftrightarrow{BC}$ and the line through B parallel to $\overleftrightarrow{AC}$ will intersect in the interior of $\angle ACB$.

16. The line through B parallel to $\overleftrightarrow{AC}$ and the line through A perpendicular to $\overleftrightarrow{BC}$ will intersect in the interior of $\angle ACB$.

Use the indirect method to prove Exercises 17–19.

C

17. Given: The plane figure;
    $a \parallel c;\ b \parallel c$
    Prove: $a \parallel b$

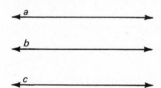

18. Given: The plane figure;
    $a \perp l;\ b \perp l$
    Prove: $a \parallel b$

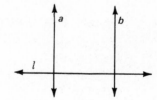

19. Given: Plane $R \parallel$ plane S
    Prove: $\overleftrightarrow{AB} \parallel \overleftrightarrow{CD}$

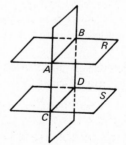

20. Prove Theorem 3-6. (See the proof of Theorem 3-5. The proof will consist of two parts.)

Self-Test

1. Write the converse of "If two lines do not intersect, the lines are skew lines." Is the given statement true? Is the converse true?

2. If $s \parallel l$, state the theorem that permits you to conclude that $\angle 2 \cong \angle 3$.

3. In the plane figure, if $\angle 1 \cong \angle 3$, state the postulate that permits you to conclude that $s \parallel l$.

4. If two lines are perpendicular to a third line, are the two lines necessarily parallel?

5. In a plane, if $a \perp k$ and $b \perp k$, state the theorem that permits you to conclude that $a \parallel b$.

6. If $b \perp l$, state the theorem that permits you to conclude that a, c, and d are not perpendicular to l.

7. If $d \parallel l$, state the theorem that permits you to conclude that a, b, and c are not parallel to l.

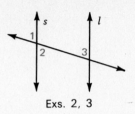

Exs. 2, 3

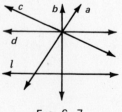

Exs. 6, 7

Applying Parallel Lines to Polygons

Objectives

1. Classify triangles according to sides and according to angles.
2. Identify the remote interior angles of a triangle with respect to a given exterior angle.
3. State and apply the theorem, and the corollaries, about the sum of the measures of the angles of a triangle.
4. State and apply the theorem about the measure of an exterior angle of a triangle.
5. Recognize and name convex polygons and regular polygons.
6. Know and use the formula for the sum of the measures of the interior angles of any polygon.
7. Use the fact that the sum of the measures of the exterior angles of any convex polygon, one angle at each vertex, is 360.

3-6 *The Angles of a Triangle*

A triangle ($\triangle$) is the union of the three segments determined by three noncollinear points.

Each of the three points, R, S and T, is a vertex of the triangle. (The plural of vertex is vertices.) $\overline{RS}$, $\overline{ST}$, and $\overline{RT}$ are the sides of the triangle. $\angle R$, $\angle S$, and $\angle T$ are the angles of the triangle.

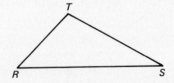

A triangle divides the plane into three sets of points: (1) the triangle, (2) the interior of the triangle, (3) the exterior of the triangle.

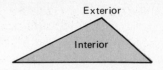

It is convenient to classify triangles according to the number of congruent sides they have and also according to their angles.

Classified according to sides:

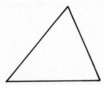

A scalene △ is a △ with no two sides ≅.

An isosceles (isos.) △ is a △ with at least two sides ≅.

An equilateral △ is a △ with all sides ≅.

Classified according to angles:

An acute △ is a △ with three acute ⊾.

An obtuse △ is a △ with an obtuse ∠.

A right △ is a △ with a right ∠.

An equiangular △ is a △ with all angles ≅.

If $\overrightarrow{BD}$ is opposite to $\overrightarrow{BA}$, then ∠CBD is called an **exterior angle** of △ABC. Two of the angles of the triangle are not adjacent to ∠CBD. These two angles, ∠A and ∠C, are called remote interior angles with respect to ∠CBD. If a ray were drawn opposite to $\overrightarrow{BC}$, it would, with $\overrightarrow{BA}$, form a second exterior angle with vertex B. There are also exterior angles at A and C.

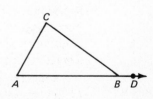

THEOREM 3-7 The sum of the measures of the angles of a triangle is 180.

Given: $\triangle DEF$

Prove: $m\angle 1 + m\angle 2 + m\angle 3 = 180$

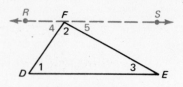

Proof:

STATEMENTS	REASONS
1. Through F draw $\overleftrightarrow{RS} \parallel \overleftrightarrow{DE}$.	1. Through a point outside a line __?__.
2. $\angle 4$ is supp. to $\angle DFS$.	2. If the exterior sides of two adj. $\angle$s __?__ .
3. $m\angle 4 + m\angle DFS = 180$	3. Definition of supp. $\angle$s.
4. $m\angle DFS = m\angle 2 + m\angle 5$	4. Angle Addition Postulate
5. $m\angle 4 + m\angle 2 + m\angle 5 = 180$	5. Substitution Principle
6. $\angle 1 \cong \angle 4$; $\angle 3 \cong \angle 5$	6. If two $\parallel$ lines are __?__ .
7. $m\angle 1 = m\angle 4$; $m\angle 3 = m\angle 5$	7. __?__
8. $m\angle 1 + m\angle 2 + m\angle 3 = 180$	8. Substitution Principle

Each of the four statements that follow could be called a theorem. At times, however, when a statement can be proved easily by applying a theorem, the statement is called a corollary of the theorem. Corollaries, like theorems, can be used as reasons in proofs.

COROLLARY 1 If two angles of one triangle are congruent to two angles of another triangle, the third angles are congruent.

COROLLARY 2 Each angle of an equiangular triangle has measure 60.

COROLLARY 3 In a triangle, there can be at most one right angle or obtuse angle.

COROLLARY 4 The acute angles of a right triangle are complementary.

The proofs of some of the above corollaries are left as exercises.

THEOREM 3-8 The measure of an exterior angle of a triangle is equal to the sum of the measures of the two remote interior angles.

Given: $\triangle ABC$ with exterior $\angle 1$

Prove: $m\angle 1 = m\angle A + m\angle C$

Proof:

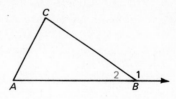

STATEMENTS	REASONS
1. $m\angle A + m\angle C + m\angle 2 = 180$	1. ___?___
2. $\angle 1$ is supp. to $\angle 2$.	2. If the exterior sides of two adj. $\underline{\textit{\&}}$ ___?___ .
3. $m\angle 1 + m\angle 2 = 180$	3. Definition of supp. $\textit{\&}$.
4. $m\angle 1 + m\angle 2$ $= m\angle A + m\angle C + m\angle 2$	4. ___?___
5. $m\angle 1 = m\angle A + m\angle C$	5. Subtraction property of equality

Oral Exercises

Classify each statement as true or false.

1. All equilateral triangles are isosceles triangles. *T*
2. Some scalene triangles are isosceles triangles. *T-*
3. The union of any three segments is a triangle. *T-*
4. A triangle may have two obtuse angles. *F*
5. Every equilateral triangle is an acute triangle. *T*
6. If one angle of a triangle has measure 90, then the other angles of the triangle are acute angles. *T*
7. Each vertex of a triangle lies in the interior of the triangle. *F*
8. It is possible for an exterior angle of a triangle to be an acute angle. *7*
9. A corollary may be used as a reason in a proof. *7*
10. If two angles of a triangle are complementary, the triangle is a right triangle. *T*
11. If two angles of a triangle are congruent, the triangle is an acute triangle. *F*
12. A right triangle can be an isosceles triangle. *T*

13. $\angle 3$ is an exterior angle of $\triangle RST$. *T*
14. $\angle 7$ is an exterior angle of $\triangle RST$. *F*
15. $\angle 4$ and $\angle 6$ are remote interior angles with respect to $\angle 2$. *T*
16. $m\angle 1 = m\angle 4 + m\angle 5$ *T*

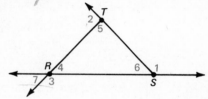

In Exercises 1–8, draw a triangle that satisfies the conditions stated. If no triangle can satisfy the conditions, write *Not Possible* on your paper.

A
1. An acute scalene triangle
2. An obtuse scalene triangle
3. An obtuse isosceles triangle
4. A scalene isosceles triangle

5. An obtuse equilateral triangle
6. An isosceles right triangle
7. A triangle with three acute ext. ∡
8. A scalene right triangle

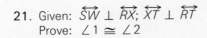

EXAMPLE. $m\angle 2 = 50$; $m\angle 4 = 150$. Find $m\angle 1$.
SOLUTION: $m\angle 4 = m\angle 1 + m\angle 2$
150 = $m\angle 1 + 50$
$m\angle 1 = 100$

Exs. 9–16

9. $m\angle 1 = 105$; $m\angle 2 = 40$. Find $m\angle 4$. 145
10. $m\angle 1 = 108$; $m\angle 4 = 156$. Find $m\angle 2$. 111
11. $m\angle 1 = 112$; $m\angle 2 = 48$. Find $m\angle 3$. 20
12. $m\angle 2 = 55$; $m\angle 3 = 24$. Find $m\angle 1$. 101
13. $m\angle 1 = 46x + 6$; $m\angle 2 = 18x + 4$; $m\angle 4 = 70x - 2$. Find x. 2
14. $m\angle 1 = 27x - 4$; $m\angle 2 = 11x + 4$; $m\angle 4 = 50x - 48$. Find x. 4
15. $m\angle 1 = 6x + 10$; $m\angle 2 = 2x + 4$; $m\angle 3 = x + 4$. Find x. 18
16. $m\angle 1 = 8x - 9$; $m\angle 2 = 2x - 7$; $m\angle 3 = 3x + 1$. Find x. 15

B
17. Explain briefly how Corollary 2 follows from Theorem 3-7.
18. Explain briefly how Corollary 3 follows from Theorem 3-7.
19. Prove Corollary 1 of Theorem 3-7.
20. Prove Corollary 4 of Theorem 3-7.

21. Given: $\overleftrightarrow{SW} \perp \overrightarrow{RX}$; $\overleftrightarrow{XT} \perp \overleftrightarrow{RT}$
Prove: $\angle 1 \cong \angle 2$

22. Given: $\overleftrightarrow{SW} \perp \overrightarrow{RX}$; $\overleftrightarrow{XT} \perp \overleftrightarrow{RT}$
Prove: $\angle 3 \cong \angle 4$

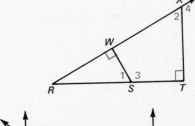

23. In the plane figure, $\overleftrightarrow{CA} \perp \overleftrightarrow{AB}$ and $\overrightarrow{DB} \perp \overrightarrow{AB}$. If $m\angle 1 = 40$ and $m\angle 8 = 70$, find the measures of the other numbered angles.

24. In the plane figure, $\overleftrightarrow{CA} \parallel \overleftrightarrow{DB}$ and $\overleftrightarrow{AB} \perp \overleftrightarrow{CA}$. If $m\angle 1 = 42$ and $m\angle 8 = 72$, find the measures of the other numbered angles.

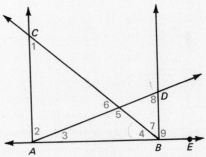

25. In the plane figure on the bottom of page 100, $m\angle 1 = 2m\angle 3$, $m\angle 2 = 3m\angle 3$, $m\angle 8 = 65$, and $m\angle CBE = 132$. Find the measures of the numbered angles.

26. In the plane figure on the bottom of page 100, $m\angle 1 = 13x + 1$, $m\angle 2 = 24x - 12$, $m\angle 3 = 10x + 2$, $m\angle 8 = 20x$, and $m\angle CBE = 45x - 3$. Find the measures of the numbered angles.

C 27. In the plane figure, $\overline{DE} \perp \overline{AC}$ and $\overline{BF} \perp \overline{AC}$. If $m\angle 1 = 2x$, $m\angle 2 = 3y + 2$, $m\angle 3 = 2y + 10$, and $m\angle 4 = 3x - 12$, find the values of x and y.

28. In the plane figure, $\overline{DE} \perp \overline{AC}$ and $\overline{BF} \perp \overline{AC}$. If $m\angle 1 = 3c - \frac{1}{2}d$ and $m\angle 4 = 2m\angle 2$, express the measure of $\angle 3$ in terms of c and d.

29. In the plane figure, $\overline{AB} \parallel \overline{DC}$ and $\overline{AD} \parallel \overline{BC}$. If $m\angle 1 = \frac{1}{2}a + \frac{1}{4}b$, $m\angle 5 = 5a - \frac{1}{3}b$, and $m\angle 7 = \frac{1}{2}a + \frac{5}{2}b$, express the measure of $\angle BDC$ as a single fraction in terms of a and b.

30. Given: $\overline{DF} \perp \overline{AG}$; $\angle CBG \cong \angle EGF$
Prove: $m\angle ABC = 90 + m\angle FEG$

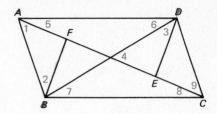
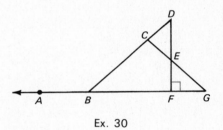

Exs. 27–29

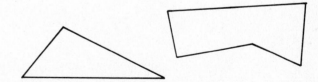

Ex. 30

3-7 *The Angles of a Polygon*

The figures below are *polygons*.

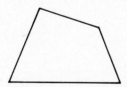

Note that each figure is the union of three or more coplanar segments (called *sides*) such that:

1. No two segments with a common endpoint are collinear.

2. Each segment intersects exactly two other segments, but only in endpoints.

The following figures are not polygons.

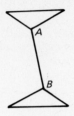

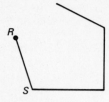

$\overline{AB}$ intersects more than two segments.

$\overline{AC}$ and $\overline{BD}$ do not intersect in end-points.

$\overline{RS}$ intersects only one segment.

In most of our work in this book we shall restrict our discussion to *convex polygons*. A convex polygon is a polygon such that no line containing a side of the polygon will contain a point in the interior of the polygon.

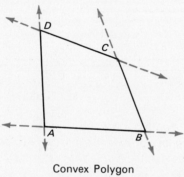

Convex Polygon

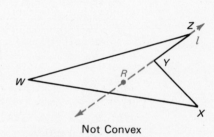

Not Convex

Note that in polygon *WXYZ*, line l containing $\overline{YZ}$ contains points, such as *R*, in the interior of the polygon. This polygon is not a convex polygon.

When referring to a polygon, we name the vertices in order. Polygon *ABCDE* and polygon *DCBAE* are two of several correct names for the polygon shown.

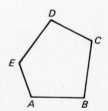

Terms such as vertex, side, interior angle, exterior angle, equilateral, equiangular, interior, and exterior, that we used in the previous section on triangles, will also be used for other polygons.

The endpoints of one side of a polygon are called *consecutive vertices*. *J* and *K* are consecutive vertices.

Two sides that intersect are called *consecutive sides*. $\overline{JK}$ and $\overline{KL}$ are consecutive sides.

A segment joining two nonconsecutive vertices is called a *diagonal* of the polygon. $\overline{NK}$ is a diagonal.

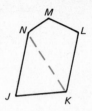

Some polygons are given special names according to the number of sides they have. Polygons with 3, 4, 5, 6, 8, 10 and *n* sides are called triangles, quadrilaterals, pentagons, hexagons, octagons, decagons, and *n*-gons, respectively.

A regular polygon is a convex polygon with all sides congruent and all angles congruent.

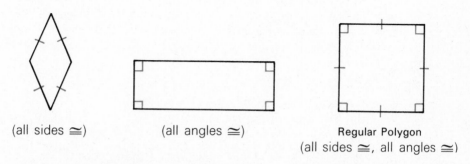

(all sides ≅)   (all angles ≅)   **Regular Polygon**
(all sides ≅, all angles ≅)

Note that two conditions are required for a convex polygon to be a regular polygon. The polygon must be equilateral and it must be equiangular. As shown in the polygons above, one condition does not necessarily dictate the other condition.

Consider the following polygons.

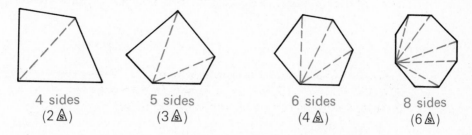

4 sides   5 sides   6 sides   8 sides
(2 △)   (3 △)   (4 △)   (6 △)

In each polygon a vertex was selected and all possible diagonals from that vertex were drawn. Note that the number of triangles formed in each polygon is two less than the number of sides. Since the sum of the measures of the interior angles of the polygon is the sum of the measures of the angles of the triangles, we have the following results.

Number of Sides of the Polygon	Number of △ Formed By Drawing All the Diagonals From One Vertex	Sum of the Measures of the Interior Angles of the Polygon
4	4 − 2, or 2	2 × 180, or 360
5	5 − 2, or 3	3 × 180, or 540
6	6 − 2, or 4	4 × 180, or 720
8	8 − 2, or 6	6 × 180, or 1080

Inductive thinking suggests the following statement which can be proved for any particular integer n, where $n \geq 3$.

The sum of the measures of the interior angles of any convex polygon of n sides is $(n - 2)180$.

EXAMPLE 1

Given: A regular decagon
Find: (a) The sum of the measures of the interior angles of the decagon.
  (b) The measure of one interior angle of the decagon.

SOLUTION: (a) Sum of the measures of the interior ∡ =
    $(10 − 2)180 = 1440$
  (b) The measure of each interior $\angle = \frac{1440}{10} = 144$

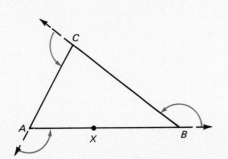
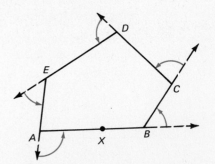

Imagine that you start at point X and walk in a counter-clockwise direction around either of the two polygons shown. When you reach vertex B, you turn through one exterior angle of the polygon and then continue toward vertex C. At vertex C you turn through another exterior angle. If you continue until you return to point X, you make one complete revolution, or turn through 360°. Intuition suggests that the sum of the measures of the exterior angles of a convex polygon, one angle at each vertex, is 360.

If we use our knowledge of the sum of the interior angles of a convex polygon, we can formally demonstrate what we feel intuitively about the sum of the measures of the exterior angles.

At each vertex of a convex n-gon, the interior angle and an exterior angle are supplementary ($m\angle 1 + m\angle 2 = 180$). Since the polygon has n vertices, the sum of the measures of the interior and exterior angles is $180n$. Hence if we subtract the sum of the measures of the interior angles from $180n$, we have the sum of the measures of the exterior angles.

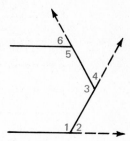

$180n - (n - 2)180$ $\quad or \quad$ $180n - 180n + 360$ $\quad or \quad$ 360

> The sum of the measures of the exterior angles of any convex n-gon, one angle at each vertex, is 360.

EXAMPLE 2. One exterior angle of a regular convex polygon has measure 30. Find the number of sides of the polygon.

SOLUTION: Let $n =$ the number of sides.
Then $30n = 360$
and $n = 12$.

Oral Exercises In Exercises 1–8, state whether the figure shown is a polygon. If it is not a polygon, explain why.

1.

4.

7.

2.

5.

8.

3.

6.

In Exercises 9–16, classify each statement as true or as false.

9. Polygon *ABCDEF* is a pentagon. F

10. It is possible to draw three diagonals from vertex *E*. T

11. Vertices *A* and *E* are a pair of nonconsecutive vertices.

12. $\overline{BC}$ and $\overline{DC}$ are a pair of consecutive sides.

13. If polygon *ABCDEF* is equilateral, then $\angle A \cong \angle B$.

14. If polygon *ABCDEF* is equiangular, then $m\angle A = 60$. F

15. $m\angle 1 + m\angle EDC = 180$ T

16. $\angle 2$ is an exterior angle of polygon *ABCDEF*.

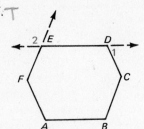

Written Exercises

In Exercises 1–10 complete each of the statements with one of the words *Always, Sometimes,* or *Never.*

A

1. A triangle is __?__ a polygon. always

2. The sum of the measures of the interior angles of a convex polygon is __?__ 360.

3. A regular polygon is __?__ equilateral.

4. The sum of the measures of the exterior angles of a convex polygon is __?__ 180.

5. An equiangular polygon is __?__ a regular polygon.

6. The interior angle and an exterior angle at one vertex of a convex polygon are __?__ supplementary.

7. A side of a polygon is __?__ a diagonal of the polygon.

8. The number of diagonals that can be drawn from one vertex of a convex polygon is __?__ greater than 2.

9. An equilateral triangle is __?__ a regular polygon.

10. The length of a side of a polygon is __?__ less than the length of a diagonal of the polygon.

In Exercises 11–16, find the sum of the measures of the interior angles of the indicated convex polygon.

11. Triangle

12. Pentagon

13. Octagon

14. Hexagon

15. Decagon

16. An *n*-gon with $n = 14$ 36

In Exercises 17–22, the measure of an exterior angle of a regular convex polygon is given. How many sides does the polygon have?

17. 120 3

18. 45 8

19. 90 4

20. 40 9

21. 36 10

22. 72 5

In Exercises 23–26, find the sum of the measures of the exterior angles of the convex polygon, one angle at each vertex.

23. Quadrilateral *360*
24. 7-gon *360*

25. 11-gon *360*
26. 25-gon *360*

In Exercises 27–32 find the measure of an interior angle of a regular convex polygon with the indicated number of sides.

B 27. 6 *120* 28. 10 *144* 29. 12 *150* 30. 15 *156* 31. 16 *157.5* 32. $\frac{(k-2)180}{k}$

In Exercises 33–38, the measure of one interior angle of a regular convex polygon is given. Find the number of sides.

33. 60 *3* 34. 108 *5* 35. 135 *8* 36. 144 *10* 37. 160 *18* 38. k $\frac{360}{180-k}$

39. If each of four interior angles of a convex pentagon has a measure of 105, find the measure of the fifth interior angle. *120*

40. If the sum of the measures of the interior angles of a regular convex polygon is 2160, find the measure of each interior angle. *154 2/7*

C 41. Prove: The sum of the measures of the interior angles of a convex quadrilateral is 360.

42. Prove: The sum of the measures of the exterior angles of a convex quadrilateral, one at each vertex, is 360. *43. 20*

43. What is the total number of diagonals that can be drawn in a convex octagon?

44. Express, in terms of *n*, the total number of diagonals that can be drawn in a convex polygon with *n* sides. $\frac{n(n-3)}{2}$

Self-Test

Exercises 1–7 refer to the figure.

1. Name the sides of $\triangle ABC$.
2. Name the interior angles of $\triangle ABC$.
3. Name the two remote interior angles with respect to $\angle DAB$.
4. Name an angle that is neither an interior nor an exterior angle of $\triangle ABC$.
5. If $m\angle B = 41$ and $m\angle BAC = 84$, find $m\angle ACF$.
6. If $\overline{AB} \cong \overline{AC}$, what kind of triangle is $\triangle ABC$? *equilateral*
7. If $\angle ABC \cong \angle ACB \cong \angle BAC$, what kind of triangle is $\triangle ABC$?

8. What is the sum of the measures of the interior angles of a convex 11-gon?
9. What is the definition of a regular polygon?
10. Explain why it is not possible for the measure of an exterior angle of a regular convex polygon to equal 22.

CHAPTER SUMMARY

1. Two distinct lines intersect, are parallel, or are skew.
2. Two distinct planes either intersect or are parallel.
3. When two parallel lines are cut by a transversal:
   a. Corresponding angles are congruent.
   b. Alternate interior angles are congruent.
   c. If the transversal is perpendicular to one of the lines, it is perpendicular to the other also.
4. Two lines cut by a transversal are parallel if:
   a. Corresponding angles are congruent.
   b. Alternate interior angles are congruent.
   c. Both lines are perpendicular to the transversal.
5. To start an indirect proof, you suppose the negation of what you want to prove is true. You then show that the negation leads to the contradiction of a known fact.
6. Through a point outside a line there is exactly one line parallel to the given line and exactly one line perpendicular to the given line.
7. The sum of the measures of the angles of a triangle is 180.
   The measure of an exterior angle of a triangle is equal to the sum of the measures of the two remote interior angles.
   The sum of the measures of the angles of a convex n-gon is $(n - 2)180$.
   The sum of the measures of the exterior angles of a convex polygon, one angle at each vertex, is 360.

CHAPTER TEST

In Exercises 1–10, complete each statement with one of the words *Always, Sometimes,* or *Never*.

1. Two lines that have no points in common are __?__ parallel.
2. Two planes that have no points in common are __?__ parallel.
3. If two parallel lines are cut by a transversal, alternate interior angles are __?__ congruent.
4. If lines k and t are each parallel to plane X, then k is __?__ parallel to t.
5. If lines m and n intersect at point X and line m is parallel to line k, then n is __?__ parallel to k.
6. In an obtuse triangle, there is __?__ one angle whose measure is greater than 90.
7. A scalene triangle is __?__ an acute triangle.
8. An acute triangle is __?__ a right triangle.
9. The sum of the measures of the exterior angles of any convex n-gon, one angle at each vertex, is __?__ 360.
10. An equilateral polygon is __?__ a regular polygon.

In Exercises 11–15, $a \parallel b$.

11. Name three angles that are congruent to $\angle 1$.

12. If $m\angle 6 = 120$, then $m\angle 2 = \underline{\ ?\ }$ 120

13. If $m\angle 8 = 58$, then $m\angle 3 = \underline{\ ?\ }$ 122

14. If $m\angle 5 = 7x + 4$ and $m\angle 4 = 10x - 20$, then $x = \underline{\ ?\ }$.

15. $m\angle 4 + m\angle 6 + m\angle 9 + m\angle 10 = \underline{\ ?\ }$ 360

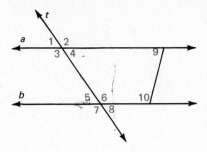

16. In a plane, $\overleftrightarrow{AB} \perp \overleftrightarrow{BD}$ and $\overleftrightarrow{CD} \perp \overleftrightarrow{BD}$. Write the theorem which supports the statement: $\overleftrightarrow{AB} \parallel \overleftrightarrow{CD}$.

17. If $m\angle 5 = 55$ and $m\angle 6 = 95$, then $m\angle 7 = \underline{\ ?\ }$ 108

18. If $m\angle 8 = 152$ and $m\angle 6 = 98$, then $m\angle 5 = \underline{\ ?\ }$ 54

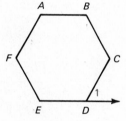

In Exercises 19–22 polygon *ABCDEF* is a regular polygon.

19. The sum of the measures of the interior angles of the polygon is $\underline{\ ?\ }$.

20. The sum of the measures of the exterior angles of the polygon, one angle at each vertex, is $\underline{\ ?\ }$ 360

21. $m\angle 1 = \underline{\ ?\ }$ 60

22. How many diagonals can be drawn from vertex *B*?

In Exercises 23 and 24, write a complete indirect proof.

23. Prove: If *n* is a number such that $n^2 = 4n$, then $n \neq 2$.

24. Prove: If $\angle 1 \not\cong \angle 2$, then $\angle 1$ and $\angle 2$ are not vertical angles.

25. Given: Plane figure with $\angle 1$ supp. to $\angle 3$, and $\angle 2$ supp. to $\angle 4$.
    Prove: $a \parallel b$

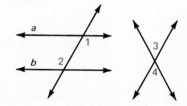

CHAPTER REVIEW

3-1 *Definitions*

1. Are two lines that have no points in common necessarily parallel?
2. If two planes have no points in common, the planes are __?__ .
3. A line that intersects two or more coplanar lines in different points is called a __?__ *Train*
4. When a transversal intersects two lines, how many pairs of corresponding angles are formed? *↑*

3-2 *When Lines are Parallel*

In Exercises 5–8, $l \parallel m$.

5. If $m\angle 6 = 80$, $m\angle 2 = $ __ __ .
6. If $m\angle 6 = 75$, $m\angle 3 = $ __ __ .
7. If $m\angle 3 = 7x - 6$ and $m\angle 7 = 6x + 6$, $x = $ __?__ .
8. If $m\angle 5 = 13x + 6$ and $m\angle 4 = 15x - 10$, $m\angle 3 = $ __?__ .

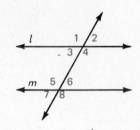

3-3 *Indirect Proof*

9. To begin an indirect proof, you suppose that the negation of what you wish to prove is __?__ . *↑*
10. Jim wanted to use the indirect method to prove "If $3x = 15$, then $x \neq 6$." He started his proof by writing, "Suppose $3x \neq 15$." Was he correct? *No*
11. The success of an indirect proof depends on finding a contradiction of a __?__ . *I know I part*

3-4 *Converses of Theorems*

12. State the converse of: If two parallel lines are cut by a transversal, the alternate exterior angles are congruent.
13. Which lines, if any, in the plane figure shown, must be parallel when:
    a. $\angle 1 \cong \angle 5$
    b. $\angle 2 \cong \angle 3$
    c. $\angle 3 \cong \angle 6$

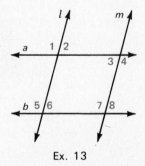

Ex. 13

3-5 *A Parallel and a Perpendicular to a Line*

In Exercises 14–17, restrict yourself to the plane that contains quadrilateral *RSTW*.

14. How many lines can be drawn through T that are parallel to $\overleftrightarrow{RS}$?
15. How many lines can be drawn through T that are parallel to $\overleftrightarrow{WR}$?

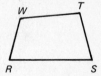

16. How many lines can be drawn through T that are perpendicular to $\overleftrightarrow{RS}$?

17. How many lines can be drawn through S that are perpendicular to $\overleftrightarrow{ST}$?

3-6 *The Angles of a Triangle*

18. Name the angles of $\triangle ABC$ that are remote interior angles with respect to $\angle CBD$.

19. $m\angle 1 + m\angle 2 + m\angle 3 = \underline{\quad?\quad}$ *90*

20. If $m\angle 4 = 145$ and $m\angle 2 = 95$, then $m\angle 1 = \underline{\quad?\quad}$ *50*

21. If $\angle 2$ is a right angle, then $m\angle 1 + m\angle 3 = \underline{\quad?\quad}$.

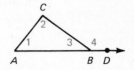

3-7 *The Angles of a Polygon*

22. If a polygon is equilateral and equiangular, it is called a $\underline{\quad?\quad}$ polygon.

23. The sum of the measures of the exterior angles of a convex n-gon, one angle at each vertex, is $\underline{\quad?\quad}$.

24. The sum of the measures of the interior angles of a convex hexagon is $\underline{\quad?\quad}$.

25. The measure of each interior angle of a regular pentagon is $\underline{\quad?\quad}$.

26. The measure of an interior angle of a regular polygon is 135. The polygon has $\underline{\quad?\quad}$ sides.

programming in BASIC

We can have the computer help us to classify a triangle as being "right," "acute," or "obtuse," given the measures of any two angles of the triangle. The angles of the triangle could be called A, B, and C. Another way of naming the angles is Angle 1, Angle 2, and Angle 3 or A_1, A_2, and A_3. The numbers to the lower right of the A's are called *subscripts*. For the computer, subscripts are written A[1], A[2], and A[3]. Subscripts are especially useful when there are many values to consider, such as the percent scores of all the geometry students in your school on a given test.

Before we write a computer program in which many decisions must be made, we should consider carefully all the decisions we would have to make if we had to do the work ourselves. A flow chart is one way of showing these decisions.

The flow chart on the next page uses ovals for start and stop, rectangles for computation, parallelograms for input and output, and diamonds for decisions. To keep things simple, let's assume that A[1] and A[2] represent positive numbers.

Following the flow chart is the program based on the plan of the flow chart.

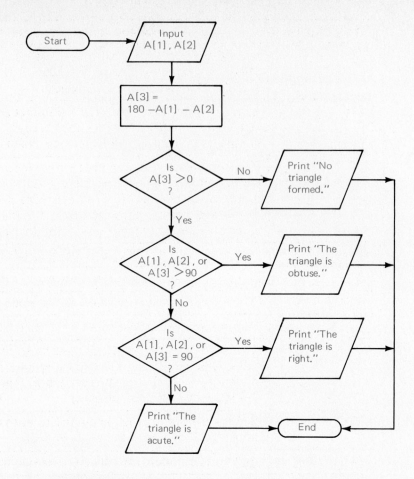

```
10   DIM A[3]
20   PRINT "WHAT ARE THE MEASURES OF TWO ANGLES";
30   INPUT A[1],A[2]
40   LET A[3]=180-A[1]-A[2]
50   IF A[3]>0 THEN 80
60   PRINT "NO TRIANGLE FORMED."
70   STOP
80   FOR I=1 TO 3
90   IF A[I]>90 THEN 140
100   IF A[I]=90 THEN 160
110   NEXT I
120   PRINT "THE TRIANGLE IS ACUTE."
130   STOP
140   PRINT "THE TRIANGLE IS OBTUSE."
150   STOP
160   PRINT "THE TRIANGLE IS RIGHT."
170   END
```

Line Number	Instruction to the Computer
10	(In any program using subscripts we must show how many values there are, in this case 3 for the three angles. DIM stands for DIMENSION.)
20	Print the information between the quotation marks. (A semicolon in a PRINT statement causes the computer to wait on the same line for another instruction.)
30	(The computer prints a question mark for input. Notice we use the "?" printed by the computer to complete the question on line 20. The user types the measures of the two angles, separated by a comma. The computer calls the first measure A[1] and the second A[2].)
40	Compute 180-A[1]-A[2] and let A[3] take that value.
50	Branch to line 80 if A[3] is positive.
60	Print the information between the quotation marks.
70, 130, 150	Stop the program. (We could have used GOTO 170.)
80-110	(The FOR-NEXT loop checks each angle for being greater than or equal to 90. Notice that we do not have to write A[1], A[2], and A[3] separately. The subscripts and the loop take care of that.)
120	(Since the tests for each angle failed, each angle must be acute. Therefore the triangle is acute.)
140, 160	PRINT the information between the quotation marks.
170	END

Exercises

1. Type, LIST, and RUN the above program. Use the following pairs of measures: 30,60; 18,118; 40,60; 120,90.

2. Using lines 10 through 70, write a program to classify a triangle as being equiangular, isosceles, or scalene given the measures of two angles of the triangle.

3. Write a program to accept the measures of the three sides of a triangle and to classify the triangle as equilateral, isosceles, or scalene. Be sure to check in your program whether the three given sides determine a triangle. Note: Use these first lines.

```
10 DIM S[3]
20 PRINT "WHAT ARE THE MEASURES OF THE THREE SIDES";
30 INPUT S[1], S[2], S[3]
```

Classify each statement as true or false.

A
1. For all numbers a and b, $|a - b| = a - b$.
2. The intersection of sets C and D contains those elements that lie in both C and D.
3. A point that lies on one side of an angle is said to lie in the interior of the angle.
4. When line c is a transversal of lines j and k, the three lines are coplanar.
5. If three lines intersect in a point, the lines must be coplanar.
6. If $\overline{AB}$ lies in plane Z, then $\overleftrightarrow{AB}$ lies in Z.
7. It is possible for two vertical angles to be complementary.
8. If point P lies outside plane Z, then any line that contains P must be parallel to Z.
9. Basic assumptions are called theorems.
10. If $AX = BX$, then point X must lie on $\overline{AB}$.
11. Inductive thinking takes place when a person makes a general statement that is based upon observation of individual cases.
12. If $a < b$ and c is a negative number, then $a + c > b + c$.
13. The hypothesis of a conditional states what is given.
14. If $\overrightarrow{AB}$ is a side of both $\angle 1$ and $\angle 2$, then $\angle 1$ and $\angle 2$ must be adjacent angles.
15. If the exterior sides of two adjacent angles lie in perpendicular lines, the angles must be supplementary.
16. Two lines that do not intersect must be parallel.
17. To begin an indirect proof you suppose that the negation of what you wish to prove is true.
18. When a conditional is false, the converse must also be false.
19. Through a point outside a line, many lines can be drawn parallel to the given line.
20. In every triangle there must be at least two acute angles.

Complete each sentence with the most appropriate word, phrase, or numeral.

21. If the exterior sides of two adjacent angles lie in a line, the angles must be __?__ angles as well as adjacent angles.
22. In mathematics, a basic assumption is called a __?__.
23. If point A is a vertex of a polygon with seven sides, then it is possible to draw __?__ diagonals that have A as endpoint.
24. If $\angle A$ of $\triangle ABC$ is an obtuse angle, then the exterior angles at both B and C must be __?__ angles.
25. A convex polygon with twelve sides has __?__ interior angles.
26. The sum of the measures of the interior $\angle$ of a convex pentagon is __?__.
27. $|-8| - |-4| = $ __?__

28. When two lines are not parallel yet do not intersect, the lines are __?__ lines.
29. Each exterior angle of a certain regular polygon has measure 18. The polygon has __?__ sides.
30. When two parallel lines are cut by a transversal, the number of pairs of alternate angles formed is __?__. *Two*

Express the measure of a supplement of ∠A.

31. $m\angle A = 102$ 32. $m\angle A = j + 30$ 33. $m\angle A = 90 - x$
supplement

Name the property of equality that supports each step in the solution of the equation $9 = 3x - 6$.

34. $3x - 6 = 9$ 35. $3x = 15$ 36. $x = 5$

Given: The plane figure with $\overline{AX} \perp \overline{YZ}$.
State the definition, postulate, or theorem
that supports the assertion.

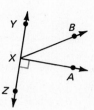

B 37. $\angle AXZ$ is a rt. ∠.
38. $\angle AXB$ and $\angle BXY$ are comp. ∡.
39. $ZX + XY = ZY$
40. $\angle YXB$ and $\angle BXZ$ are supp. ∡.

In Exercises 41–44, $m\angle 1 = 3x - 1$ and $m\angle 2 = x + 7$.

41. If $\angle 1$ and $\angle 2$ are vertical angles, $x =$ __?__.
42. If $\angle 1$ and $\angle 2$ are complementary angles, $x =$ __?__.
43. If $\angle 2$ is one of the angles formed when $\angle 1$ is bisected, $x =$ __?__.
44. If $\angle 1$ and $\angle 2$ are exterior angles on the same side of a transversal that cuts two parallel lines, $x =$ __?__.

C 45. Given: $\overline{CZ} \perp \overline{AE}$; $\overline{BZ} \perp \overline{DZ}$
    Prove: $\angle 1$ and $\angle 4$ are comp. ∡.

46. Given: $m\angle 2 = m\angle 4$
    Prove: $m\angle 5 = 2(m\angle 1)$

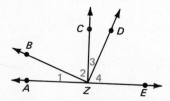

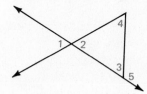

47. Write a complete demonstration: When two parallel lines are cut by a transversal, the lines that bisect two alternate exterior angles are parallel.

48. The sides of a regular n-gon are extended to form an n-pointed star. Derive a formula for the measure of the angle at one of the n points of the star.

CONGRUENT TRIANGLES

Proving That Triangles Are Congruent

Objectives

1. When given a correspondence statement or a congruence statement about two triangles, identify the six pairs of corresponding parts.
2. Apply the reflexive, symmetric, and transitive properties to congruence of triangles.
3. Use the SSS Postulate and the SAS Postulate to prove two triangles congruent.
4. Use the LL Theorem and the HL Postulate to prove two right triangles congruent.

4-1 *Congruence of Triangles*

Suppose we match the vertices of $\triangle ABC$ with those of $\triangle DEF$ in the following way:

$$A \leftrightarrow D \quad B \leftrightarrow E \quad C \leftrightarrow F$$

This enables us to speak of a correspondence between the triangles:

$$\triangle ABC \leftrightarrow \triangle DEF$$

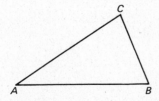 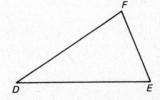

In this correspondence, the first vertices named, A and D, are corresponding vertices. So are the second vertices and the third vertices named.

Because A and D are corresponding vertices, $\angle A$ and $\angle D$ are called corresponding angles (corr. ⁂) of the triangles. Other corresponding angles are $\angle B$ and $\angle E$; $\angle C$ and $\angle F$.

Because vertices A and B correspond to vertices D and E, $\overline{AB}$ and $\overline{DE}$ are called corresponding sides. Other corresponding sides are $\overline{BC}$ and $\overline{EF}$; $\overline{AC}$ and $\overline{DF}$.

When the following six statements are true for $\triangle ABC$ and $\triangle DEF$, the triangles are said to be congruent triangles (≅⁂).

$$\angle A \cong \angle D \qquad \overline{AB} \cong \overline{DE}$$
$$\angle B \cong \angle E \qquad \overline{BC} \cong \overline{EF}$$
$$\angle C \cong \angle F \qquad \overline{AC} \cong \overline{DF}$$

We say that $\triangle ABC$ is congruent to $\triangle DEF$ ($\triangle ABC \cong \triangle DEF$). Notice that two triangles are congruent if the six parts (the sides and angles) of one triangle are congruent to the six corresponding parts of the other triangle.

To indicate that particular sides or angles of two triangles are congruent, we can use check marks in a diagram, as shown below.

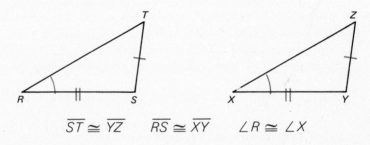

$$\overline{ST} \cong \overline{YZ} \qquad \overline{RS} \cong \overline{XY} \qquad \angle R \cong \angle X$$

Is the statement $\triangle RST \cong \triangle XYZ$ correct? The information given so far does not enable us to decide. Suppose we now secure additional information: $m\angle S = 97$; $m\angle Y = 98$. Clearly, $\angle S \not\cong \angle Y$. Then $\triangle RST \not\cong \triangle XYZ$, for there is a part of one triangle that is not congruent to the corresponding part of the other triangle.

Sometimes it is convenient to describe a side of a triangle in terms of its position with respect to angles of the triangle.

$\overline{GJ}$ lies opposite $\angle H$.

$\overline{GJ}$ is *included* between $\angle G$ and $\angle J$.

$\angle G$ lies *opposite* $\overline{HJ}$.

$\angle G$ is *included* between $\overline{GH}$ and $\overline{GJ}$.

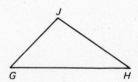

Recall that congruence of segments and angles is reflexive, symmetric, and transitive. This fact can be used, together with the definition of congruent triangles, to establish the following theorem.

THEOREM 4-1 Congruence of triangles is reflexive, symmetric, and transitive.

Proof of the third part of the theorem is left as Exercise 29.

Oral
Exercises

Given the correspondence △ABC ↔ △NOK

1. The three pairs of corresponding angles are __?__.
2. The three pairs of corresponding sides are __?__.

Given the statement △DEF ≅ △JQV.

3. The three pairs of corresponding angles are __?__.
4. The three pairs of corresponding sides are __?__.

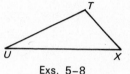

5. The angle opposite $\overline{XT}$ is __?__.
6. The side opposite ∠T is __?__.
7. The angle included between $\overline{XT}$ and $\overline{XU}$ is __?__.
8. The side included between ∠X and ∠T is __?__.

Exs. 5–8

In Exercises 9–14, the vertices of two triangles are matched as shown.

A ↔ N   B ↔ R   C ↔ S

State whether the correspondence is expressed correctly.

9. △ABC ↔ △RSN
10. △ABC ↔ △NSR
11. △ABC ↔ △NRS
12. △CBA ↔ △SRN
13. △CAB ↔ △SNR
14. △BAC ↔ △RSN

In Exercises 15–20, state whether the diagram suggests that the statement might be correct.

15. △DUH ≅ △EZK
16. △DUH ≅ △EKZ
17. △DUH ≅ △KEZ
18. △HDU ≅ △ZKE
19. △UHD ≅ △EKZ
20. △UDH ≅ △EKZ

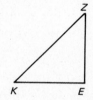

Written Exercises

A 1–6. List the six requirements that must be met for the statement $\triangle RST \cong \triangle NGA$ to be true.

7–12. Given the statement $\triangle BDF \cong \triangle HJM$. Write six statements that follow from the definition of congruent triangles.

It is known that $\triangle ABC$ and $\triangle XYZ$ are scalene triangles.

13. If $\triangle ABC \cong \triangle XYZ$, is $\triangle BCA \cong \triangle YZX$?
14. If $\triangle ABC \cong \triangle XYZ$, is $\triangle ABC \cong \triangle XZY$?
15. If $\triangle ABC \cong \triangle XYZ$, is $\triangle ABC \cong \triangle ZYX$?
16. If $\triangle BAC \cong \triangle ZYX$, is $\triangle ACB \cong \triangle YXZ$?

State whether the figure suggests that the statement might be correct.

17. $\triangle DFE \cong \triangle RST$
18. $\triangle DEF \cong \triangle RST$
19. $\triangle DFE \cong \triangle RTS$
20. $\triangle FED \cong \triangle RST$

Given the congruence shown, list the six pairs of corresponding parts of the triangles named.

B 21. $\triangle AMD \cong \triangle BMD$
22. $\triangle CDM \cong \triangle ADM$

23. $\triangle PRS \cong \triangle YRS$
24. $\triangle SRY \cong \triangle STU$

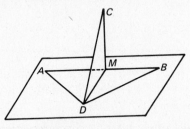

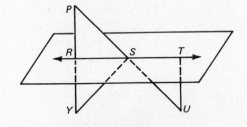

25. $\triangle ABC \cong \triangle CDA$
26. $\triangle ADX \cong \triangle CBX$

27. $\triangle FTG \cong \triangle ETJ$
28. $\triangle EFG \cong \triangle JEF$

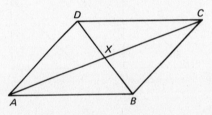

c 29. Prove that congruence of triangles is transitive.

Given: $\triangle ABC \cong \triangle RST$;
$\triangle RST \cong \triangle XYZ$

Prove: $\triangle ABC \cong \triangle XYZ$

(Hint: $\overline{AB} \cong \overline{RS}$ and $\overline{RS} \cong \overline{XY}$. Therefore $\overline{AB} \cong \overline{XY}$.)

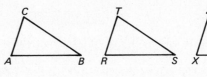

30. Each angle of each triangle has measure 60. Each side has length 13. Complete the statement $\triangle DEF \cong \triangle \underline{\ ?\ }$ in six correct ways.

4-2 *Some Ways to Prove Triangles Congruent*

Suppose you have three sticks.

You fasten the sticks together at the ends to form a triangle.

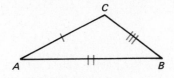

Now suppose you take a duplicate set of sticks and try to form a different-looking triangle by joining the sticks at their ends. You cannot do it. For three particular sticks only one kind of triangle is possible.

The idea suggested by the sticks is taken as a postulate of geometry.

**POSTULATE 13
(SSS POSTULATE)**   If three sides of one triangle are congruent to the corresponding parts of another triangle, the triangles are congruent.

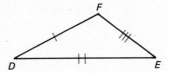

According to Postulate 13:

If $\overline{AB} \cong \overline{DE}$, $\overline{BC} \cong \overline{EF}$, and $\overline{AC} \cong \overline{DF}$, then $\triangle ABC \cong \triangle DEF$.

Suppose you have two sticks.

You fasten them together to form a 60° angle.

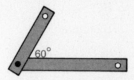

There is only one way to finish forming a triangle. A third stick must have just the right length.

POSTULATE 14 **If two sides and the included angle of one**
(SAS POSTULATE) triangle are congruent to the corresponding
parts of another triangle, the triangles are congruent.

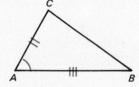 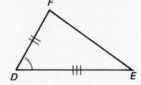

According to Postulate 14:

If $\overline{AB} \cong \overline{DE}$, $\overline{AC} \cong \overline{DF}$, and $\angle A \cong \angle D$,
then $\triangle ABC \cong \triangle DEF$.

Oral Exercises

In Exercises 1–6, the goal is to prove two triangles congruent.

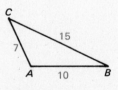

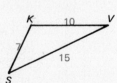

1. Pair vertex A with vertex __?__ .
2. Pair vertex C with vertex __?__ .
3. $\angle B$ and $\angle$ __?__ are corr. ∡.
4. $\overline{CB}$ and __?__ are corr. sides.
5. To support the statement $\overline{AB} \cong \overline{KV}$, a person can use the reason __?__ .
6. Which statement is correct, $\triangle ABC \cong \triangle KSV$ or $\triangle ABC \cong \triangle KVS$?

In Exercises 7–12, the goal is to prove two triangles congruent.

7. Pair vertex D with vertex _?_ , and vertex E with vertex _?_ .

8. $\overline{DF}$ and _?_ are corr. sides.

9. $\overline{EF}$ and _?_ are corr. sides.

10. What reason supports the statement $\angle D \cong \angle Z$?

11. Is the statement $\triangle DEF \cong \triangle ZJO$ correct?

12. Is the statement $\triangle OZJ \cong \triangle FDE$ correct?

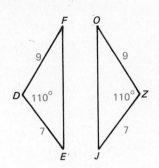

13. To use the SSS Postulate to prove $\triangle DEF \cong \triangle RUN$, a person must show:

$\overline{DE} \cong$ _?_ , $\overline{EF} \cong$ _?_ , $\overline{DF} \cong$ _?_

14. To use the SAS Postulate to prove $\triangle DEF \cong \triangle RUN$, a person who uses $\angle D \cong \angle R$ must also show:

$\overline{DE} \cong$ _?_ , $\overline{DF} \cong$ _?_

15. To use the SSS Postulate to prove $\triangle DEF \cong \triangle URN$, a person must show:

$\overline{DE} \cong$ _?_ , $\overline{EF} \cong$ _?_ , $\overline{DF} \cong$ _?_

16. To use the SAS Postulate to prove $\triangle DEF \cong \triangle URN$, a person who uses $\angle F \cong \angle N$ must also show:

$\overline{FD} \cong$ _?_ , $\overline{FE} \cong$ _?_

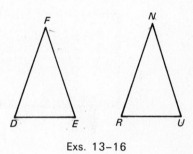

Exs. 13–16

Written Exercises

Copy everything shown. Complete the proof by supplying reasons.

Given: $\overline{XZ} \cong \overline{XW}$; $\overline{YZ} \cong \overline{YW}$

Prove: $\triangle XYZ \cong \triangle XYW$

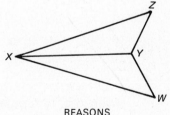

Proof:

STATEMENTS	REASONS
A 1. $\overline{XZ} \cong \overline{XW}$	1. _?_
2. $\overline{XY} \cong \overline{XY}$	2. _?_
3. $\overline{YZ} \cong \overline{YW}$	3. _?_
4. $\triangle XYZ \cong \triangle XYW$	4. _?_

Given: $m\angle C = 80$; $m\angle T = 80$;
$\overline{AC} \cong \overline{RT}$; $\overline{BC} \cong \overline{VT}$

Prove: $\triangle ABC \cong \triangle RVT$

Proof:

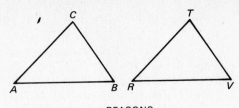

STATEMENTS	REASONS
5. $\overline{AC} \cong \overline{RT}$	5. ?
6. $m\angle C = 80$; $m\angle T = 80$	6. ?
7. $m\angle C = m\angle T$	7. ?
8. $\angle C \cong \angle T$	8. ?
9. $\overline{BC} \cong \overline{VT}$	9. ?
10. $\triangle ABC \cong \triangle RVT$	10. ?

Given: $\overline{ABCD}$; $\overline{AB} \cong \overline{CD}$;
$\overline{BY} \cong \overline{CX}$; $\overline{YD} \cong \overline{XA}$

Prove: $\triangle DYB \cong \triangle AXC$

Proof:

STATEMENTS	REASONS
11. $\overline{AB} \cong \overline{CD}$	11. ?
12. $AB = CD$	12. ?
13. $BC = BC$	13. ?
14. $AB + BC = BC + CD$	14. ?
15. $AB + BC = AC$	15. ?
16. $BC + CD = BD$	16. ?
17. $AC = BD$	17. ?
18. $\overline{AC} \cong \overline{BD}$	18. ?
19. $\overline{BY} \cong \overline{CX}$; $\overline{YD} \cong \overline{XA}$	19. ?
20. $\triangle DYB \cong \triangle AXC$	20. ?

Given the information stated in each exercise, you are to prove $\triangle RSJ \cong \triangle RSK$. Write a proof in two-column form.

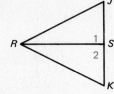

B 21. $\overline{RJ} \cong \overline{RK}$; $\overline{SJ} \cong \overline{SK}$

22. $\angle JRS \cong \angle KRS$; $\overline{RJ} \cong \overline{RK}$

23. $\angle 1$ and $\angle 2$ are rt. $\angle\!\!\!\!\!\angle$; $\overline{JS} \cong \overline{KS}$

24. $RJ = 13$; $RK = 13$; $\overline{RS}$ bisects $\overline{JK}$.

Write proofs in two-column form.

25. Given: $\overline{AB}$ and $\overline{CD}$ bisect each other.
    Prove: $\triangle AXC \cong \triangle BXD$

26. Given: $\angle A \cong \angle B$; X is the midpoint of $\overline{AB}$; $\overline{AC} \cong \overline{BD}$
    Prove: $\triangle AXC \cong \triangle BXD$

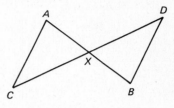

27. Given: $\overline{ZT}$ bisects $\overline{RS}$; $\overline{RZ} \cong \overline{SZ}$
    Prove: $\triangle RTZ \cong \triangle STZ$

28. Given: $\overline{RS} \perp$ plane M; $\overline{RT} \cong \overline{ST}$
    Prove: $\triangle RTZ \cong \triangle STZ$

29. Given: $\overline{XY} \cong \overline{XZ}$; $\overline{PY} \cong \overline{PZ}$
    Prove: $\triangle PXY \cong \triangle PXZ$

30. Given: $\angle PYX \cong \angle PYZ$; $\overline{YX} \cong \overline{YZ}$
    Prove: $\triangle PXY \cong \triangle PZY$

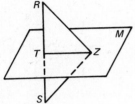

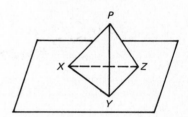

C 31. Given: $\angle 1 \cong \angle 2$; $\overline{AB} \cong \overline{DC}$; $\overline{BK} \cong \overline{CK}$
    Prove: $\triangle ABK \cong \triangle DCK$.

32. Given: $\overline{AB} \cong \overline{CD}$; $\overline{AK} \cong \overline{DK}$; $\angle A \cong \angle D$
    Prove: $\triangle ACK \cong \triangle DBK$

33. Given: $\overline{RS} \perp$ plane M; $ST = 5$, $SW = 5$
    Prove: $\triangle RST \cong \triangle RSW$

34. Given: $\overline{SJ}$ bisects $\overline{TW}$; $\overline{RT} \cong \overline{RW}$
    Prove: $\triangle RJT \cong \triangle RJW$

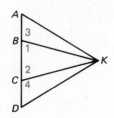

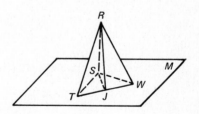

4-3 *Some Ways to Prove Right Triangles Congruent*

$\overline{RT}$ is the *hypotenuse* of the right triangle pictured. $\overline{RS}$ and $\overline{TS}$ are *legs*. In any right triangle the side opposite the right angle is called the hypotenuse; the other two sides are called legs.

THEOREM 4-2
(LL THEOREM)

If two legs of one right triangle are congruent to the corresponding parts of another right triangle, the triangles are congruent.

Given: $\triangle RST$ and $\triangle XYZ$;
$\angle S$ and $\angle Y$ are rt. $\angle$s;
$\overline{RS} \cong \overline{XY}$; $\overline{ST} \cong \overline{YZ}$

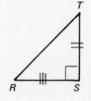

Prove: $\triangle RST \cong \triangle XYZ$

Proof:

STATEMENTS	REASONS
1. $\angle S$ and $\angle Y$ are rt. $\angle$s.	1. Given
2. $\angle S \cong \angle Y$	2. All rt. $\angle$s are $\cong$.
3. $\overline{RS} \cong \overline{XY}$; $\overline{ST} \cong \overline{YZ}$	3. Given
4. $\triangle RST \cong \triangle XYZ$	4. SAS Postulate

In the diagram below, stick m is fastened rigidly to stick RS so that $\angle S$ is a right angle. Stick RT can rotate about a bolt at point R.

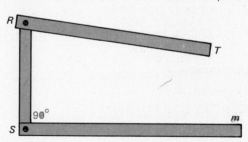

Stick RT is rotated until tip T just reaches stick m.

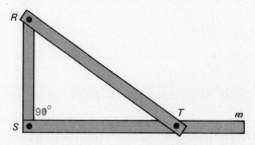

The extra wood on m is sawed off, and a bolt is secured at T. For particular sticks RS and RT, and a right angle at S, only one kind of triangle is possible.

Postulate 15 is related to the experiment described above.

POSTULATE 15
(HL POSTULATE) If the hypotenuse and a leg of one right triangle are congruent to the corresponding parts of another right triangle, the triangles are congruent.

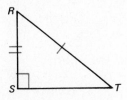
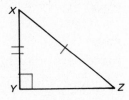

According to Postulate 15:

If △ *RST* and *XYZ* are rt. △ with rt. ∠ *S* and *Y*, $\overline{RT} \cong \overline{XZ}$, and $\overline{RS} \cong \overline{XY}$,
then △*RST* ≅ △*XYZ*.

Oral Exercises

In the figure it is given that $\overline{XC} \perp \overline{AE}$, $\overline{AX} \perp \overline{XD}$, and $\overline{BX} \perp \overline{XE}$. Name a right triangle that has:

1. Hypotenuse $\overline{XD}$
2. Hypotenuse $\overline{XE}$ ⁣*N°*
3. $\overline{XD}$ as one of its legs *BXD*
4. $\overline{BX}$ as one of its legs *BXE*
5. $\overline{AD}$ as its hypotenuse *AXD*
6. Name every right triangle that has $\overline{XC}$ as one of its legs.

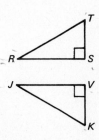

∠*S* and ∠*V* are rt. ∠. You wish to prove that △*RST* ≅ △*JVK*.

7. If you intend to use the HL Postulate and have proved $\overline{RS} \cong \overline{JV}$, you also need to prove *R?T* ≅ *J?K* .
8. If you intend to use the SSS Postulate, you need to prove *J? ≅ R?, R?T ≅ J?V*, and *R?S ≅ J?K* .
9. If you intend to use the LL Theorem, you need to prove *R?T ≅ J?V* and *R?S ≅ J?K* .
10. If you intend to use the SAS Postulate, you need to prove ∠*S* ≅ ∠*V*, __?__ ≅ __?__ , and __?__ ≅ __?__ .

Written Exercises State the postulate or theorem that directly supports the conclusion $\triangle DEF \cong \triangle MJK$.

A 1. Given: $\angle D$ and $\angle M$ are rt. $\angle s$; $\overline{FE} \cong \overline{KJ}$; $\overline{DF} \cong \overline{MK}$
    2. Given: $\angle F \cong \angle K$; $\overline{DF} \cong \overline{MK}$; $\overline{FE} \cong \overline{KJ}$ SAS
    3. Given: $\overline{DF} \cong \overline{MK}$; $\overline{DE} \cong \overline{MJ}$; $\overline{FE} \cong \overline{KJ}$ SSS
    4. Given: $\angle D$ and $\angle M$ are rt. $\angle s$; $\overline{DF} \cong \overline{MK}$; $\overline{DE} \cong \overline{MJ}$

Name each right triangle shown in the figure.

5. Given: $\angle ACB$ is a rt. $\angle$; $\overline{CD} \perp \overline{AB}$.

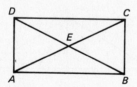

7. Given: $\overline{AB} \perp$ plane N

DCX = BCY

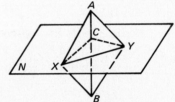

6. Given: $\angle ABC$, $\angle BCD$, $\angle CDA$, and $\angle DAB$ are rt. $\angle s$.

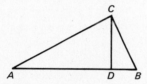

8. Given: $\overline{VW} \perp$ plane of $\triangle XYZ$

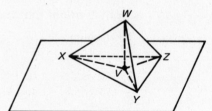

9. Examine the triangles. Do you believe that we shall have an AAA theorem or postulate for congruence of triangles?

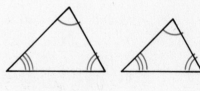

10. Examine the triangles. Do you believe that we shall have an SSA theorem or postulate for congruence of triangles?

Supply the reasons needed to complete the proof.

Given: $\overline{AB}$ and $\overline{CD}$ are ⊥ bisectors of each other.

Prove: $\triangle AKD \cong \triangle BKC$

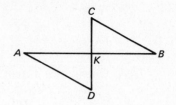

Proof:

STATEMENTS	REASONS
11. $\overline{CD} \perp \overline{AB}$	11. __?__
12. $\angle AKD$ and $\angle BKC$ are rt. ∠s.	12. __?__
13. $\triangle AKD$ and $\triangle BKC$ are rt. ⧍s.	13. __?__
14. $\overline{CD}$ bisects $\overline{AB}$; $\overline{AB}$ bisects $\overline{CD}$.	14. __?__
15. $\overline{AK} \cong \overline{BK}$; $\overline{DK} \cong \overline{CK}$	15. __?__
16. $\triangle AKD \cong \triangle BKC$	16. __?__

Write proofs in two-column form.

17. Given: $\angle 3$ and $\angle 4$ are rt. ∠s;
    $\overline{HJ} \cong \overline{HK}$
    Prove: $\triangle GHJ \cong \triangle GHK$

18. Given: $\angle 3$ and $\angle 4$ are rt. ∠s;
    $\overline{GJ} \cong \overline{GK}$
    Prove: $\triangle GHJ \cong \triangle GHK$

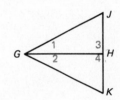

B 19. Given: $\overline{RS} \perp \overline{TS}$; $\overline{RS} \perp \overline{ZS}$; $\overline{RT} \cong \overline{RZ}$
    Prove: $\triangle RST \cong \triangle RSZ$

20. Given: $\overline{RS} \perp \overline{TS}$; $\overline{RS} \perp \overline{ZS}$; $\overline{ST} \cong \overline{SZ}$
    Prove: $\triangle RST \cong \triangle RSZ$

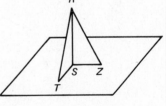

21. Given: $\overline{AB}$ is the ⊥ bisector of $\overline{CD}$;
    $\overline{AC} \cong \overline{BD}$
    Prove: $\triangle AXC \cong \triangle BXD$

22. Given: X is the midpoint of both $\overline{AB}$ and $\overline{CD}$; $\overline{CD} \perp$ plane M
    Prove: $\triangle AXC \cong \triangle BXD$

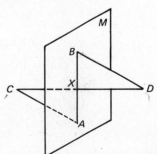

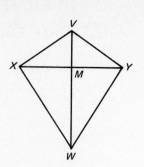

23. Given: $\angle VXW$ and $\angle VYW$ are rt. $\angle\!\!\!/\,s$;
    $\overline{VX} \cong \overline{VY}$
    Prove: $\triangle VXW \cong \triangle VYW$

24. Given: $\overline{VW}$ is the $\perp$ bisector of $\overline{XY}$.
    Prove: $\triangle VMX \cong \triangle VMY$

C 25. Given: $\angle GBK$ is a rt. $\angle$;
    $\angle H$ is comp. to $\angle K$;
    $\overline{AK} \cong \overline{BK}$; $\overline{GK} \cong \overline{HK}$
    Prove: $\triangle GBK \cong \triangle HAK$

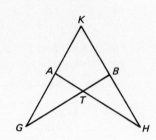

26. Given: $\overline{GB} \perp \overline{HK}$; $\overline{HA} \perp \overline{GK}$;
    $\overline{GK} \cong \overline{HK}$; $\overline{AK} \cong \overline{BK}$;
    $\overline{GT} \cong \overline{HT}$
    Prove: $\triangle GAT \cong \triangle HBT$

27. Given: $\overline{PS} \perp \overline{XY}$;
    $\overline{RS}$ bisects $\overline{XY}$.
    Prove: $\triangle PSX \cong \triangle PSY$

28. Given: $\overline{PZ} \perp$ plane M;
    $PX = 15$; $PY = 15$
    Prove: $\triangle PZY \cong \triangle PZX$

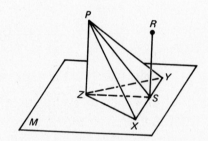

Self-Test 1. In the correspondence $\triangle SEW \leftrightarrow \triangle TJN$, vertex E is paired with vertex __?__ .
2. For the statement $\triangle SEW \cong \triangle TJN$ to be true it is necessary that $\angle S \cong \angle$ __?__ and $\overline{SW} \cong$ __?__ .
3. Write a complete statement of the SSS Postulate.
4. Write a complete statement of the HL Postulate.

In Exercises 5 and 6 it is given that $m\angle KBA = 90$, $m\angle CBA = 90$, $\overline{KB} \cong \overline{CB}$.

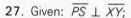

5. Use a right triangle method to prove $\triangle KBA \cong \triangle CBA$.
6. Use another method to prove $\triangle KBA \cong \triangle CBA$.

Check your answers with those printed at the back of the book.

Methods Involving Two Angles

Objectives

1. Use the ASA Postulate and the AAS Theorem to prove two triangles congruent.
2. Use the HA Theorem and the LA Theorem to prove two right triangles congruent.

4-4 *More Ways to Prove Triangles Congruent*

Three sticks are shown. Bolts at *A* and *B* are loose enough so that sticks *s* and *t* can be turned.

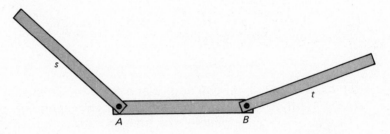

Let the goal be to form a triangle with a 60° angle at *A* and a 40° angle at *B*.

Sticks *s* and *t* are rotated to form the desired angles.

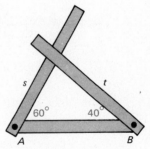

Extra wood is sawed off, and a bolt is fastened at *C*.

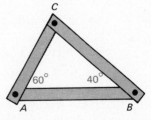

For a particular stick *AB*, a given angle measure at *A* and a given angle measure at *B*, only one kind of triangle can be made.

POSTULATE 16	If two angles and the included side of one
(ASA POSTULATE)	triangle are congruent to the corresponding parts of another triangle, the triangles are congruent.

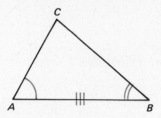 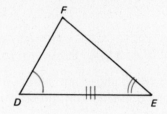

According to Postulate 16:

If $\angle A \cong \angle D$, $\overline{AB} \cong \overline{DE}$, and $\angle B \cong \angle E$,
then $\triangle ABC \cong \triangle DEF$.

THEOREM 4-3 If two angles and a not-included side of one triangle
(AAS THEOREM) are congruent to the corresponding parts of another
triangle, the triangles are congruent.

Given: $\triangle ABC$ and DEF; $\angle A \cong \angle D$;
$\angle C \cong \angle F$; $\overline{AB} \cong \overline{DE}$

Prove: $\triangle ABC \cong \triangle DEF$

 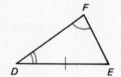

The proof is left as Exercise 24.

Oral Exercises

Name the side that is included between the angles named.

1. $\angle A$, $\angle B$ 2. $\angle B$, $\angle C$ 3. $\angle A$, $\angle C$

Name the two sides that are not included between the angles named.

4. $\angle D$, $\angle E$ 5. $\angle E$, $\angle F$ 6. $\angle D$, $\angle F$

Some congruent segments and angles are indicated. Can the triangles be proved congruent? If so, what theorem or postulate can be used?

7.

10.

8.

11.

9.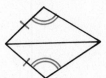

12.

Written Exercises

Supply the reasons needed to complete the proof.

Given: $\overline{ABCD}$; $\overline{AX} \parallel \overline{BY}$;
$\overline{AB} \cong \overline{CD}$; $\angle X \cong \angle Y$

Prove: $\triangle ACX \cong \triangle BDY$

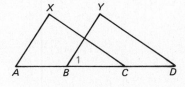

Proof:

STATEMENTS	REASONS
A 1. $\overline{AB} \cong \overline{CD}$	1. __?__
2. $AB = CD$	2. __?__
3. $BC = BC$	3. __?__
4. $AB + BC = BC + CD$	4. __?__
5. $AB + BC = AC$	5. __?__
6. $BC + CD = BD$	6. __?__
7. $AC = BD$	7. __?__
8. $\overline{AC} \cong \overline{BD}$	8. __?__
9. $\overline{AX} \parallel \overline{BY}$	9. __?__
10. $\angle A \cong \angle 1$	10. __?__
11. $\angle X \cong \angle Y$	11. __?__
12. $\triangle ACX \cong \triangle BDY$	12. __?__

In each exercise you are to prove △RST ≅ △RSP.
Write a proof in two-column form.

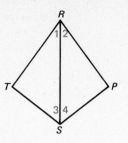

13. Given: ∠1 ≅ ∠2; ∠T ≅ ∠P

14. Given: ∠1 ≅ ∠2; ∠3 ≅ ∠4

15. Given: ∠T ≅ ∠P; RS⃗ bisects ∠TRP.

16. Given: ∠T and ∠P are rt. ∡s; ∠1 ≅ ∠2

Write proofs in two-column form.

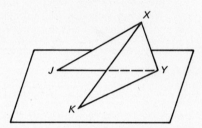

17. Given: ∠J ≅ ∠K;
    ∠JXY ≅ ∠KXY
    Prove: △XYJ ≅ △XYK

18. Given: XJ ≅ XK; YJ ≅ YK
    Prove: △XYJ ≅ △XYK

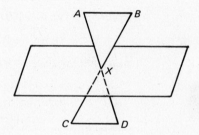

19. Given: AD bisects BC;
    ∠B ≅ ∠C
    Prove: △AXB ≅ △DXC

20. Given: AB ∥ CD;
    BC bisects AD.
    Prove: △AXB ≅ △DXC

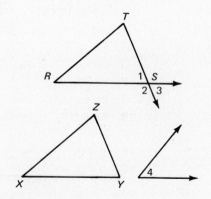

B 21. Given: ∠T ≅ ∠Z; RT ≅ XZ;
    ∠R is comp. to ∠4;
    ∠X is comp. to ∠4
    Prove: △RST ≅ △XYZ

22. Given: ∠3 ≅ ∠Y; ∠R ≅ ∠X;
    RS ≅ XY
    Prove: △RST ≅ △XYZ

23. Given: ∠Y is supp. to ∠2;
    ∠T ≅ ∠Z; RT ≅ XZ
    Prove: △RST ≅ △XYZ

24. Write a complete demonstration of Theorem 4-3. (*Hint:* Refer to the figure on page 132. You can use Corollary 1 of Theorem 3-7 to prove that $\angle B \cong \angle E$. Then prove the triangles congruent by applying the ASA Postulate.)

C 25. Given: $\overline{HG} \parallel \overline{EF}$; $\overline{GH} \cong \overline{EF}$
   Prove: $\triangle HMG \cong \triangle FME$

26. Given: $\angle HEF \cong \angle FGH$; $\overline{EH} \parallel \overline{FG}$
   Prove: $\triangle EHF \cong \triangle GFH$

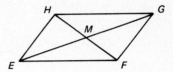

27. Given: $\triangle XEJ \cong \triangle YEJ$; $\overline{XE} \perp$ plane M;
   $\angle JYE \cong \angle KXE$; $\overline{JY} \cong \overline{KX}$.
   Prove: $\triangle XEJ \cong \triangle XEK$

28. Given: $\angle XEK \cong \angle XEJ$; $\angle XEJ \cong \angle YEJ$;
   $\angle KXE \cong \angle JXE$; $\overrightarrow{JE}$ bisects $\angle XJY$
   Prove: $\triangle XEK \cong \triangle YEJ$

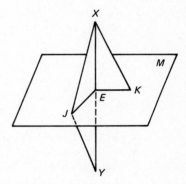

4-5 *More Ways to Prove Right Triangles Congruent*

The ASA Postulate and the AAS Theorem lead to two more ways to prove that right triangles are congruent.

THEOREM 4-4
(HA THEOREM)
If the hypotenuse and an acute angle of one right triangle are congruent to the corresponding parts of another right triangle, the triangles are congruent.

Given: $\triangle ABC$ and DEF; $\angle B$ and $\angle E$
are rt. $\&$; $\overline{AC} \cong \overline{DF}$; $\angle A \cong \angle D$

Prove: $\triangle ABC \cong \triangle DEF$

The proof is left as Exercise 9.

THEOREM 4-5
(LA THEOREM)
If a leg and an acute angle of one right triangle are congruent to the corresponding parts of another right triangle, the triangles are congruent.

CASE 1

Given: △RST and XYZ; ∠S and ∠Y are rt. ⧀; $\overline{RS} \cong \overline{XY}$; ∠R ≅ ∠X

Prove: △RST ≅ △XYZ

The proof is left as Exercise 10.

CASE 2

Given: △RST and XYZ; ∠S and ∠Y are rt. ⧀; $\overline{RS} \cong \overline{XY}$; ∠T ≅ ∠Z

Prove: △RST ≅ △XYZ

The proof is left as Exercise 11.

Oral Exercises Some congruent parts of two right triangles are indicated by checkmarks. State whether the HA Theorem, the LA Theorem, or some other right triangle method can be used to prove that the triangles are congruent.

1.

2.

3.

4.

5.

6.

7.

8.

Written Exercises

Write proofs in two-column form.

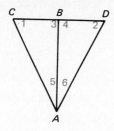

A

1. Given: $\angle 3$ and $\angle 4$ are rt. $\angle$s; $\angle 1 \cong \angle 2$
   Prove: $\triangle ABC \cong \triangle ABD$

2. Given: $\angle 3$ and $\angle 4$ are rt. $\angle$s; $\angle 5 \cong \angle 6$
   Prove: $\triangle ABC \cong \triangle ABD$

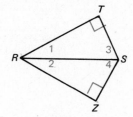

3. Given: $\angle T$ and $\angle Z$ are rt. $\angle$s; $\angle 1 \cong \angle 2$
   Prove: $\triangle RTS \cong \triangle RZS$

4. Given: $\angle T$ and $\angle Z$ are rt. $\angle$s;
   $\overrightarrow{SR}$ bisects $\angle TSZ$
   Prove: $\triangle RTS \cong \triangle RZS$

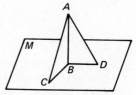

5. Given: $\overline{AB} \perp \overline{BC}$; $\overline{AB} \perp \overline{BD}$; $\angle C \cong \angle D$
   Prove: $\triangle ABC \cong \triangle ABD$

6. Given: $\overline{AB} \perp$ plane M; $\angle BAC \cong \angle BAD$
   Prove: $\triangle ABC \cong \triangle ABD$

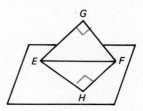

7. Given: $\angle G$ and $\angle H$ are rt. $\angle$s;
   $\overline{EG} \cong \overline{EH}$
   Prove: $\triangle EGF \cong \triangle EHF$

8. Given: $\angle G$ and $\angle H$ are rt. $\angle$s;
   $m\angle GEF = 42$; $m\angle HEF = 42$
   Prove: $\triangle EGF \cong \triangle EHF$

B

9. Copy what is shown for Theorem 4-4. Complete the demonstration.
10. Copy Theorem 4-5, Case 1. Complete the demonstration.
11. Copy Theorem 4-5, Case 2. Complete the demonstration.

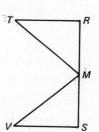

12. Given: $\angle R$ and $\angle S$ are rt. $\angle$s;
    M is the midpoint of $\overline{RS}$;
    $\angle T \cong \angle V$
    Prove: $\triangle MRT \cong \triangle MSV$

13. Given: $\overline{TR} \perp \overline{RS}$; $\overline{VS} \perp \overline{RS}$;
    $\angle T$ is comp. to $\angle VMS$;
    $\overline{TM} \cong \overline{VM}$
    Prove: $\triangle MRT \cong \triangle MSV$

14. Given: $\angle R$ and $\angle S$ are rt. $\angle$s;
    $\angle RMV \cong \angle TMS$; $\overline{TR} \cong \overline{VS}$
    Prove: $\triangle MRT \cong \triangle MSV$

15. Given: $\overline{ZW} \perp \overline{WY}$; $\overline{JK} \perp \overline{WY}$;
    $\overline{XY} \perp \overline{WY}$; $\angle 7 \cong \angle 8$
    Prove: $\triangle ZWY \cong \triangle XYW$

16. Given: $\overline{ZW} \perp \overline{WY}$; $\overline{JK} \perp \overline{WY}$;
    $\overline{XY} \perp \overline{WY}$; $\angle 1 \cong \angle 2$
    Prove: $\triangle ZWY \cong \triangle XYW$

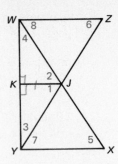

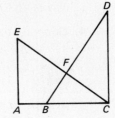

C 17. Given: $\overline{EA} \perp \overline{AC}$; $\overline{DC} \perp \overline{AC}$;
    $\overline{EA} \cong \overline{BC}$; $\angle D$ is comp. to $\angle E$.
    Prove: $\triangle EAC \cong \triangle BCD$

18. Given: $\overline{BD} \perp \overline{EC}$; $\overline{EA} \perp \overline{AC}$;
    $\overline{DC} \perp \overline{AC}$; $\overline{EC} \cong \overline{BD}$
    Prove: $\triangle EAC \cong \triangle BCD$

In each exercise, write what is to be
proved. Write a proof in two-column
form.

19. Given: $\overline{VX} \perp \overline{AB}$; $\overline{VY} \perp \overline{BC}$;
    $\angle BVX \cong \angle VBY$
    Prove: $\triangle \underline{\ ?\ } \cong \triangle \underline{\ ?\ }$

20. Given: $\overline{VX} \perp \overline{AB}$; $\overline{VY} \perp \overline{BC}$;
    $\overline{VY} \cong \overline{AX}$;
    $\angle AVX$ is comp. to $\angle CVY$.
    Prove: $\triangle \underline{\ ?\ } \cong \triangle \underline{\ ?\ }$

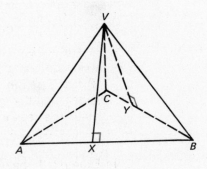

Self-Test State whether the statement $\triangle PDC \cong$
$\triangle PDN$ can be proved by use of the postulate or theorem indicated.

1. ASA
2. AAS
3. HA
4. LA

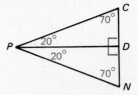

In Exercises 5 and 6, write proofs in two-
column form. It is given that $\overline{ZX} \perp \overline{XY}$,
$\overline{WY} \perp \overline{XY}$, and M is the midpoint of $\overline{XY}$.

5. Use a right triangle method to prove
   $\triangle ZXM \cong \triangle WYM$.

6. Use a method that does not refer to right
   triangles to prove $\triangle ZXM \cong \triangle WYM$.

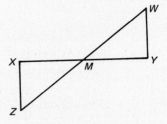

Congruent Segments and Angles

Objectives

1. Prove two segments or two angles congruent by first proving that two triangles are congruent.
2. Use auxiliary lines correctly.
3. Apply the theorems about isosceles triangles in proofs and numerical exercises.

4-6 *Proving Corresponding Parts Congruent*

When two triangles are congruent, each part of one triangle is congruent to the corresponding part of the other triangle. You can sometimes prove that two segments or two angles are congruent by showing that they are corresponding parts of congruent triangles.

One way to prove two segments or two angles congruent:

1. Identify two triangles in which the two segments or angles are corresponding parts.
2. Prove that the triangles are congruent.
3. State that the two parts are congruent, supporting the statement with the reason: "Corr. parts of ≅ △ are ≅."

In Example 1, below, the proof ends with the statement that two corresponding parts are congruent. Notice, in Example 2, how we can go on from a statement about congruence to prove something else.

EXAMPLE 1

Given: $\overline{AB}$ and $\overline{CD}$ bisect each other.

Prove: $\overline{AC} \cong \overline{BD}$

Proof:

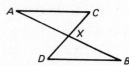

STATEMENTS	REASONS
1. $\overline{CD}$ bisects $\overline{AB}$; $\overline{AB}$ bisects $\overline{CD}$.	1. Given
2. $\overline{AX} \cong \overline{BX}$; $\overline{CX} \cong \overline{DX}$	2. Def. of bisect
3. $\angle AXC \cong \angle BXD$	3. Vert. ∡ are ≅.
4. $\triangle AXC \cong \triangle BXD$	4. SAS Postulate
5. $\overline{AC} \cong \overline{BD}$	5. Corr. parts of ≅ △ are ≅.

EXAMPLE 2

Given: $\overline{AB}$ and $\overline{CD}$ bisect each other.

Prove: $\overline{AC} \parallel \overline{BD}$

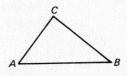

Proof:

STATEMENTS	REASONS
1–4. Same as in Example 1	1–4. Same as in Example 1
5. $\angle C \cong \angle D$	5. Corr. parts of $\cong$ ▲ are $\cong$.
6. $\overline{AC} \parallel \overline{BD}$	6. When two lines are cut by a trans. so that alt. int. ∡ are $\cong$, the lines are $\parallel$.

Ways to Prove Two Triangles Congruent

All Triangles	Right Triangles
SSS	HL
SAS	LL
ASA	HA
AAS	LA

Oral Exercises   State the postulate or theorem you would use to prove $\triangle ABC \cong \triangle DEF$.

1. Given: $\angle C$ and $\angle F$ are rt. ∡; $\overline{AB} \cong \overline{DE}$; $\overline{AC} \cong \overline{DF}$
2. Given: $\angle C$ and $\angle F$ are rt. ∡; $\overline{AC} \cong \overline{DF}$; $\angle B \cong \angle E$
3. Given: $\angle A \cong \angle D$; $\angle C \cong \angle F$; $\overline{AC} \cong \overline{DF}$
4. Given: $\angle A \cong \angle D$; $\angle C \cong \angle F$; $\overline{BC} \cong \overline{EF}$
5. Given: $\angle C$ and $\angle F$ are rt. ∡; $\overline{AC} \cong \overline{DF}$; $\overline{BC} \cong \overline{EF}$
6. Given: $\angle A \cong \angle D$; $\overline{AB} \cong \overline{DE}$; $\angle B \cong \angle E$
7. Given: $\angle A \cong \angle D$; $\overline{AC} \cong \overline{DF}$; $\overline{AB} \cong \overline{DE}$
8. Given: $\overline{BC} \perp \overline{AC}$; $\overline{EF} \perp \overline{DF}$; $\overline{AB} \cong \overline{DE}$; $\angle B \cong \angle E$
9. Given: $\overline{AB} \cong \overline{DE}$; $\overline{BC} \cong \overline{EF}$; $\overline{AC} \cong \overline{DF}$
10. Given: $\overline{AC} \cong \overline{DF}$; $\angle C \cong \angle F$; $\overline{BC} \cong \overline{EF}$

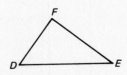

Written Exercises

Write proofs in two-column form.

A

1. Given: $\angle 3$ and $\angle 4$ are rt. $\angle$s; $\overline{AC} \cong \overline{BC}$
   Prove: $\overline{AX} \cong \overline{BX}$

2. Given: $\angle 1 \cong \angle 2$; $\angle 3 \cong \angle 4$
   Prove: $\overline{AC} \cong \overline{BC}$

3. Given: $\overline{AC} \cong \overline{BC}$; $\overline{AX} \cong \overline{BX}$
   Prove: $\angle 1 \cong \angle 2$

4. Given: $\angle 3$ and $\angle 4$ are rt. $\angle$s; $\overline{AX} \cong \overline{BX}$
   Prove: $\angle A \cong \angle B$

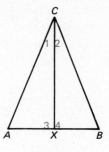

Exs. 1–4

5. Given: $\overline{XY} \cong \overline{ZW}$; $\overline{YZ} \cong \overline{WX}$
   Prove: $\angle Y \cong \angle W$

6. Given: $\overline{XY} \cong \overline{ZW}$; $\angle 1 \cong \angle 2$
   Prove: $\overline{XW} \cong \overline{ZY}$

7. Given: $\angle 1 \cong \angle 2$; $\angle 3 \cong \angle 4$
   Prove: $\overline{XY} \cong \overline{ZW}$

8. Given: $\angle 1 \cong \angle 2$; $\angle Y \cong \angle W$
   Prove: $\overline{YZ} \cong \overline{WX}$

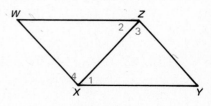

Exs. 5–12

9. Given: $\overline{XY} \parallel \overline{WZ}$; $\overline{XW} \parallel \overline{YZ}$
   Prove: $\overline{XW} \cong \overline{ZY}$

10. Given: $\overline{XY} \parallel \overline{WZ}$; $\overline{XY} \cong \overline{ZW}$
    Prove: $\angle 3 \cong \angle 4$

11. Given: $\overline{XW} \parallel \overline{YZ}$; $XW = ZY$
    Prove: $XY = ZW$

12. Given: $XY = ZW$; $ZY = XW$
    Prove: $m\angle 1 = m\angle 2$

B

13. Given: $\overleftrightarrow{RS}$ bisects $\angle TRV$ and $\angle TSV$.
    Prove: $\overline{TS} \cong \overline{VS}$

14. Given: $\overline{RT} \perp \overline{TS}$; $\overline{RV} \perp \overline{VS}$; $\angle 1 \cong \angle 2$
    Prove: $\overline{RT} \cong \overline{RV}$

15. Given: $RT = 23$; $RV = 23$; $m\angle 1 = m\angle 2$; $m\angle T = 92$
    Prove: $m\angle V = 92$

16. Given: $\angle 1 \cong \angle 2$; $\overline{RT} \cong \overline{RV}$; $\angle T$ is a rt. $\angle$.
    Prove: $\angle V$ is a rt. $\angle$.

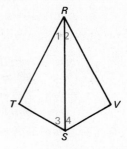

Exs. 13–16

17. Given: $\overrightarrow{ZW}$ bisects $\angle XZY$;
    $\overline{XZ} \cong \overline{YZ}$
    Prove: $\overline{ZW} \perp \overline{YX}$

18. Given: $\overleftrightarrow{ZW}$ is the $\perp$ bisector of $\overline{XY}$.
    Prove: $\overrightarrow{ZW}$ bisects $\angle XZY$.

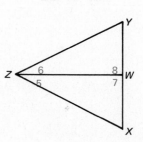

19. Given: $\angle 3 \cong \angle 4$; $\overline{BC} \cong \overline{DA}$
    Prove: $\overline{AB} \parallel \overline{DC}$

20. Given: $\overline{AB} \cong \overline{CD}$; $\overline{AB} \parallel \overline{DC}$
    Prove: $\overline{AD} \parallel \overline{BC}$

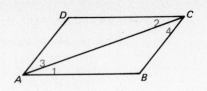

21. Given: $\angle 2 \cong \angle 1$; $\angle M \cong \angle P$
    Prove: $\overline{JM} \cong \overline{JP}$

22. Given: $\overleftrightarrow{KJ}$ bisects $\angle MKP$; $\overline{KM} \cong \overline{KP}$
    Prove: $\angle 1 \cong \angle 2$

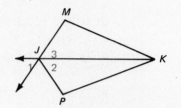

C 23. Given: $\overline{TV} \cong \overline{ZV}$; $\angle TVS \cong \angle ZVS$
    Prove: $\overline{RT} \cong \overline{RZ}$

24. Given: $\overleftrightarrow{RS}$ bisects $\angle TRZ$ and $\angle TVZ$;
    $\angle STV \cong \angle SZV$
    Prove: $\angle RTS \cong \angle RZS$

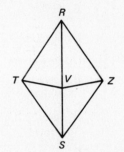

25. Given: M is the midpoint of $\overline{AB}$
    and $\overline{CD}$.

    Prove: M is the midpoint of $\overline{EF}$.
    (*Hint:* Show $\triangle AMC \cong$
    $\triangle BMD$. Then select some
    corresponding parts that
    will enable you to prove
    $\triangle AME \cong \triangle BMF$.)

26. Given: $\overline{AE} \parallel \overline{FB}$; $\overline{AC} \cong \overline{BD}$
    Prove: $\overline{AE} \cong \overline{BF}$

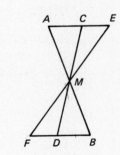

27. Given: $\overline{PV} \perp$ plane M;
    R is the midpoint of $\overline{PV}$.
    Prove: $\angle SPT \cong \angle SVT$

28. Given: $\overline{SR}$ bisects $\overline{PV}$;
    $\overline{PT} \cong \overline{VT}$
    Prove: $\overline{TR} \perp \overline{PV}$

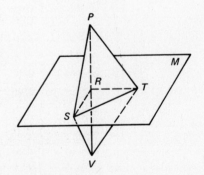

Write a demonstration of the statement.

29. In a plane, if a line is perpendicular to a ray that bisects an angle, the points where that line intersects the sides of the angle are equally distant from the vertex of the angle.

30. If, from a point on the bisector of an angle, perpendicular segments are drawn to the sides of the angle, those segments are congruent.

Challenge

Given: $\overline{VA}$, $\overline{VB}$, $\overline{VC}$, $\overline{AB}$, $\overline{BC}$, and $\overline{AC}$ are all $\cong$;
P is the midpoint of $\overline{VC}$;
T is the midpoint of $\overline{AB}$.

Prove: $\overline{PT} \perp \overline{AB}$; $\overline{PT} \perp \overline{VC}$

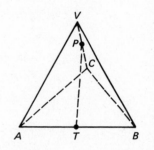

4-7 Isosceles Triangles

Recall that an isosceles triangle is a triangle with two congruent sides. The congruent sides are called legs, and the third side is called the base.

$\angle 1$ and $\angle 2$ are *base angles*.
$\angle 3$ is the *vertex angle*.

Two terms that are used in connection with all triangles, including isosceles triangles, are *altitude* and *median*. In each of the figures below, $\overline{AH}$ is an altitude and $\overline{AM}$ is a median of $\triangle ABC$.

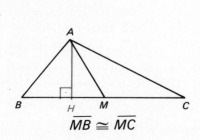

$\overline{MB} \cong \overline{MC}$

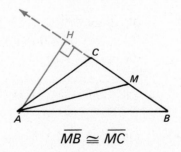

$\overline{MB} \cong \overline{MC}$

CONGRUENT TRIANGLES **143**

An altitude of a triangle is the segment drawn from any vertex perpendicular to the line that contains the opposite side. A median of a triangle is the segment that joins a vertex and the midpoint of the opposite side. Every triangle has three altitudes and three medians.

Given △RST, one can say, "Draw the altitude from T to $\overleftrightarrow{RS}$," for there is exactly one perpendicular from T to $\overleftrightarrow{RS}$. On the other hand, one can say, "Draw the median from T to $\overline{RS}$." But it would not be correct to say, "From T draw the segment that is both an altitude and a median of the triangle." The last sentence would place on the auxiliary segment conditions that might be contradictory.

If △RST were an isosceles triangle, you could draw the altitude to the base and then prove that the altitude is also a median. See Exercise 26.

THEOREM 4-6 If two sides of a triangle are congruent, the angles opposite those sides are congruent.

Given: △ABC; $\overline{AC} \cong \overline{BC}$

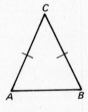

Prove: $\angle A \cong \angle B$

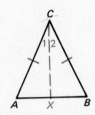

Proof:

STATEMENTS	REASONS
1. Draw the bisector of $\angle C$ and let X be the point where the bisector intersects $\overline{AB}$.	1. An angle has exactly one bisector.
2. $\angle 1 \cong \angle 2$	2. Def. of angle bisector
3. $\overline{AC} \cong \overline{BC}$	3. Given
4. $\overline{CX} \cong \overline{CX}$	4. Reflexive property of congruence
5. △CAX ≅ △CBX	5. SAS Postulate
6. $\angle A \cong \angle B$	6. Corr. parts of ≅ ▲ are ≅.

COROLLARY 1 An equilateral triangle is also equiangular.

COROLLARY 2 Each angle of an equilateral triangle has measure 60.

THEOREM 4-7 If two angles of a triangle are congruent, the sides opposite those angles are congruent.

Given: $\triangle ABC$; $\angle A \cong \angle B$

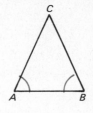

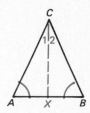

Prove: $\overline{AC} \cong \overline{BC}$

Proof:

STATEMENTS	REASONS
1. Draw the bisector of $\angle C$ and let X be the point where the bisector intersects $\overline{AB}$.	1. An angle has exactly one bisector.
2. $\angle 1 \cong \angle 2$	2. Def. of angle bisector
3. $\angle A \cong \angle B$	3. Given
4. $\overline{CX} \cong \overline{CX}$	4. Reflexive property of congruence
5. $\triangle CAX \cong \triangle CBX$	5. AAS Theorem
6. $\overline{AC} \cong \overline{BC}$	6. Corr. parts of $\cong \triangle$ are $\cong$.

COROLLARY An equiangular triangle is also equilateral.

Oral Exercises

An isosceles triangle is shown. Name:

1. The base
2. The legs
3. The vertex angle
4. The base angles

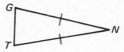

5. Given $\overline{PX} \cong \overline{PY}$, you can deduce: $\angle \underline{\ X\ ?} \cong \angle \underline{\ Y\ ?}$
   You support the conclusion with the reason: $\underline{\ ?\ }$
6. Given $\angle X \cong \angle Y$, you can deduce: $\underline{\ ?\ } \cong \underline{\ ?\ }$
   You support the conclusion with the reason: $\underline{\ ?\ }$

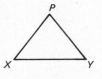

7. Suppose $\overline{ZA} \cong \overline{ZD}$. Then $\angle \underline{\ ?\ } \cong \angle \underline{\ ?\ }$.
8. Suppose $\overline{ZB} \cong \overline{ZC}$. Then $\angle \underline{\ ?\ } \cong \angle \underline{\ ?\ }$.
9. A supplement of $\angle 5$ is $\angle \underline{\ ?\ }$ and a supplement of $\angle 6$ is $\angle \underline{\ ?\ }$.
10. Suppose $\angle 5 \cong \angle 6$. Then $\angle 3 \cong \angle 4$ because $\underline{\ ?\ }$.
11. Suppose $\angle 1 \cong \angle 2$. Then $\underline{\ ?\ } \cong \underline{\ ?\ }$.
12. Suppose $\angle 5 \cong \angle 6$. Then $\underline{\ ?\ } \cong \underline{\ ?\ }$.

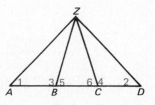

Exs. 7–12

In Exercises 13–16, treat the sentences as steps in a proof, not as directions you are to follow. In each case tell whether the directions for drawing an auxiliary line are satisfactory.

13. Draw $\overleftrightarrow{XT}$.

14. Draw $\overleftrightarrow{XT} \perp \overleftrightarrow{TS}$.

15. Draw $\overleftrightarrow{XR} \parallel \overleftrightarrow{TS}$.

16. Draw the ray that bisects $\angle T$.

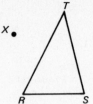

Written Exercises

A

In Exercises 1–8, $\overline{RJ} \cong \overline{RK}$.

1. If $m\angle 1 = 72$, $m\angle J = $ ___?_24°_

2. If $m\angle 1 = 70$, $m\angle R = $ ___?__.

3. If $m\angle 2 = 110$, $m\angle R = $ ___?__.

4. If $m\angle J = 2m\angle R$, $m\angle R = $ ___?__.

5. If $m\angle R = x$ and $m\angle J = x + 30$, $x = $ ___?__.

6. If $m\angle R$ is represented by c, then $m\angle J + m\angle 1$ is represented by ___?__.

7. If $m\angle 1$ is represented by d, then $m\angle J$ is represented by ___?__ and $m\angle R$ is represented by ___?__.

8. If $m\angle R$ is represented by e, then $m\angle J$ is represented by ___?__.

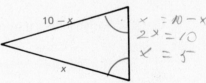

In Exercises 9–12, congruent angles are marked. Find the numerical value of x.

9.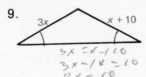

$3x$ $x + 10$

$3x = x + 10$
$3x - 1x = 10$
$2x = 10$
$x = 5$

11.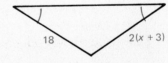

$10 - x$ x

$x = 10 - x$
$2x = 10$
$x = 5$

10.

x $4x - 12$

12.

18 $2(x + 3)$

Write proofs in two-column form.

13. Given: $\overline{AC} \cong \overline{BC}$
    Prove: $\angle 1 \cong \angle 5$

14. Given: $\angle 3 \cong \angle 4$
    Prove: $\overline{AC} \cong \overline{BC}$

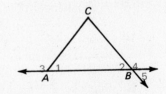

15. Given: $EJ = EK$; $JM = KN$
    Prove: $\angle M \cong \angle N$

16. Given: $\overline{EJ} \cong \overline{EK}$; $\overline{JK} \parallel \overline{MN}$
    Prove: $\angle M \cong \angle N$

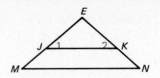

B 17. Given: $\overline{VX} \cong \overline{VW}$; $\overline{XY} \cong \overline{WZ}$
    Prove: $\angle 5 \cong \angle 6$

18. Given: $\angle X \cong \angle W$; $\overline{VY} \cong \overline{VZ}$
    Prove: $\angle 5 \cong \angle 6$

19. Given: $\angle 5 \cong \angle 6$; $\angle 3 \cong \angle 4$
    Prove: $\overline{VX} \cong \overline{VW}$

20. Given: $\overline{VX} \cong \overline{VW}$; $\overline{XY} \cong \overline{WZ}$
    Prove: $\angle XVZ \cong \angle WVY$

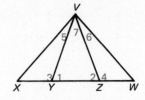

Exs. 17–20

21. Given: $\overline{AC} \cong \overline{BC}$;
    D is the midpoint of $\overline{AC}$;
    E is the midpoint of $\overline{BC}$;
    $\overline{DG} \perp \overline{AB}$; $\overline{EH} \perp \overline{AB}$
    Prove: $\triangle AGD \cong \triangle BHE$

22. Given: $\angle A \cong \angle B$; $\angle 1 \cong \angle 2$;
    $\overline{AG} \cong \overline{BH}$
    Prove: $DC = EC$

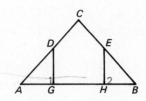

In Exercises 23 and 24, a regular pentagon and two diagonals are shown.

23. $m\angle 1 = \underline{\quad ? \quad}$

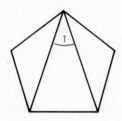

24. $m\angle 2 = \underline{\quad ? \quad}$

Write complete demonstrations.

C 25. The bisector of the vertex angle of an isosceles triangle is perpendicular to the base.

26. The altitude to the base of an isosceles triangle is also a median of the triangle.

27. Prove Theorem 4-6 by showing
    $\triangle JXK \cong \triangle KXJ$, given that
    $\overline{JX} \cong \overline{KX}$.

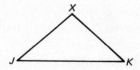

Self-Test $\overline{ABCD}$ in the figure shown.

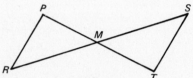

1. State whether the directions for drawing an auxiliary line are satisfactory.
   a. Draw the line that bisects $\overline{AD}$ and $\overline{BC}$.
   b. Draw the line that bisects $\angle KBC$.

2. To prove that $\angle 1 \cong \angle 2$ you could try to show that $\triangle\ \underline{\ ?\ } \cong \triangle\ \underline{\ ?\ }$.

3. If $\angle 3 \cong \angle 4$, $x = \underline{\ ?\ }$.

4. If $\overline{RT} \cong \overline{ST}$, $y = \underline{\ ?\ }$.

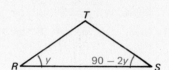

5. It is known that $\triangle JAV \cong \triangle KEZ$. What reason supports the assertion that $\overline{AV} \cong \overline{EZ}$?

6. Given: M is the midpoint of $\overline{PT}$ and $\overline{RS}$.
   Prove: $\angle R \cong \angle S$

CHAPTER SUMMARY

1. Ways to prove two triangles congruent.

All triangles:		Right triangles:	
SSS	ASA	LL	HA
SAS	AAS	HL	LA

2. A common way to prove that two angles or two segments are congruent is to show that they are corresponding parts of congruent triangles.

3. If two sides of a triangle are congruent, the angles opposite those sides are congruent.

4. If two angles of a triangle are congruent, the sides opposite those angles are congruent.

CHAPTER TEST

1. If $\triangle ABC \cong \triangle PQR$, then $\overline{AC} \cong \underline{PR}$.

2. In $\triangle DEF$, $\overline{DE}$ lies opposite $\angle \underline{F}$.

3. In $\triangle MND$, sides $\overline{MN}$ and $\overline{ND}$ include $\angle \underline{N}$.

4. If $\triangle RST$ and $\triangle XYZ$ are scalene triangles such that $\triangle RST \cong \triangle XYZ$, then $\triangle SRT \cong \triangle \underline{YXZ}$

5. In a triangle, a segment that joins a vertex of the triangle and the midpoint of the opposite side is called a __?__ of the triangle.

6. The congruent sides of an isosceles triangle are called __?__ .

7. Each angle of an equilateral triangle has measure __?__ 60 60

8. If two angles of a triangle are congruent, the sides opposite those angles are __?__

In Exercises 9–14, identify the congruence method you would use to prove $\triangle ABC \cong \triangle RST$.

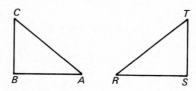

9. Given: $\angle C \cong \angle T$; $\overline{AC} \cong \overline{RT}$; $\overline{BC} \cong \overline{ST}$ = SAS

10. Given: $\angle C \cong \angle T$; $\angle B \cong \angle S$; $\overline{BC} \cong \overline{ST}$

11. Given: $\overline{AB} \perp \overline{BC}$; $\overline{RS} \perp \overline{ST}$; $\overline{AC} \cong \overline{RT}$; $\overline{BC} \cong \overline{ST}$ = SAL

12. Given: $\angle B \cong \angle S$; $\angle A \cong \angle R$; $\overline{AC} \cong \overline{RT}$

13. Given: $\overline{AB} \perp \overline{BC}$; $\overline{RS} \perp \overline{ST}$; $\angle C \cong \angle T$; $\overline{AB} \cong \overline{RS}$

14. Given: $\angle B$ and $\angle S$ are rt. $\angle$s; $\overline{AC} \cong \overline{RT}$; $\angle A \cong \angle R$

In Exercises 15–25, write the reasons that are needed to complete the proof.

Given: Polygon $ABCDE$ is a regular pentagon; M is the midpoint of $\overline{AB}$.

Prove: $\angle 1 \cong \angle 2$

Proof:

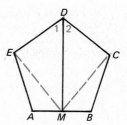

STATEMENTS	REASONS
15. Draw $\overline{EM}$ and $\overline{CM}$.	15. __?__
16. $\overline{EA} \cong \overline{CB}$	16. __?__
17. $\angle A \cong \angle B$	17. __?__
18. M is the midpt. of $\overline{AB}$.	18. __?__
19. $\overline{AM} \cong \overline{BM}$	19. __?__
20. $\triangle EAM \cong \triangle CBM$	20. __?__
21. $\overline{EM} \cong \overline{CM}$	21. __?__ Given
22. $\overline{ED} \cong \overline{CD}$	22. __?__
23. $\overline{DM} \cong \overline{DM}$	23. __?__
24. $\triangle EMD \cong \triangle CMD$	24. __?__
25. $\angle 1 \cong \angle 2$	25. __?__

26. In isosceles $\triangle DEF$, $\overline{DE} \cong \overline{FE}$. If $m\angle D = 6x + 8$, $m\angle F = 6y - 4$, and $m\angle E = 2x + 2y$, find x.

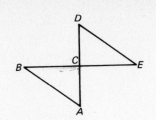

27. Given: $\angle 1$ is a rt. $\angle$;
    $\overline{AB} \cong \overline{DE}$; $\overline{AC} \cong \overline{DC}$
    Prove: $\triangle ABC \cong \triangle DEC$

28. Given: $\angle 1 \cong \angle 2$; $\angle C \cong \angle D$
    Prove: $\overline{AC} \cong \overline{BD}$

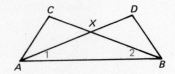

CHAPTER REVIEW

4-1 *Congruence of Triangles*

1. In $\triangle ABC$, the side opposite $\angle A$ is ? *B.C*

2. In $\triangle CDE$, the side included between $\angle E$ and $\angle D$ is *ED*.

3. If vertices A and B correspond to vertices D and E, then $\overline{AB}$ and ? are corresponding sides.

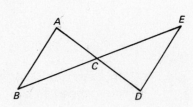

4. If $\triangle ABC \cong \triangle DEC$, then $\triangle BAC \cong \triangle$? *ECD*

4-2 *Some Ways to Prove Triangles Congruent*

5. Write a full statement of the SSS Postulate.

6. Write a full statement of the SAS Postulate.

7. Given: $\overline{DC} \cong \overline{BC}$ and $\overline{AD} \cong \overline{AB}$. It is possible to prove $\triangle ADC \cong \triangle ABC$ by the ? method.

8. Given: $\overline{DC} \cong \overline{BC}$ and $\angle 1 \cong \angle 2$. It is possible to prove $\triangle ADC \cong \triangle ABC$ by the ? method.

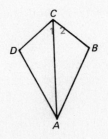

4-3 *Some Ways to Prove Right Triangles Congruent*

In the plane figure shown, $\overline{DB} \perp \overline{AC}$ and $\overline{AD} \perp \overline{DC}$.

9. The legs of rt. $\triangle DBC$ are ? and ? .

10. The hypotenuse of $\triangle ADC$ is ? .

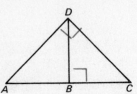

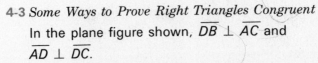

11. Given: $\overline{AB} \cong \overline{CB}$. It is possible to prove
    $\triangle ABD \cong \triangle CBD$ by the __?__ method.

12. Given: $\overline{AD} \cong \overline{CD}$. It is possible to prove
    $\triangle ABD \cong \triangle CBD$ by the __?__ method.

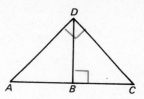

4-4 *More Ways to Prove Triangles Congruent*

13. Write a full statement of the AAS
    Theorem.

14. Given: $\angle P \cong \angle T$; $\overline{PR} \cong \overline{TR}$
    Prove: $\triangle PVR \cong \triangle TSR$

15. Given: $\angle P \cong \angle T$; $\overline{PV} \cong \overline{TS}$
    Prove: $\triangle PVR \cong \triangle TSR$

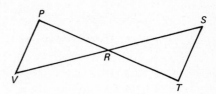

4-5 *More Ways to Prove Right Triangles Congruent*

In Exercises 16–18, the figure is
a plane figure and $\angle 1$ and $\angle 2$ are
right angles.

16. Given: $\overline{AE} \cong \overline{DC}$; $\angle 3 \cong \angle 4$
    Prove: $\triangle ABE \cong \triangle DBC$

17. Given: $\overline{BE} \cong \overline{BC}$; $\angle 4$ is comple-
    mentary to $\angle 5$.
    Prove: $\triangle ABE \cong \triangle DBC$

18. If $\overline{BE} \cong \overline{BC}$ and $\angle 5 \cong \angle 4$, must
    $\triangle ABE$ be congruent to $\triangle DBC$?

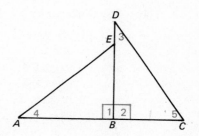

4-6 *Proving Corresponding Parts Congruent*

19. If $\triangle DEF \cong \triangle LMN$, then $\angle EFD \cong \angle$ __?__ .

20. If $\triangle ABC \cong \triangle SZW$, then $\overline{AC} \cong$ __?__ .

21. Given: $\overline{SR} \parallel \overline{TP}$; $\overline{SR} \cong \overline{TP}$
    Prove: $\angle P \cong \angle R$

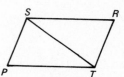

4-7 *Isosceles Triangles*

22. In $\triangle ABC$, if $\angle 1 \cong \angle 2$, then __?__ $\cong$ __?__ .

23. In $\triangle ADC$, if $\overline{AD} \cong \overline{DC}$, then

24. Is it correct to say "Draw $\overrightarrow{AX}$ bisecting $\angle 1$
    and also $\perp$ to $\overleftrightarrow{BC}$?"

25. In $\triangle ABC$, if $\overline{AB} \cong \overline{BC}$, $m\angle 1 = 6x + 2$,
    and $m\angle 2 = 8x - 20$, find $m\angle B$.

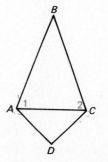

REVIEWING ALGEBRAIC SKILLS

Solve each equation by the method of factoring.

EXAMPLE. $x^2 + 4x - 12 = 0$

SOLUTION: $(x + 6)(x - 2) = 0$

$$x + 6 = 0 \quad \text{or} \quad x - 2 = 0$$
$$x = -6 \quad \text{or} \quad x = 2$$

The solution set is $\{-6, 2\}$.

1. $x^2 - 5x - 6 = 0$
2. $x^2 + 3x - 10 = 0$
3. $x^2 - 9x + 18 = 0$
4. $x^2 - 8x + 15 = 0$
5. $x^2 + 4x = 32$
6. $x^2 - 24 = 2x$

7. $2x^2 + x - 3 = 0$
8. $3x^2 + 2x - 8 = 0$
9. $6x^2 - 7x = 3$
10. $12x^2 - x = 6$
11. $2x = 24 - 15x^2$
12. $x + 20 = 30x^2$

Solve each equation by using the quadratic formula.

EXAMPLE. $x^2 + 5x + 2 = 0$

SOLUTION: $x = \dfrac{-b \pm \sqrt{b^2 - 4ac}}{2a}$

$$a = 1 \quad b = 5 \quad c = 2$$

$$x = \frac{-5 \pm \sqrt{25 - 8}}{2}$$

$$x = \frac{-5 \pm \sqrt{17}}{2}$$

The solution set is $\left\{ \dfrac{-5 + \sqrt{17}}{2}, \dfrac{-5 - \sqrt{17}}{2} \right\}$.

13. $x^2 + 7x + 3 = 0$
14. $x^2 + 8x + 5 = 0$
15. $x^2 - 5x + 1 = 0$
16. $x^2 - 3x - 3 = 0$
17. $x^2 + 5x = 3$
18. $x^2 + 1 = 11x$

19. $2x^2 + x - 4 = 0$
20. $3x^2 + 5x - 3 = 0$
21. $5x^2 - 13x + 3 = 0$
22. $4x^2 - 7x - 1 = 0$
23. $7x^2 - x - 5 = 0$
24. $5x^2 + 5x + 1 = 0$

Solve by factoring or by using the quadratic formula.

25. $6x^2 = 2 - x$
26. $9x^2 - 20 = 3x$
27. $8x^2 + 8x = x - 1$

28. $5x^2 - x + 6 = 5 - 12x$
29. $2x^2 + 12.5x = 10.5$
30. $x^2 = 2 - \frac{1}{2}x$

The Hypotenuse-Leg Proposition

extra for experts

It would be possible to develop the geometry of this text with the use of a shorter set of postulates than we have used. In particular, the statement taken as Postulate 15 could be proved as a theorem based on Postulate 14, Theorem 4-3, and Theorem 4-6. It is important to note that the proofs of Theorems 4-3 and 4-6 do not depend, directly or indirectly, on Postulate 15. A demonstration of the hypotenuse-leg proposition, complete except for reasons, follows:

If the hypotenuse and a leg of one right triangle are congruent to the corresponding parts of another right triangle, the right triangles are congruent.

Given: $\triangle RST$ and $\triangle XYZ$;
$\angle S$ and $\angle Y$ are rt. $\angle$s;
$\overline{RT} \cong \overline{XZ}$; $\overline{ST} \cong \overline{YZ}$

Prove: $\triangle RST \cong \triangle XYZ$

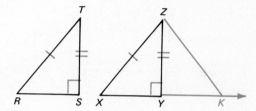

Proof:

STATEMENTS	STATEMENTS (continued)
1. On $\overrightarrow{XY}$ take K such that $KY = RS$.	9. $\angle S \cong \angle KYZ$
	10. $\triangle RST \cong \triangle KYZ$
2. Draw $\overline{KZ}$.	11. $\overline{KZ} \cong \overline{RT}$
3. $\overline{RS} \cong \overline{KY}$	12. $\overline{RT} \cong \overline{XZ}$
4. $\overline{ST} \cong \overline{YZ}$	13. $\overline{KZ} \cong \overline{XZ}$
5. $\angle XYZ$ is a rt. $\angle$.	14. $\angle K \cong \angle X$
6. $\overline{ZY} \perp \overline{XK}$	15. $\angle KYZ \cong \angle XYZ$
7. $\angle KYZ$ is a rt. $\angle$.	16. $\triangle KYZ \cong \triangle XYZ$
8. $\angle S$ is a rt. $\angle$.	17. $\triangle RST \cong \triangle XYZ$

Supply reasons to complete the demonstration above.

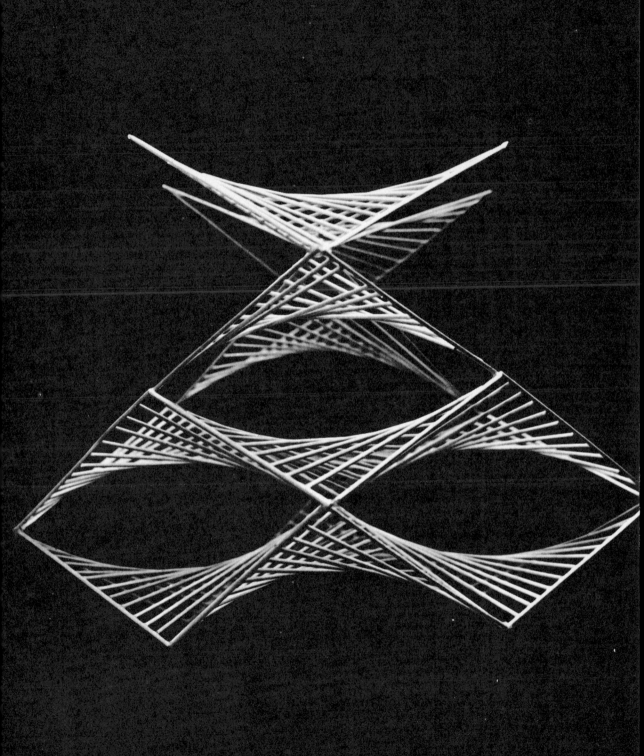

APPLYING CONGRUENT TRIANGLES

Parallelograms

Objectives

1. State the definition of a parallelogram.
2. State and apply the theorem and corollaries that relate to the properties of a parallelogram.
3. State and apply the theorems that can be used to prove that a quadrilateral is a parallelogram.

5-1 *Properties of Parallelograms*

A parallelogram ($\square$) is a quadrilateral in which both pairs of opposite sides are parallel. In referring to the parallelogram shown, we write "$\square ABCD$."

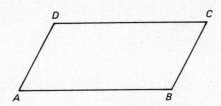

Suppose you drew one of the diagonals, say $\overline{AC}$, in the above parallelogram. Do you think that the two triangles which are formed by drawing $\overline{AC}$ are congruent?

THEOREM 5-1 A diagonal of a parallelogram separates the parallelogram into two congruent triangles.

Given: ▱RSTW with diagonal $\overline{RT}$

Prove: △RST ≅ △TWR

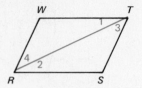

Proof:

STATEMENTS	REASONS
1. RSTW is a ▱.	1. Given
2. $\overline{RS} \parallel \overline{WT}$	2. Definition of a ▱
3. ∠2 ≅ ∠1	3. If 2 ∥ lines are cut ~~S/A S~~
4. $\overline{RT} \cong \overline{RT}$	4. _?_
5. $\overline{RW} \parallel \overline{ST}$	5. Definition of a ▱
6. ∠3 ≅ ∠4	6. _?_
7. △RST ≅ △TWR	7. _?_

COROLLARY 1 Opposite sides of a parallelogram are congruent.
The proof is left as Exercise 19.

COROLLARY 2 Opposite angles of a parallelogram are congruent.
The proof is left as Exercise 20.

THEOREM 5-2 The diagonals of a parallelogram bisect each other.

Given: ▱JKLM with diagonals $\overline{JL}$ and $\overline{KM}$

Prove: $\overline{JE} \cong \overline{LE}$; $\overline{KE} \cong \overline{ME}$

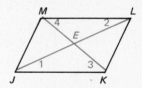

Proof:

STATEMENTS	REASONS
1. JKLM is a ▱.	1. Given
2. $\overline{JK} \parallel \overline{ML}$	2. Definition of a ▱
3. ∠1 ≅ ∠2	3. _?_
4. $\overline{JK} \cong \overline{LM}$	4. _?_
5. ∠3 ≅ ∠4	5. _?_
6. △JEK ≅ △LEM	6. _?_
7. $\overline{JE} \cong \overline{LE}$; $\overline{KE} \cong \overline{ME}$	7. _?_

Oral Exercises

Classify each statement as true or false.

1. Every quadrilateral is a parallelogram. _True_
2. Every parallelogram is a quadrilateral. _True_
3. If quadrilateral *RSTW* is a parallelogram, then $\overline{RS} \cong \overline{TW}$. _True_
4. If quadrilateral *DEFG* is a parallelogram, then $\overline{DE} \parallel \overline{EF}$. _false_
5. There exists a parallelogram with all sides congruent.
6. There exists a parallelogram with all angles congruent.
7. There exists a parallelogram *ABCD* such that $m\angle A = 70$ and $m\angle C = 80$. _false_
8. $\overline{WY}$ is a diagonal of $\square WXYZ$. _True_
9. If $\overline{AC}$ is drawn in $\square ABCD$, then $\triangle ABC \cong \triangle CDA$. _True_
10. There exists a parallelogram that is not a plane figure. _false_

Exercises 11–18 refer to $\square RSTW$. Complete each statement.

11. $\overline{RS} \parallel$ __?__ *WT*
12. $\overline{TS} \cong$ __?__ *WR*
13. $\overline{WX} \cong$ __?__ *SX*
14. $\angle WRS \cong$ __?__ *TS*
15. $\triangle RST \cong$ __?__ *TS*
16. $WT =$ __?__ *RS*
17. $TX =$ __?__ *RX*
18. $m\angle RWT = m\angle$ __?__ *TW*

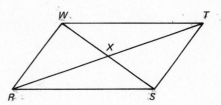

Written Exercises

A

Exercises 1–14 refer to $\square CDEF$. Using the given information, find the indicated measure.

1. $CE = 12$; $CX =$ __?__ *6*
2. $FX = 8$; $FD =$ __?__ *16*
3. $m\angle CDE = 72$; $m\angle EFC =$ __?__ *72*
4. $m\angle 1 + m\angle 2 = 106$; $m\angle FCD =$ __?__ *106*
5. $m\angle 3 = 88$; $m\angle 2 =$ __?__ *88*
6. $m\angle 4 = 41$; $m\angle 1 =$ __?__
7. $m\angle CFE = 10x + 1$; $m\angle EDC = 12x - 9$; $x =$ __?__ *5*
8. $m\angle FCD = 7x - 3$; $m\angle DEF = 5x + 31$; $x =$ __?__ *17*
9. $m\angle 3 = 4x + 4$; $m\angle 4 = 6x$; $m\angle FED = 104$; $x =$ __?__ *10*
10. $m\angle 1 = 7x + 8$; $m\angle 2 = 10x + 1$; $m\angle FCD = 111$; $x =$ __?__
11. $FX = 7y - 6$; $FD = 16$; $y =$ __?__ *2*
12. $XE = 2y + 2$; $CE = 12$; $y =$ __?__ *2*
13. $CE = 5y + 3$; $XE = 7$; $y =$ __?__
14. $FD = 6y - 5$; $DX = 11$; $y =$ __?__

In Exercises 15 and 16, assume that the lines that appear to be parallel are parallel. State the number of parallelograms in each figure.

15.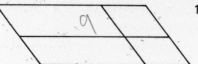

16.

B 17. Given: $\square ABCD$; $BR = \frac{1}{3}BD$; $DS = \frac{1}{3}BD$

Prove: $\overline{AS} \cong \overline{CR}$

18. Given: $\square ABCD$; $\overline{BS} \cong \overline{DR}$

Prove: $\overline{AS} \cong \overline{CR}$

19. Prove Corollary 1 of Theorem 5-1.

20. Prove Corollary 2 of Theorem 5-1.

21. Given: $\square RSTW$; $\square TWXY$

Prove: $RS = XY$

22. Given: $\square RSYX$; $\square RSTW$;

$\angle WRX \cong \angle TSY$

Prove: $\overline{WX} \cong \overline{TY}$

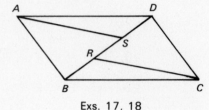

Exs. 17, 18

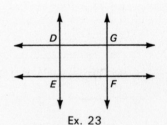

Exs. 21, 22

Ex. 23

C 23. Given: $\overleftrightarrow{DG} \parallel \overleftrightarrow{EF}$; $\overleftrightarrow{DE} \perp \overleftrightarrow{EF}$;

$\overleftrightarrow{GF} \perp \overleftrightarrow{EF}$

Prove: $DE = GF$

24. Given: Points R, S, T, and W are the midpoints of the sides of $\square ABCD$.

Prove: $\overline{RS} \cong \overline{TW}$

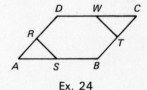

Ex. 24

25. Prove: The bisectors of a pair of opposite angles of a non-equilateral parallelogram are parallel to each other.

26. Prove: Any two consecutive angles of a parallelogram are supplementary.

5-2 *Proving that Certain Quadrilaterals Are Parallelograms*

In the development of our geometry, it becomes necessary at times to prove that certain quadrilaterals are parallelograms. One way to prove that a quadrilateral is a parallelogram is to show that the quadrilateral satisfies the definition of a parallelogram. The theorems in this section will provide other methods.

THEOREM 5-3 If two sides of a quadrilateral are congruent and parallel, the quadrilateral is a parallelogram.

Given: $\overline{RS} \cong \overline{TW}$
$\overline{RS} \parallel \overline{TW}$

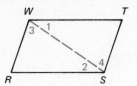

Prove: Quad. $RSTW$ is a ▱.

Proof:

STATEMENTS	REASONS
1. Draw $\overleftrightarrow{WS}$.	1. Through any two points there is exactly one line.
2. $\overline{RS} \cong \overline{TW}$; $\overline{RS} \parallel \overline{TW}$	2. Given
3. $\angle 1 \cong \angle 2$	3. _?_
4. $\overline{WS} \cong \overline{WS}$	4. _?_
5. $\triangle RSW \cong \triangle TWS$	5. _?_
6. $\angle 3 \cong \angle 4$	6. Corr. parts of ≅ ⧍ are ≅.
7. $\overline{RW} \parallel \overline{ST}$	7. If two lines are cut by a trans. so that _?_ .
8. Quad. $RSTW$ is a ▱.	8. Def. of a ▱

THEOREM 5-4 If both pairs of opposite sides of a quadrilateral are congruent, the quadrilateral is a parallelogram.

Given: $\overline{AB} \cong \overline{CD}$; $\overline{BC} \cong \overline{DA}$

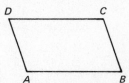

Prove: Quad. $ABCD$ is a ▱.

The proof is left as Exercise 19.

THEOREM 5-5 If the diagonals of a quadrilateral bisect each other, the quadrilateral is a parallelogram.

Given: $\overline{DR} \cong \overline{FR}$
$\overline{GR} \cong \overline{ER}$

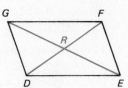

Prove: Quad. $DEFG$ is a ▱.

The proof is left as Exercise 20.

We now have four ways to prove that a quadrilateral is a parallelogram:

1. Show that both pairs of opposite sides are parallel.
2. Show that both pairs of opposite sides are congruent.
3. Show that one pair of opposite sides are congruent and parallel.
4. Show that the diagonals bisect each other.

THEOREM 5-6 If three parallel lines cut off congruent segments on one transversal, they cut off congruent segments on every transversal.

Given: $k \parallel l \parallel m$; trans. $\overleftrightarrow{AC}$ and $\overleftrightarrow{RT}$; $\overline{AB} \cong \overline{BC}$

Prove: $\overline{RS} \cong \overline{ST}$

For a proof, see Exercises 1–13.

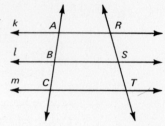

Oral Exercises

In Exercises 1–4, certain information is given. State the definition or theorem that supports the statement "Quad. *ABCD* is a parallelogram."

1. $\overline{AB} \parallel \overline{DC}$; $\overline{AD} \parallel \overline{BC}$
2. $\overline{AB} \parallel \overline{DC}$; $\overline{AB} \cong \overline{DC}$
3. $\overline{AX} \cong \overline{XC}$; $\overline{BX} \cong \overline{XD}$
4. $\overline{AB} \cong \overline{DC}$; $\overline{AD} \cong \overline{BC}$

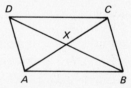

In Exercises 5–8, classify each statement as true or false.

5. If exactly one pair of opposite sides of a quadrilateral are congruent, the quadrilateral is a parallelogram.
6. Every parallelogram is a regular quadrilateral.
7. The opposite sides of a parallelogram are congruent.
8. If three parallel lines are cut by a transversal, they always cut off congruent segments on the transversal.

In Exercises 9–12, complete each statement using one of the words *Always, Sometimes,* or *Never.*

9. A pentagon is __?__ a parallelogram.
10. The diagonals of a quadrilateral __?__ bisect each other.
11. If the diagonals of a quadrilateral bisect each other, the quadrilateral is __?__ a parallelogram.
12. If both pairs of opposite sides of a quadrilateral are parallel, the quadrilateral is __?__ a parallelogram.

In Exercises 1–13, provide the reasons for a proof of Theorem 5–6.

Given: $k \parallel l \parallel m$; trans. $\overleftrightarrow{AC}$ and $\overleftrightarrow{RT}$;
$\overline{AB} \cong \overline{BC}$

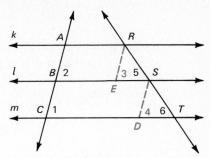

Prove: $\overline{RS} \cong \overline{ST}$

Proof:

STATEMENTS	REASONS
A 1. $k \parallel l \parallel m$; trans. $\overleftrightarrow{AC}$ and $\overleftrightarrow{RT}$	1. ___?___
2. Through R and S draw lines parallel to $\overleftrightarrow{AC}$. Label points of intersection with l and m as E and D.	2. ___?___
3. Quad. $ABER$ is a $\square$; quad. $BCDS$ is a $\square$.	3. ___?___
4. $\overline{RE} \cong \overline{AB}$; $\overline{BC} \cong \overline{SD}$	4. ___?___
5. $\overline{AB} \cong \overline{BC}$	5. ___?___
6. $\overline{RE} \cong \overline{SD}$	6. ___?___
7. $\angle 3 \cong \angle 2$	7. ___?___
8. $\angle 2 \cong \angle 1$	8. ___?___
9. $\angle 1 \cong \angle 4$	9. ___?___
10. $\angle 3 \cong \angle 4$	10. ___?___
11. $\angle 5 \cong \angle 6$	11. ___?___
12. $\triangle ERS \cong \triangle DST$	12. ___?___
13. $\overline{RS} \cong \overline{ST}$	13. ___?___

14. Given: $\triangle AED \cong \triangle CFB$; $\overline{DE} \parallel \overline{BF}$
Prove: Quad. $DEBF$ is a $\square$.

15. Given: Quad. $ABCD$ is a $\square$;
$\overline{DE} \parallel \overline{BF}$
Prove: Quad. $DEBF$ is a $\square$.

16. Given: $\overline{EB} \cong \overline{DF}$;
$\triangle AED \cong \triangle CFB$
Prove: Quad. $DEBF$ is a $\square$.

B   17. Given: $\overline{AE} \cong \overline{CF}$;
Quad. $ABCD$ is a $\square$.
Prove: Quad. $DEBF$ is a $\square$.

18. Given: Plane figure with $\overline{AE} \cong \overline{CF}$; $\overline{EB} \cong \overline{FD}$;
$\overline{AB} \parallel \overline{DC}$
Prove: Quad. $ABCD$ is a $\square$.

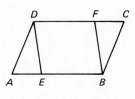

Exs. 14–18

19. Prove Theorem 5-4.
20. Prove Theorem 5-5.

21. Given: Plane figure with
    $\overline{EB} \cong \overline{DC}$; $\angle 1 \cong \angle 2 \cong \angle 3$
    Prove: Quad. *ABCD* is a ▱.
22. Given: Plane figure with
    $\angle 3 \cong \angle 4$; $\angle 3 \cong \angle 2$; $\overline{AB} \cong \overline{BE}$
    Prove: Quad. *ABCD* is a ▱.

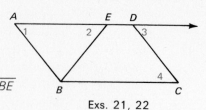

Exs. 21, 22

C 23. In ▱*MNOP*, point *A* is the intersection of the diagonals. If *X* is the midpoint of $\overline{AP}$ and *Y* is the midpoint of $\overline{NA}$, prove that quad. *MXOY* is a parallelogram.

24. Prove that any segment that includes the point of intersection of the diagonals of a parallelogram and whose endpoints lie on a pair of opposite sides of the parallelogram is bisected by the diagonals.

25. Prove that if the opposite angles of a quadrilateral are congruent, the quadrilateral is a parallelogram.

26. Prove Theorem 5-6 for the case shown. (*Hint:* See Exercises 1–13.)

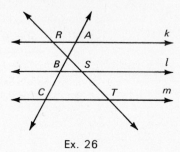

Ex. 26

Self-Test

1. By definition, a parallelogram is a quadrilateral whose opposite sides are __?__ .
2. The opposite angles of a parallelogram are __?__ .
3. If the diagonals of a quadrilateral bisect each other, the quadrilateral is a __?__ .
4. The diagonals of a parallelogram _____?_____ be congruent.
   (can / cannot)

In Exercises 5–10, state whether the given information is sufficient to support the statement "Quad. *ABCD* is a ▱."

5. $\overline{AB} \parallel \overline{DC}$; $\overline{AD} \parallel \overline{BC}$
6. $\overline{AB} \cong \overline{DC}$; $\overline{AD} \cong \overline{BC}$
7. $\overline{AB} \cong \overline{DC}$; $\overline{AB} \parallel \overline{DC}$
8. $\overline{AX} \cong \overline{XC}$
9. $\overline{AX} \cong \overline{XC}$; $\overline{BX} \cong \overline{XD}$
10. $\angle 1 \cong \angle 2$

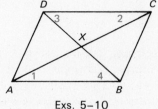

Exs. 5–10

Check your answers with those printed at the back of the book.

Other Quadrilaterals

Objectives

1. Know and use the definition of a rectangle, a rhombus, and a square.
2. Identify the special properties of a rectangle, a rhombus, and a square.
3. State the definition of a trapezoid.
4. State and apply the theorem about the median of a trapezoid.
5. State and apply the theorem about the segment that joins the midpoints of two sides of a triangle.

5-3 *Rectangles, Rhombuses, Squares*

A *rectangle* may be defined in several different ways, but we shall use the following definition. A rectangle (rect.) is a parallelogram with four right angles.

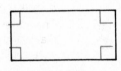

Rectangle

Note that in rectangle *ABCD*, $\overline{AC}$ appears to be congruent to $\overline{BD}$. The theorem that follows states that this relationship is true for every rectangle.

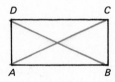

THEOREM 5-7   The diagonals of a rectangle are congruent.

For a proof, see Exercises 11–18.

Another special kind of parallelogram is a *rhombus*. A rhombus is a parallelogram with four congruent sides. The next two theorems state two properties of a rhombus that are not common to all parallelograms.

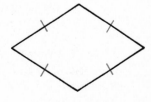

Rhombus

THEOREM 5-8 The diagonals of a rhombus are perpendicular.

Given: Rhombus *RSTW* with diagonals $\overline{SW}$ and $\overline{RT}$

Prove: $\overline{RT} \perp \overline{SW}$

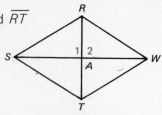

Proof:

STATEMENTS	REASONS
1. Rhombus *RSTW* with diagonals $\overline{SW}$ and $\overline{RT}$	1. Given
2. $\overline{RS} \cong \overline{RW}$	2. *Given*
3. $\overline{SA} \cong \overline{WA}$	3. Diagonals of a ▱ bisect each other. (By definition a rhombus is a ▱.)
4. $\overline{RA} \cong \overline{RA}$	4. _?_ *Same line*
5. $\triangle RSA \cong \triangle RWA$	5. SSS Postulate
6. $\angle 1 \cong \angle 2$	6. _?_
7. $\overline{RT} \perp \overline{SW}$	7. If two lines form _?_ .

THEOREM 5-9 Each diagonal of a rhombus bisects a pair of opposite angles.

Given: Rhombus *ABCD* with diagonal $\overline{AC}$.

Prove: $\angle 1 \cong \angle 2$; $\angle 3 \cong \angle 4$

The proof is left as Exercise 21.

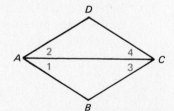

The most special kind of parallelogram is the *square*. A **square** is a rectangle with four congruent sides. Since every square is a parallelogram as well as a rhombus and a rectangle, it has all the special properties of all these quadrilaterals.

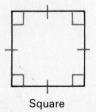

Square

It is possible to define the words *rectangle, rhombus,* and *square* in several different ways. Which of the following statements would you classify as acceptable definitions? Which are the definitions used in this book?

1. A rectangle is a parallelogram with four right angles. *True*
2. A rectangle is a quadrilateral with four right angles. *True*
3. A rectangle is a parallelogram with one right angle. *True*
4. A rectangle is an equiangular parallelogram. *True*
5. A rhombus is a parallelogram with four congruent sides. *True*
6. A rhombus is an equilateral quadrilateral. *True*
7. A rhombus is a parallelogram in which two consecutive sides are congruent. *True*
8. A quadrilateral with two congruent sides is a rhombus. *F*
9. A square is a rectangle with four congruent sides. *True*
10. A square is a rhombus with one right angle. *True*
11. A square is a regular quadrilateral. *True*
12. A square is a rectangle in which two consecutive sides are congruent.

Written Exercises

In Exercises 1–10, copy and complete the following chart by placing checks in the appropriate blanks.

A

	PROPERTY	PARALLELOGRAM	RECTANGLE	RHOMBUS	SQUARE
1.	Opposite sides are ‖				
2.	Opposite sides are ≅				
3.	Opposite ∠ are ≅				
4.	Diagonal forms two ≅ △				
5.	Diagonals bisect each other				
6.	Diagonals are ≅				
7.	Diagonals are ⊥				
8.	Diagonals bisect opposite ∠				
9.	All ∠ are rt. ∠				
10.	All sides are ≅				

In Exercises 11–18, supply the reasons needed to complete the proof of Theorem 5-7.

Given: Rect. RSTW with diagonals
$\overline{RT}$ and $\overline{WS}$

Prove: $\overline{RT} \cong \overline{WS}$

Proof:

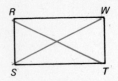

STATEMENTS	REASONS
11. Rect. RSTW with diagonals $\overline{RT}$ and $\overline{WS}$	11. ?
12. Rect. RSTW is a ▱.	12. ?
13. $\overline{SR} \cong \overline{TW}$	13. ?
14. ∠RST and ∠WTS are rt ⓪.	14. ?
15. ∠RST ≅ ∠WTS	15. ?
16. $\overline{ST} \cong \overline{ST}$	16. ?
17. △RST ≅ △WTS	17. ?
18. $\overline{RT} \cong \overline{WS}$	18. ?

19. Draw a quadrilateral that has congruent diagonals but is not a rectangle.

20. Draw a quadrilateral that has perpendicular diagonals but is not a rhombus.

B 21. Prove Theorem 5-9.

22. Given: Quad. ABCD is a ▱;
∠1 ≅ ∠2
Prove: Quad. ABCD is a rhombus.

23. Given: Quad. ABCD is a ▱;
$\overline{AC} \perp \overline{BD}$
Prove: Quad. ABCD is a rhombus.

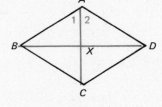

24. Prove that a quadrilateral in which the four sides are congruent is a rhombus.

25. Prove that a parallelogram in which two consecutive sides are congruent is a rhombus.

26. Prove that the quadrilateral formed by joining, in order, the midpoints of the sides of a rectangle is a rhombus.

C 27. Prove that if the diagonals of a parallelogram are congruent, the parallelogram is a rectangle.

28. Given: Quad. ABCD is a square.
$\overline{AR} \cong \overline{DW} \cong \overline{CT} \cong \overline{BS}$
Prove: Quad. RSTW is a square.

5-4 Trapezoids

Note that each of the following quadrilaterals has exactly one pair of parallel sides. ($\overline{AB} \parallel \overline{CD}$)

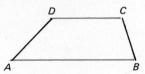

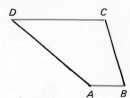

A quadrilateral with exactly one pair of parallel sides is called a trapezoid. The parallel sides are bases and the non-parallel sides are legs. The segment joining the midpoints of the legs is called the median.

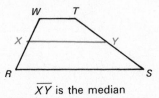
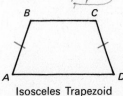

$\overline{XY}$ is the median

Isosceles Trapezoid

If the legs of a trapezoid are congruent, the quadrilateral is called an isosceles trapezoid.

At this stage of our study of geometry, detailed proofs of the next two theorems would be tedious. Proofs by the methods of coordinate geometry are more appealing, and are included in Chapter 11.

THEOREM 5-10 The median of a trapezoid is parallel to the bases and has a length equal to half the sum of the lengths of the bases.

Given: Trapezoid $RSTW$; median $\overline{MN}$

Prove: $\overline{MN} \parallel \overline{ST}$; $\overline{MN} \parallel \overline{RW}$
$MN = \frac{1}{2}(ST + RW)$

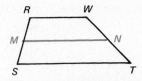

THEOREM 5-11 The segment joining the midpoints of two sides of a triangle is parallel to the third side and its length is half the length of the third side.

Given: $\triangle ABC$;
    R is the midpoint of $\overline{AC}$;
    S is the midpoint of $\overline{BC}$.

Prove: $\overline{RS} \parallel \overline{AB}$; $RS = \frac{1}{2}AB$

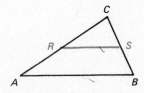

Classify each statement as true or false.

1. A trapezoid has two bases.
2. The parallel sides of a trapezoid are called the legs.
3. The median of a trapezoid is the segment joining the midpoints of the bases of the trapezoid.
4. It is possible for a trapezoid to have a right angle.
5. There exists a trapezoid with three congruent sides.
6. The legs of an isosceles trapezoid are congruent.

In Exercises 7–10, points M and N are the midpoints of $\overline{AB}$ and $\overline{BC}$. Using the given information, state the indicated length.

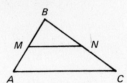

7. $AC = 12$; $MN = \underline{6}$
8. $MN = 7$; $AC = \underline{?}$
9. $AC = k$; $MN = \underline{?}$
10. $MN = l$; $AC = \underline{?}$

In Exercises 11–14, $\overline{RS}$ is the median of trapezoid $ABCD$.

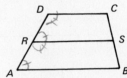

11. If $AB = 10$ and $DC = 8$, $RS = \underline{?}$.
12. If $RS = 7$, then $AB + DC = \underline{?}$
13. If $BC = 12$, $CS = \underline{?}$
14. If $m\angle A = 80$, $m\angle DRS = \underline{?}$.

In Exercises 1–6, $\overline{XY}$ is the median of trapezoid $MNRS$. Using the given information, find the indicated measure.

A
1. $RS = 15$; $MN = 7$; $XY = \underline{?}$
2. $RS = 13.7$; $MN = 6.1$; $XY = \underline{?}$
3. $XY = 12$; $RS = 15$; $MN = \underline{?}$
4. $XY = 11.3$; $MN = 8.4$; $RS = \underline{?}$
5. $MN = 5\frac{1}{3}$; $RS = 7\frac{1}{3}$; $XY = \underline{?}$
6. $MN = 9$; $RS = 14\frac{2}{3}$; $XY = \underline{?}$

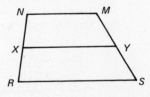

In Exercises 7–12, points R and S are the midpoints of $\overline{AB}$ and $\overline{BC}$.

7. If $AC = 14.4$, $RS = \underline{?}$.
8. If $RS = 5.6$, $AC = \underline{?}$.
9. If $AC = x + 6$ and $RS = x - 1$, then $x = \underline{?}$.
10. If $AC = 3x + 1$ and $RS = x + 3$, then $RS = \underline{?}$.
11. If $AC = x^2 + x + 1$ and $x = 3$, then $RS = \underline{?}$.
12. If $RS = x^2 - x + 3$ and $x = 2$, then $AC = \underline{?}$.

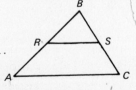

13. Given: Points *A* and *D* are the midpoints of $\overline{BE}$ and $\overline{CE}$.

    Prove: Quad. *ABCD* is a trapezoid.

14. Given: Points *A* and *D* are the midpoints of $\overline{BE}$ and $\overline{CE}$; $\overline{BC} \cong \overline{EC}$

    Prove: $AD = \frac{1}{2}EC$

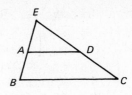

In Exercises 15–18, exactly one of the lengths denoted by *k*, *l*, and *m* can be found. Find that length.

15.

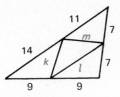

17.

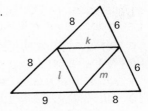

16.

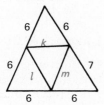

18.

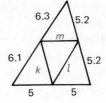

B 19. Prove: The base angles of an isosceles trapezoid are congruent. (*Hint:* Draw the auxiliary segments shown. Show that quad. *ARSD* is a ▱ and hence $\overline{AR} \cong \overline{DS}$. Then prove $\triangle ABR \cong \triangle DCS$.)

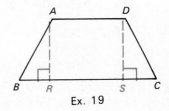

Ex. 19

20. Prove: The diagonals of an isosceles trapezoid are congruent. (You may use the statement of Exercise 19 as a reason in your proof.)

21. Given: Quad. *ABCD* is a trapezoid; $\overline{AD} \cong \overline{BC}$; $\overline{AC} \cong \overline{BD}$

    Prove: $\triangle ARD \cong \triangle BRC$

22. Given: Quad. *ABCD* is a trapezoid; $\angle 1 \cong \angle 2$

    Prove: $\overline{AD} \cong \overline{BC}$

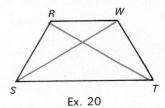

Ex. 20

C 23. Given: Quad. *ABCD* is a trapezoid; $\overline{DR} \cong \overline{CR}$

    Prove: $\overline{AD} \cong \overline{BC}$

24. Explain why diagonals $\overline{AC}$ and $\overline{BD}$ of trapezoid *ABCD* cannot bisect each other.

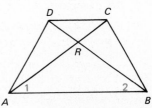

Exs. 21–24

In Exercises 25–28, $\overline{RS}$ is the median of trapezoid $ABCD$.

25. If $AB = 3x^2 + 10$, $RS = 2x^2 + x + 6$, and
    $DC = 18 - 4x$, find x.
26. If $AB = x^2 + 6x + 2$, $RS = 3x^2 + x + 1$, and
    $DC = x^2 + 5x - 2$, find x.
27. If $AB = x^2 - x$, $RS = 2x^2 + 2x - 3$, and
    $DC = x^2 - 3$, find x.
28. If $AB = 2x^3 + x^2 - 4x$, $DC = 2x^2 + 5$, and
    $RS = x^3 + 2x^2 - 3x + 1$, find x.

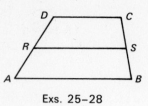

Exs. 25–28

Self-Test   Complete each of the following, using one of the words *Always, Sometimes,* or *Never.*

1. A parallelogram is __?__ a quadrilateral.
2. A parallelogram is __?__ a rectangle.
3. A rhombus is __?__ a square.
4. A trapezoid is __?__ a parallelogram.
5. The diagonals of a trapezoid __?__ bisect each other.
6. The diagonals of a rectangle are __?__ congruent.
7. If the diagonals of a parallelogram are perpendicular to each other, the parallelogram is __?__ a square.
8. If a segment joins the midpoints of two sides of a triangle, the segment is __?__ parallel to the third side.
9. The length of the median of a trapezoid is __?__ equal to the sum of the lengths of the bases.
10. If the measure of each of two angles of a quadrilateral is 90, the quadrilateral is __?__ a trapezoid.

Inequalities

Objectives

1. State and apply the inequality relations for one triangle.
2. State and apply the inequality relations for two triangles.

5-5 *Inequalities for One Triangle*

In most of our work thus far, we have restricted our study to angles and segments that have equal measures. We now consider some of the relationships that exist between angles and segments that do not have equal measures.

Note $\triangle ABC$ with $\overline{AC} \not\cong \overline{BC}$. The figure suggests that $\angle A \not\cong \angle B$, and more specifically, that $m\angle A > m\angle B$. In order to prove such relationships we shall use the following theorem about real numbers a, b, and c.

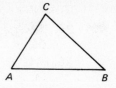

If $a = b + c$ and c is a positive number, then $a > b$.

EXAMPLE 1

Since $12 = x + 5$ and $5 > 0$, we can conclude $12 > x$.

EXAMPLE 2

Given: $\overline{DEF}$

Prove: $DF > DE$

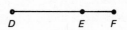

Proof:

STATEMENTS	REASONS
1. $\overline{DEF}$	1. Given
2. $DF = DE + EF$	2. Def. of between
3. $DF > DE$	3. If $a = b + c$ and $c > 0$, then $a > b$.

In the above example, we had $DF = a$, $DE = b$, and $EF = c$. Since EF is a length, we know that EF is a positive number.

EXAMPLE 3

Given: The plane figure

Prove: $m\angle RST > m\angle RSD$

Proof:

STATEMENTS	REASONS
1. $m\angle RST = m\angle RSD + m\angle DST$	1. Angle Addition Postulate
2. $m\angle RST > m\angle RSD$	2. If $a = b + c$ and $c > 0$, then $a > b$.

In Example 3 we can say $\angle RST$ is *larger* than $\angle RSD$. Just as we call one segment *longer* than another when its length is greater, we also call one angle *larger* than another when its measure is greater.

THEOREM 5-12 If one side of a triangle is longer than a second side, then the angle opposite the first side is larger than the angle opposite the second side.

Given: $\triangle ABC$, $AB > BC$

Prove: $m\angle C > m\angle A$

Proof:

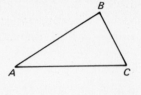

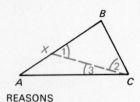

STATEMENTS	REASONS
1. On $\overrightarrow{BA}$ take point X so that $BX = BC$.	1. On a ray there is exactly one point at a given distance from the endpoint of the ray.
2. Draw $\overline{CX}$.	2. _?_
3. $m\angle 1 = m\angle 2$	3. Base $\angle$s of an isosceles $\triangle$ _?_.
4. $m\angle 1 = m\angle A + m\angle 3$	4. The measure of an exterior $\angle$ of a $\triangle$ _?_.
5. $m\angle 1 > m\angle A$	5. If $a = b + c$ and $c > 0$, then $a > b$.
6. $m\angle 2 > m\angle A$	6. Substitution principle (Steps 3 and 5)
7. $m\angle ACB = m\angle 2 + m\angle 3$	7. Angle Addition Postulate
8. $m\angle ACB > m\angle 2$	8. If $a = b + c$ and _?_.
9. $m\angle ACB > m\angle A$, or $m\angle C > m\angle A$	9. Transitive property of inequality (Steps 6 and 8)

THEOREM 5-13 If one angle of a triangle is larger than a second angle, then the side opposite the first angle is longer than the side opposite the second angle.

Given: $\triangle DEF$, $m\angle D > m\angle E$

Prove: $EF > DF$

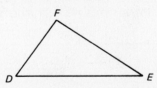

Proof: Suppose $EF \not> DF$. Then either $EF = DF$ or $EF < DF$. If $EF = DF$, then $m\angle D = m\angle E$ (base angles of an isosceles $\triangle$ are $\cong$), and if $EF < DF$, then $m\angle D < m\angle E$ (by Theorem 5-12). But both conclusions contradict the given fact that $m\angle D > m\angle E$. Hence our assumption that $EF \not> DF$ must be false, and it follows that $EF > DF$.

COROLLARY 1 The perpendicular segment from a point to a line is the shortest segment from the point to the line.

The proof is left as Exercise 19.

COROLLARY 2 The perpendicular segment from a point to a plane is the shortest segment from the point to the plane.

The proof is left as Exercise 20.

Oral Exercises

In Exercises 1–4, state the largest and smallest angles of each triangle.

1.
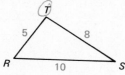

3.
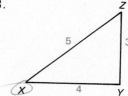

2.
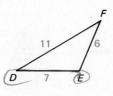

4.
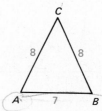

In Exercises 5–8, state the longest and shortest sides of each triangle.

5.
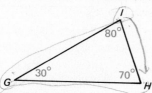

7.
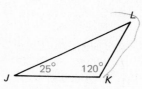

6.
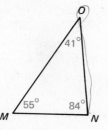

8.
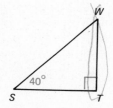

In Exercises 9–14, classify each statement as true or false.

9. If $9 = x + 5$, then $9 > x$. T
10. If $12 = y - 2$, then $12 > y$. T
11. If $219 = \sqrt{x} + 73$, then $219 > \sqrt{x}$. T
12. If $AB = BC + 6$, then $AB > BC$. T
13. If $m\angle A = m\angle 1 + m\angle 2$, then $m\angle 1 > m\angle 2$. F
14. If $m\angle R = m\angle 3 + m\angle 4$, then $m\angle R > m\angle 3$. T

Written Exercises

In Exercises 1–6, write the name of the longest and shortest sides of each triangle.

A 1.

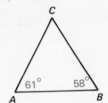

3.

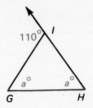

5.

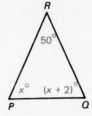

2.

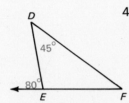

4.

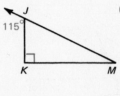

6.

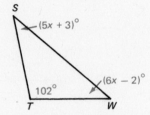

7. Given: $\overline{ABC}$
   Prove: $AC > AB$

8. Given: $\overline{ABC}$; $BC = 5$
   Prove: $AC > 5$

9. Given: $\overline{ABC}$; $AB > 7$
   Prove: $AC > 7$

10. Given: $\overline{ABC}$; $AC = k$
    Prove: $k > AB$

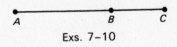

Exs. 7–10

11. Given: The plane figure
    Prove: $m\angle ARB > m\angle 1$

12. Given: The plane figure;
    $m\angle 2 = m\angle 3$
    Prove: $m\angle ARB > m\angle 3$

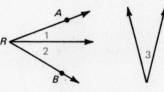

Exs. 11, 12

B 13. Prove: An exterior angle of a triangle is larger than each remote interior angle.

14. Given: $\overline{ACD}$; $\overline{BCE}$;
    $m\angle B > m\angle A$;
    $m\angle E > m\angle D$
    Prove: $AD > BE$

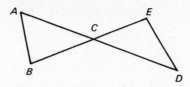

15. Given: $\triangle RTW$; $m\angle R > m\angle T$
    Prove: $WT > WS$ (*Hint:* Use the
    fact that $m\angle 1 > m\angle R$.)

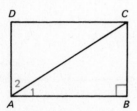

17. Given: The plane figure
    Prove: $m\angle 4 + m\angle 5 > 180$

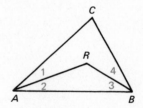

16. Given: Quad $ABCD$ is a rect.;
    $AB > BC$
    Prove: $m\angle 2 > m\angle 1$

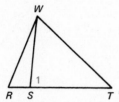

18. Given: $\triangle ABC$; $AC > BC$;
    $\angle 1 \cong \angle 2$; $\angle 3 \cong \angle 4$
    Prove: $AR > RB$

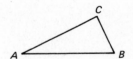

C 19. Prove Corollary 1 of Theorem 5-13.
   20. Prove Corollary 2 of Theorem 5-13.

21. Given: $\triangle ABC$; $AC > BC$; $m\angle B = 45$
    Prove: $\angle C$ is an obtuse angle.
22. Given: $\triangle ABC$; $AC > BC$; $m\angle A = 46$
    Prove: $\angle C$ is an acute angle.

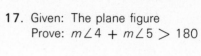

Challenge

Explain how to pass a plane through a cube in such a way that the intersection
is (**a**) an equilateral triangle, (**b**) a trapezoid, (**c**) a pentagon, and (**d**) a hexagon.

5-6 *The Triangle Inequality*

The relationship stated in the following theorem is commonly referred to as *the triangle inequality*.

THEOREM 5-14 The sum of the lengths of any two sides of a triangle is greater than the length of the third side.

Given: $\triangle ABC$

Prove: $AC + AB > CB$

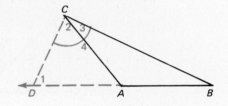

Proof:

STATEMENTS	REASONS
1. On $\overrightarrow{BA}$ take point D such that $\overline{DAB}$ and $DA = AC$.	1. On a ray there is exactly one point __?__.
2. $m\angle 1 = m\angle 2$	2. __?__
3. $m\angle 4 = m\angle 2 + m\angle 3$	3. Angle Addition Postulate
4. $m\angle 4 > m\angle 2$	4. If $a = b + c$ and $c > 0$, $a > b$.
5. $m\angle 4 > m\angle 1$	5. Substitution principle
6. $DB > CB$	6. If one angle of one $\triangle$ is larger than __?__.
7. $DB = DA + AB$	7. Definition of between
8. $DA + AB > CB$	8. Substitution principle (Steps 6 and 7)
9. $AC + AB > CB$	9. Substitution principle (Steps 1 and 8)

Oral Exercises

State whether it is possible for a triangle to exist with sides of the given lengths.

1. 4, 5, 6
2. 8, 10, 12
3. 1, 2, 3
4. 8, 8, 10
5. 8, 2, 5
6. 7, 15, 6

7. $x, 2x, x$ $(x > 0)$
8. $3x, 2x, 4x$ $(x > 0)$
9. $x, x + 3, x + 4$ $(x > 1)$
10. $x, y, x + y$ $(x \text{ and } y > 0)$
11. $x, y, x - y$ $(x \text{ and } y > 0)$
12. $2x, 2x + 2, 4x + 3$ $(x > 0)$

13. If the lengths of two sides of a triangle are 5 and 8, then the length of the third side must be greater than __?³__ .

14. If the lengths of two sides of a triangle are 7 and 7, then the length of the third side must be greater than __?⁰__ .

Written Exercises

In Exercises 1–10 the lengths of two sides of a triangle are given. If x is the length of the third side of the triangle and the domain of x is the set $\{\frac{1}{2}, 1, 4, 7, 9.3, 14, 19\}$, find all possible values for x.

A

1. 7, 8
2. 5, 5
3. 1, 8
4. 3, 6
5. 10, 10
6. 5, 11
7. 5.1, 4.4
8. 3.9, 2.3
9. $2\frac{1}{2}, 5\frac{1}{2}$
10. $6\frac{1}{3}, 4\frac{1}{3}$

In Exercises 13 and 14 you may use as a reason in your proof the theorem "If $a > b$ and $c > d$, then $a + c > b + d$."

11. Given: $\triangle ABC$; $AB > BD$
    Prove: $AC + BC > BD$

12. Given: $\triangle ABC$; $AC > BD$
    Prove: $BC + AB > BD$

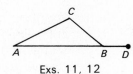

Exs. 11, 12

B 13. Given: Quad. $RSTW$
    Prove: $RS + ST + TW + WR > 2SW$

14. Given: Quad. $RSTW$
    Prove: $RS + ST + TW + WR > RT + SW$
    (*Hint:* Use Ex. 13 and the inequality $RS + ST + TW + WR > 2RT$.)

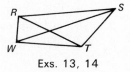

Exs. 13, 14

15. The lengths of two sides of a triangle are 7 and 10. Between what two numbers does the length of the third side lie? 17

16. The length of a leg of an isosceles triangle is 9. Between what two numbers does the length of the third side lie? 18 < n > 0

17. The lengths of three sides of a quadrilateral are 4, 7, and 10. Between what two numbers does the length of the fourth side lie? 21

18. The lengths of four sides of a pentagon are 3, 4, 6, and 14. Between what two numbers does the length of the fifth side lie? 0 and 27

C 19. Given: $\triangle ABC$
    Prove: $\frac{1}{2}(AC + AB + BC) > CR$

20. Given: The plane figure; $\overline{WX} \cong \overline{WT}$
    Prove: $SR + RX > ST$

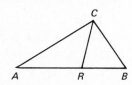

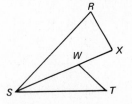

21. Given: Quad. *ABCD*
Prove: Perimeter of quad. *ABCD* is greater than perimeter of △*DRC*. (You may use "If $a > b$ and $c > d$, then $a + c > b + d$.")

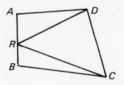

22. Given: △*ABC*; *M* is the midpoint of $\overline{AB}$
Prove: $AC + BC > 2CM$
(*Hint:* Use Theorem 5-11.)

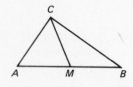

5-7 *Inequalities for Two Triangles*

Suppose you attach an elastic string to the ends of the legs of two identical compasses. Consider the two compasses shown.

If the two compasses are opened the same amount, it is apparent that △*ABC* ≅ △*RST* (SAS Postulate) and $\overline{BC} \cong \overline{ST}$.

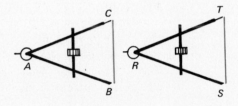

However, if the compasses are opened unequal amounts as shown ($m\angle A > m\angle R$), we note that $\overline{BC}$ is not congruent to $\overline{ST}$; in fact, $BC > ST$.

Although it may be easy to see this relationship, it is not very easy to prove it.

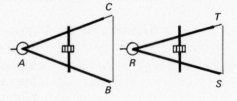

THEOREM 5-15 If two sides of one triangle are congruent to two sides of another triangle, but the included angle of the first triangle is larger than the included angle of the second, then the third side of the first triangle is longer than the third side of the second.

Given: $\overline{AB} \cong \overline{JK}$;
$\overline{AC} \cong \overline{JL}$;
$m\angle A > m\angle J$

Prove: $BC > KL$

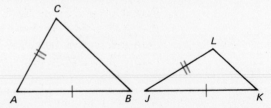

Outline of Proof:

Draw $\overrightarrow{AT}$ such that $\angle BAT \cong \angle KJL$. On $\overrightarrow{AT}$ take point Z such that $AZ = JL$.

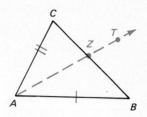

Case 1

If point Z lies on $\overline{BC}$, we have $BC = BZ + ZC$, and hence $BC > BZ$. Since $\triangle ABZ \cong \triangle JKL$ (SAS Postulate), $BZ = KL$. Then by substitution $BC > KL$.

Case 2

If point Z does not lie on $\overline{BC}$, draw $\overrightarrow{AX}$, the bisector of $\angle CAZ$. Label the intersection of $\overrightarrow{AX}$ and $\overline{BC}$ point Y. Draw $\overline{YZ}$. Since $AC = JL = AZ$, $\triangle ACY \cong \triangle AZY$ (SAS Postulate) and $CY = ZY$. If we draw $\overline{BZ}$, we can see that $BY + ZY > BZ$ and hence that $BY + CY > BZ$. Therefore $BC > BZ$. But since $\triangle ZAB \cong \triangle LJK$ (SAS Postulate), we have $KL = BZ$. Now by substituting in $BC > BZ$, we can conclude $BC > KL$.

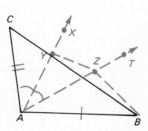

THEOREM 5-16 If two sides of one triangle are congruent to two sides of another triangle, but the third side of the first triangle is longer than the third side of the second, then the included angle of the first triangle is larger than the included angle of the second.

Given: $\overline{DE} \cong \overline{RS}$;

$\overline{DF} \cong \overline{RT}$;

$EF > ST$

Prove: $m\angle D > m\angle R$

Proof: Suppose $m\angle D \not> m\angle R$. Then either $m\angle D = m\angle R$ or $m\angle D < m\angle R$. If $m\angle D = m\angle R$, then $\triangle DEF \cong \triangle RST$ (SAS Postulate) and $EF = ST$. But this contradicts the fact that $EF > ST$. If $m\angle D < m\angle R$, then, by Theorem 5-15, $EF < ST$. Again this contradicts the fact that $EF > ST$. Hence our assumption that $m\angle D \not> m\angle R$ is false, and it follows that $m\angle D > m\angle R$.

Oral Exercises Exercises 1–4 refer to the triangles shown. Classify each statement as true or false.

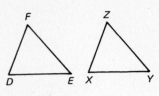

1. If $\overline{DE} \cong \overline{XY}$, and $\overline{DF} \cong \overline{XZ}$, then $\overline{FE}$ must be congruent to $\overline{ZY}$.

2. If $m\angle F > m\angle Z$ and $\overline{DF} \cong \overline{XZ}$, then DE must be greater than XY.

3. If $\overline{ED} \cong \overline{YX}$, $\overline{EF} \cong \overline{YZ}$, and $DF > XZ$, then $m\angle E > m\angle Y$.

4. If $m\angle D > m\angle X$, $\overline{DE} \cong \overline{XY}$, and $\overline{DF} \cong \overline{XZ}$, then $FE > ZY$.

In Exercises 5–8, state whether $\angle 1$ or $\angle 2$ is the larger angle.

5.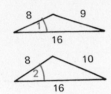

7.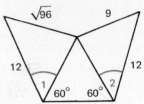

6.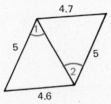

8.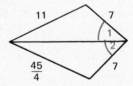

In Exercises 9 and 10, state whether $\overline{AB}$ or $\overline{BD}$ is the longer segment.

9.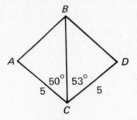

10.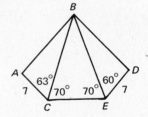

Written Exercises In Exercises 1–6, complete each statement, using one of the words *Always, Sometimes,* or *Never.*

A

1. If $\overline{AB} \cong \overline{RS}$ and $\overline{BC} \cong \overline{ST}$, then $\overline{AC}$ is __?__ congruent to $\overline{RT}$.

2. If $\overline{AB} \cong \overline{RS}$ and $\overline{AC} \cong \overline{RT}$, then $m\angle A$ is __?__ equal to $m\angle R$.

3. If $\overline{AB} \cong \overline{RS}$, $\overline{AC} \cong \overline{RT}$, and $\angle A \not\cong \angle R$, then $\overline{BC}$ is __?__ congruent to $\overline{ST}$.

4. If $\overline{AC} \cong \overline{RT}$, $\overline{BC} \cong \overline{ST}$, and $AB > RS$, then $m\angle C$ is __?__ greater than $m\angle T$.

5. If $\overline{AC} \cong \overline{RT}$, $\overline{BC} \cong \overline{ST}$, and $m\angle C > m\angle T$, then AB is __?__ greater than RS.

6. If $m\angle A = m\angle R$, $m\angle B = m\angle S$, and $AB > RS$, then AC is __?__ less than RT.

In Exercises 7–10, state whether AB or BD is the greater measure.

7.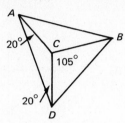

9.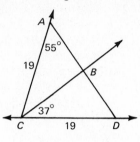

8.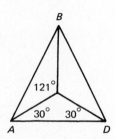

10.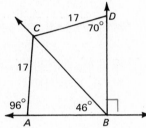

11. Given: $\overline{DT} \cong \overline{FT}$;
$\qquad m\angle 1 > m\angle 2$
Prove: $DE > FE$

12. Given: $DE > FE$;
$\qquad \overline{DT} \cong \overline{FT}$
Prove: $m\angle 1 > m\angle 2$

B 13. Given: $RX = XS = XT$;
$\qquad m\angle 1 = 100$
Prove: $RT > ST$

14. Given: $RX = XS = XT$;
$\qquad RT > ST$
Prove: $m\angle 1 > 90$

15. Given: $m\angle 1 = 70$; $m\angle 2 = 72$;
$\qquad \overline{AT} \cong \overline{TC}$
Prove: $AB > BC$

16. Given: $\angle TAC \cong \angle TCA$; $m\angle 1 = 69$;
$\qquad m\angle 2 = 72$
Prove: $AB > BC$

C 17. Given: $\overline{AT} \cong \overline{CT}$; $CB = AR$
$\qquad$ Prove: $m\angle ATB > m\angle CTB$

18. Given: $\overline{AT} \cong \overline{CT}$; $CB = AR$
$\qquad$ Prove: $m\angle 2 > m\angle 1$

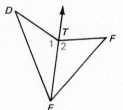

Exs. 11, 12

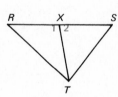

Exs. 13, 14

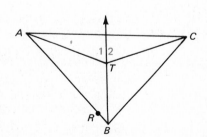

Exs. 15–18

19. Given: Quad. *ABCD* is a ▱;
m∠1 = 30; m∠2 = 35
Prove: *AC* > *BD*

20. Given: Quad. *ABCD* is a ▱;
AC > *BD*
Prove: ∠*ABC* is an obtuse angle.

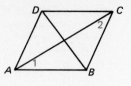

21. Given: Point *X* not in plane of △*RST*;
$\overline{RS} \cong \overline{ST}$; m∠*SRT* = 60;
m∠*RTX* > m∠*XTS*
Prove: m∠*XSR* > m∠*XRS*

22. Given: *RT* = *XT* = *TS*; m∠*XRT* = 58;
m∠*XSW* = 121; *RX* = 4*y* + 5;
XS = 26 + *y*
Prove: *y* > 7

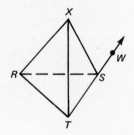

Self-Test Exercises 1–4 refer to △*DEF*.

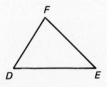

1. If *DE* > *EF*, then m∠*F* > m∠ __?__ .
2. If m∠*F* > m∠*E*, then *DE* > __?__ .
3. If *DF* = 5 and *FE* = 6, then *DE* < __?__ .
4. If *DE* = 7 and *FE* = 6, then *DF* > __?__ .

Exercises 5–8 refer to the plane figure shown.

5. If $\overline{ST} \cong \overline{TW}$ and m∠3 < m∠4,
then *RS* ___?___ *RW*.
   (<, =, >)

6. If $\overline{ST} \cong \overline{TW}$ and *RW* > *RS*, then
m∠4 ___?___ m∠3.
   (<, =, >)

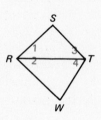

7. If $\overline{RS} \cong \overline{RW}$ and $\overline{ST} \cong \overline{TW}$, then
m∠1 ___?___ m∠2.
   (<, =, >)

8. If *RS* = *ST* = *TW* = 8 and *RT* = 10, then *RW* < __?__ .

CHAPTER SUMMARY

1. In a parallelogram:
   a. opposite sides are parallel. c. opposite angles are congruent.
   b. opposite sides are congruent. d. diagonals bisect each other.
2. You can prove a quadrilateral is a parallelogram by showing any one of the
following is true:
   a. opposite sides are parallel.
   b. opposite sides are congruent.
   c. two sides are congruent and parallel.
   d. diagonals bisect each other.

3. If parallel lines cut off congruent segments on one transversal, they cut off congruent segments on every transversal.

4. Rectangles, rhombuses, and squares are special parallelograms.

5. The median of a trapezoid is parallel to the base and its length is half the sum of the lengths of the bases.

6. The segment joining the midpoints of two sides of a triangle is parallel to, and half as long as, the third side.

7. In $\triangle ABC$:
   a. if $m\angle A > m\angle B$, then $BC > AC$
   b. if $BC > AC$, then $m\angle A > m\angle B$
   c. $AB + BC > AC$

8. In $\triangle ABC$ and $\triangle A'B'C'$ with $AB = A'B'$ and $BC = B'C'$,
   a. if $m\angle B > m\angle B'$, then $AC > A'C'$
   b. if $AC > A'C'$, then $m\angle B > m\angle B'$

CHAPTER TEST

Classify each statement as true or false.

1. The opposite sides of a parallelogram are congruent.

2. The opposite angles of a parallelogram are congruent.

3. If the diagonals of a quadrilateral bisect each other, the quadrilateral is a parallelogram.

4. The diagonals of every parallelogram bisect the angles of the parallelogram.

5. The diagonals of a nonsquare rectangle are perpendicular to each other.

6. There exists a trapezoid whose diagonals are congruent.

7. The median of a trapezoid is the segment that joins the midpoints of the bases.

8. If three parallel lines cut off congruent segments on one transversal, they cut off congruent segments on every transversal.

9. Any two consecutive angles of a parallelogram are supplementary.

10. There exists a triangle whose sides have lengths 3, 9, and 5.

Exercises 11–13 refer to the figure shown. $RS = ST$ and $WT > WR$

11. $m\angle 1 \underline{\quad ? \quad} m\angle 2$
    $(<, =, >)$

12. $m\angle R \underline{\quad ? \quad} m\angle T$
    $(<, =, >)$

13. $RS \underline{\quad ? \quad} WT + WS$
    $(<, =, >)$

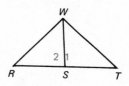

Exercises 14–16 refer to trapezoid $ABCD$. $\overline{MN}$ is the median.

14. If $AB = 16$ and $DC = 10$, then $MN = \underline{\quad ? \quad}$ 13

15. If $DC = 12$ and $MN = 15$, then $AB = \underline{\quad ? \quad}$

16. If $AB = 6x - 1$, $MN = 5x - 1$, and $DC = 3x + 2$, then $x = \underline{\quad ? \quad}$

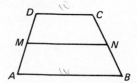

In Exercises 17–20, state whether the given information is sufficient to support the statement "Quad. *WXYZ* is a $\square$."

17. $\overline{OX} \cong \overline{OZ}$; $\overline{OW} \cong \overline{OY}$
18. $\overline{XW} \cong \overline{ZY}$; $\overline{WZ} \parallel \overline{XY}$
19. $\overline{XY} \cong \overline{WZ}$; $\overline{XY} \parallel \overline{WZ}$
20. $\overline{WX} \parallel \overline{ZY}$; $\angle 1 \cong \angle 2$

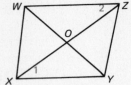

Exercises 21–23 refer to $\triangle DEF$.
$\overline{FR} \cong \overline{RD}$ and $\overline{FS} \cong \overline{SE}$.

21. $RS = \frac{1}{2}$? $\overline{DE}$
22. If $DE = 14$, $RS = $? .
23. If $RS = 2x + 2$ and $DE = 6x - 4$, then $x = $? .

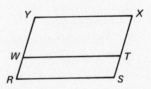

24. Given: $AC = k$
    Prove: $k > BC$

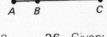

25. Given: $\square ABCD$; $\angle 1 \cong \angle 2$
    Prove: $\overline{DC} \cong \overline{AE}$

26. Given: $\square RSTW$; $\square RSXY$
    Prove: Quad. *WTXY* is a parallelogram.

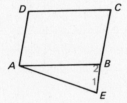

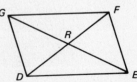

CHAPTER REVIEW

5-1 *Properties of Parallelograms*

Quadrilateral *PTRS* is a parallelogram.

1. $\triangle PTS \cong \triangle$?
2. If $m\angle P = 14x + 8$ and $m\angle R = 16x - 2$, $x = $? .
3. $\angle 1 \cong$?
4. If $PT = 10x$ and $SR = 8x + 6$, $x = $? .

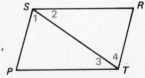

5-2 *Proving That Certain Quadrilaterals Are Parallelograms*

Using the information given in each exercise, write the reason why quadrilateral *DEFG* is a parallelogram.

5. $\overline{DE} \parallel \overline{GF}$; $\overline{DG} \parallel \overline{EF}$
6. $\overline{DE} \cong \overline{GF}$; $\overline{DG} \cong \overline{EF}$
7. $\overline{DE} \cong \overline{GF}$; $\overline{DE} \parallel \overline{GF}$
8. $\overline{DR} \cong \overline{RF}$; $\overline{GR} \cong \overline{RE}$

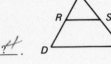

5-3 Rectangles, Rhombuses, Squares

Classify each statement as true or false.

9. Every rectangle is a parallelogram. T
10. The diagonals of a rhombus are perpendicular. T
11. Every rhombus is a regular polygon. F
12. If a rectangle is equilateral, then it is a square. F

5-4 Trapezoids

Quadrilateral *PTRS* is a trapezoid; $\overline{PM} \cong \overline{MS}$; $\overline{TN} \cong \overline{NR}$.

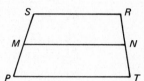

13. The legs of the trapezoid are __?__ and __?__ .
14. If the trapezoid were isosceles, then $\angle$ __?__ $\cong \angle$ __?__ .
15. $\overline{MN}$ is the __?__ of trapezoid *PTRS*.
16. If $SR = 14$ and $PT = 20$, then $MN = $ __?__ .

5-5 Inequalities for One Triangle

17. If $a = b + c$ and $c > 0$, then a ____?____ b.
    $$(<, =, >)$$
18. In $\triangle ABC$, if $AC > BC$, then $m\angle B > m\angle$ __?__ .
19. In $\triangle ABC$, if $m\angle C > m\angle B$,
    then $AB > $ __?__ .
20. The shortest segment that can
    be drawn from point *C* to $\overleftrightarrow{AB}$
    is the __?__ segment from *C* to
    $\overleftrightarrow{AB}$.

5-6 The Triangle Inequality

21. If the lengths of two sides of a triangle are 3 and 5, then the length
    of the third side must be less than __?__ .

22. If the lengths of two sides of a triangle are 4 and 7, then the length
    of the third side must be greater than __?__ .

23. Is it possible for a triangle to have sides with lengths 5, 11, and 4?

5-7 Inequalities for Two Triangles

24. If $\overline{RT} \cong \overline{ST}$ and $RX > SX$,
    then $m\angle 1$ ____?____ $m\angle 2$.
    $$(<, =, >)$$
25. If $\overline{RX} \cong \overline{SX}$ and $m\angle 3 > m\angle 4$,
    then RT ____?____ ST.
    $$(<, =, >)$$
26. If $\overline{RT} \cong \overline{ST}$ and $m\angle 1 = m\angle 2$,
    then RX ____?____ SX.
    $$(<, =, >)$$

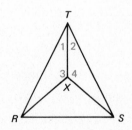

Mathematics and Magic

*extra
for
experts*

When a magician appears to saw his assistant in half, people realize that trickery is involved. Yet some of those people are so gullible mathematically that they do not look for trickery when they see an alleged proof of an obviously false statement. The proof, outlined below, that *every triangle is isosceles* is *not* valid. You should hunt for the place where the proof breaks down.

Given: △ABC

Prove: $\overline{AC} \cong \overline{BC}$

Outline of proof:
Let *j* be the bisector of ∠C and *k* be the perpendicular bisector of $\overline{AB}$. Either *j* ∥ *k* or *j* ∦ *k*.

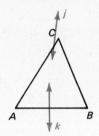

I. If *j* ∥ *k*, then *j* ⊥ $\overline{AB}$.
   Show rt. △AXC ≅ rt. △BXC.
   Then $\overline{AC} \cong \overline{BC}$.

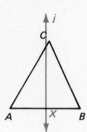

Case I

II. If *j* ∦ *k*, then *j* and *k* intersect at some point *P*.
   a. If *P* lies in the interior of △ABC:
      From *P* drop perpendiculars to $\overline{AC}$ and $\overline{BC}$.
      Draw $\overline{PA}$ and $\overline{PB}$.
      △ATP ≅ △BTP; $\overline{AP} \cong \overline{BP}$
      △CRP ≅ △CSP; $\overline{RC} \cong \overline{SC}$, $\overline{RP} \cong \overline{SP}$
      △ARP ≅ △BSP; $\overline{AR} \cong \overline{BS}$
      Since $\overline{AR} \cong \overline{BS}$ and $\overline{RC} \cong \overline{SC}$, $\overline{AC} \cong \overline{BC}$.

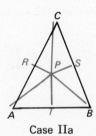

Case IIa

   b. If *P* lies on △ABC:
      △APC ≅ △BPC; $\overline{AC} \cong \overline{BC}$
   c. If *P* lies in the exterior of △ABC:
      From *P* drop perpendiculars to $\overleftrightarrow{AC}$ and $\overleftrightarrow{BC}$.
      Draw $\overline{PA}$ and $\overline{PB}$.
      △ATP ≅ △BTP; $\overline{AP} \cong \overline{BP}$
      △CXP ≅ △CYP; $\overline{CX} \cong \overline{CY}$; $\overline{PX} \cong \overline{PY}$
      △AXP ≅ △BYP; $\overline{AX} \cong \overline{BY}$
      Since $\overline{CX} \cong \overline{CY}$ and $\overline{AX} \cong \overline{BY}$, $\overline{AC} \cong \overline{BC}$.

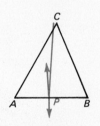

Case IIb

Explain the mistake in the argument above.

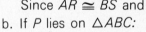

Case IIc

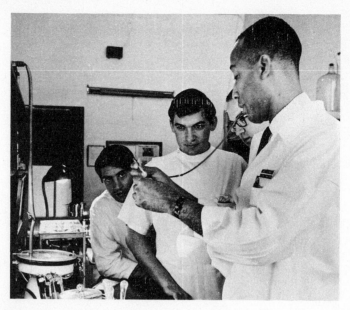

Careers

Medicine

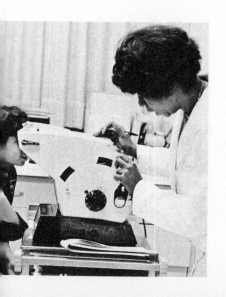

The field of medicine includes such diverse areas of specialization as dental hygiene, optometry, x-ray technology, nursing, therapy, and audiology. All contribute to the diagnosis and treatment of illness, to preventive medicine, and to research.

In any health service occupation, precision instruments are an important means of obtaining accurate data quickly. Microscopes and automatic analyzers, for example, are necessary to examine bacteria cultures, blood cholesterol level, and tissue samples. In recent years, the computer has provided an efficient tool for the storage of vast quantities of medical information; in some cases, the computer has even been programmed to make a preliminary diagnosis.

Mathematics is an important part of the ''equipment'' needed for a career in medicine. Analyzing data, preparing medication, and performing chemical tests all require careful calculations, and a practical understanding of mathematical techniques.

SIMILAR POLYGONS

Definitions and Properties

Objectives

1. Express a ratio in simplest form.
2. Determine an unknown term in a given proportion.
3. Transform a proportion into an equivalent equation.
4. State and apply the properties of similar polygons.

6-1 Ratio and Proportion

The ideas in this chapter are based on the concepts of *ratio* and *proportion*. Although you may remember the meaning of those words, the following discussion will give you an opportunity to refresh your memory.

Numbers such as $\frac{5}{7}$, $\frac{1}{9}$, and $\frac{\sqrt{5}}{11}$ are called ratios. For all numbers k and l ($l \neq 0$), the **ratio** of k to l is the number $\frac{k}{l}$. Do you understand why l cannot have the value zero?

EXAMPLE 1. If $m\angle R = 40$ and $m\angle T = 70$, find the ratio of the measure of $\angle R$ to the measure of $\angle T$.

SOLUTION: $\dfrac{m\angle R}{m\angle T} = \dfrac{40}{70} = \dfrac{4}{7}$

In Example 1 we found the *ratio of the measures* of two angles, not the ratio of two angles. When we write a ratio, we are comparing two numbers. Measures are numbers, whereas angles are sets of points, not numbers.

EXAMPLE 2. If $k = 12$ and $t = 16$, find the ratio of:

        a. k to t **b.** t to k

SOLUTION: **a.** $\dfrac{k}{t} = \dfrac{12}{16} = \dfrac{3}{4}$ **b.** $\dfrac{t}{k} = \dfrac{16}{12} = \dfrac{4}{3}$

Note that for positive numbers k and t the ratio of k to t is not the same as the ratio of t to k unless k is equal to t.

EXAMPLE 3. What is the ratio of the length, l, of a rectangle to its width, w, if the rectangle is 360 centimeters long and 3 meters wide?

SOLUTION: To form the ratio, we select a common unit of measure. If we convert to centimeters, we have

$$\frac{l}{w} = \frac{360}{300} = \frac{6}{5}$$

If we had converted to meters, or any other common unit of measure, the ratio of l to w, in reduced form, would still equal $\frac{6}{5}$. The choice of the common unit of measure has no bearing on the final ratio.

It is convenient, at times, to write the ratio of k to t in the form $k:t$. This is especially true when comparing more than two numbers. The statement that three numbers are in the ratio $3:5:7$ means that:

1. The ratio of the first to the second is $3:5$.
2. The ratio of the first to the third is $3:7$.
3. The ratio of the second to the third is $5:7$.

Some examples of three numbers in the ratio $3:5:7$ follow:

$$6, 10, 14 \qquad 15, 25, 35 \qquad 1.5, 2.5, 3.5$$

A sentence of the form illustrated below is called a proportion.

$$\frac{a}{b} = \frac{c}{d} \qquad (b \neq 0 \text{ and } d \neq 0)$$

We can also write a proportion using the form $a:b = c:d$. Each statement can be read "a is to b as c is to d" or "a divided by b equals c divided by d."

A proportion, by definition, is an equation whose members are ratios. Hence we may use all the properties of equality when working with proportions.

Each of the numbers a, b, c, and d in the proportion $\frac{a}{b} = \frac{c}{d}$ is called

a *term* of the proportion.

a is the *first term* $\qquad$ c is the *third term*
b is the *second term* $\qquad$ d is the *fourth term*

If there is a need to show that three or more ratios are equal, we can

write an *extended proportion*. $\frac{a}{b} = \frac{c}{d} = \frac{3}{5}$ is an example of an extended

proportion.

1. A proportion is an equation, each of whose members is a ___?___ .
2. In reduced form, the ratio of 2 to 4 is ___?___ .
3. If three numbers are in the ratio $7:9:13$, then the ratio of the first number to the third number is ___?___ .
4. The third term of the proportion $\dfrac{x}{4} = \dfrac{y}{7}$ is ___?___ .

Classify each statement as true or false.

5. $\dfrac{7}{13}$ is an example of a proportion.
6. The value of a ratio may be greater than 1.
7. The ratio $3:4$ is the same as the ratio $4:3$.
8. If the numerator and denominator of a fraction are multiplied by 5, the new ratio is equal to the given ratio.
9. If 4 is added to both the numerator and the denominator of $\frac{3}{4}$, the new ratio is equal to the given ratio.
10. If the ratio of the lengths of two segments measured in meters is $2:3$, the ratio of the lengths when measured in centimeters is less than $2:3$.
11. $4:3 = 20:12$ is a correct statement.
12. It is possible for the second and third terms of a proportion to be the same number.

In Exercises 13–16, express in reduced form the ratio $k:l$.

13. $k = 6$
   $l = 9$

15. $k = 19$
   $l = 37$

14. $k = 12$
   $l = 10$

16. $k = \frac{5}{3}$
   $l = \frac{2}{3}$

Written Exercises

In Exercises 1–8, use the number line to find the value of the indicated ratio.

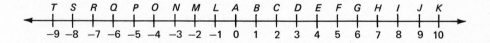

A

1. $TA:BE$
2. $JM:QH$

3. $LB:SD$
4. $EB:NC$

5. $KA:RI$
6. $BS:DJ$

7. $GS:PE$
8. $CQ:AD$

In Exercises 9–12, the length and width of a rectangle are given. Find the ratio of the length to the width. Express each ratio in reduced form.

	length	width
9.	24 centimeters	12 centimeters
10.	4 meters	180 centimeters

	length	width
11.	2.5 centimeters	0.2 meter
12.	240 centimeters	$3\frac{1}{4}$ meters

In Exercises 13–18, find the ratio of the area of the shaded portion to the area of the unshaded portion.

13.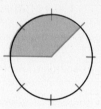

15.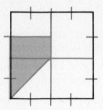

17.

14.

16.

18.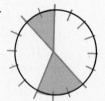

In Exercises 19–28, find the value of x.

EXAMPLE. $\dfrac{4}{5} = \dfrac{6}{x}$

SOLUTION: $5x\left(\dfrac{4}{5}\right) = 5x\left(\dfrac{6}{x}\right)$ (multiplication property of equality)

$\qquad 4x = 30$ (simplifying each member)

$\qquad x = \dfrac{30}{4} = \dfrac{15}{2}$ (division property of equality)

19. $\dfrac{5}{8} = \dfrac{10}{x}$

20. $\dfrac{3}{7} = \dfrac{5}{x}$

21. $\dfrac{x}{5} = \dfrac{12}{3}$

22. $\dfrac{x}{6} = \dfrac{7}{4}$

23. $\dfrac{9}{x} = \dfrac{6}{5}$

24. $\dfrac{18}{x} = \dfrac{4}{3}$

B 25. $\dfrac{2x + 1}{3} = \dfrac{4}{5}$

26. $\dfrac{3x + 4}{6} = \dfrac{2}{5}$

27. $\dfrac{14}{4x + 3} = \dfrac{7}{2}$

28. $\dfrac{3}{5x + 1} = \dfrac{2}{9}$

EXAMPLE. The ratio of the measures of two complementary angles is $3:7$. Find the measure of each angle.

SOLUTION: Let $3x =$ measure of smaller angle
$7x =$ measure of larger angle
$3x + 7x = 90$ (The angles are complementary.)
$10x = 90$
$x = 9$

Therefore $3x = 27$ and $7x = 63$.

29. The ratio of the measures of two complementary angles is $4:5$. Find the measure of each angle.
30. The ratio of the measures of two complementary angles is $2:3$. Find the measure of each angle.
31. The ratio of the measures of two supplementary angles is $1:2$. Find the measure of each angle.
32. The ratio of the measures of two supplementary angles is $11:25$. Find the measure of each.
33. A 36-centimeter segment is divided into three parts whose lengths have the ratio $2:3:7$. Find the length of each segment.
34. A 60-centimeter segment is divided into three parts whose lengths have the ratio $3:4:8$. Find the length of each segment.
35. A quadrilateral with a perimeter of 31 cm has one side 7 cm long. Find the lengths of the remaining three sides if their ratio is $3:4:5$.
36. The measure of one angle of a quadrilateral is 100. Find the measures of the remaining three angles if their ratio is $3:4:6$.

In Exercises 37–40, find the ratio of x to y.

C 37. $\dfrac{x + 3y}{x - y} = \dfrac{2}{3}$

39. $\dfrac{1}{6x - 14y} = \dfrac{y}{x^2 - 5y^2}$

38. $\dfrac{2}{3x + y} = \dfrac{3}{x - 6y}$

40. $\dfrac{y}{y^2 - 2x^2} = \dfrac{2}{3y - 4x}$

6-2 *Properties of Proportions*

As stated in Section 6-1, a proportion is an equation whose members are ratios. In some of the work in this chapter it will be necessary to transform proportions into equivalent equations. The properties listed on the following page will be used to help us in this work. In all the statements listed on page 194, the letters denote any nonzero real numbers.

Properties of Proportions

1. $\dfrac{a}{b} = \dfrac{c}{d}$ is equivalent to $ad = bc$.

   EXAMPLE. $\dfrac{3}{4} = \dfrac{6}{8}$ is equivalent to $3 \cdot 8 = 4 \cdot 6$.

2. $\dfrac{a}{b} = \dfrac{c}{d}$ is equivalent to $\dfrac{a}{c} = \dfrac{b}{d}$.

   EXAMPLE. $\dfrac{3}{4} = \dfrac{6}{8}$ is equivalent to $\dfrac{3}{6} = \dfrac{4}{8}$.

3. $\dfrac{a}{b} = \dfrac{c}{d}$ is equivalent to $\dfrac{b}{a} = \dfrac{d}{c}$.

   EXAMPLE. $\dfrac{3}{4} = \dfrac{6}{8}$ is equivalent to $\dfrac{4}{3} = \dfrac{8}{6}$.

4. $\dfrac{a}{b} = \dfrac{c}{d}$ is equivalent to $\dfrac{a+b}{b} = \dfrac{c+d}{d}$.

   EXAMPLE. $\dfrac{3}{4} = \dfrac{6}{8}$ is equivalent to $\dfrac{3+4}{4} = \dfrac{6+8}{8}$.

5. $\dfrac{a}{b} = \dfrac{c}{d}$ is equivalent to $\dfrac{a-b}{b} = \dfrac{c-d}{d}$.

   EXAMPLE. $\dfrac{3}{4} = \dfrac{6}{8}$ is equivalent to $\dfrac{3-4}{4} = \dfrac{6-8}{8}$.

6. If $\dfrac{a}{b} = \dfrac{c}{d} = \dfrac{e}{f} = \cdots$, then $\dfrac{a+c+e+\cdots}{b+d+f+\cdots} = \dfrac{a}{b} = \dfrac{c}{d} = \cdots$

   EXAMPLE. Since $\dfrac{3}{4} = \dfrac{6}{8} = \dfrac{9}{12}$, then $\dfrac{3+6+9}{4+8+12} = \dfrac{3}{4} = \dfrac{6}{8} = \dfrac{9}{12}$.

When any one of these properties is needed as a reason in a proof, the phrase *a property of proportions* can be used.

Oral Exercises In Exercises 1–8, classify each statement as true or false.

1. If $\dfrac{3}{x} = \dfrac{7}{y}$, then $3y = 7x$.

2. If $\dfrac{x}{5} = \dfrac{4}{y}$, then $4x = 5y$.

3. If $\dfrac{k}{l} = \dfrac{r}{t}$, then $\dfrac{k}{r} = \dfrac{l}{t}$.

4. If $\dfrac{x}{5} = \dfrac{7}{9}$, then $\dfrac{7}{x} = \dfrac{9}{5}$.

5. If $\dfrac{y}{7} = \dfrac{2}{11}$, then $\dfrac{7}{y} = \dfrac{11}{2}$.

6. If $5x = 7y$, then $\dfrac{x}{5} = \dfrac{y}{7}$.

7. If $\dfrac{5}{6} = \dfrac{9}{x}$, then $\dfrac{5+6}{6} = \dfrac{9+x}{x}$.

8. If $\dfrac{13}{4} = \dfrac{x}{6}$, then $\dfrac{13-4}{4} = \dfrac{x-6}{6}$.

Complete each statement.

9. If $\dfrac{a}{5} = \dfrac{b}{7}$, then $5b = \underline{\ ?\ }$.

10. If $\dfrac{x}{3} = \dfrac{y}{5}$, then $\dfrac{3}{?} = \dfrac{5}{?}$.

11. If $\dfrac{2}{5} = \dfrac{x}{3}$, then $\dfrac{2+5}{5} = \dfrac{?}{3}$.

12. If $\dfrac{x}{6} = \dfrac{y}{8}$, then $\dfrac{x}{y} = \dfrac{?}{?}$.

13. If $x^2 = 7y$, then $\dfrac{7}{x} = \dfrac{?}{y}$.

14. If $5x = 9y$, then $\dfrac{x}{y} = \dfrac{?}{?}$.

Written Exercises

In Exercises 1–4, complete the proportion.

A

1. If $kl = st$, $\dfrac{k}{s} = \dfrac{?}{?}$.

2. If $kl = st$, $\dfrac{k}{t} = \dfrac{?}{?}$.

3. If $xy = ab$, $\dfrac{x}{?} = \dfrac{a}{?}$.

4. If $ab = rs$, $\dfrac{?}{r} = \dfrac{?}{b}$.

In Exercises 5–12, find the value of x.

5. $3x = 17$

6. $5x = 26$

7. $\dfrac{x}{6} = \dfrac{7}{3}$

8. $\dfrac{x}{10} = \dfrac{6}{5}$

9. $\dfrac{3}{x} = \dfrac{7}{5}$

10. $\dfrac{4}{11} = \dfrac{x}{2}$

11. $6:x = 3:7$

12. $x:4 = 7:3$

In Exercises 13–18, $\dfrac{TD}{DR} = \dfrac{TE}{ES}$. Three lengths are given. Find the indicated length.

13. $TD = 2$; $DR = 4$; $TE = 3$. $ES = \underline{\ ?\ }$.
14. $TE = 4$; $ES = 8$; $DR = 4$. $TD = \underline{\ ?\ }$.
15. $DR = 5$; $ES = 7$; $TD = 3$. $TE = \underline{\ ?\ }$.
16. $ES = 7$; $TD = 4$; $TE = 5$. $DR = \underline{\ ?\ }$.
17. $TD = 4$; $TE = 5$; $ES = 6$. $TR = \underline{\ ?\ }$.
18. $ES = 8$; $TD = 4$; $DR = 7$. $TS = \underline{\ ?\ }$.

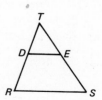

In Exercises 19–26, find the value of x.

B 19. $\dfrac{x + 4}{6} = \dfrac{4}{3}$

20. $\dfrac{x + 1}{8} = \dfrac{2}{3}$

21. $\dfrac{3x - 1}{3} = \dfrac{6}{5}$

22. $\dfrac{8x - 3}{2} = \dfrac{5}{3}$

23. $\dfrac{x + 1}{x - 2} = \dfrac{x + 5}{x - 6}$

24. $\dfrac{x - 3}{x + 2} = \dfrac{x - 5}{x + 7}$

25. $\dfrac{(2x - 5)^2}{(x - 5)(x + 1)} = \dfrac{4}{1}$

26. $\dfrac{3}{(3x + 1)^2} = \dfrac{2}{(3x + 4)(2x - 1)}$

In Exercises 27–30, find the values of x and y for the given system of equations.

C 27. $\dfrac{3x - 2y}{6} = 1$

$\dfrac{3(x - 5)}{y} = \dfrac{1}{2}$

28. $\dfrac{2x - 3y}{6} = \dfrac{2}{1}$

$\dfrac{5x + 3y}{17} = \dfrac{3}{1}$

29. $\dfrac{3y - 2x}{6xy} = \dfrac{1}{6}$

$\dfrac{2y - 3x}{5} = \dfrac{6xy}{6}$

30. $\dfrac{4y + x}{5} = \dfrac{2x^2y}{x}$

$\dfrac{y + 4x}{10} = \dfrac{xy}{2}$

6-3 *Similar Polygons*

Note that the two polygons to the right differ in size but are alike in shape. The two polygons are said to be *similar*.

    A formal definition of similar ($\sim$) polygons includes terms such as *one-to-one correspondence, corresponding angles,* and *corresponding sides*. As you may recall, these terms were also used in our discussion of congruent triangles.

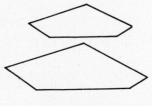

Same Shape

    Two polygons are said to be similar if and only if there is a one-to-one correspondence between their vertices such that:

1. Corresponding angles are congruent.
2. Lengths of corresponding sides are in proportion.

    The two polygons shown at the top of page 197 are similar. When we say polygon *CDEF* is similar to polygon *VWXY* (polygon *CDEF* $\sim$ polygon *VWXY*), we are asserting that the vertices have been paired as follows:

$$C \leftrightarrow V \qquad D \leftrightarrow W \qquad E \leftrightarrow X \qquad F \leftrightarrow Y$$

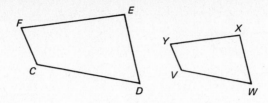

With this pairing of vertices, the definition permits us to conclude the following:

1. $\angle C \cong \angle V \qquad \angle D \cong \angle W$
   $\angle E \cong \angle X \qquad \angle F \cong \angle Y$

2. $\dfrac{CD}{VW} = \dfrac{DE}{WX} = \dfrac{EF}{XY} = \dfrac{FC}{YV}$

At this stage, if we wish to show that two polygons are similar, we must establish that both conditions of the definition are met. The following figures show that meeting just one condition is not sufficient.

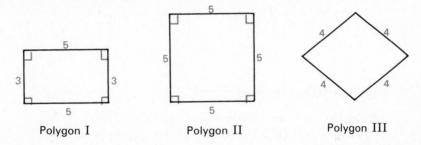

Polygon I   Polygon II   Polygon III

Notice that although the corresponding angles of polygons I and II are congruent, the lengths of corresponding sides are not in proportion. The polygons have different shapes; they are not similar.

Now look at polygons II and III. In this case the lengths of corresponding sides are in proportion but the corresponding angles are not congruent. Again the polygons are not similar.

The following theorem about similar polygons will enable us to shorten some of our proofs.

THEOREM 6-1 Similarity of polygons is reflexive, symmetric, and transitive.

For a proof of the transitive property, see Exercises 11–18. The proofs of the reflexive and symmetric properties are left as Exercises 29 and 30.

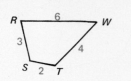

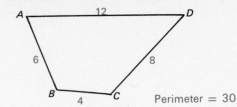

Perimeter = 15   Perimeter = 30

The *perimeter of a polygon* is the sum of the lengths of its sides. Consider the perimeters of the similar quadrilaterals pictured above. Note that the ratio of the perimeter of quadrilateral *RSTW* to the perimeter of quadrilateral *ABCD* is 15:30 or 1:2. How does this ratio compare with the ratio of the lengths of each pair of corresponding sides?

THEOREM 6-2 If two polygons are similar, the ratio of their perimeters equals the ratio of the lengths of any pair of corresponding sides.

Given: Polygon *MORST* is similar to polygon *M'O'R'S'T'*; the polygons have perimeters p and p' respectively.

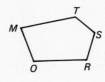   

Prove: $\dfrac{p}{p'} = \dfrac{MO}{M'O'}$

Proof:

STATEMENTS	REASONS
1. $MORST \sim M'O'R'S'T'$	1. Given
2. $\dfrac{MO}{M'O'} = \dfrac{OR}{O'R'} = \dfrac{RS}{R'S'} = \cdots$	2. Lengths of corr. sides of $\sim$ polygons are in proportion.
3. $\dfrac{MO + OR + RS + \cdots}{M'O' + O'R' + R'S' + \cdots}$ $= \dfrac{MO}{M'O'}$	3. A property of proportions
4. $\dfrac{p}{p'} = \dfrac{MO}{M'O'}$	4. Substitution principle

Oral Exercises

Classify each statement as true or false.

1. Every polygon is similar to itself.
2. All triangles are similar.
3. All rectangles are similar.
4. All squares are similar.
5. If two polygons are each similar to a third polygon, the two polygons are similar to each other.
6. Similarity of polygons is symmetric.
7. The perimeter of a square, with a side of length s, is $4s$.
8. The ratio of the measures of two corresponding angles of two similar polygons is $1:1$.
9. If two quadrilaterals are similar, the quadrilaterals must be rectangles.
10. If the ratio of the lengths of two corresponding sides of two similar triangles is $1:1$, the triangles are congruent.
11. If two polygons are similar, then they are congruent.
12. If two triangles have the same perimeter, then they are congruent.

In Exercises 13–18, state why the polygons are, or are not, similar.

13.

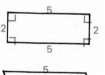

15.

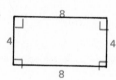

17.

14.

16.

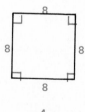

18.

SIMILAR POLYGONS **199**

Written Exercises

In Exercises 1–10 complete each statement with one of the words *Always*, *Sometimes*, or *Never*.

A

1. Two rectangles are __?__ similar.
2. Two squares are __?__ similar.
3. Two similar polygons are __?__ congruent.
4. A pentagon is __?__ similar to a hexagon.
5. The perimeter of a polygon is __?__ less than 1.
6. If polygon **I** is similar to polygon **II** and polygon **II** is similar to polygon **III**, then polygon **I** is __?__ similar to polygon **III**.
7. If two polygons are regular polygons, the polygons are __?__ similar.
8. If an angle of one rhombus is congruent to an angle of another rhombus, the two rhombuses are __?__ similar.
9. If quad. *ABCD* is similar to quad. *HIJK*, then quad. *HIJK* is __?__ similar to quad. *ABCD*.
10. If the perimeter of △*ABC* is 12 and the perimeter of △*DEF* is 17, then the ratio of *AB* to *DE* is __?__ 12 to 17.

In Exercises 11–18, provide the reasons for the proof.

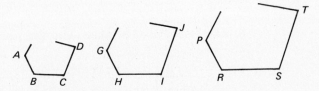

Given: Polygon *ABCD* ⋯ ∼ polygon *GHIJ* ⋯
polygon *GHIJ* ⋯ ∼ polygon *PRST* ⋯

Prove: Polygon *ABCD* ⋯ ∼ polygon *PRST* ⋯

Proof:

STATEMENTS	REASONS
11. $\angle A \cong \angle G$, $\angle G \cong \angle P$, ⋯	11. __?__
12. $\angle A \cong \angle P$, ⋯	12. __?__
13. $\dfrac{AB}{GH} = \dfrac{BC}{HI}$, $\dfrac{GH}{PR} = \dfrac{HI}{RS}$, ⋯	13. __?__
14. $\dfrac{AB}{BC} = \dfrac{GH}{HI}$, $\dfrac{GH}{HI} = \dfrac{PR}{RS}$, ⋯	14. __?__
15. $\dfrac{AB}{BC} = \dfrac{PR}{RS}$, $\dfrac{BC}{CD} = \dfrac{RS}{ST}$, ⋯	15. __?__
16. $\dfrac{AB}{PR} = \dfrac{BC}{RS}$, $\dfrac{BC}{RS} = \dfrac{CD}{ST}$, ⋯	16. __?__
17. $\dfrac{AB}{PR} = \dfrac{BC}{RS} = \dfrac{CD}{ST} = $ ⋯	17. __?__
18. polygon *ABCD* ⋯ ∼ polygon *PRST* ⋯	18. __?__

In Exercises 19–24, the lengths of certain sides of the similar polygons are given. Find the lengths of the other sides.

EXAMPLE. quad. *ABCD* ~ quad. *RSTW*

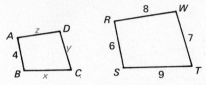

SOLUTION: The ratio of the lengths of one pair of corresponding sides is 4:6, or 2:3. Using variables to represent the lengths, we can write:

$$\frac{x}{9} = \frac{2}{3} \qquad \frac{y}{7} = \frac{2}{3} \qquad \frac{z}{8} = \frac{2}{3}$$

$$x = 6 \qquad y = \frac{14}{3} \qquad z = \frac{16}{3}$$

B 19.

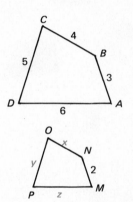

quad. *ABCD* ~ quad. *MNOP*

21.

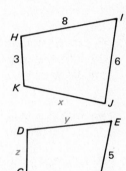

quad. *HIJK* ~ quad. *DEFG*

20.

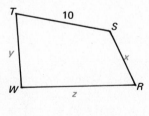

quad. *RSTW* ~ quad. *ABCD*

22.

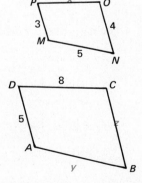

quad. *ABCD* ~ quad. *MNOP*

23.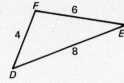

24.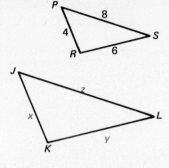

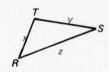

$\triangle DEF \sim \triangle RST$
Perimeter of $\triangle RST$ is 12.

$\triangle PRS \sim \triangle JKL$
Perimeter of $\triangle JKL$ is 27.

In Exercises 25–28, $\triangle RMN \sim \triangle RST$.

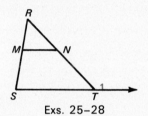

25. If $m\angle R = 55$ and $m\angle RNM = 45$,
$m\angle 1 = \underline{\ ?\ }$.

26. If $m\angle R = 53$ and $m\angle RNM = 43$,
$m\angle S = \underline{\ ?\ }$.

27. If $RM = 3$, $MS = 4$, and $NT = 5$, $RT = \underline{\ ?\ }$.

28. If $RM = 3$, $MS = 4$, and $MN = 4$, $ST = \underline{\ ?\ }$.

Exs. 25–28

C **29.** Prove: Similarity of polygons is reflexive. (Use a quadrilateral.)

30. Prove: Similarity of polygons is symmetric. (Use two triangles.)

Self-Test

1. Express the ratio of 18 to 24 as a fraction in reduced form.

2. Is $5x = 7y$ equivalent to $\dfrac{x}{y} = \dfrac{5}{7}$?

3. Is $\dfrac{AB}{BC} = \dfrac{RS}{ST}$ equivalent to $\dfrac{AB}{RS} = \dfrac{BC}{ST}$?

4. If $\dfrac{x}{y} = \dfrac{5}{7}$, then $\dfrac{7}{y} = \dfrac{?}{?}$.

5. If $\dfrac{x}{8} = \dfrac{5}{6}$, then $x = \underline{\ ?\ }$.

Classify each statement as true or false.

6. If $\triangle ABC \sim \triangle RST$, then $\overline{AC}$ corresponds to $\overline{RT}$.

7. If quad. $ABCD \sim$ quad. $RSTV$, then $\angle B$ must be congruent to $\angle T$.

8. If two similar polygons have perimeters of 24 and 16, then the ratio of the lengths of a pair of corresponding sides is $3:2$.

9. If $\triangle DEF \sim \triangle XYZ$, then $\dfrac{DE}{DF} = \dfrac{XY}{XZ}$.

10. If two triangles are congruent, they are similar.

Check your answers with those printed at the back of the book.

Careers

Graphic Arts

You have probably been struck by an eye-catching advertisement in a magazine or attracted by a pleasing design on a book or record cover. These are all products of graphic artists.

The finished product, whether it is a magazine cover, an advertising display, or a brochure, is the result of the work of many people. After the designer has created a preliminary sketch of the project, a variety of specialists go to work to bring it into being. Commercial artists draw the art that is needed, photographers take the necessary pictures, and letterers and typographers select and draw appropriate styles of type. A layout specialist arranges the various elements of art and type on the page in a pleasing manner. The efforts of graphic artists as well as mathematicians went into the creation of this book.

Working with Similar Triangles

Objectives

1. State and use the AA Postulate and Theorem 6-3 for proving triangles similar.
2. State and apply the corollaries to the AA Postulate.
3. State and apply Theorem 6-4 and its corollary.
4. State and apply the theorem about the bisector of an angle of a triangle.

6-4 *Proving Triangles Similar*

At this point in our discussion of similar polygons, the only way that we can prove two triangles are similar is by showing that the triangles satisfy the definition of similar polygons. In this section we will introduce a postulate that will provide a simpler method for proving triangles are similar.

The postulate may be more meaningful to you if you do the following experiment.

1. On a piece of paper draw two segments, $\overline{AB}$ and $\overline{RS}$, such that $AB = \frac{2}{3}RS$.

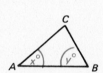 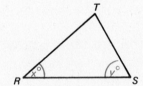

2. Select a point C, not on $\overleftrightarrow{AB}$, and draw $\overline{AC}$ and $\overline{BC}$.

3. Use a protractor and draw angles at R and S that are congruent to $\angle A$ and $\angle B$ respectively. Label the third vertex of the triangle T.

4. Compare the measures of $\angle C$ and $\angle T$. Measure $\overline{AC}$ and $\overline{RT}$. Is $\frac{AC}{RT}$ approximately equal to $\frac{2}{3}$? Is $\frac{BC}{ST}$ approximately equal to $\frac{2}{3}$? Are the lengths of the sides of the two triangles in proportion? Are the corresponding angles congruent? Do the two triangles appear to be similar?

If you were careful in all the work in this experiment, the answers to all the questions in Part 4 should be *yes*. If you repeat this experiment by drawing any two triangles such that two angles of one triangle are congruent to two angles of the other, you should again observe that the lengths of the corresponding sides are in proportion.

POSTULATE 17
(AA POSTULATE)
If two angles of one triangle are congruent to two angles of another triangle, the triangles are similar.

EXAMPLE 1

Given: Plane figure with $\angle 1 \cong \angle 2$

Prove: $\triangle DEF \sim \triangle CEB$

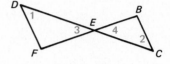

Proof:

STATEMENTS	REASONS
1. $\angle 3 \cong \angle 4$	1. Vertical angles are $\cong$.
2. $\angle 1 \cong \angle 2$	2. Given
3. $\triangle DEF \sim \triangle CEB$	3. AA Postulate

The notation we use in Statement 3 must be consistent with the reasoning shown in Steps 1 and 2. Since $\angle 1$ was congruent to $\angle 2$, we pair vertex D with vertex C. The statement $\angle 3 \cong \angle 4$ tells us to pair vertex E with vertex E. The remaining vertices, F and B, are then paired.

Suppose, in the example, we had been asked to prove $\dfrac{DE}{CE} = \dfrac{DF}{CB}$. Our proof would follow the pattern of the example with the addition of the following statement and reason.

STATEMENT	REASON
4. $\dfrac{DE}{CE} = \dfrac{DF}{CB}$	4. Lengths of corr. sides of $\sim \triangle$ are in proportion.

Note how the notation used in Statement 3, $\triangle DEF \sim \triangle CEB$, shows that $\overline{DE}$ corresponds to $\overline{CE}$ and that $\overline{DF}$ corresponds to $\overline{CB}$.

Suppose you want to prove that the product of the lengths of two segments is equal to the product of the lengths of two other segments. One way is to prove two triangles are similar, write a proportion, and then apply a property of proportions. Example 2, on the following page, shows how this method can be used.

EXAMPLE 2

Given: $\triangle ABC$; $\overline{MN} \parallel \overline{AB}$

Prove: $MN \cdot BC = AB \cdot NC$

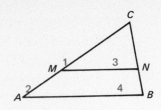

Proof:

STATEMENTS	REASONS
1. $\overline{MN} \parallel \overline{AB}$	1. Given
2. $\angle 1 \cong \angle 2$; $\angle 3 \cong \angle 4$	2. If two parallel lines are cut __?__ .
3. $\triangle MNC \sim \triangle ABC$	3. AA Postulate
4. $\dfrac{MN}{AB} = \dfrac{NC}{BC}$	4. Lengths of corr. sides of similar $\triangle$ are in proportion.
5. $MN \cdot BC = AB \cdot NC$	5. A property of proportions

The proofs of the following statements are left as Exercises 19 and 20.

If an acute angle of one right triangle is congruent to an acute angle of another right triangle, the triangles are similar.

If two isosceles triangles have congruent vertex angles, the triangles are similar.

The following theorem provides another way to prove that two triangles are similar.

THEOREM 6-3   If an angle of one triangle is congruent to an angle of another triangle and the lengths of the sides including those angles are proportional, the triangles are similar.

Given: $\triangle ABC$ and $\triangle RST$ with $\angle C \cong \angle T$;

$$\frac{AC}{RT} = \frac{BC}{ST}$$

Prove: $\triangle ABC \sim \triangle RST$

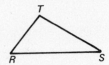

The proof is left as Exercise 27.

Oral Exercises

Classify each statement as true or false. Exercises 1–8 refer to similar triangles *ABC* and *RST*.

1. $\angle A \cong \angle R$
2. If $m\angle R = 70$, then $m\angle A = 70$.
3. If $AB = 5$, then RS must equal 5.
4. $\dfrac{AC}{RT} = \dfrac{TS}{CB}$
5. If $\dfrac{AB}{RS} = \dfrac{3}{5}$, then $\dfrac{AC}{RT} = \dfrac{3}{5}$.
6. The ratio of $m\angle C$ to $m\angle T$ is $1:1$.
7. If $\triangle ABC$ is a right $\triangle$, then $\triangle RST$ is a right $\triangle$.
8. If $m\angle B = 30$ and $m\angle C = 80$, then $m\angle R = 60$.

9. All isosceles triangles are similar.
10. All equilateral triangles are similar.
11. All isosceles right triangles are similar.
12. If $\triangle RST \sim \triangle DEF$, then $\dfrac{RS}{DE} = \dfrac{ST}{DF}$.
13. If $\triangle ABC \sim \triangle XYZ$, then $\dfrac{AC}{XZ} = \dfrac{BC}{YZ}$.
14. If $\triangle MNO \sim \triangle GHK$, then $\angle MON \cong \angle GHK$.

Written Exercises

In Exercises 1–6, state whether the triangles are similar.

A

1.

4.
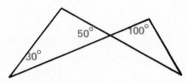

2.
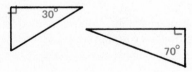

5.
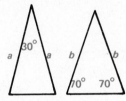

3.

6.
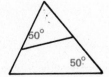

Exercises 7–10 refer to △*RST* with ∠1 ≅ ∠2.

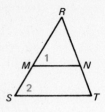

7. △*RST* ～ △ __?__

8. Complete the extended proportion

$$\frac{?}{RS} = \frac{?}{ST} = \frac{?}{RT}.$$

9. If *RM* = 3, *MN* = 4, and *RS* = 7, then *ST* = __?__ .

10. If *RM* = 4, *MN* = 5, and *ST* = 8, then *RS* = __?__ .

11. Given: $\overline{AB} \parallel \overline{DE}$
    Prove: △*ABC* ～ △*EDC*

12. Given: ∠*B* and ∠*D* are rt. ⧸.
    Prove: △*ABC* ～ △*EDC*

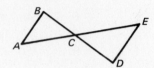

13. Given: *m*∠1 = *t*; *m*∠2 = *t*
    Prove: △*TDE* ～ △*TRS*

14. Given: $\overline{DE} \parallel \overline{RS}$
    Prove: △*TDE* ～ △*TRS*

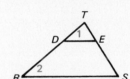

15. Given: $\overline{AC} \perp \overline{BD}$;
    ∠1 ≅ ∠2
    Prove: △*BAC* ～ △*EDC*

16. Given: $\overline{AC} \perp \overline{BD}$;
    m∠1 = 30; *m*∠2 = 30
    Prove: △*BAC* ～ △*EDC*

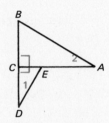

B 17. Given: Quad. *ABCD* is a ▱.
    Prove: △*ABF* ～ △*EDA*

18. Given: Quad. *ABCD* is a ▱.
    Prove: △*ABH* ～ △*EDH*

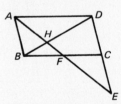

19. Prove that if an acute angle of one right triangle is congruent to an acute angle of another right triangle, then the triangles are similar.

20. Prove that if two isosceles triangles have congruent vertex angles, then the triangles are similar.

In Exercises 21 and 22, △*RST* is similar to △*DEF*.

21. If *m*∠*S* = 42, *m*∠*F* = 8*x* + 6, and *m*∠*D* = 44, then *x* = __?__ .

22. If *m*∠*E* = 38, *m*∠*R* = 43, and *m*∠*T* = 7*x* + 8, then *x* = __?__ .

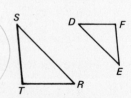

C 23. Given: $\triangle ABC \sim \triangle DEF$;
       $\angle 1 \cong \angle 2$; $\angle 3 \cong \angle 4$
    Prove: $\triangle ACX \sim \triangle DFY$

24. Given: $\triangle ACX \sim \triangle DFY$;
       $\angle 2 \cong \angle 4$
    Prove: $\dfrac{AC}{DF} = \dfrac{AB}{DE}$

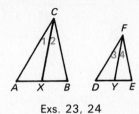

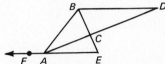

Exs. 23, 24

25. Given: $\overrightarrow{BE}$ bisects $\angle ABD$;
       $m\angle DBC = \dfrac{1}{2}m\angle FAB$
    Prove: $AD \cdot BC = BE \cdot DC$

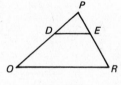

26. Prove: If the lengths of two sides of a triangle are k and l, the lengths of
    the altitudes to those sides are in the ratio of l to k.

27. Prove Theorem 6-3, page 206.
    (*Hint:* On $\overline{TR}$ pick point X such that
    $TX = CA$. Draw $\overleftrightarrow{XY} \parallel \overleftrightarrow{RS}$.)

28. Given: $\triangle POR$; $\dfrac{PD}{DO} = \dfrac{PE}{ER}$
    Prove: $\overleftrightarrow{DE} \parallel \overleftrightarrow{OR}$

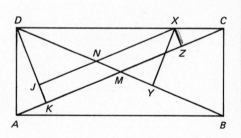

Ex. 28

Challenge

Quad. $ABCD$ is a rectangle;
$\overline{XY} \perp \overline{BD}$; $\overline{XZ} \perp \overline{AC}$;
$\overline{DK} \perp \overline{AC}$; $\overline{XJ} \perp \overline{DK}$;
$AB = 156$; $BC = 65$; $DK = 60$

$XY + XZ = \underline{\quad ? \quad}$

6-5 *Segments Divided Proportionally*

Suppose Y and Z are points on $\overline{AB}$ and $\overline{CD}$ respectively. If $\dfrac{AY}{YB} = \dfrac{CZ}{ZD}$, then $\overline{AB}$ and $\overline{CD}$ are
said to be divided proportionally.

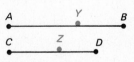

THEOREM 6-4 If a line is parallel to one side of a triangle and inter-sects the other two sides, it divides them propor-tionally.

Given: $\triangle ABC$; $\overline{YZ} \parallel \overline{AB}$

Prove: $\dfrac{AY}{YC} = \dfrac{BZ}{ZC}$

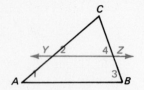

Proof:

STATEMENTS	REASONS
1. $\overline{YZ} \parallel \overline{AB}$	1. Given
2. $\angle 1 \cong \angle 2$; $\angle 3 \cong \angle 4$	2. If two $\parallel$ lines are __?__ .
3. $\triangle ACB \sim \triangle YCZ$	3. __?__
4. $\dfrac{AC}{YC} = \dfrac{BC}{ZC}$	4. Lengths of corr. sides of $\sim \triangle$ are __?__ .
5. $\dfrac{AC - YC}{YC} = \dfrac{BC - ZC}{ZC}$	5. A property of proportions
6. $AY + YC = AC$; $BZ + ZC = BC$	6. __?__
7. $AY = AC - YC$; $BZ = BC - ZC$	7. Subtraction property of equality
8. $\dfrac{AY}{YC} = \dfrac{BZ}{ZC}$	8. Substitution principle

Using the properties of proportions, it can be shown that the following three proportions are equivalent.

$$\frac{AY}{YC} = \frac{BZ}{ZC}$$

$$\frac{AC}{YC} = \frac{BC}{ZC}$$

$$\frac{AC}{AY} = \frac{BC}{BZ}$$

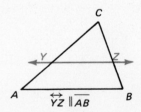

We shall agree that Theorem 6-4 may be used as a reason in a proof to support any of the three proportions.

EXAMPLE

Given $\triangle ABC$ with $\overline{YZ} \parallel \overline{AB}$.
Find the ratio of:

a. CZ to ZB b. BC to ZC c. BC to BZ

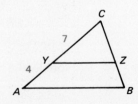

SOLUTION:

a. $\dfrac{CZ}{ZB} = \dfrac{CY}{YA} = \dfrac{7}{4}$ b. $\dfrac{BC}{ZC} = \dfrac{AC}{YC} = \dfrac{11}{7}$ c. $\dfrac{BC}{BZ} = \dfrac{AC}{AY} = \dfrac{11}{4}$

COROLLARY If three parallel lines intersect two transversals, they divide them proportionally.

Given: $\overleftrightarrow{AK} \parallel \overleftrightarrow{BM} \parallel \overleftrightarrow{CN}$

Prove: $\dfrac{AB}{BC} = \dfrac{KM}{MN}$

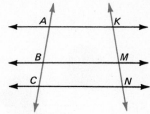

For a proof, see Exercises 1-4.

THEOREM 6-5 If a ray bisects an angle of a triangle, it divides the opposite side into segments whose lengths are proportional to the lengths of the other two sides.

Given: $\triangle ABC$ with $\angle 1 \cong \angle 2$

Prove: $\dfrac{AD}{DB} = \dfrac{CA}{CB}$

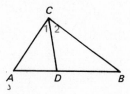

The proof is left as Exercise 28.

Oral Exercises Exercises 1–9 refer to $\triangle RST$ with $\overline{DE} \parallel \overline{ST}$. Classify each statement as true or false.

1. $\dfrac{RD}{DS} = \dfrac{RE}{ET}$ 4. $\dfrac{SD}{SR} = \dfrac{TE}{TR}$ 7. $\dfrac{TE}{SD} = \dfrac{RD}{RE}$

2. $\dfrac{RS}{RD} = \dfrac{RT}{RE}$ 5. $\dfrac{RE}{RD} = \dfrac{DS}{ET}$ 8. $\triangle RDE \sim \triangle RST$

3. $\dfrac{RD}{RE} = \dfrac{DS}{ET}$ 6. $\dfrac{RS}{RT} = \dfrac{RD}{DE}$ 9. $\dfrac{RD}{RS} = \dfrac{DE}{ST}$

Exercises 10 and 11 refer to $\triangle DEF$ with $\angle 1 \cong \angle 2$. Complete each of the following.

10. $\dfrac{DH}{HE} = \dfrac{?}{?}$

11. If $\dfrac{FD}{FE} = \dfrac{5}{9}$, then $\dfrac{DH}{HE} = \dfrac{?}{?}$.

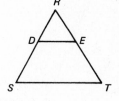

In Exercises 12–14, $k \parallel l \parallel m$.

12. If $AB = BC$, must $DE = EF$?

13. If $\dfrac{AB}{BC} = \dfrac{4}{5}$, what is the ratio of DE to EF?

14. If $AB = DE$, must $BC = EF$?

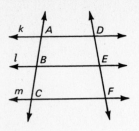

Provide the reasons for the following proof of the Corollary, page 211.

Written Exercises

Given: The plane figure with
$\overleftrightarrow{AK} \parallel \overleftrightarrow{BM} \parallel \overleftrightarrow{CN}$

Prove: $\dfrac{AB}{BC} = \dfrac{KM}{MN}$

Proof:

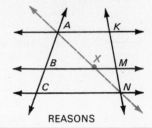

STATEMENTS	REASONS
A 1. $\overleftrightarrow{AK} \parallel \overleftrightarrow{BM} \parallel \overleftrightarrow{CN}$	1. _?_
2. Draw $\overleftrightarrow{AN}$. (Call the intersection of $\overleftrightarrow{AN}$ and $\overleftrightarrow{BM}$, X.)	2. _?_
3. $\dfrac{AB}{BC} = \dfrac{AX}{XN}$; $\dfrac{KM}{MN} = \dfrac{AX}{XN}$	3. _?_
4. $\dfrac{AB}{BC} = \dfrac{KM}{MN}$	4. _?_

Exercises 5–12 refer to $\triangle DEF$ with $\overleftrightarrow{RS} \parallel \overleftrightarrow{EF}$. In each exercise three lengths are given. You are to find the indicated length.

5. $DR = 4$; $RE = 5$; $DS = 5$; $SF =$ _?_

6. $DS = 6$; $SF = 8$; $DR = 4$; $RE =$ _?_

7. $DE = 12$; $DR = 5$; $DF = 15$; $DS =$ _?_

8. $DF = 16$; $DS = 6$; $DE = 12$; $DR =$ _?_

9. $DR = 4$; $DE = 10$; $DF = 14$; $SF =$ _?_

10. $DF = 18$; $SF = 10$; $DE = 14$; $DR =$ _?_

11. $DE = 7$; $DS = 6$; $SF = 10$; $DR =$ _?_

12. $DF = 15$; $DR = 4$; $RE = 6$; $SF =$ _?_

Exercises 13–16 refer to $\triangle ABC$ with $\angle 1 \cong \angle 2$.

13. Complete the proportion: $\dfrac{AD}{DB} = \dfrac{?}{?}$

14. Complete the proportion: $\dfrac{AC}{AD} = \dfrac{?}{?}$

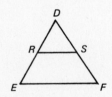

15. If $AD = 6$, $DB = 4$, and $AC = 8$, then $BC = \underline{\quad?\quad}$.

16. If $AD = 8$, $DB = 6$, and $BC = 8$, then $AC = \underline{\quad?\quad}$.

B 17. Given: $\triangle ABC$; $\angle 1 \cong \angle 2$

   Prove: $\dfrac{AE}{EB} = \dfrac{AD}{DC}$

18. Given: $\triangle ABC$; $m\angle 1 = k$; $m\angle 2 = k$

   Prove: $\dfrac{AB}{EB} = \dfrac{AC}{DC}$

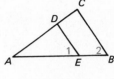

Exs. 17, 18

Exercises 19 and 20 refer to $\triangle PTR$ with $\angle 1 \cong \angle 2$.

19. If $PS = 6$, $ST = 8$, and the perimeter of $\triangle PTR$ is 42, find PR.

20. If $PS = 5$, $ST = 7$, and the perimeter of $\triangle PTR$ is 36, find RT.

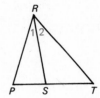

21. Given: $\triangle DEF$; $m\angle 1 = j$; $m\angle 2 = j$
   Prove: $DE \cdot RF = DF \cdot SE$

22. Given: $\triangle DEF$; $\overline{FE} \perp \overline{DE}$; $\overline{RS} \perp \overline{DE}$
   Prove: $DR \cdot SE = DS \cdot RF$

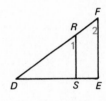

Exs. 21, 22

Exercises 23–26 refer to $\triangle MNO$ with $\overline{AB} \parallel \overline{MN}$. In each exercise find the numerical value of x.

C 23. $OA = x + 2$; $OB = 4x - 2$;
   $AM = 4x - 2$; $BN = 5x - 1$

24. $OA = 2x - 2$; $OB = 2x + 1$;
   $AM = 3x - 4$; $BN = 2x + 4$

25. $OA = x + 1$; $OB = 2x - 2$;
   $OM = 4x - 2$; $ON = 5x - 1$

26. $AM = 4x - 6$; $BN = 6x - 5$;
   $OM = 2x + 6$; $ON = 8x - 2$

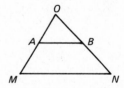

27. Prove: If two triangles are similar, the lengths of two corresponding altitudes have the same ratio as the lengths of two corresponding sides.

28. Prove Theorem 6-5. (*Hint:* Draw $\overleftrightarrow{BC}$ and also draw $\overleftrightarrow{AX} \parallel \overleftrightarrow{CD}$. Use Theorem 6-4.)

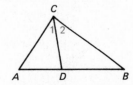

Self-Test Exercises 1–4 refer to △ABC.

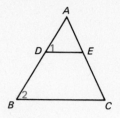

1. If ∠1 ≅ ∠2, what postulate or theorem supports the statement that "△ADE ∼ △ABC"?

2. If △ADE ∼ △ABC, then $\dfrac{AD}{AB} = \dfrac{DE}{?}$.

3. If $\overline{DE} \parallel \overline{BC}$, then $\dfrac{AE}{EC} = \dfrac{?}{DB}$.

4. If $\dfrac{AD}{DB} = \dfrac{AE}{EC}$, then $AD \cdot \underline{\;?\;} = AE \cdot \underline{\;?\;}$.

In Exercises 5–8 complete each statement with one of the words *Always, Sometimes,* or *Never.*

5. If △ABC and △RST are right triangles, △ABC is __?__ similar to △RST.

6. If two isosceles triangles have congruent vertex angles, the triangles are __?__ similar.

7. If three parallel lines intersect two transversals, they __?__ divide the transversals into congruent segments.

8. If a ray bisects an angle of a triangle, it __?__ divides the opposite side into segments whose lengths are proportional to the lengths of the other two sides.

Check your answers with those printed at the back of the book.

CHAPTER SUMMARY

1. A ratio is a number. The number $\dfrac{a}{b}$, or $a:b$, $(b \neq 0)$ is the ratio of a to b.

2. An equation of the form $\dfrac{a}{b} = \dfrac{c}{d}$ $(b \neq 0$ and $d \neq 0)$ is a proportion.

3. The properties of proportions are used to change proportions into equivalent equations.

4. If two convex polygons are similar:
   a. Corresponding angles are congruent.
   b. Lengths of corresponding sides are in proportion.
   c. The ratio of the perimeters equals the ratio of the lengths of any pair of corresponding sides.

5. Two triangles are similar if two angles of one triangle are congruent to two angles of the other triangle.

6. In any triangle:
   a. A line that is parallel to one side and intersects the other two sides divides them proportionally.
   b. A ray that bisects an angle divides the opposite side into segments whose lengths are proportional to the lengths of the other two sides.

CHAPTER TEST

1. In reduced form, the ratio $16:24$ is __?__ .

2. The ratio of the measure of a right angle to the sum of the measures of the angles of a quadrilateral is __?__ .

3. $\dfrac{3}{4} = \dfrac{x}{7}$ is equivalent to $\dfrac{7}{4} = \dfrac{?}{?}$.

4. If $9y = 5x$, then $\dfrac{x}{y} = \dfrac{?}{?}$.

5. If $\triangle DEF \sim \triangle RST$ and $DE:RS = 2:5$, then the perimeters of the two triangles are in the ratio __?__ .

6. If $\triangle XYZ \sim \triangle PQR$, then $\dfrac{XY}{PQ} = \dfrac{XZ}{?}$.

Exercises 7–10 refer to $\triangle DEF$ with $\overline{TW} \parallel \overline{EF}$.

7. $\dfrac{DT}{TE} = \dfrac{?}{WF}$

8. $\dfrac{DT}{TW} = \dfrac{?}{EF}$

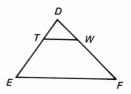

9. If $DT = 5$, $ET = 2$, and $WF = 3$, $DW =$ __?__ .

10. If $DW = 8$, $WF = 4$, and $EF = 14$, $TW =$ __?__ .

11. In $\triangle GHK$, $\overline{KE}$ bisects $\angle GKH$.
If $GE = 8$, $EH = 5$, and $GK = 12$,
$KH =$ __?__ .

In Exercises 12–20, write the reasons that are needed to complete the proof.

Given: $\overline{AB} \parallel \overline{ED}$

Prove: $AD \cdot CE = BE \cdot DC$

Proof:

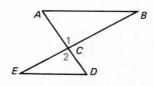

STATEMENTS	REASONS
12. $\overline{AB} \parallel \overline{ED}$	12. __?__
13. $\angle A \cong \angle D$	13. __?__
14. $\angle 1 \cong \angle 2$	14. __?__
15. $\triangle ABC \sim \triangle DEC$	15. __?__
16. $\dfrac{AC}{DC} = \dfrac{BC}{CE}$	16. __?__
17. $\dfrac{AC + DC}{DC} = \dfrac{BC + CE}{CE}$	17. __?__
18. $AC + DC = AD$; $BC + CE = BE$	18. __?__
19. $\dfrac{AD}{DC} = \dfrac{BE}{CE}$	19. __?__
20. $AD \cdot CE = BE \cdot DC$	20. __?__

21.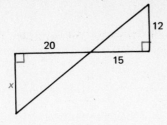

$x = \underline{\quad ? \quad}$

23.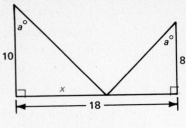

$x = \underline{\quad ? \quad}$

22.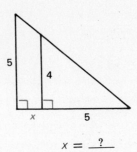

$x = \underline{\quad ? \quad}$

24.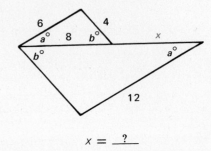

$x = \underline{\quad ? \quad}$

25. Given: $\angle C \cong \angle B$
Prove: $\triangle AXC \sim \triangle DXB$

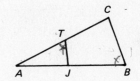

26. Given: $m\angle B = 70; \ m\angle 1 = 70$
Prove: $\dfrac{AT}{AB} = \dfrac{JT}{CB}$

CHAPTER REVIEW

6-1 *Ratio and Proportion*

1. Find the ratio of 12 cm to 32 cm.
2. Find the ratio of x to y if $x = 80$ cm and $y = 2$ meters.
3. In the proportion $\dfrac{3}{5} = \dfrac{x}{y}$, the third term is $\underline{\quad ? \quad}$.
4. If $\dfrac{x}{4} = \dfrac{3}{2}$, $x = \underline{\quad ? \quad}$.

6-2 Properties of Proportions

Classify each statement as true or false. All variables represent non-zero numbers.

5. If $\dfrac{x}{y} = \dfrac{k}{t}$, then $xt = yk$.

6. If $\dfrac{3}{5} = \dfrac{9}{x}$, then $\dfrac{x}{5} = \dfrac{3}{9}$.

7. If $\dfrac{2}{7} = \dfrac{y}{6}$, then $\dfrac{7}{2} = \dfrac{6}{y}$.

8. If $\dfrac{5}{7} = \dfrac{y}{3}$, then $\dfrac{5 + 7}{7} = \dfrac{y + 3}{y}$.

6-3 Similar Polygons

9. If $\triangle ABC \sim \triangle RST$, then $\triangle BAC \sim \triangle \underline{\ ?\ }$.

10. If $\triangle DEF \sim \triangle PQR$, then $\angle EFD \cong \angle \underline{\ ?\ }$.

11. If quad. $ABCD \sim$ quad. $PQRS$, then $\dfrac{AB}{PQ} = \dfrac{DA}{?}$.

12. If $\triangle DEF \sim \triangle KMN$ and $DE:KM = 3:2$, then the ratio of the perimeters of the two triangles is $\underline{\ ?\ }$.

6-4 Proving Triangles Similar

13. If $\angle A \cong \angle E$, is $\triangle ABC \sim \triangle EDC$?

14. If $\triangle ABC \sim \triangle EDC$, then $\dfrac{AB}{?} = \dfrac{AC}{?} = \dfrac{BC}{?}$.

15. If $AC = BC$ and $EC = DC$, is $\triangle ABC \sim \triangle EDC$?

16. Given: $m\angle B = 90$; $m\angle D = 90$.
Prove: $\triangle ABC \sim \triangle EDC$

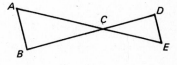

6-5 Segments Divided Proportionally

17. If $\overline{RS} \parallel \overline{DF}$, then $\dfrac{ER}{RD} = \dfrac{?}{?}$.

18. If $\angle 1 \cong \angle 2$, then $\dfrac{ES}{SF} = \dfrac{DE}{?}$.

19. If $\overline{RS} \parallel \overline{DF}$, $ER = 3$, $ED = 8$, and $ES = 4$, find SF.

20. If $\angle 1 \cong \angle 2$, $ED = 15$, $DF = 18$, and $EF = 11$, find ES.

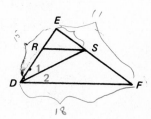

programming in BASIC

Two computer programs dealing with proportions are introduced in this section. Only part of each one is given. You will be expected to complete the programs as exercises.

The first one computes the missing term of a proportion. Notice the new statement in line 40: MAT INPUT P. This is one way of giving the computer input for *all* of the subscripted variables that you have allowed for in the DIMENSION statement. In this case, you must input a value for P[1], P[2], P[3], and P[4].

```
 10   DIM P[4]
 20   PRINT "TYPE THE TERMS OF THE PROPORTION,"
 30   PRINT "USING ZERO FOR THE UNKNOWN VALUE."
 40   MAT INPUT P
 50   IF P[1]=0 THEN 110
 60   IF P[2]=0 THEN 130
 70   IF P[3]=0 THEN 150
 80   IF P[4]=0 THEN 170
 90   PRINT "ONE OF THE TERMS SHOULD HAVE BEEN ZERO."
100   STOP
110   LET X=P[2]*P[3]/P[4]
120   GOTO 180
  .
  .
  .
180   PRINT "THE MISSING TERM IS ";X
190   END
```

There are several ways that a proportion can be changed into another form. These were discussed in Section 6-2. The following program was written to take the four numbers of a proportion and change them into a selected form. There is a new statement in this program:

$$210 \quad GOTO \quad C \quad OF \quad 220,240,260,280,300,320$$

This statement is called a *computed* GOTO. If C is 1, the program branches to line 220; if C is 2, it branches to the second line number, 240, and so on. Line 340 branches the program for input of another proportion to be changed. When you wish to stop a program of this type, you hold down the Control Key and type C; then push the Return Key.

```
10   PRINT "CHANGING THE FORM OF A PROPORTION."
20   DIM X[4]
30   PRINT "A:B=C:D IS EQUIVALENT TO:"
40   PRINT "    1.   AD=BC"
50   PRINT "    2.   A:C=B:D"
60   PRINT "    3.   B:A=D:C"
70   PRINT "    4.   (A+B):B=(C+D):D"
80   PRINT "    5.   (A-B):B=(C-D):D"
90   PRINT "    6.   (A+C):(B+D)=A:B"
100  PRINT
110  PRINT "TYPE THE FOUR TERMS OF THE PROPORTION."
120  MAT INPUT X
130  IF X[1]*X[4]=X[2]*X[3] THEN 160
140  PRINT "YOU DID NOT TYPE THE TERMS OF A PROPORTION."
150  GOTO 110
160  PRINT "WHAT WAY DO YOU WANT IT CHANGED";
170  INPUT C
180  PRINT
190  PRINT X[1];" :";X[2];" =";X[3];" :";X[4]
200  PRINT "IS EQUIVALENT TO"
210  GOTO C OF 220,240,260,280,300,320
220  PRINT X[1];" *";X[4];" =";X[2];" *";X[3]
230  GOTO 330
         .
         .
         .
320  PRINT X[1]+X[3];" :";X[2]+X[4];" =";X[1];" :";X[2]
330  PRINT
340  GOTO 100
350  END
```

Exercises

1. Complete the first program. Then use it to find the missing term of each proportion.

   a. $\dfrac{5}{8} = \dfrac{x}{56}$ b. $\dfrac{7}{18} = \dfrac{1.4}{z}$ c. $\dfrac{105}{8} = \dfrac{y}{4}$

2. Complete the second program and use it to change each proportion in Exercise 1 into another form.

3. In the proportion $a{:}x = x{:}b$, x is called the *geometric mean*. Write a program to find the geometric mean of each pair of numbers.
   a. 4 and 9   b. 3 and 5   c. 6 and 0.2

In our work in this chapter, the AA method for proving two triangles similar was stated as a postulate. By using a sequence of postulates and theorems different from those in this text, we could have used area properties to establish the theorem: *If a line is parallel to one side of a triangle and intersects the other two sides, it divides them proportionally*. The latter theorem could then have been used to prove an AAA Theorem, which follows.

THEOREM If three angles of one triangle are congruent to three angles of another triangle, the triangles are similar.

Given: $\angle A \cong \angle P$
$\angle B \cong \angle O$
$\angle C \cong \angle R$

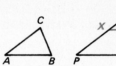

Prove: $\triangle ABC \sim \triangle POR$

Plan of Proof:

By definition, two polygons are similar if the corresponding angles are congruent and the lengths of the corresponding sides are in proportion. We must show that $\dfrac{CA}{RP} = \dfrac{CB}{RO} = \dfrac{BA}{OP}$.

Proof:

STATEMENTS	REASONS
1. Let X be a point on $\overline{RP}$ such that $\overline{RX} \cong \overline{CA}$.	1. On a ray there is exactly one point at a given distance from the endpoint of the ray.
2. At X draw $\overrightarrow{XY}$ so that $\angle RXY \cong \angle P$. Let T be the intersection of $\overrightarrow{XY}$ and $\overline{RO}$.	2. In a half-plane, through the endpoint of a ray that lies in the edge of the half-plane, there is exactly one other ray such that the angle formed by the two rays has a given measure.
3. $\overline{XT} \parallel \overline{PO}$	3. _?_
4. $\angle A \cong \angle P$	4. _?_
5. $\angle RXT \cong \angle A$	5. Transitive property of congruence
6. $\angle R \cong \angle C$	6. _?_
7. $\triangle RXT \cong \triangle CAB$	7. ASA Postulate
8. $\overline{RT} \cong \overline{CB}$	8. _?_

9. $\dfrac{RX}{RP} = \dfrac{RT}{RO}$	9. If a line is ∥ to one side of a triangle and intersects the other two sides, it divides them proportionally.
10. $\dfrac{CA}{RP} = \dfrac{CB}{RO}$	10. Def. of ≅ segments and substitution principle
11. If point Z is taken on $\overleftrightarrow{PO}$ so that $\overline{PZ} \cong \overline{AB}$, it can be shown that $\dfrac{CA}{RP} = \dfrac{BA}{OP}$.	11. By same reasoning as Steps 1–10
12. $\dfrac{CA}{RP} = \dfrac{CB}{RO} = \dfrac{BA}{OP}$	12. Transitive property of equality
13. $\triangle ABC \sim \triangle POR$	13. Definition of similar polygons

Exercises

1. Use the theorem above to prove "If two angles of one triangle are congruent to two angles of another triangle, the triangles are similar."

2. Prove: If an angle of one triangle is congruent to an angle of another triangle and the lengths of the sides including those angles are proportional, the triangles are similar. (You may use as a reason "If a line intersects two sides of a triangle so that the lengths of corresponding segments are proportional, the line is parallel to the third side.")

CUMULATIVE REVIEW: CHAPTERS 1–6

True-False Exercises

A 1. Every rectangle is equilateral.
  2. Some rhombuses are equiangular.
  3. If point C is the midpoint of $\overline{AB}$, then $AC = \frac{1}{2}BC$.
  4. If two lines do not intersect, they must be parallel.
  5. If two sides of a triangle lie in a plane, the third side of the triangle must lie in that plane.
  6. If $\overline{RX} \cong \overline{SX}$, then X must be the midpoint of $\overline{RS}$.
  7. If $\angle PZY$ and $\angle QZY$ are adjacent angles, point Y must lie in the interior of $\angle PZQ$.
  8. When a conditional is true, the converse must be true.
  9. If lines j and k are both perpendicular to line g, then j and k must be parallel.
 10. If $\triangle ABC \cong \triangle HXD$, then $\triangle BAC \cong \triangle XHD$.

B 11. In triangles RST and DEF, if $RS > DE$ and $ST > EF$, then RT must be greater than DF.
 12. If plane P and plane R both contain points G, H, and J, then P and R must be the same plane.
 13. A point and a line not containing that point lie in exactly one plane.
 14. If lines j and k are perpendicular, and lines g and k are parallel, then g and j must be coplanar.
 15. The sum of the measures of the interior angles of a nonequilateral convex pentagon is 540.
 16. If the lengths of the sides of a triangle are x, y, and z, then $x > y - z$.
 17. A line that is parallel to a plane must be parallel to every line in that plane.
 18. It is possible to have a triangle whose sides have lengths 8.3, 6.5, and 1.91.

Algebraic Exercises

In Exercises 1–20 state the numerical value of x.

A 1. The lengths of the legs of an isosceles triangle are $3x$ and $x + 12$.
  2. The measures of two vertical angles are $5x - 21$ and $2x$.
  3. An angle has measure x. A complement of the angle has measure $x + 10$.
  4. An angle and a supplement of the angle have measures $x + 20$ and $x - 20$.
  5. Opposite angles of a parallelogram have measures $3x + 5$ and $2x + 21$.
  6. When two parallel lines are cut by a transversal, alternate interior angles have measures $2(x + 12)$ and $3(x - 15)$.
  7. A segment 41 cm long is divided into two segments that are x cm and $(3x - 7)$ cm long.
  8. The measures of the angles of a triangle are $x - 10$, x, and $x + 10$.

9. The measures of the angles of a quadrilateral are x, x, $x + 15$, and $x + 45$.
10. An angle with measure x is bisected. One of the angles formed has measure $x - 40$.
11. On a number line, one endpoint of a segment has coordinate -5. The other endpoint has coordinate $2x$. The midpoint has coordinate 6.
12. Two complementary angles have measures $x + 3y$ and $x - 3y$.

13. $\dfrac{x}{14} = \dfrac{3}{7}$

14. $\dfrac{8}{x} = \dfrac{24}{25}$

15. $\dfrac{1}{2} = \dfrac{x - 5}{20}$

16. $\dfrac{3}{8} = \dfrac{6}{x + 1}$

17. $\dfrac{5}{7} = \dfrac{3}{x}$

18. $\dfrac{3}{2} = \dfrac{8}{x - 5}$

19. $\dfrac{x + 9}{x - 9} = \dfrac{7}{2}$

20. $\dfrac{x}{x + 3} = \dfrac{x}{x - 5}$

B 21. A 35-cm segment is divided into two parts that have lengths in the ratio $2:3$. Find the length of the shorter part.

22. The measures of two supplementary angles are in the ratio $7:3$. Find the measure of the larger angle.

23. The measures of two complementary angles are in the ratio $1:4$. Find the measure of the smaller angle.

24. A 70-cm segment is divided into three parts having lengths in the ratio $2:3:5$. Find the length of the longest part.

25. The measures of the angles of a triangle are in the ratio $1:2:3$. Find the measure of each angle.

26. The measures of the angles of a triangle are in the ratio $5:5:2$. Find the measure of each angle.

27. In a regular polygon, the ratio of the measure of an interior angle to the measure of an exterior angle is $2:1$. How many sides does the polygon have?

28. The lengths of two sides of a triangle have the ratio $3:5$. The bisector of the included angle intersects a side that is 48 cm long. Find the lengths of the two segments of that side.

29. The sides of a triangle are 20, 24, and 33 cm long. The largest angle is bisected. Find the lengths of the segments into which the side opposite that angle is divided.

30. The perimeter of a triangle is 40. One side is cut by the bisector of the opposite angle into two segments having lengths 6 and 10. Find the lengths of the two shorter sides of the triangle.

31. An angle has measure $\dfrac{k}{2}$. Represent, by a single fraction, the measure of a complement of the angle.

32. Three angles of a convex quadrilateral have measures h, $\dfrac{j}{2}$, and $\dfrac{k}{3}$. Represent, by a single fraction, the measure of the fourth angle.

Completion Exercises

Write the correct expression on your paper.

A 1. When the sum of the measures of two angles is 180, the angles are called __?__ angles.

2. The definition of an isosceles triangle specifies that two __?__ be congruent.

3. Two points on a number line have coordinates c and n. The distance between the points is represented by __?__.

4. For $\frac{d}{f}$ to be a ratio, it is necessary that $f \neq$ __?__.

5. A quadrilateral with exactly two parallel sides is called a __?__.

6. Two angles are complementary if the sum of their measures is __?__.

7. The vertex angle of an isosceles triangle has measure 50. Each base angle has measure __?__.

8. The sum of the measures of the exterior angles of a decagon, one angle at each vertex, is __?__.

9. When the letters a, b, x, y represent nonzero numbers, and $\frac{a}{b} = \frac{x}{y}$, then $\frac{a}{x} = \frac{?}{?}$.

10. When the letters r, s, j, k represent nonzero numbers, and $rs = jk$, then $\frac{r}{j} = \frac{?}{?}$.

11. The measure of a base angle of an isosceles triangle is represented by h. The measure of the vertex angle, represented in terms of h, is __?__.

12. A parallelogram with congruent diagonals must be a __?__.

13. A quadrilateral with four congruent sides may be a __?__, but it must be a __?__.

14. If $\triangle ABC \cong \triangle RKN$, then $\overline{AC} \cong$ __?__.

15. If two polygons are similar, corresponding angles must be __?__.

16. The ratio of the lengths of two corresponding sides of two similar triangles is $5:7$. The ratio of the perimeters is __?__.

17. If $\angle RZK$ and $\angle NZK$ are adjacent acute angles, a point that must lie in the interior of $\angle RZN$ is point __?__.

18. If $\overrightarrow{OC}$ bisects $\angle HOJ$ and $m\angle HOC = 17$, then $m\angle HOJ =$ __?__.

19. The SAS Postulate is to be applied to prove $\triangle ABC \cong \triangle DEF$. If $\overline{BC} \cong \overline{EF}$ and $\angle C \cong \angle F$ are used, you must also show that __?__.

20. The AAS Theorem is to be applied to prove $\triangle ABC \cong \triangle DEF$. If $\overline{BC} \cong \overline{EF}$ and $\angle B \cong \angle E$ are used, you must also show that __?__.

B 21. If $xy \neq 0$ and $4x = 7y$, then the ratio of x to y equals __?__.

22. The diagonals of a quadrilateral are not congruent, but they bisect each other. The quadrilateral must be a __?__, but it cannot be a __?__.

23. Points R, S, and T are not collinear. The union of $\overrightarrow{SR}$ and $\overrightarrow{ST}$ is __?__.

24. X, the midpoint of $\overline{JK}$, corresponds to $4\frac{2}{5}$ on a number line. J corresponds to $6\frac{1}{5}$. K corresponds to __?__.

25. In simplified form, $|c - 9| - |9 - c| =$ __?__.

26. If the measure of each exterior angle of a regular n-gon is less than 25, then n must be greater than __?__.

27. Points R, A, and N are collinear. N lies on $\overrightarrow{AR}$ but not on $\overrightarrow{RA}$. Point __?__ lies between points __?__ and __?__.

28. The diagonals of a quadrilateral are congruent, and they are perpendicular bisectors of each other. The quadrilateral can best be described as a __?__.

29. Two distinct lines both perpendicular to a third line can be __?__, __?__, or __?__ lines.

30. To begin an indirect proof, you suppose that the __?__ of the __?__ is true.

31. If the union of $\overrightarrow{PN}$ and $\overrightarrow{PK}$ is not an angle, then points P, N, and K are __?__ points.

32. The greatest number of right angles a convex pentagon can have is __?__.

Multiple-Choice Exercises

Write the letter that indicates the best answer.

A 1. The union of $\overrightarrow{ST}$ and $\overrightarrow{TS}$ is:
  a. $\overline{ST}$ b. $\overrightarrow{TS}$ c. $\angle STS$ d. $\overleftrightarrow{ST}$ e. none of these

2. No congruence postulate or theorem has been abbreviated by:
  a. SSS   b. SSA   c. SAS   d. AAS   e. none of these

3. A figure that has P and R as endpoints is:
  a. $\overrightarrow{PR}$ b. $\overrightarrow{RP}$ c. $\overleftrightarrow{PR}$ d. PR e. none of these

4. Two numbers that cannot be the measures of two complementary angles are:
  a. 20 and 70   c. 45.1 and 44.9   e. none of these
  b. 89 and 1   d. $40\frac{2}{3}$ and $50\frac{1}{3}$

5. The total number of diagonals in a hexagon is:
  a. 9   b. 6   c. 3   d. 12   e. none of these

6. Four rays are drawn in a half-plane from a point in the edge of the half-plane. The total number of angles formed by the four rays is:
  a. 7   b. 6   c. 5   d. 4   e. none of these

7. The angle formed by $\overrightarrow{TX}$ and $\overrightarrow{TR}$ is:
  a. $\angle R$ c. $\angle RXT$ e. none of these
  b. $\angle RTS$ d. $\angle XTR$

8. One point in the exterior of $\triangle RST$ is:
  a. R b. S c. Z d. X e. none of these

9. One point that lies on exactly three of the angles shown is:
  a. X b. S c. T d. Z e. none of these

10. One point that lies in the interior of exactly two of the angles shown is:
  a. R b. X c. Z d. Y e. none of these

Exs. 7–10

B 11. If $\triangle ABC \cong \triangle NXT$, then it is also true that:
  a. $\triangle TNX \cong \triangle CAB$
  d. $\triangle BAC \cong \triangle TNX$
  b. $\triangle TXN \cong \triangle CAB$
  e. none of these
  c. $\triangle ACB \cong \triangle NXT$

12. Four of the angles of a pentagon have measures 85, 90, 95, and 110. The smallest of all the exterior angles has measure:
  a. 5   b. 20   c. 70   d. 85   e. none of these

13. The fact that corresponding sides of congruent triangles are congruent comes from a:
  a. definition
  d. inductive argument
  b. postulate
  e. none of these
  c. theorem

14. At 1:15 the hands of a clock form an angle with measure:
  a. 90   b. 60   c. 30   d. 15   e. none of these

15. At 6:40 the hands of a clock form an angle with measure:
  a. 10   b. 20   c. $30\frac{1}{12}$ d. 40   e. none of these

16. If point R lies between points N and A, then:
  a. N lies on $\overline{RA}$
  d. $NA + AR = NR$
  b. N lies on $\overrightarrow{RA}$
  e. none of these
  c. $NR = NA - AR$

17. In $\triangle RST$, $RS < ST < RT$. The longest of the three altitudes contains vertex:
  a. R b. S c. T d. cannot tell

18. A quadrilateral in which diagonals are congruent must be a:
  a. trapezoid
  d. rectangle
  b. parallelogram
  e. none of these
  c. rhombus

19. If four coplanar lines r, s, t, and q are such that $s \perp r$, $t \parallel s$, $q \perp t$, then:
  a. $r \parallel q$
  d. $r \parallel t$
  b. $r \perp q$
  e. none of these
  c. $s \parallel q$

20. Points X, Y, and Z lie on $\triangle GHJ$ in positions such that $\overline{YX} \parallel \overline{GH}$ and $\overline{XZ} \parallel \overline{JG}$. The number of pairs of similar triangles (don't include self-similarities) in the figure is:
  a. 2   b. 3   c. 4   d. 6   e. none of these

Always, Sometimes, or Never Exercises

Write A, S, or N to indicate your answer.

A 1. Two skew lines __?__ lie in one plane.

2. Three lines, each line parallel to the other two, are __?__ coplanar.

3. A conclusion reached by inductive thinking is __?__ correct.

4. A right triangle is __?__ isosceles.

5. An equilateral triangle is __?__ isosceles.

6. A trapezoid with three congruent sides is __?__ isosceles.

7. If $a = b + c$, and $c > 0$, then a is __?__ greater than b.

8. If two angles have a common side, the angles are __?__ adjacent angles.

9. The supplement of an obtuse angle is __?__ an obtuse angle.

10. The sum of the measures of the exterior angles of a convex n-gon, one angle at each vertex, is __?__ 720.

11. Complementary angles are __?__ congruent.

12. A ray __?__ has a midpoint.

13. Supplementary angles are __?__ adjacent angles.

14. Equiangular polygons are __?__ regular polygons.

15. The negation of a false statement is __?__ true.

16. Congruent angles are __?__ supplementary.

B 17. The diagonals of a trapezoid are __?__ perpendicular.

18. Lines parallel to the same plane are __?__ parallel to each other.

19. If $AB + BC > AC$, then it is __?__ true that $\overline{ABC}$.

20. If a, b, c, and d are nonzero numbers such that $ab = cd$, then it is __?__ true that $\dfrac{a}{c} = \dfrac{d}{b}$.

21. An altitude to the base of an isosceles triangle is __?__ congruent to the base.

22. If $\triangle ABC \cong \triangle RST$, and $\angle A$ is an obtuse angle, then it is __?__ true that $ST > AB$.

23. The median of an isosceles trapezoid is __?__ shorter than either leg.

24. If $\overline{AB}$ and $\overline{CD}$ are perpendicular bisectors of each other, then quadrilateral $ACBD$ is __?__ a square.

25. When $RS = ST$, point S is __?__ the midpoint of $\overline{RT}$.

26. When two lines are cut by a transversal and lines that bisect two alternate interior angles are drawn, the two lines are __?__ parallel lines.

27. In a convex n-gon it is __?__ possible to draw a total of $(n - 2)$ diagonals from one vertex.

28. An exterior angle of a triangle is __?__ complementary to a remote interior angle.

Miscellaneous Exercises

In the plane figure, $\overrightarrow{SY} \perp \overleftrightarrow{RT}$.

A 1. Name a pair of opposite rays.

2. Name a pair of complementary angles.

3. $m\angle RSX + m\angle XST = $ __?__ .

4. $RT - ST = $ __?__ .

5. If $m\angle XSY = 38$, $m\angle XST = $ __?__ .

6. State the postulate or theorem that supports the assertion: $\angle TSX$ is supplementary to $\angle XSR$.

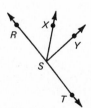

In the plane figure, $\angle AZC$ is a rt. $\angle$ and $\overrightarrow{ZB} \perp \overrightarrow{ZD}$. State the reason that supports the assertion.

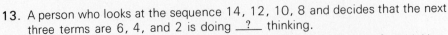

7. $\overleftrightarrow{AZ} \perp \overleftrightarrow{ZC}$

8. $\angle BZD$ is a rt. $\angle$.

9. $m\angle 1 + m\angle 2 = m\angle AZC$

10. $m\angle AZC = 90$

11. $\angle 2$ and $\angle 3$ are comp. $\angle$s

12. $\angle 1 \cong \angle 3$

13. A person who looks at the sequence 14, 12, 10, 8 and decides that the next three terms are 6, 4, and 2 is doing __?__ thinking.

14. A person who concludes from $7n = 14$ that $n = 2$ is doing __?__ thinking.

15. Given the fact that points A and B lie in plane P, what can you deduce about $\overleftrightarrow{AB}$?

16. Given that lines m and n are parallel and transversal j is perpendicular to m, what can you deduce?

17. The measures of the angles of a triangle are 40, 60, and 80. Find the measure of the largest exterior angle.

18. Three angles of a convex quadrilateral each have measure 80. Find the measure of the fourth angle.

19. An exterior angle of a triangle has measure 107, and a remote interior angle has measure 49. Find the measure of the other remote interior angle.

20. All the diagonals that contain a particular vertex of a 9-gon are drawn. How many triangles are formed?

In the figure for Exercises 21–24, $\overline{CD} \parallel \overline{AB}$.

21. $PC = 8$, $CA = 4$, $PD = 10$ $DB =$ __?__

22. $CD = 12$, $AB = 16$, $PA = 12$ $PC =$ __?__

23. $PA = 6$, $PB = 9$, $PC = 4$ $PD =$ __?__

24. $PC = 5$, $AC = 3$, $PB = 7$ $PD =$ __?__

In the figure for Exercises 25–28, $\angle ZXY \cong \angle WXY$.

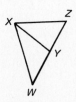

25. $XZ = 3$, $XW = 5$, $YZ = 2$ $WY =$ __?__

26. $XZ = 8$, $XW = 12$, $ZW = 16$ $ZY =$ __?__

27. $YZ = 5$, $WZ = 13$, $XZ = 6$ $XW =$ __?__

28. $YW = 2 \cdot YZ$, $XZ = 13$ $XW =$ __?__

In the figure for Exercises 29–32, $\overleftrightarrow{AB} \parallel \overleftrightarrow{CD}$.

29. If $m\angle BAC : m\angle DCA = 5:4$, then $m\angle BAC =$ __?__.

30. If $\angle CAK$, $\angle ACK$, and $\angle K$ have measures that are in the ratio $4:3:2$, then $m\angle K =$ __?__.

31. If $m\angle BAK = \frac{1}{4} m\angle BAC$ and $m\angle DCK = \frac{1}{4} m\angle DCA$, then $m\angle K = \underline{\ \ ?\ \ }$.

32. If $m\angle BAK = 20$ and $m\angle DCK = 15$, then $m\angle K = \underline{\ \ ?\ \ }$.

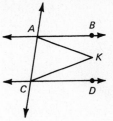

33. If each interior angle of a regular n-gon has measure 144, $n = \underline{\ \ ?\ \ }$.

34. The measure of a supplement of $\angle X$ is four times the measure of a complement of $\angle X$. Find the measure of $\angle X$.

35. The shortest sides of two similar polygons have lengths 5 and 8. The sum of the perimeters is 403. Find the perimeter of the smaller polygon.

36. The measures of the angles of a convex hexagon are in the ratio $2:4:5:5:5:6$. Find the measure of the smallest angle.

C 37. In $\triangle RST$, $m\angle T = 84$. $\overrightarrow{RX}$ and $\overrightarrow{SX}$ bisect the exterior $\angle$s at R and S. Find $m\angle RXS$.

38. In the figure, $\overline{AB}$, $\overline{CD}$, and $\overline{EF}$ are perpendicular to $\overline{BF}$. $AB = 24$ and $EF = 40$. Find CD.

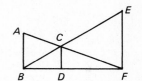

Proof Exercises

A 1. Given: $\angle 1 \cong \angle 2$; $\overline{AC} \cong \overline{AD}$
Prove: $\triangle AKC \cong \triangle AKD$

2. Given: $\angle 3 \cong \angle 4$; $\angle ACB \cong \angle ADB$
Prove: $\triangle ACB \cong ADB$

3. Given: $\overline{AB} \perp \overline{CD}$; $\angle 3 \cong \angle 4$
Prove: $\triangle CKB \cong \triangle DKB$

4. Given: $\overline{AB} \perp \overline{CD}$; $\overrightarrow{AB}$ bisects $\angle CAD$
Prove: $\triangle CAK \cong \triangle DAK$

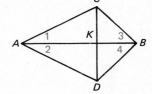

Exs. 1–4

5. Given: $\overline{DG} \cong \overline{FE}$; $\overline{GP} \cong \overline{EO}$;
$\angle GPD$ and $\angle EOF$ are rt. $\angle$s
Prove: $\triangle GPD \cong \triangle EOF$

6. Given: $\angle GPF$ and $\angle EOD$ are rt. $\angle$s;
$\overline{GF} \parallel \overline{DE}$
Prove: $\triangle GPF \sim \triangle EOD$

7. Given: Quad. $DEFG$ is a $\square$;
$\overline{GP} \perp \overline{DF}$; $\overline{EO} \perp \overline{DF}$
Prove: $\triangle GPF \cong \triangle EOD$

8. Given: $\triangle GDF \cong \triangle EFD$
Prove: $\overline{GF} \parallel \overline{DE}$

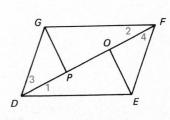

Exs. 5–8

9. Given: $\angle 1 \cong \angle R$
   Prove: $\angle 2 \cong \angle S$

10. Given: $\overline{TX} \cong \overline{TY}$; $\angle 1 \cong \angle R$
    Prove: $\angle 2 \cong \angle R$

11. Given: $TX = TY$; $XR = YS$
    Prove: $\triangle RTS$ is isos.

12. Given: $\overline{TR} \cong \overline{TS}$; $\overline{XY} \parallel \overline{RS}$
    Prove: $\angle 1 \cong \angle 2$

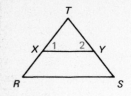

Exs. 9–12

13. Given: $j \parallel k$; $l \parallel m$
    Prove: $\angle 1 \cong \angle 11$

14. Given: $j \parallel k$; $l \parallel m$
    Prove: $\angle 3 \cong \angle 9$

15. Given: $l \parallel m$; $\angle 1 \cong \angle 11$
    Prove: $j \parallel k$

16. Given: $j \parallel k$; $\angle 4 \cong \angle 10$
    Prove: $l \parallel m$

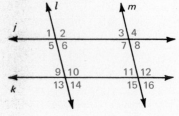

Exs. 13–16

B 17. Given: $\angle C \cong \angle D$
    Prove: $\angle A \cong \angle B$

18. Given: $\angle A \cong \angle XYZ$; $\overline{DB} \parallel \overline{YX}$
    Prove: $\overline{AC} \parallel \overline{DB}$

19. Given: $\triangle AZC \sim \triangle YZX$; $\overline{BD} \parallel \overline{YX}$
    Prove: $\triangle AZC \sim \triangle BZD$

20. Given: $\triangle AZC \sim \triangle BZD$; $\overline{YX} \parallel \overline{DB}$
    Prove: $\dfrac{AC}{YX} = \dfrac{AZ}{YZ}$

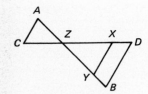

Exs. 17–20

21. Given: $\overline{GM} \cong \overline{HM}$; $\angle 2 \cong \angle 4$; $\overline{GH} \parallel \overline{KJ}$
    Prove: $\angle G \cong \angle H$

22. Given: $\angle GKJ \cong \angle HJK$; $\angle 1 \cong \angle 3$
    Prove: $\overline{MK} \cong \overline{MJ}$

23. Given: $\angle GKJ \cong \angle HJK$; $\overline{MK} \cong \overline{MJ}$; $\overline{GH} \parallel \overline{KJ}$
    Prove: $\overline{GM} \cong \overline{HM}$

24. Given: M is the midpoint of $\overline{GH}$;
    $\angle G \cong \angle H$; $\angle 1 \cong \angle 3$
    Prove: $\angle 2 \cong \angle 4$

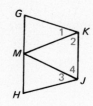

Exs. 21–24

25. Given: $\angle TAD \cong \angle TCB$
    Prove: $\triangle ANB \sim \triangle CND$

26. Given: $\triangle TBC \sim \triangle TDA$
    Prove: $\triangle BNA \sim \triangle DNC$

27. Given: $\angle B \cong \angle D$
    Prove: $\dfrac{TB}{TD} = \dfrac{TC}{TA}$

28. Given: $\angle BAN \cong \angle DCN$
    Prove: $TC \cdot DA = TA \cdot BC$

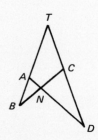

Exs. 25–28

In Exercises 29–34, it is given that:
$\overline{RS} \perp \overline{WX}$; $\overline{RS} \perp \overline{WY}$; $\overline{RW} \cong \overline{SW}$.
Anything you prove in one exercise
you may use as a statement in later
exercises, writing as your reason, for
example, *Proved in Exercise 29*.

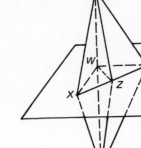

29. Prove: $\overline{RX} \cong \overline{SX}$
30. Prove: $\overline{RY} \cong \overline{SY}$
31. Prove: $\angle RXY \cong \angle SXY$
32. Prove: $\overline{RZ} \cong \overline{SZ}$
33. Prove: $\triangle RWZ \cong \triangle SWZ$
34. Prove: $\overline{WZ}$ is a perpendicular bisector of $\overline{RS}$.

C 35. Given: $\overline{CM} \cong \overline{DM}$; $\overline{GM} \cong \overline{HM}$
    Prove: $\overline{AG} \cong \overline{AH}$
36. Given: $\overline{AC} \cong \overline{AD}$; $\overline{BC} \cong \overline{BD}$
    Prove: $\triangle CMD$ is isos.
37. Given: $\overline{AC} \cong \overline{AD}$; $\overrightarrow{AB}$ bisects $\angle CAD$
    Prove: $\angle 3 \cong \angle 4$
38. Given: $\angle 1 \cong \angle 2$; $\overrightarrow{MA}$ bisects $\angle GMH$
    Prove: $\overline{AC} \cong \overline{AD}$

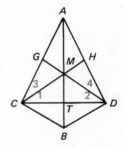

39. Given: $\angle 1 \cong \angle 2$
    Prove: $(ST)^2 = SR \cdot SP$

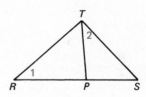

40. Given: A plane figure;
    $\overline{DF} \perp \overline{XY}$; $\overline{GH} \perp \overline{XZ}$; $\overline{EJ} \perp \overline{YZ}$
    Prove: $\dfrac{DE}{DG} = \dfrac{XY}{XZ}$

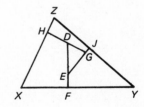

RIGHT TRIANGLES

The Pythagorean Theorem

Objectives

1. Determine the geometric mean between two numbers.
2. State and apply the relationships that exist when the altitude is drawn to the hypotenuse of a right triangle.
3. State and apply the Pythagorean Theorem and its converse.
4. Determine the lengths of two sides of a 45°-45°-90° or 30°-60°-90° triangle when the length of the third side is given.
5. Apply the Pythagorean Theorem in working with a rectangular solid.

7-1 The Altitude to the Hypotenuse of a Right Triangle

If a, b, and x are positive numbers and $\dfrac{a}{x} = \dfrac{x}{b}$, then x is called the geometric mean between a and b.

EXAMPLE 1. Find the geometric mean between 3 and 12.

SOLUTION: Let x = the geometric mean. Then: $\dfrac{3}{x} = \dfrac{x}{12}$

$$x^2 = 36$$
$$x = \sqrt{36} = 6$$

EXAMPLE 2. Find the geometric mean between 3 and 7.

SOLUTION: Let x = the geometric mean. Then: $\dfrac{3}{x} = \dfrac{x}{7}$

$$x^2 = 21$$
$$x = \sqrt{21}$$

Note that in Example 1 the geometric mean is a rational number, while in Example 2 the geometric mean is an irrational number.

Since much of the work in this chapter will involve *radicals* and their properties, the following is provided as a review.

1. A **radical** is an indicated root of a number.

$$\sqrt{5}, \; \sqrt[3]{7}, \; \sqrt[6]{2} \text{ are radicals.}$$

2. The symbol $\sqrt{}$ means the *positive square root* of a number.
3. The number appearing under the radical sign is called the *radicand*.
4. A term such as $\sqrt{x}$ is said to be in *simplified form* when:
   a. No integral factor of the radicand, other than 1, is a perfect square.
   b. No radicand is a fraction.
   c. No radical appears in a denominator.

5. For all positive values of a and b, $\sqrt{a} \cdot \sqrt{b} = \sqrt{ab}$.

6. For all positive values of a and b, $\sqrt{\dfrac{a}{b}} = \dfrac{\sqrt{a}}{\sqrt{b}}$.

EXAMPLE 3. Simplify: $\sqrt{50}$

SOLUTION: $\sqrt{50} = \sqrt{25 \cdot 2} = \sqrt{25} \cdot \sqrt{2} = 5\sqrt{2}$

EXAMPLE 4. Simplify: $\sqrt{\frac{5}{3}}$

SOLUTION: $\sqrt{\dfrac{5}{3}} = \dfrac{\sqrt{5}}{\sqrt{3}} = \dfrac{\sqrt{5}}{\sqrt{3}} \cdot \dfrac{\sqrt{3}}{\sqrt{3}} = \dfrac{\sqrt{15}}{\sqrt{9}} = \dfrac{\sqrt{15}}{3}$

EXAMPLE 5. Simplify: $6\sqrt{\frac{8}{5}}$

SOLUTION: $6\sqrt{\dfrac{8}{5}} = \dfrac{6\sqrt{8}}{\sqrt{5}} = 6 \cdot \dfrac{\sqrt{8}}{\sqrt{5}} \cdot \dfrac{\sqrt{5}}{\sqrt{5}} = \dfrac{6\sqrt{40}}{5}$

$$= \dfrac{6\sqrt{4 \cdot 10}}{5} = \dfrac{12\sqrt{10}}{5}$$

Certain relationships which exist when the altitude is drawn to the hypotenuse of a right triangle are stated in the theorem and corollary that follow.

THEOREM 7-1 If the altitude is drawn to the hypotenuse of a right triangle, the two triangles formed are similar to the given triangle and to each other.

Given: Rt. $\triangle ACB$; $\angle ACB$ is rt. $\angle$; $\overline{CD} \perp \overline{AB}$

Prove: $\triangle ADC \sim \triangle ACB$; $\triangle CDB \sim \triangle ACB$; $\triangle ADC \sim \triangle CDB$

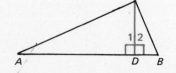

Proof:

STATEMENTS	REASONS
1. $\angle ACB$ is a rt. $\angle$; $\overline{CD} \perp \overline{AB}$	1. Given
2. $\angle 1$ is a rt. $\angle$.	2. $\perp$ lines form rt. $\angle$s.
3. In rt. $\triangle ADC$ and ACB, $\angle A \cong \angle A$.	3. Reflexive property of congruence
4. $\triangle ADC \sim \triangle ACB$	4. If an acute $\angle$ of one rt. $\triangle$ is $\cong$ to __?__ .
5. $\angle 2$ is a rt. $\angle$.	5. $\perp$ lines form rt. $\angle$s.
6. In rt. $\triangle CDB$ and ACB, $\angle B \cong \angle B$.	6. Reflexive property of congruence
7. $\triangle CDB \sim \triangle ACB$	7. Same as Reason 4
8. $\triangle ADC \sim \triangle CDB$	8. Similarity of $\triangle$s is transitive.

When $\overline{CD}$ is perpendicular to hypotenuse $\overline{AB}$, $\overline{AD}$ is called the segment of the hypotenuse *adjacent* to leg $\overline{AC}$. The segment of the hypotenuse adjacent to leg $\overline{BC}$ is $\overline{BD}$.

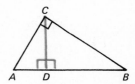

COROLLARY   If the altitude is drawn to the hypotenuse of a right triangle, the length of a leg of the right triangle is the geometric mean between the length of the hypotenuse and the length of the segment of the hypotenuse adjacent to that leg.

Given: Rt. $\triangle ACB$; $\angle ACB$ is a rt. $\angle$; $\overline{CD} \perp \overline{AB}$

Prove: I. $\dfrac{AB}{AC} = \dfrac{AC}{AD}$ II. $\dfrac{BA}{BC} = \dfrac{BC}{BD}$

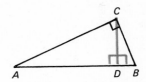

Proof:

STATEMENTS	REASONS
1. $\angle ACB$ is a rt. $\angle$; $\overline{CD} \perp \overline{AB}$	1. Given
2. $\triangle ACB \sim \triangle ADC$	2. If the altitude is drawn to the hypotenuse of a rt. $\triangle$, the two __?__ .
3. $\dfrac{AB}{AC} = \dfrac{AC}{AD}$	3. __?__

The proof of Part **II** is left as Exercise 33.

In Exercises 1–10, classify each statement as true or false.

1. The symbol $\sqrt{}$ denotes the positive square root of a number.
2. $\sqrt{9} \cdot \sqrt{25} = 15$
3. The simplified form of $\sqrt{18}$ is $2\sqrt{3}$.
4. The simplified form of $\sqrt{\dfrac{1}{2}}$ is $\dfrac{\sqrt{2}}{2}$.
5. $\sqrt{32}$ is in simplified form.
6. In the proportion $\dfrac{5}{x} = \dfrac{x}{6}$, x is the geometric mean between 5 and 6.
7. $\dfrac{3}{x} = \dfrac{x}{5}$ is equivalent to $2x = 15$.
8. $\sqrt{\dfrac{7}{3}}$ is equivalent to $\dfrac{\sqrt{7}}{\sqrt{3}}$.
9. The simplified form of $3\sqrt{8}$ is $6\sqrt{2}$.
10. If $\overline{RX}$ is the altitude to the hypotenuse of rt. $\triangle RST$, then point R is the vertex of one of the acute angles of the triangle.

Exercises 11–18 refer to rt. $\triangle ACB$ with $\overline{CX} \perp \overline{AB}$ and $m\angle ACB = 90$.

11. Name the hypotenuse of rt. $\triangle ACB$.
12. Name the altitude to the hypotenuse of rt. $\triangle ACB$.
13. Is $\triangle ACB \sim \triangle AXC$?
14. Is $\triangle BXC \sim \triangle CXA$?
15. The segment of the hypotenuse adjacent to $\overline{BC}$ is __?__.
16. The segment of the hypotenuse adjacent to $\overline{AC}$ is __?__.
17. $\dfrac{AB}{AC} = \dfrac{AC}{?}$
18. $\dfrac{AB}{BC} = \dfrac{BC}{?}$

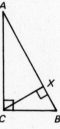

Express each radical in simplified form.

1. $\sqrt{49}$
2. $\sqrt{81}$
3. $\sqrt{200}$
4. $\sqrt{45}$

5. $3\sqrt{27}$
6. $4\sqrt{18}$
7. $\sqrt{\tfrac{1}{2}}$
8. $\sqrt{\tfrac{2}{3}}$

9. $4\sqrt{\tfrac{3}{2}}$
10. $9\sqrt{\tfrac{5}{3}}$
11. $6\sqrt{\tfrac{4}{3}}$
12. $10\sqrt{\tfrac{9}{5}}$

Find a positive number x for which the equation is true.

13. $x^2 = 100$
14. $x^2 = 64$

15. $x^2 = 28$
16. $x^2 = 63$

17. $x^2 = \tfrac{7}{2}$
18. $x^2 = \tfrac{11}{3}$

Express, in simplified form, the geometric mean between:

19. 4 and 9   **21.** 6 and 8   **23.** 5 and 7

20. 3 and 12   **22.** 4 and 6   **24.** 3 and 11

Exercises 25–32 refer to $\triangle DFE$ with $m \angle DFE = 90$ and $\overline{FM} \perp \overline{DE}$.

EXAMPLE. $DE = 12$; $DM = 3$; $DF = \underline{\;?\;}$

SOLUTION: Let $x = DF$

$$\frac{3}{x} = \frac{x}{12} \qquad \text{(by the corollary to Theorem 7-1)}$$

$$x^2 = 36$$

$$x = \sqrt{36} = 6$$

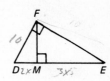

B **25.** $DE = 8$; $DM = 2$; $DF = \underline{\;?\;}$ **28.** $ME = 5$; $EF = 10$; $DE = \underline{\;?\;}$

26. $DE = 16$; $ME = 9$; $FE = \underline{\;?\;}$ **29.** $DM = 4$; $ME = 6$; $FE = \underline{\;?\;}$

27. $DM = 4$; $DF = 6$; $DE = \underline{\;?\;}$ **30.** $DM = 3$; $ME = 8$; $DF = \underline{\;?\;}$

31. $FE = 6$; $DM = x$; $ME = 2x$; $x = \underline{\;?\;}$

32. $DF = 10$; $DM = 2x$; $ME = 3x$; $x = \underline{\;?\;}$

33. Prove Part **II** of the corollary to Theorem 7-1.

34. Prove: The length of the altitude drawn to the hypotenuse of a right triangle is the geometric mean between the lengths of the segments of the hypotenuse.

35. Prove: In a right triangle, the product of the lengths of the hypotenuse and the altitude to the hypotenuse is equal to the product of the lengths of the legs.

Exercises 36–38 refer to $\triangle RST$. $m \angle RST = 90$ and $\overline{SY} \perp \overline{RT}$. (*Hint:* Use Exercise 34.)

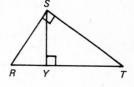

C **36.** $RY = x + 1$; $YT = 4x - 3$; $SY = 2x$; $x = \underline{\;?\;}$

37. $RY = x - 1$; $YT = 3x$; $SY = x + 2$; $x = \underline{\;?\;}$

38. $RY = x - 2$; $YT = 3x - 3$; $SY = x + 1$; $x = \underline{\;?\;}$

7-2 *The Pythagorean Theorem*

The following theorem states an interesting relationship that exists between the lengths of the three sides of a right triangle. The theorem is called the Pythagorean Theorem. Pythagoras, a Greek mathematician and philosopher, is credited with offering one of the first proofs of this useful and famous theorem. A more recent proof is shown on the next page.

THEOREM 7-2 In any right triangle the square of the length of the hypotenuse is equal to the sum of the squares of the lengths of the legs.

Given: Rt. $\triangle ACB$; $\angle ACB$ is a rt. $\angle$.

Prove: $c^2 = a^2 + b^2$

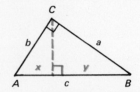

Proof:

STATEMENTS	REASONS
1. Draw a perpendicular from C to $\overline{AB}$.	1. Through a point outside a line there is exactly one perpendicular to that line.
2. $\dfrac{c}{a} = \dfrac{a}{y}$; $\dfrac{c}{b} = \dfrac{b}{x}$	2. The length of a leg of a right triangle is __?__ .
3. $cy = a^2$ and $cx = b^2$	3. A property of proportions
4. $cy + cx = a^2 + b^2$	4. Addition property of equality
5. $c(y + x) = a^2 + b^2$	5. Distributive property
6. $c^2 = a^2 + b^2$	6. Substitution principle ($y + x = c$)

The converse of the Pythagorean Theorem is also true.

THEOREM 7-3 If the sum of the squares of the lengths of two sides of a triangle is equal to the square of the length of the third side, the triangle is a right triangle.

Given: $\triangle ACB$ with $a^2 + b^2 = c^2$

Prove: $\triangle ACB$ is a rt. $\triangle$.

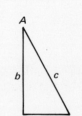

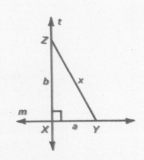

Proof:

STATEMENTS	REASONS
1. At point X on line m, draw a line $t \perp m$.	1. In a plane, through a given point on a line, __?__ .
2. On m mark off $XY = a$ and on t mark off $XZ = b$.	2. On a ray there is exactly one point at a given distance from the endpoint of the ray.
3. Draw $\overline{YZ}$.	3. Through any two __?__ .
4. In rt. $\triangle ZXY$, $a^2 + b^2 = x^2$	4. __?__
5. $a^2 + b^2 = c^2$	5. Given
6. $c^2 = x^2$, and $c = x$	6. Substitution principle (and Algebra)
7. $\triangle ACB \cong \triangle ZXY$	7. SSS Postulate
8. $\angle C \cong \angle ZXY$	8. Corr. $\angle$ of $\cong$ $\triangle$ are $\cong$.
9. $m\angle C = m\angle ZXY$	9. Definition of $\cong$ $\angle$.
10. $m\angle ZXY = 90$	10. $\perp$ lines form rt. $\angle$.
11. $m\angle C = 90$	11. Substitution principle
12. $\triangle ACB$ is a rt. $\triangle$.	12. A triangle that contains a rt. $\angle$ is a rt. $\triangle$.

Oral Exercises

In Exercises 1–6, state an equation that can be used to find the length x in each of the right triangles shown.

1.

3.

5.

2.

4.

6.

In Exercises 7–12, the lengths of three sides of a triangle are given. State whether the triangle is a right triangle.

7. 2, 3, 4

8. 3, 4, 5

9. 3, 3, 4

10. 4, 5, 6

11. 6, 8, 10

12. 2, 2, $\sqrt{8}$

Exercises 13–18 refer to rt. $\triangle RST$ with $m\angle S = 90$.
Classify each statement as true or false.

13. $r^2 + t^2 = s^2$
14. $s^2 - t^2 = r^2$
15. $r^2 - s^2 = t^2$

16. $s = \sqrt{t^2 + r^2}$
17. $s^2 = (r + t)^2$
18. $r = \sqrt{s^2 - t^2}$

Written Exercises

Exercises 1–10 refer to rt. $\triangle ACB$ with $m\angle C = 90$. The lengths of two sides of the triangle are given. Express the length of the third side in simplified radical form.

A
1. $AC = 6$; $BC = 8$; $AB = $ __?__
2. $AC = 5$; $BC = 12$; $AB = $ __?__
3. $AC = 4$; $AB = 5$; $BC = $ __?__
4. $BC = 5$; $AB = 6$; $AC = $ __?__
5. $AC = 4$; $BC = 6$; $AB = $ __?__
6. $AC = 4$; $BC = 8$; $AB = $ __?__
7. $AB = 14$; $AC = 8$; $BC = $ __?__
8. $AB = 12$; $BC = 10$; $AC = $ __?__
9. $AC = 3\sqrt{3}$; $BC = 3$; $AB = $ __?__
10. $AC = 5\sqrt{3}$; $BC = 5$; $AB = $ __?__

In Exercises 11–18, determine if a triangle with sides of the given lengths is a right triangle.

11. 5, 12, 13
12. 9, 12, 15
13. 8, 10, 13
14. 5, 7, 8

15. 10, 24, 26
16. 11, 60, 61
17. 8, 4, $4\sqrt{3}$
18. $6\sqrt{2}, 6\sqrt{2}, 12$

Write answers in simplified radical form.

19. The length and width of a rectangle are 6 cm and 4 cm. Find the length of a diagonal of the rectangle.
20. The length of a side of a square is 5 cm. Find the length of a diagonal of the square.
21. Quadrilateral $ABCD$ is a square. If $AC = 12$, find AB.
22. Quadrilateral $DEFG$ is a rectangle. If $DE = 4$ and $DF = 10$, find EF.

In Exercises 23–30, the lengths of two sides of a right triangle are given. Find two possible values for the length of the third side. (*Hint:* The third side is not necessarily the hypotenuse.)

B
23. 3, 4
24. 4, 5

25. 4, 6
26. 8, 10

27. $3\sqrt{2}, 4\sqrt{2}$
28. $4\sqrt{3}, 2\sqrt{3}$

29. $\frac{5}{2}, \frac{3}{2}$
30. $\frac{7}{3}, \frac{2}{3}$

Exercises 31–34 refer to equilateral triangle *ABC* with $\overline{CX} \perp \overline{AB}$.

31. If $AC = 8$, $CX =$ __?__ .
32. If $BX = 3$, $CX =$ __?__ .
33. If the perimeter of $\triangle ABC$ is 36, $CX =$ __?__ .
34. If the perimeter of $\triangle ABC$ is 30, $CX =$ __?__ .

Exercises 35–38 refer to rhombus *RSTW*.

35. If $SW = 12$ and $RT = 18$, then $RS =$ __?__ .
36. If $SW = 10$ and $RT = 16$, then $WT =$ __?__ .
37. If $RS = 8$ and $RT = 14$, then $SW =$ __?__ .
38. If $RW = 7$ and $SW = 10$, then $RT =$ __?__ .

C 39. In rt. $\triangle ABC$, the measure of $\angle C$ is 90. If $AB = 4x - 3$, $BC = 2x + 6$, and $AC = 3x - 6$, find x.

40. In rt. $\triangle RST$, the measure of $\angle T$ is 90. If $RS = 6x - 1$, $ST = 4x + 6$, and $RT = 2x + 1$, find x.

41. X is a point in the interior of rectangle *PTRS*. If $XP = 4$, $XT = 6$, and $XR = 5$, find XS.

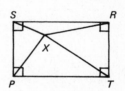

42. In the solid shown, $AE = EB$, $DF = FC$, and $\overline{AB} \cong \overline{BC} \cong \overline{AC} \cong \overline{AD} \cong \overline{BD} \cong \overline{DC}$. If $AB = 4$, find EF.

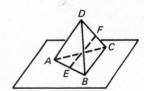

Challenge

A room is 10 meters long, 4 meters wide, and 4 meters high. A spider is at the middle of an end wall, $\frac{1}{3}$ meter from the floor. A fly is at the middle of the other end wall, $\frac{1}{3}$ meter from the ceiling, too frightened to move. The spider crawls to the fly. What is the shortest distance? (14 meters is not the correct answer.)

7-3 Special Right Triangles

In each of the special right triangles shown below, if you are given the length of any one side of the triangle, you can readily find the lengths of the other two sides.

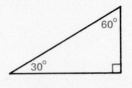

45°-45°-90° triangle   30°-60°-90° triangle

The triangle at the left is called a 45°-45°-90° triangle, or an isosceles right triangle. The triangle at the right is a 30°-60°-90° triangle.

The Pythagorean Theorem, which applies to all right triangles, is used to prove the following relationships that exist in these two special right triangles.

THEOREM 7-4   If each acute angle of a right triangle has measure 45, the hypotenuse is $\sqrt{2}$ times as long as a leg.

Given: Rt. $\triangle RST$; $m\angle R = m\angle T = 45$;
  $RS = l$

Prove: $RT = l\sqrt{2}$

Outline of Proof:

Since $\angle R \cong \angle T$, $RS = TS$. Since $RS = l$, $TS = l$.

By the Pythagorean Theorem,

$$(RT)^2 = l^2 + l^2 = 2l^2.$$

Hence $RT = \sqrt{2l^2} = l\sqrt{2}$.

EXAMPLE 1. In the 45°-45°-90° triangle shown, $DE = 12$. Find DF.

SOLUTION: $DF = 12\sqrt{2}$ (By Theorem 7-4)

EXAMPLE 2. In the 45°-45°-90° triangle shown, $BC = 10$. Find AB.

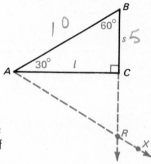

SOLUTION: Let $AB = x$.

Then: $x\sqrt{2} = 10$

$$x = \frac{10}{\sqrt{2}} = \frac{10}{\sqrt{2}} \cdot \frac{\sqrt{2}}{\sqrt{2}} = \frac{10\sqrt{2}}{2} = 5\sqrt{2}$$

THEOREM 7-5   If the acute angles of a right triangle have measures 30 and 60:
(a) The hypotenuse is twice as long as the shorter leg.
(b) The longer leg is $\sqrt{3}$ times as long as the shorter leg.

Given: Rt. $\triangle ACB$; $m \angle BAC = 30$;
$m \angle B = 60$; $BC = s$; $AC = l$

Prove: a. $AB = 2s$
b. $l = s\sqrt{3}$

Outline of Proof:

a. Draw $\overrightarrow{BC}$. Draw $\overrightarrow{AX}$ so that $m \angle BAX = 60$. Let R be the point of intersection of $\overrightarrow{BC}$ and $\overrightarrow{AX}$. $\triangle BAR$ is an equilateral triangle, and hence $AB = BR = 2s$.

b. $s^2 + l^2 = (AB)^2$
$s^2 + l^2 = (2s)^2 = 4s^2$
Thus $l^2 = 3s^2$
and $l = \sqrt{3s^2} = s\sqrt{3}$.

EXAMPLE 3. The length of the hypotenuse of a 30°-60°-90° triangle is 8. Find the length of:
a. the shorter leg   b. the longer leg

SOLUTION: Draw and label a figure.
a. $2s = 8$ b. $l = s\sqrt{3}$
$s = 4$ $l = 4\sqrt{3}$

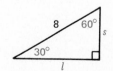

EXAMPLE 4. An altitude of an equilateral triangle has length 6. Find the length of a side of the triangle.

SOLUTION: Draw and label a figure.

$$s\sqrt{3} = 6$$

$$s = \frac{6}{\sqrt{3}} = \frac{6}{\sqrt{3}} \cdot \frac{\sqrt{3}}{\sqrt{3}} = \frac{6\sqrt{3}}{3}$$

$$= 2\sqrt{3}$$

$$c = 2s. \text{ Hence } c = 2(2\sqrt{3}) = 4\sqrt{3}.$$

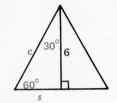

Oral Exercises

Classify each statement as true or false.

1. If the measure of one acute angle of a right triangle is 30, the measure of the other acute angle is 60.
2. If the legs of a right triangle are congruent, each acute angle has measure 45.
3. The legs of a 30°-60°-90° triangle are unequal in length.
4. The legs of a 45°-45°-90° triangle are unequal in length.
5. There exists a 10°-80°-90° triangle.
6. The hypotenuse of a 30°-60°-90° triangle is twice as long as the shorter leg.
7. The shorter leg of a 30°-60°-90° triangle is $\sqrt{3}$ times the longer leg.
8. When a diagonal of a square is drawn, the two triangles formed are 45°-45°-90° triangles.
9. The hypotenuse of a 45°-45°-90° triangle is $\sqrt{2}$ times as long as a leg.
10. If $\overline{AB}$ is the hypotenuse of rt. $\triangle ACB$, then $\overline{AB}$ must be twice as long as $\overline{AC}$ or $\overline{BC}$.

Exercises 11–14 refer to the 30°-60°-90° triangle.

11. If $EF = 4$, then $DF = \underline{\quad?\quad}$.
12. If $EF = 3$, then $DE = \underline{\quad?\quad}$.
13. If $DF = 10$, then $EF = \underline{\quad?\quad}$.
14. If $DF = 12$, then $DE = \underline{\quad?\quad}$.

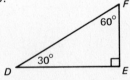

Exercises 15 and 16 refer to the 45°-45°-90° triangle.

15. If $PR = 7$, then $RS = \underline{\quad?\quad}$.
16. If $SR = 6$, then $PS = \underline{\quad?\quad}$.

Exercises 1–14 refer to the 30°-60°-90° triangle. Using the given information, find the indicated length.

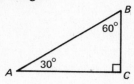

A

1. $AB = 14$; $BC =$ ___?___
2. $AB = 22$; $BC =$ ___?___
3. $BC = 9$; $AB =$ ___?___
4. $BC = 7$; $AB =$ ___?___
5. $BC = 6$; $AC =$ ___?___
6. $BC = 8$; $AC =$ ___?___

7. $AB = 16$; $AC =$ ___?___

8. $AB = 20$; $AC =$ ___?___
9. $AC = 8\sqrt{3}$; $BC =$ ___?___
10. $AC = 9\sqrt{3}$; $BC =$ ___?___
11. $AB = 13$; $AC =$ ___?___
12. $AB = 15$; $AC =$ ___?___
13. $AC = 4\sqrt{3}$; $AB =$ ___?___
14. $AC = \dfrac{11\sqrt{3}}{2}$; $AB =$ ___?___

Exercises 15–22 refer to the 45°-45°-90° triangle. Using the given information, find the indicated length.

15. $XY = 7$; $XZ =$ ___?___
16. $YZ = 10$; $XZ =$ ___?___
17. $XY = 5\sqrt{2}$; $XZ =$ ___?___
18. $YZ = 7\sqrt{2}$; $XZ =$ ___?___
19. $XZ = 11\sqrt{2}$; $XY =$ ___?___
20. $XZ = 15\sqrt{2}$; $YZ =$ ___?___
21. $XZ = 10$; $XY =$ ___?___
22. $XZ = 12$; $YZ =$ ___?___

Exercises 23–32 refer to $\triangle DEF$ with $m\angle DEF = 90$, $m\angle D = 30$, and $\overline{EX} \perp \overline{DF}$.

B

23. $FX = 5$; $EF =$ ___?___
24. $EF = 12$; $FX =$ ___?___
25. $EF = 6$; $DE =$ ___?___
26. $EF = 8$; $DE =$ ___?___
27. $XF = 4$; $DX =$ ___?___
28. $XF = 6$; $DX =$ ___?___
29. $DX = 6\sqrt{3}$; $XF =$ ___?___
30. $DX = 8\sqrt{3}$; $XF =$ ___?___
31. $DE = 12$; $FX =$ ___?___
32. $EF = 8$; $DX =$ ___?___

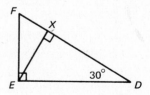

Exercises 33–36 refer to equilateral triangle *ABC* with $BX = XC$, $\overline{YZ} \perp \overline{AC}$, and $m\angle 1 = 105$.

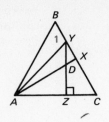

C   33. If $YZ = 12$, then $XY = \underline{\quad?\quad}$.

   34. If $AD = 10$, then $XY = \underline{\quad?\quad}$.

   35. Find the ratio of *BY* to *YX*.

   36. If the perimeter of $\triangle AZD$ is $12 + 4\sqrt{3}$, find the perimeter of $\triangle YXD$.

7-4 *Rectangular Solids*

The Pythagorean Theorem can be used to find the lengths of segments in solids, or three-dimensional figures. Once you develop the ability to recognize right triangles in a solid, the work is no more difficult than with two-dimensional figures.

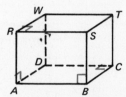

One of the most common three-dimensional figures is the rectangular solid.

Rectangular Solid

The following vocabulary is used when we speak of a rectangular solid.

Face: The rectangular solid has six rectangular faces. For example, rectangle *RSTW* bounds one face and rectangle *BCTS* bounds another.

Edge: The segment formed by the intersection of two faces is an edge. A rectangular solid has twelve edges. $\overline{AR}$ is one edge. $\overline{BC}$ is another edge.

Vertex: The intersection of two edges is a vertex. A rectangular solid has eight vertices. Point *A* is one vertex, and point *T* is another.

Diagonal of a rectangular solid: A diagonal of a solid is a segment whose endpoints are two vertices that do not lie in the same face. $\overline{WB}$ is a diagonal of the solid shown. A rectangular solid has four congruent diagonals. The other diagonals, not drawn in the figure, are $\overline{SD}$, $\overline{RC}$, and $\overline{AT}$. Note that $\overline{DB}$ is *not* a diagonal of the solid. $\overline{DB}$ is a diagonal of one of the faces.

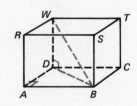

The length of a diagonal of a rectangular solid can be expressed in terms of the length, width, and height of the solid. The Pythagorean Theorem is used to derive the relationship.

Let $AB = l$, $AD = w$, and $WD = h$.

In rt. $\triangle DAB$:　　$(DB)^2 = l^2 + w^2$
In rt. $\triangle WDB$:　　$(WB)^2 = (DB)^2 + h^2$
　　　　　　　　　　$= l^2 + w^2 + h^2$　(by substitution)
　　　　Hence $WB = \sqrt{l^2 + w^2 + h^2}$.

EXAMPLE. In the given rectangular solid, $AB = 3$, $BC = 2$, and $TC = 4$. Find the indicated lengths.
　　a. WT　　c. BD
　　b. RW　　d. BW

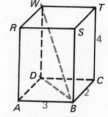

SOLUTION:　a. $WT = AB = 3$
　　　b. $RW = BC = 2$
　　　c. $(BD)^2 = (AD)^2 + (AB)^2$
　　　　　　$= 2^2 + 3^2 = 4 + 9 = 13$
　　　　Hence $BD = \sqrt{13}$
　　　d. $BW = \sqrt{l^2 + w^2 + h^2} = \sqrt{3^2 + 2^2 + 4^2}$
　　　　　$= \sqrt{9 + 4 + 16}$, or $BW = \sqrt{29}$

Oral Exercises

1. How many edges does the solid have?
2. How many faces does the solid have?
3. Name the edges that are parallel to $\overline{RN}$.
4. Name the edges that have the same length as $\overline{WR}$.
5. Name four edges that are perpendicular to $\overline{SO}$.
6. When $\overline{MO}$ is drawn, is $\overline{MO}$ a diagonal of the solid?
7. When $\overline{TN}$ is drawn, is $\overline{TN}$ a diagonal of the solid?
8. Name the right angle in $\triangle PMN$.
9. Name the right angle in $\triangle PNR$.
10. $PR \underline{\quad ? \quad} PN$
　　　　$(<, =, >)$

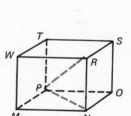

11. $TR \underline{\quad ? \quad} WS$
　　　　$(<, =, >)$
12. $(PN)^2 = (PM)^2 + (\underline{\ ?\ })^2$
13. $(PN)^2 + (RN)^2 = (\underline{\ ?\ })^2$

14. Is it possible for all the edges of a rectangular solid to be congruent?
15. Arrange PN, MN, and PR in increasing order of magnitude.

Exercises 1–8 refer to the rectangular solid shown. Find the indicated lengths.

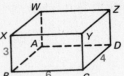

1. *AB*
2. *WZ*
3. *AW*
4. *WX*

5. *CZ*
6. *AC*
7. *WC*
8. *BZ*

Exercises 9–20 refer to the rectangular solid shown. In Exercises 9–16 find the indicated lengths.

9. *RS*
10. *WD*
11. *AS*
12. *RD*

13. *AC*
14. *BT*
15. *WB*
16. *AT*

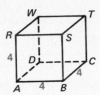

17. *AC* ____?____ *BD*
        $(<, =, >)$

18. *RD* ____?____ *AW*
        $(<, =, >)$

19. *AC* ____?____ *DS*
        $(<, =, >)$

20. *WS* ____?____ *AT*
        $(<, =, >)$

B 21. The bottom of a rectangular box is bounded by a square with a side whose length is 4 cm. If the height of the box is 6 cm, find the length of a diagonal of the box.

22. The bottom of a rectangular box is bounded by a rectangle 6 cm long and 4 cm wide. If the height of the box is 10 cm, find the length of a diagonal of the box.

23. The bottom of a rectangular box is bounded by a square whose diagonal has a length of $8\sqrt{2}$ cm. If the height of the box is 4 cm, find the length of a diagonal of the box.

24. The bottom of a rectangular box is bounded by a rectangle whose diagonal has a length of $2\sqrt{13}$ cm. If the height of the box is 5 cm, find the length of a diagonal of the box.

25. A *cube* is a rectangular solid with all edges congruent. Find the length of a diagonal of a cube with an edge 5 cm long.

26. Find the length of a diagonal of a cube with an edge 4 cm long.

27. The length of a diagonal of a cube is $3\sqrt{3}$ cm. Find the length of an edge of the cube.

28. The length of a diagonal of a cube is $5\sqrt{3}$ cm. Find the length of an edge of the cube.

The figure shown for Exercises 29–34 is called a *regular square pyramid*. Quad. *ABCD* is a square. The other faces are bounded by congruent isosceles triangles. $\overline{VM} \perp \overline{MO}$; $\overline{VO} \perp \overline{BC}$; $\overline{VM} \perp \overline{MB}$

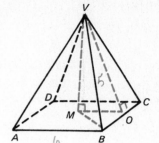

C 29. If $VO = 12$ and $VC = 13$, find BC.
   30. If $AB = 6$ and $VB = 5$, find VM.
   31. If $BC = 8$ and $VB = 8$, find VM.
   32. If $VM = 8$ and $VB = 10$, find AB.
   33. If $m\angle MBV = 60$ and $AB = 8$, find VO.
   34. If $m\angle MVB = 30$ and $VA = 10$, find VM.

Self-Test In Exercises 1–3, find the value of x.

1.

2.
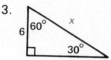

3.
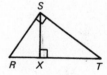

4. The geometric mean between 4 and 25 is __?__ .
5. The geometric mean between 6 and 12 is __?__ .

Exercises 6–8 refer to rt. $\triangle RST$ with $\overline{SX} \perp \overline{RT}$.

6. $\dfrac{RT}{SR} = \dfrac{SR}{?}$

7. $(SX)^2 + (XT)^2 = $ __?__

8. If $RS = 8$ and $RX = 3$, then $SX = $ __?__ .

Check your answers with those printed at the back of the book.

Challenge

Each face of a pyramid is an equilateral triangle. Each edge of the pyramid has length 6. Find the length of **(a)** the altitude of the pyramid, **(b)** the radius of the sphere that contains the four vertices of the pyramid.

Trigonometry

Objectives

1. State the definitions of the tangent, sine, and cosine ratios for an acute angle of a right triangle.
2. Solve a right triangle problem by correct selection and use of the tangent, sine, and cosine ratios.
3. Know the meaning of an angle of elevation and an angle of depression.

7-5 *The Tangent Ratio*

Many distances can be found directly by use of a ruler or tape measure, but some distances cannot be measured directly. Such distances can sometimes be found by using the principles of *trigonometry*. The word trigonometry comes from Greek words meaning "triangle measurement."

We shall confine this brief discussion of trigonometry to three of the special relationships that exist in any right triangle.

Consider the four right triangles shown in the diagram below.

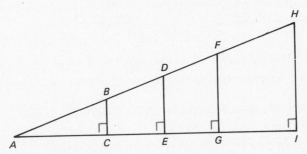

Since each of the triangles contains $\angle A$ and a right angle, the triangles are similar to each other (AA Postulate). We can then conclude that:

$$\frac{BC}{AC} = \frac{DE}{AE} = \frac{FG}{AG} = \frac{HI}{AI}$$

We call this ratio the *tangent ratio*.

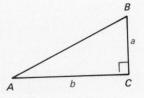

The **tangent** (tan) of an acute angle of a right triangle is the ratio of the length of the leg opposite the acute angle to the length of the leg adjacent to the acute angle.

We usually write tan A for tan $\angle A$ and abbreviate the definition as follows:

$$\tan A = \frac{\text{length of opposite side}}{\text{length of adjacent side}} = \frac{a}{b}$$

We can find an approximation for the tangent of a given acute angle by measuring the legs of a right triangle that contains the angle and then performing the indicated division. Fortunately, tables exist that show the values of the tangent ratios for acute angles with particular measures. Such a table is shown on page 262.

EXAMPLE 1. Find tan 35°.

SOLUTION: Using the table on page 262, locate 35° in the column labeled Angle. Read .7002 in the column labeled Tangent. tan 35° $\doteq$ .7002 (We read this "tan 35° is approximately equal to .7002.")

EXAMPLE 2. In the right triangle shown, find:
a. tan A b. tan B

SOLUTION: a. tan $A = \frac{7}{15}$ b. tan $B = \frac{15}{7}$

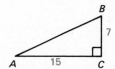

EXAMPLE 3. Find tan R.

SOLUTION: Let $RS = x$.
$$x^2 + 5^2 = 13^2$$
$$x^2 + 25 = 169$$
$$x^2 = 144$$
$$x = 12$$
$$\tan R = \frac{5}{12}$$

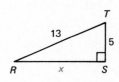

EXAMPLE 4. Find x correct to two digits.

SOLUTION:
$$\tan 40° = \frac{x}{12}$$
$$.8391 \doteq \frac{x}{12}$$
$$x \doteq 12(.8391)$$
$$x \doteq 10.0692, \text{ or } 10$$

EXAMPLE 5. Find x to the nearest degree.

SOLUTION:
$$\tan x° = \frac{9}{12}$$
$$\tan x° = .7500$$

Note, on page 262, that .7500 is closer to .7536 than to .7265.

$$x \doteq 37$$

In Exercises 1–4, state the tangent of ∠A.

1.

3.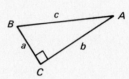

2.

4.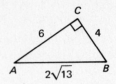

In Exercises 5–8, use the table on page 262.

5. tan 27° ≐ __?__

7. tan 45° ≐ __?__

6. tan 49° ≐ __?__

8. tan 76° ≐ __?__

In Exercises 9–12, find x correct to the nearest degree. Use the table on page 262.

9. tan x° ≐ .6745

11. tan x° ≐ 1.5281

10. tan x° ≐ .1944

12. tan x° ≐ .5390

In Exercises 1–8, find tan ∠1.

1.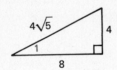

4.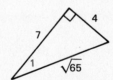

2.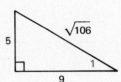

5.

3.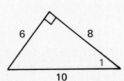

6.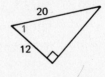

7.

8.

169
144
25

In Exercises 9–14, find x correct to two digits.

9.

10.

11.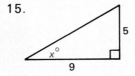

12.

13.

14.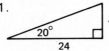

In Exercises 15–20, find x correct to the nearest degree.

B 15.

16.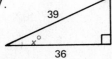

17.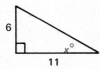

18.

19.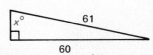

20.

21. In the plane figure shown, $\overline{AC} \cong \overline{BC}$, $\overline{CD} \perp \overline{AB}$, and $m\angle 1 = 62$. If $AB = 40$, find CD.

22. In the plane figure shown, $\angle A \cong \angle B$, $\overline{CD} \perp \overline{AB}$, and $m\angle 1 = 64$. If $CD = 10$, find AB.

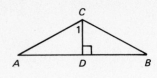

C 23. In $\triangle ABC$, $\overline{BD} \perp \overline{AC}$. If $BD = 8$, find AC.

24. In $\triangle ABC$, $\overline{BD} \perp \overline{AC}$. If $BD = 10$, find AC.

25. Quadrilateral $ABCD$ is a trapezoid with $m\angle A = 75$, $m\angle B = 55$, $AB = 30$, and $DC = 20$. Find the length of an altitude.

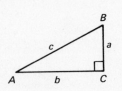

26. The length of an edge of a cube is 10 cm. Find, to the nearest degree, the measure of the smaller angle formed by the intersection of two diagonals of the cube.

7-6 *The Sine and Cosine Ratios*

Suppose you want to find the length x. The tangent ratio is not helpful, because it deals only with the two legs, not the hypotenuse. We need a different ratio to solve this problem.

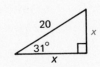

The following two ratios relate the length of the hypotenuse to the lengths of the legs of a right triangle.

The sine (sin) of an acute angle of a right triangle is the ratio of the length of the leg opposite the acute angle to the length of the hypotenuse.

The cosine (cos) of an acute angle of a right triangle is the ratio of the length of the leg adjacent to the acute angle to the length of the hypotenuse.

We shall abbreviate the definitions as follows:

$$\sin A = \frac{\text{length of opposite side}}{\text{length of hypotenuse}} = \frac{a}{c}$$

$$\cos A = \frac{\text{length of adjacent side}}{\text{length of hypotenuse}} = \frac{b}{c}$$

For angle B, we have $\sin B = \dfrac{b}{c}$ and $\cos B = \dfrac{a}{c}$.

EXAMPLE 1. Find x and y correct to two digits.

SOLUTION: a. $\sin 26° = \dfrac{x}{20}$

$.4384 \doteq \dfrac{x}{20}$

$x \doteq 20(.4384)$

$x \doteq 8.768$, or 8.8

b. $\cos 26° = \dfrac{y}{20}$

$.8988 \doteq \dfrac{y}{20}$

$y \doteq 20(.8988)$

$y \doteq 17.976$, or 18

EXAMPLE 2. In rt. $\triangle RST$, $RT = 12$ and $TS = 9$.
Find x correct to the nearest degree.

SOLUTION: $\sin x° = \frac{9}{12}$

$\sin x° = .7500$

$x \doteq 49$

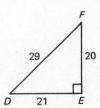

Oral
Exercises

In Exercises 1–8, use the table on page 262.

1. $\sin 19° \doteq$ __?__
2. $\cos 52° \doteq$ __?__
3. $\cos 81° \doteq$ __?__
4. $\sin 16° \doteq$ __?__

5. $\sin 20° \doteq$ __?__
6. $\cos 70° \doteq$ __?__
7. $\sin 45° \doteq$ __?__
8. $\cos 45° \doteq$ __?__

Exercises 9–16 refer to rt. $\triangle DEF$. Classify each statement as true or false.

9. $\sin D = \frac{20}{29}$
10. $\cos F = \frac{20}{29}$
11. $\tan D = \frac{20}{21}$
12. $\tan F > \tan D$

13. $\cos D = \frac{29}{21}$
14. $\sin D > \cos D$
15. $\sin D = \cos F$
16. $m \angle D > 45$

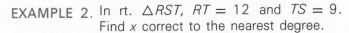

In Exercises 17–20, state the values of sin *A* and cos *A* as fractions in reduced and simplified radical form.

17.

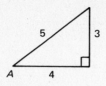

19.

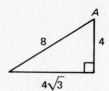

18.

20.

Written Exercises

In Exercises 1–8, use the table on page 262. Find the measure of each angle to the nearest degree.

A

1. sin *A* ≐ .2588
2. cos *C* ≐ .4848
3. cos *R* ≐ .9781
4. sin *E* ≐ .9744

5. sin *D* ≐ .6050
6. cos *F* ≐ .5200
7. cos *H* ≐ .1644
8. sin *M* ≐ .1826

Exercises 9–16 refer to the right triangle shown. Classify each statement as true or false.

9. $\sin 28° = \dfrac{x}{12}$

10. $\cos 62° = \dfrac{12}{x}$

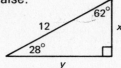

11. $\sin 62° = \dfrac{y}{12}$

12. $\sin 62° = \cos 28°$

13. $y = 12 \cos 28°$

14. $x = 12 \sin 28°$

15. $x^2 + y^2 = 12$

16. $\tan 28° = \dfrac{x}{y}$

In Exercises 17–22, find *x* correct to two digits.

17.

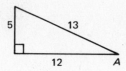

18.

19.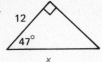

21.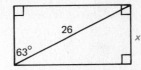

20.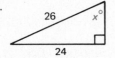

22.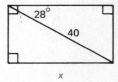

In Exercises 23 and 24, find *x* correct to the nearest degree.

B **23.**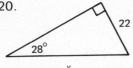

24.

In Exercises 25–28, *do not use* the table on page 262. Find the exact value of *x*.

25. $x = (\sin 30°)^2 + (\cos 30°)^2$
(*Hint:* See Theorem 7-5.)

26. $x = (\sin 60°)^2 + (\cos 60°)^2$

27. $x = (\sin 45°)^2 + (\cos 45°)^2$
(*Hint:* See Theorem 7-4.)

28. $x = (\tan 30°)(\tan 60°)$

C **29.** Quad. *RSTW* is an isosceles trapezoid. If *WR* = 8, *WT* = 12, and *RS* = 20, find *x* correct to the nearest degree.

30. Quad. *RSTW* is an isosceles trapezoid. If *WT* = 16, *RS* = 30, and $m\angle T$ = 110, find *WR* correct to two digits.

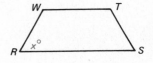

31. In $\triangle ACB$, $m\angle C = 90$, $m\angle A = 25$, and $m\angle 1 = 50$. If *AB* = 30, find *BD* correct to two digits.

32. In $\triangle ACB$, $m\angle C = 90$, $m\angle 2 = 40$, and $m\angle 3 = 22$. If *DC* = 16, find *AB* correct to two digits.

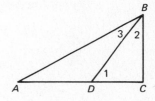

7-7 *Using the Three Trigonometric Ratios*

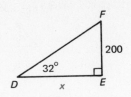

The arithmetic needed to solve some problems can be simplified if a wise choice is made in setting up the trigonometric ratio.

Suppose that we are working with right triangle *DEF* and want to find *x*, the length of $\overline{DE}$.

If we use the tangent ratio with $\angle D$, we have $\tan 32° = \dfrac{200}{x}$. Hence $x = \dfrac{200}{\tan 32°} \doteq \dfrac{200}{.6249}$. In order to compute the value of *x*, it is necessary to divide 200 by .6249. If you do this long division, you will find the value of *x*, correct to two digits, is 320.

The arithmetic in the above problem is much easier if we use the tangent ratio with $\angle F$.

$$\tan 58° = \frac{x}{200}, \text{ or } x = 200 \,(\tan 58°) \doteq 200(1.6003) = 320$$

Notice that the long division has been replaced with an easier multiplication, and again *x*, correct to two digits, is 320.

In the practical applications of trigonometry, engineers and surveyors frequently measure an *angle of elevation* or an *angle of depression*. The **angle of elevation** of an object is the angle in a vertical plane between a horizontal line and the line of sight to the object. It is the acute angle through which a telescope must be elevated from the horizontal to sight on an object. The **angle of depression** is the acute angle through which a telescope must be depressed from the horizontal to sight on an object. Note that $m\angle E = m\angle D$.

$\angle D$ is the angle of depression for a person at *D* sighting *E*.

$\angle E$ is the angle of elevation for a person at *E* sighting *D*.

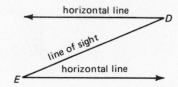

Oral Exercises

In Exercises 1–6, assume that you are to find the value of *x*. State whether the arithmetic involved would require division or multiplication.

1. $\tan 56° = \dfrac{x}{19}$

2. $\cos 19° = \dfrac{x}{27}$

3. $\sin 14° = \dfrac{16}{x}$

4. $\tan x° = \dfrac{18}{95}$

5. $x \sin 16° = 41$

6. $.7632 \doteq \dfrac{x}{36}$

In Exercises 7–10, state the values of sin A, cos A, and tan A as fractions.

7.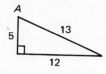

9.

8.

10.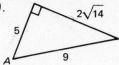

In Exercises 11–16, lines l and m are horizontal lines. Name the indicated angle.

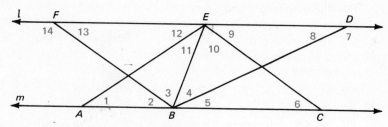

11. The angle of elevation from A to E.
12. The angle of depression from D to B.
13. The angle of elevation from B to F.
14. The angle of depression from E to C.
15. An angle congruent to the angle of depression from F to B.
16. An angle congruent to the angle of elevation from C to E.

Written Exercises

In all the exercises, find lengths correct to two digits and measures of angles correct to the nearest degree.

A

1.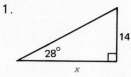

    $x \doteq$ __?__

3.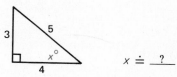

    $x \doteq$ __?__

2.

    $x \doteq$ __?__

4.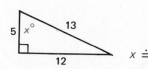

    $x \doteq$ __?__

5. Is sin 31° equal to cos 59°?
6. Is cos 24° equal to cos 66°?
7. Is sin x° equal to cos (90 − x)°?
8. Is cos y° equal to sin (90 − y)°?

9. A 10-meter ladder is leaning against the side of a building. If the foot of the ladder is 3 meters from the foot of the building, find the measure of the acute angle that the ladder makes with the building.

10. A kite string is 200 meters long. Find the height of the kite if the string makes an angle of 38° with the ground. (Assume the kite string does not sag.)

B 11. From the top of a cliff 300 meters high, the angle of depression of a boat has measure 26. How far from the cliff is the boat?

12. The pilot of an airplane finds the angle of depression of an airport to be 16°. If the altitude of the plane is 6000 meters, find the horizontal distance to the airport.

13. The length of the base of an isosceles triangle is 18 cm and the perimeter of the triangle is 78 cm. Find the measure of a base angle of the triangle.

14. The measure of a base angle of an isosceles triangle is 56 and the length of the base is 16 cm. Find the length of an altitude to one of the legs of the triangle.

15. In △ABC, AC is 8 and the length of the altitude to $\overline{AB}$ is 5. Find the measure of ∠A.

16. In △RST, the measure of ∠S is 142 and the length of $\overline{RS}$ is 10. Find the length of the altitude from vertex R.

C 17. At point A, a pilot flying toward an airport finds the angle of depression of the airport to be 22°. Five seconds later, at point B, the measure of the angle of depression is 44°. If the pilot is flying at a constant speed of 900 kilometers per hour and at a constant altitude, what is the height of the plane above the ground?

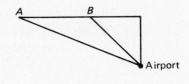

18. In right △DFC, m∠F = 90, DE = 120, m∠1 = 27, and m∠2 = 48. Find CF.

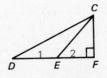

19. In right △RST, m∠S = 90, m∠1 = 60, and RT = 2TX. Find the measure of ∠R.

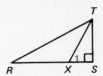

20. The solid shown is a cube with point R on $\overline{XY}$ and point S on $\overline{YZ}$. If $m\angle RAY = 30$ and $m\angle YAS = 30$, find $m\angle RAS$.

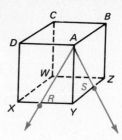

21. If x is the measure of an acute angle of a right triangle, prove that $(\sin x°)^2 + (\cos x°)^2 = 1$.

22. Prove that for any $\triangle ABC$, $\dfrac{\sin A}{\sin B} = \dfrac{a}{b}$.

(*Hint:* Draw the altitude from C.)

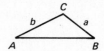

Self-Test Exercises 1–5 refer to rt. $\triangle DEF$.

1. $\tan D = \dfrac{?}{?}$

3. $\tan F = \dfrac{?}{?}$

2. $\sin D = \dfrac{?}{?}$

4. $\cos F = \dfrac{?}{?}$

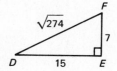

5. $m\angle D$, to the nearest degree, is ___?___ .

In Exercises 6–9, find x correct to two digits.

6.

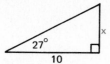

8.

7.

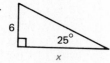

9.

10. If the angle of elevation from A to B is $40°$ and $AB = 30$ cm, find the horizontal distance from A to B.

Check your answers with those printed at the back of the book.

TABLE OF TRIGONOMETRIC RATIOS

Angle	Sine	Cosine	Tangent	Angle	Sine	Cosine	Tangent
1°	.0175	.9998	.0175	46°	.7193	.6947	1.0355
2°	.0349	.9994	.0349	47°	.7314	.6820	1.0724
3°	.0523	.9986	.0524	48°	.7431	.6691	1.1106
4°	.0698	.9976	.0699	49°	.7547	.6561	1.1504
5°	.0872	.9962	.0875	50°	.7660	.6428	1.1918
6°	.1045	.9945	.1051	51°	.7771	.6293	1.2349
7°	.1219	.9925	.1228	52°	.7880	.6157	1.2799
8°	.1392	.9903	.1405	53°	.7986	.6018	1.3270
9°	.1564	.9877	.1584	54°	.8090	.5878	1.3764
10°	.1736	.9848	.1763	55°	.8192	.5736	1.4281
11°	.1908	.9816	.1944	56°	.8290	.5592	1.4826
12°	.2079	.9781	.2126	57°	.8387	.5446	1.5399
13°	.2250	.9744	.2309	58°	.8480	.5299	1.6003
14°	.2419	.9703	.2493	59°	.8572	.5150	1.6643
15°	.2588	.9659	.2679	60°	.8660	.5000	1.7321
16°	.2756	.9613	.2867	61°	.8746	.4848	1.8040
17°	.2924	.9563	.3057	62°	.8829	.4695	1.8807
18°	.3090	.9511	.3249	63°	.8910	.4540	1.9626
19°	.3256	.9455	.3443	64°	.8988	.4384	2.0503
20°	.3420	.9397	.3640	65°	.9063	.4226	2.1445
21°	.3584	.9336	.3839	66°	.9135	.4067	2.2460
22°	.3746	.9272	.4040	67°	.9205	.3907	2.3559
23°	.3907	.9205	.4245	68°	.9272	.3746	2.4751
24°	.4067	.9135	.4452	69°	.9336	.3584	2.6051
25°	.4226	.9063	.4663	70°	.9397	.3420	2.7475
26°	.4384	.8988	.4877	71°	.9455	.3256	2.9042
27°	.4540	.8910	.5095	72°	.9511	.3090	3.0777
28°	.4695	.8829	.5317	73°	.9563	.2924	3.2709
29°	.4848	.8746	.5543	74°	.9613	.2756	3.4874
30°	.5000	.8660	.5774	75°	.9659	.2588	3.7321
31°	.5150	.8572	.6009	76°	.9703	.2419	4.0108
32°	.5299	.8480	.6249	77°	.9744	.2250	4.3315
33°	.5446	.8387	.6494	78°	.9781	.2079	4.7046
34°	.5592	.8290	.6745	79°	.9816	.1908	5.1446
35°	.5736	.8192	.7002	80°	.9848	.1736	5.6713
36°	.5878	.8090	.7265	81°	.9877	.1564	6.3138
37°	.6018	.7986	.7536	82°	.9903	.1392	7.1154
38°	.6157	.7880	.7813	83°	.9925	.1219	8.1443
39°	.6293	.7771	.8098	84°	.9945	.1045	9.5144
40°	.6428	.7660	.8391	85°	.9962	.0872	11.4301
41°	.6561	.7547	.8693	86°	.9976	.0698	14.3007
42°	.6691	.7431	.9004	87°	.9986	.0523	19.0811
43°	.6820	.7314	.9325	88°	.9994	.0349	28.6363
44°	.6947	.7193	.9657	89°	.9998	.0175	57.2900
45°	.7071	.7071	1.0000	90°	1	0	undefined

CHAPTER SUMMARY

1. In the right triangle shown:

$$c^2 = a^2 + b^2$$

$$\frac{c}{a} = \frac{a}{y} \qquad \frac{c}{b} = \frac{b}{x}$$

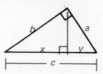

2. A triangle, with sides of lengths a, b, and c, is a right triangle if $c^2 = a^2 + b^2$.
3. In a 30°-60°-90° triangle, the lengths of the sides are in the ratio $1 : \sqrt{3} : 2$.
4. In a 45°-45°-90° triangle, the lengths of the sides are in the ratio $1 : 1 : \sqrt{2}$.
5. In the right triangle shown:

$$\tan A = \frac{a}{b}$$

$$\sin A = \frac{a}{c} \qquad \cos A = \frac{b}{c}$$

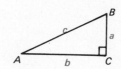

CHAPTER TEST

In $\triangle DEF$, $m\angle DEF = 90$ and $\overline{EB} \perp \overline{DF}$.

1. $\dfrac{DF}{EF} = \dfrac{EF}{?}$

2. $\dfrac{DF}{DE} = \dfrac{DE}{?}$

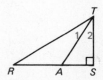

3. If $DF = 12$ and $BF = 3$, then $EF = \underline{}$.
4. If $DE = \sqrt{30}$ and $DB = 5$, then $DF = \underline{}$.
5. In $\triangle DBE$, $(DE)^2 = (DB)^2 + (\underline{})^2$.
6. If $EF = 6$ and $EB = 5$, then $BF = \underline{}$.
7. Is it possible for rt. $\triangle DEF$ to have sides whose lengths are 5, 8, and 9?

Exercises 8–12 refer to $\triangle RST$ with $m\angle S = 90$, $m\angle R = 30$, and $m\angle 1 = m\angle 2$.

8. If $RT = 10$, $TS = \underline{}$.
9. If $TS = 6$, $RS = \underline{}$.
10. If $RS = 4\sqrt{3}$, $RT = \underline{}$.
11. If $RT = 6\sqrt{3}$, $AS = \underline{}$.
12. If $RA = 4$, $RT = \underline{}$.

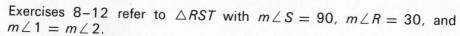

In the given rectangular solid, $DE = 6$, $EO = 6$, and $EB = 5$. Find the indicated lengths.

13. BK
14. CE

15. ME
16. DO

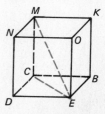

Exercises 17–20 refer to rt. △JKM.

17. $\tan J = \dfrac{?}{?}$

18. $\sin M = \dfrac{?}{?}$

19. $\cos J = \dfrac{?}{?}$

20. $m\angle J$, to the nearest degree, is ___?___. (Use a table.)

In Exercises 21–24, find x correct to two digits. Use the table on page 262.

21.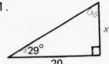

22.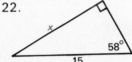

23.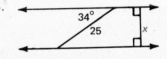

24.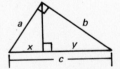
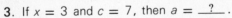

CHAPTER REVIEW

7-1 *The Altitude to the Hypotenuse of a Right Triangle*

1. The geometric mean between 4 and 9 is ___?___.
2. The simplified form of $\sqrt{72}$ is ___?___.

Exercises 3 and 4 refer to the right triangle shown.

3. If $x = 3$ and $c = 7$, then $a = $ ___?___.
4. If $b = 5$ and $c = 8$, then $y = $ ___?___.

7-2 *The Pythagorean Theorem*

5. The lengths of the sides of a triangle are 4, 6, and 8. Is the triangle a right triangle?
6. If the lengths of the legs of a right triangle are 3 and 5, then the length of the hypotenuse is ___?___.
7. If a rectangle that is 6 cm long has a diagonal that is 9 cm long, then the rectangle is ___?___ cm wide.

7-3 *Special Right Triangles*

Classify each statement as true or false.

8. The hypotenuse of a 45°-45°-90° triangle is $\sqrt{3}$ times as long as a leg.

9. The shorter leg of a 30°-60°-90° triangle is the leg opposite the 30° angle.

10. If the length of the hypotenuse of a 30°-60°-90° triangle is 10, then the length of the longer leg is $5\sqrt{3}$.

11. If the length of a diagonal of a square is 18, then the length of a side is $9\sqrt{2}$.

7-4 *Rectangular Solids*

Exercises 12–15 refer to the rectangular solid shown. Find the indicated lengths.

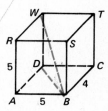

12. *DC*

13. *RW*

14. *DB*

15. *WB*

7-5 *The Tangent Ratio*

16. The table on page 262 shows that tan 57° $\doteq$ __?__ .

17. The table on page 262 shows that when tan $x \doteq .3830$, $x \doteq$ __?__ .

In Exercises 18 and 19, find tan $\angle A$.

18.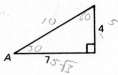

19.

7-6 *The Sine and Cosine Ratio*

In Exercises 20 and 21, find x correct to two digits.

20.

21.

In Exercises 22 and 23, find y correct to the nearest degree.

22.

23.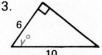

In Exercises 24–27, write the equation you would use to find x. Do not use the table and do not find the numerical value of x.

24.

26.

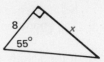

25.

27.

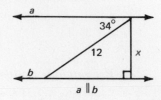

$a \parallel b$

REVIEW OF SKILLS

Find the ordered pair (x, y) that satisfies each system.

EXAMPLE. $\begin{aligned} x + y &= 2 \\ 2x - y &= 7 \end{aligned}$

SOLUTION: $\begin{aligned} x + y &= 2 \\ 2x - y &= 7 \end{aligned}$

$\qquad 3x \quad\ = 9$ (Add)

$\qquad\ x \quad\ = 3$

$\qquad 3 + y = 2$ (Substitute 3 for x in either of the original equations.

$\qquad\qquad y = -1$ We used the first equation.)

The ordered pair is $(3, -1)$.

1. $\begin{aligned} 3x + y &= 4 \\ 2x - y &= 6 \end{aligned}$ 3. $\begin{aligned} -x - 5y &= 2 \\ x - 2y &= 5 \end{aligned}$ 5. $\begin{aligned} 3x - 2y &= 14 \\ 5x + 2y &= -14 \end{aligned}$

2. $\begin{aligned} 4x - y &= 14 \\ 3x + y &= 14 \end{aligned}$ 4. $\begin{aligned} x + 5y &= 16 \\ -x + 2y &= -2 \end{aligned}$ 6. $\begin{aligned} 3x - 3y &= 21 \\ -3x + 5y &= -35 \end{aligned}$

EXAMPLE. $\begin{aligned} 2x + 2y &= 7 \\ 3x + 4y &= 11 \end{aligned}$

SOLUTION: $\begin{aligned} 2x + 2y &= 7 \ \rightarrow\ 4x + 4y = 14 \\ 3x + 4y &= 11 \rightarrow\ 3x + 4y = 11 \end{aligned}$ (Multiply by 2)

$\qquad\qquad\qquad\qquad\quad x \quad\quad = 3$ (Subtract)

$\qquad\qquad\qquad 6 + 2y = 7$

$\qquad\qquad\qquad\qquad 2y = 1$

The ordered pair is $(3, \frac{1}{2})$. $y = \frac{1}{2}$

7. $2x + 3y = 19$
   $x + y = 8$
8. $3x - 2y = 23$
   $x + y = 1$
9. $2x + 3y = 18$
   $3x - 2y = 1$

10. $2x - 13y = 5$
    $3x + 4y = -16$
11. $3x = 2y + 34$
    $6y = 10 - 5x$
12. $4x = 3(1 - y)$
    $6y = 2x + 1$

programming in BASIC

There is an infinite set of number triples {A, B, C} where A, B, and C are positive integers and $A^2 + B^2 = C^2$. A, B, and C are, in this case, the lengths of the sides of a right triangle. We therefore call any such set a Pythagorean triple.

The following program lists all such triples where A and B are less than or equal to 20.

```
10  FOR A=1 TO 20
20  FOR B=A TO 20
30  LET C=SQR(A*A+B*B)
40  IF C<>INT(C) THEN 60
50  PRINT A;B;C
60  NEXT B
70  NEXT A
80  END

RUN

3    4    5
5    12   13
6    8    10
8    15   17
9    12   15
12   16   20
15   20   25

END
```

The RUN of this program has seven triples, five of which are proportional to 3 : 4 : 5. {3, 4, 5} is called a *primitive* Pythagorean triple because there are no factors common to all three numbers.

We can find Pythagorean triples another way. Select any two positive integers U and V (U $>$ V), and calculate 2UV, $U^2 - V^2$, and $U^2 + V^2$.

Pythagorean Triples

V	U	2UV	$U^2 - V^2$	$U^2 + V^2$
1	2	4	3	5
2	5	20	21	29
1	3	6	8	10
2	8	32	60	68

In each case, the calculations give Pythagorean triples. If U and V are not both even or both odd, and have no common factor, primitive Pythagorean triples result.

There is a fascinating fact about any right triangle whose sides have lengths that are integers. If the triangle's three sides are extended, then there are exactly four circles which are tangent to these lines. These circles have radii which are integers, and the sum of the three smallest radii is equal to the largest radius.

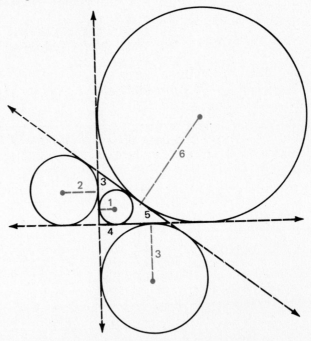

The computer program on the next page calculates and prints primitive Pythagorean triples and the radii of the corresponding circles. Only triples whose numbers are less than one hundred are given.

```
10  PRINT "PRIMITIVE PYTHAGOREAN TRIPLES"
20  PRINT "TRIPLES", "RADII"
30  FOR V=1 TO 6
40  LET U=V+1
50  LET Z=V*V+U*U
60  IF Z>100 THEN 120
70  LET X=2*U*V
80  LET Y=U*U-V*V
90  PRINT X;Y;Z,V*(U-V);V*(U+V);U*(U-V);U*(U+V)
100 LET U=U+2
110 GOTO 50
120 PRINT
130 NEXT V
140 END
```

Exercises

1. Show that $\{U^2 - V^2, 2UV, U^2 + V^2\}$ is a Pythagorean triple by substituting in the equation $a^2 + b^2 = c^2$.

2. Type and RUN the program.

3. Notice in your RUN of the program that when $X > Y$, neither the triples nor the radii are listed in order of increasing magnitude. Change the program to include the lines listed below.

   ```
   82  IF X<Y THEN 90
   84  PRINT Y;X;Z,V*(U-V);U*(U-V);V*(U+V);U*(U+V)
   86  LET U=U+2
   88  GOTO 50
   ```

4. Modify the program to print triples with numbers up to 999. The loop must be extended to 21 and the check on the size of Z must be changed.

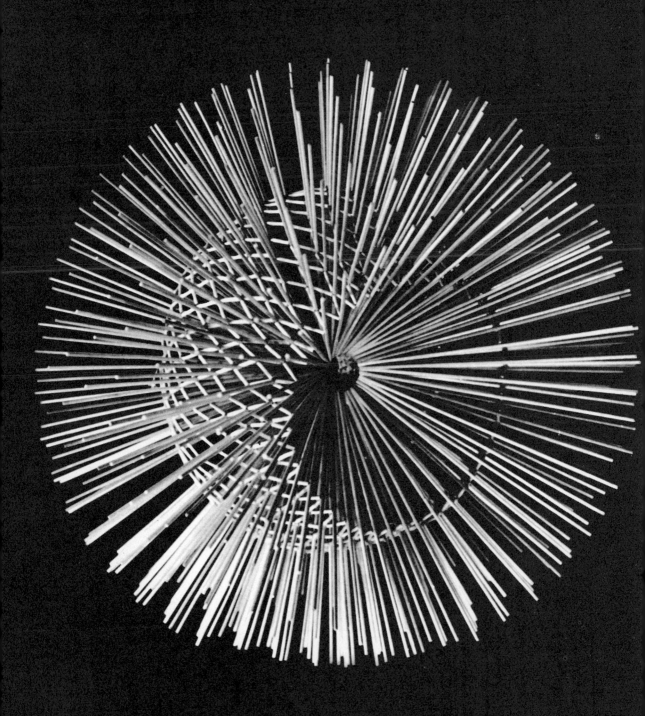

8

CIRCLES

Tangents, Arcs, and Chords

Objectives

1. Define a circle and the lines and segments related to circles.
2. Recognize polygons inscribed in, or circumscribed about, circles.
3. Apply the theorems that relate tangents and radii.
4. Use, in exercises and proofs, the properties involving arcs and central angles.
5. Apply the theorems about the chords of a circle.

8-1 *Circles and Lines*

A circle (⊙) is the set of points in a plane that are a given distance from a given point in the plane. The given point, called the center, can be used to name the circle. The circle shown is ⊙P.

A circle separates a plane into three subsets: the circle itself, the *interior* of the circle, and the *exterior*.

Point N lies in the interior, and $PN < PK$.

Point V lies in the exterior, and $PV > PK$.

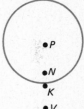

THEOREM 8-1   A line that lies in the plane of a circle and contains an interior point of the circle intersects the circle in two points.

Given: Line l lies in the plane of ⊙O; point X lies in the interior of ⊙O; l contains X.

Prove: Line l intersects ⊙O in two points.

The proof is left as Exercise 26.

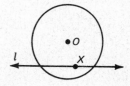

A radius of a circle is a segment that joins the center of a circle to a point on the circle. $\overline{OA}$ is a radius. $\overline{OA}$, $\overline{OB}$, and $\overline{OC}$ are *radii*.

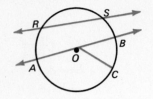

A chord (kord) is a segment whose endpoints lie on a circle. $\overline{RS}$ and $\overline{AB}$ are chords.

A diameter is a chord that contains the center. $\overline{AB}$ is a diameter.

A secant is a line that contains a chord. $\overleftrightarrow{RS}$ and $\overleftrightarrow{AB}$ are secants.

Two or more coplanar circles that have the same center are called concentric circles.

A polygon is said to be inscribed in a circle, and the circle is circumscribed about the polygon, when each vertex of the polygon lies on the circle.

Inscribed Polygons

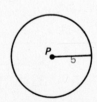

The words *radius* and *diameter* can refer to lengths of segments, as well as to the segments themselves. Thus ⊙P has radius 5 and diameter 10.

Remove the restriction "in a plane" from the definition of a circle and you have the definition of a sphere. A sphere is the set of points a given distance from a given point.

Often you can define terms that are used for spheres as well as for circles by replacing the word *circle* by the word *sphere*.

1. For the circle shown, name: the center; two radii; a diameter; three chords; a secant.

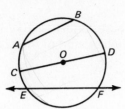

2. Repeat Exercise 1, using the sphere shown.

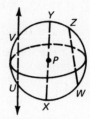

3. State the diameter of a sphere whose radius is 3; $8\frac{1}{2}$; 12.3; j.

4. State the radius of a circle in which the longest chord has length 12; 11; 8.36; $2j$; k.

5. The radius of $\odot O$ is 6. What can you say about the length OX if point X lies on the circle? If X lies in the interior? If X lies in the exterior?

6. Sphere R has radius 8. Describe the position of point Y in relation to the sphere if $RY = 8$; if $RY = 10$; if $RY < 8$.

7. Two points both lie in the interior of a circle, but neither is at the center. How many chords contain both points? How many secants? How many radii? How many diameters?

8. The radius of a sphere is 20. What can you deduce about the distance XY if both X and Y lie on the sphere? If both X and Y lie in the interior? If X lies in the interior and Y lies in the exterior?

9. How many radii can be drawn in a sphere?

10. Can the intersection of a plane and a sphere be a point? a line? a circle? the empty set?

Draw, inscribed in a circle, the figure named. If a drawing cannot be made, write *impossible*.

1. A square
2. An isosceles triangle
3. A right triangle
4. A nonregular hexagon
5. An isosceles trapezoid
6. A nonrectangular ▱

7. Draw a circle and two nonparallel chords. Draw the perpendicular bisector of each chord. Where do the perpendicular bisectors appear to intersect?

8. Draw a circle and a set of parallel chords. What kind of figure contains the midpoints of the chords?

Points *X* and *Y* lie in the interior of a circle. State the number of points in the intersection of the circle and the figure named.

9. $\overline{XY}$ 　　　　　　 10. $\overrightarrow{XY}$ 　　　　　　 11. $\overrightarrow{YX}$ 　　　　　　 12. $\overleftrightarrow{XY}$

Point *V* lies in the interior of a sphere, and point *W* lies in the exterior. State the number of points in the intersection of the sphere and the figure named.

13. $\overline{VW}$ 　　　　　　 14. $\overrightarrow{VW}$ 　　　　　　 15. $\overrightarrow{WV}$ 　　　　　　 16. $\overleftrightarrow{VW}$

Write a definition of the term.

B 17. A radius of a sphere 　　　　　 19. A diameter of a sphere
18. A chord of a sphere 　　　　　　 20. A secant of a sphere

21. The radius of ⊙*O* is 4. If radii $\overline{OA}$ and $\overline{OB}$ form a 90° angle, $AB = \underline{\ ?\ }$.
22. In ⊙*P*, radii $\overline{PX}$ and $\overline{PY}$ form a 90° angle. If $XY = 10$, $PX = \underline{\ ?\ }$.
23. The radius of ⊙*S* is 12. If radii $\overline{SC}$ and $\overline{SD}$ form a 120° angle, $CD = \underline{\ ?\ }$.
24. In ⊙*R*, radii $\overline{RZ}$ and $\overline{RW}$ form a 120° angle. If $ZW = 18$, $RZ = \underline{\ ?\ }$.

C 25. Prove: If a plane intersects a sphere in more than one point, the intersection is a circle. *Hint:* Draw a perpendicular from point *O* to plane *M*, intersecting *M* in point *P*. (You may assume that this is possible.) Let *X* and *Y* be any two points on the intersection of the sphere and the plane. Show that $PX = PY$.

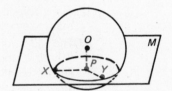

26. Prove Theorem 8-1. *Hint:* Let the line that contains *O* and is perpendicular to l intersect l at *T*. Let the radius of ⊙*O* be *r*. On line l there are two points, *A* and *B*, such that $TA = TB = \sqrt{r^2 - (OT)^2}$. Because $OA = r$ and $OB = r$, points *A* and *B* lie on ⊙*O*.

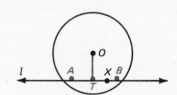

Challenge

Think of the earth as a perfect sphere. A person walks one km south, then one km west, then one km north, thereby returning precisely to the starting point. Where, other than the North Pole, can that person start from?

8-2 *Tangents*

A tangent to a circle is a line that lies in the plane of the circle and intersects the circle in exactly one point. In the diagram, $\overleftrightarrow{XY}$ is tangent to $\odot O$, and $\odot O$ is tangent to $\overleftrightarrow{XY}$. Point Y is the point of tangency. A subset of $\overleftrightarrow{XY}$ that contains the point of tangency is also referred to as a tangent. Thus $\overleftrightarrow{XY}$, $\overrightarrow{XY}$, and $\overline{XY}$ are all tangent to $\odot O$ at point Y.

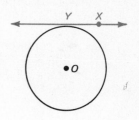

THEOREM 8-2   A tangent to a circle is perpendicular to the radius drawn to the point of tangency.

Given: Line t is tangent to $\odot O$ at point J.

Prove: $\overline{OJ} \perp t$

Indirect Proof:

Suppose $\overline{OJ}$ is not perpendicular to t. From point O there is a segment, $\overline{OK}$, that is perpendicular to t. Then $OK < OJ$. But this contradicts the fact that $OK > OJ$ (because K lies in the exterior of $\odot O$, whereas J lies on $\odot O$). The supposition that $\overline{OJ}$ is not perpendicular to t must be false. Consequently, $\overline{OJ} \perp t$.

THEOREM 8-3   A line that lies in the plane of a circle and is perpendicular to a radius at its outer endpoint is tangent to the circle.

Given: Line m lies in the plane of $\odot P$;
   $m \perp \overline{PA}$ at A.

Prove: m is tangent to $\odot P$.

Outline of Proof:

Let B be any point, other than A, on m. Since $\overline{PA} \perp m$, $PB > PA$ and point B must lie in the exterior of $\odot P$. Since all points, other than A, of line m lie in the exterior of $\odot P$, line m is tangent to $\odot P$.

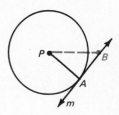

A line that is tangent to each of two coplanar circles is called a common tangent.

A common *internal* tangent intersects the segment that joins the centers.

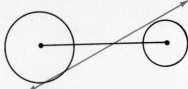

A common *external* tangent does not intersect the segment that joins the centers.

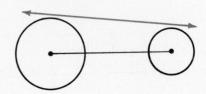

When two coplanar circles are tangent to one line at one point, the *circles are tangent* to each other.

Circles *O* and *P* are *externally* tangent. Each circle, except for point *X*, lies in the exterior of the other.

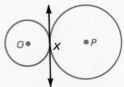

Circles *R* and *S* are *internally* tangent. Circle *R*, except for point *Y*, lies in the interior of circle *S*.

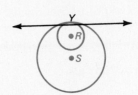

A polygon is circumscribed about a circle and the circle is inscribed in the polygon when each side of the polygon is tangent to the circle.

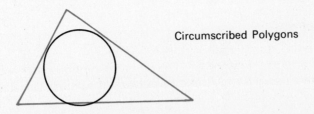

Circumscribed Polygons

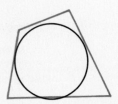

In the plane figure, circles *P, O,* and *R* are tangent to line *l*.

1. Name two internally tangent circles.
2. Name two externally tangent circles.
3. Line *l* is a common internal tangent of what two circles?
4. Line *l* is a common external tangent of what two circles?

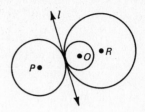

For each pair of coplanar circles, state the number of common external tangents and the number of common internal tangents that can be drawn.

5.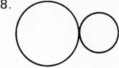

7.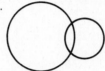

9.

6.

8.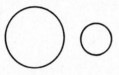

10.

State whether the triangle is inscribed in the circle, circumscribed about the circle, or neither.

11.

12.

13.

14.

A plane figure is shown.

15. It is given that line *j* is tangent to ⊙*U* at point *V*. What can you conclude about $\overline{UV}$ and *j*?
16. It is given that *j* ⊥ $\overline{UV}$ at *V*, a point of ⊙*U*. What can you conclude about line *j* and ⊙*U*?

Written Exercises

For each exercise draw a circle. Then draw a polygon, of the kind described, so that it is circumscribed about the circle.

A

1. An obtuse triangle
2. An acute isosceles triangle
3. A right triangle
4. A nonisosceles trapezoid
5. A nonrectangular rhombus
6. A rectangle (Is it necessary that the rectangle be a square?)

Draw two circles, with all their common tangents, in such a way that the number of common tangents is:

7. One
8. Two
9. Three
10. Four

Tangent relationships are indicated by diagram. Find the lengths.

11.

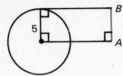

$AB = \underline{\ ?\ }$

13.

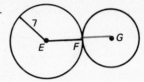

$EG = 12 \qquad FG = \underline{\ ?\ }$

12.

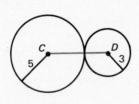

$CD = \underline{\ ?\ }$

14.

$JL = 7.1 \qquad JK = \underline{\ ?\ }$

B

15.

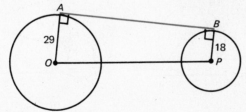

$OP = 61 \qquad AB = \underline{\ ?\ }$

16.

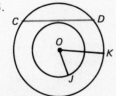

$OJ = 9 \qquad OK = 15 \qquad CD = \underline{\ ?\ }$

278 *GEOMETRY*

Line j is tangent to $\odot P$ at point T. $\overline{PS} \perp j$. Consider $\overleftrightarrow{PT}$ (not drawn in the diagram).

17. How is $\overleftrightarrow{PT}$ related to line j?

18. In the plane, how many lines can be drawn from P perpendicular to j?

19. Can $\overline{PT}$ and $\overline{PS}$ be different segments? Can T and S be different points?

20. Complete the statement: A line that contains the center of a circle and is perpendicular to a line that is tangent to the circle must pass through ___?___ .

21. Given: $\overline{XY}$ is tangent to $\odot C$ at X;
    $\overline{XY}$ is tangent to $\odot K$ at Y.

    Prove: $\overline{CX} \parallel \overline{KY}$

22. Prove: The lines tangent to a circle at the endpoints of a diameter are parallel.

23. Write a definition of a line tangent to a sphere.

24. Write a definition of a plane tangent to a sphere.

25. At a given point on a sphere, how many lines can be drawn tangent to the sphere?

26. Consider all the spheres tangent to a given plane at a given point. Make a true statement about the centers of the spheres.

C 27. Three spheres, each with a 10 cm radius, have centers that are 50 cm apart. How many planes, each one tangent to all three spheres, can be drawn?

28. How many spheres, each one tangent to all three spheres of Exercise 27, can be drawn?

29. Given: $\overline{XY}$ and $\overline{XZ}$ are tangent to $\odot O$.

    Prove: $\overline{XY} \cong \overline{XZ}$

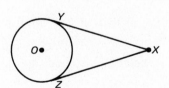

30. Given: $\overline{RS}$ and $\overline{TU}$ are common internal tangents to $\odot J$ and $\odot K$.

    Prove: $\overline{RS} \cong \overline{TU}$

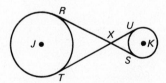

31. Prove: A line that contains the centers of two externally tangent circles contains the point of tangency.

32. Prove: A line that contains the centers of two internally tangent circles contains the point of tangency.

8-3 *Arcs and Central Angles*

A central angle of a circle is an angle whose vertex is the center of the circle. Angle 1 is a central angle of ⊙P.

A minor arc of a circle is the union of two points on the circle and all the points of the circle that lie in the interior of the central angle whose sides contain the two points.

The part of ⊙O shown in red is *minor* arc AB ($\overarc{AB}$ or $\overarc{AXB}$).

The part of ⊙O shown in black is *major* arc AYB ($\overarc{AYB}$). To name a major arc, three letters must be used.

A semicircle is the union of the endpoints of a diameter and all points of the circle lying on one side of the diameter. $\overarc{CZD}$ and $\overarc{CWD}$ are semicircles of ⊙P.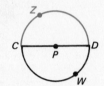

The measure of a minor arc is defined to be the measure of its central angle. If $m\angle 1 = 40$, then $m\,\overarc{AB} = 40$. Since each expression represents 40, we can write $m\,\overarc{AB} = m\angle 1$.

The measure of major arc $\overarc{ATB}$ is defined to be $360 - m\,\overarc{AB}$. If $m\,\overarc{AB} = 40$, then $m\,\overarc{ATB} = 320$.

The measure of a semicircle is 180.

Notice in the figure at the left below, but not in the figure at the right, it seems reasonable to state: $m\,\overarc{AX} + m\,\overarc{XB} = m\,\overarc{AB}$. For both figures it seems reasonable to state: $m\,\overarc{AX} + m\,\overarc{XB} = m\,\overarc{AXB}$.

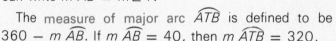

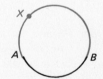

POSTULATE 18
(ARC ADDITION POSTULATE)

If the intersection of arcs $\overarc{AX}$ and $\overarc{XB}$ of a circle is the single point X, then $m\,\overarc{AX} + m\,\overarc{XB} = m\,\overarc{AXB}$.

Congruent circles are circles that have congruent radii. Circles O and P are congruent if $\overline{OA} \cong \overline{PB}$.

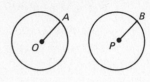

From the definitions of a circle and of congruent circles, we have two facts that are useful in proofs:

Radii of a $\odot$ are congruent.
Radii of congruent circles are congruent.

In the same circle or in congruent circles, arcs that have equal measures are called **congruent arcs**.

THEOREM 8-4   In the same circle or in congruent circles, if two central angles are congruent, their arcs are congruent.

Given: $\odot O \cong \odot P$; $\angle 1 \cong \angle 2$

Prove: $\widehat{AB} \cong \widehat{CD}$

The proof is left as Exercise 19.

THEOREM 8-5   In the same circle or in congruent circles, if two minor arcs are congruent, their central angles are congruent.

The demonstration is left as Exercise 20.

Oral Exercises   Point O is the center of the circle. State whether point X lies on the arc named.

1. $\widehat{BC}$

3. $\widehat{ABC}$

2. $\widehat{AC}$

4. $\widehat{ACB}$

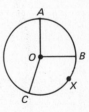

5. If $\overline{AO} \perp \overline{OB}$, then $m\,\widehat{AB} = \underline{\quad?\quad}$ and $m\,\widehat{BXA} = \underline{\quad?\quad}$.

6. Suppose $m\,\widehat{BC} = 110$. Name an arc whose measure is 250.

7. Name three central angles in the figure.

8. Without using X, name three minor arcs; three major arcs.

Point *P* is the center of the circle. $\overline{DE}$ is a diameter.

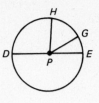

9. m $\overset{\frown}{DHE}$ = __?__ (numerical value)
10. m $\overset{\frown}{HG}$ + m $\overset{\frown}{GE}$ = m __?__
11. m $\overset{\frown}{DH}$ + m $\overset{\frown}{HG}$ = m __?__
12. If m $\overset{\frown}{GE}$ = 30, m $\overset{\frown}{DG}$ = __?__ .
13. If m $\overset{\frown}{DG}$ = 150 and m $\overset{\frown}{HG}$ = 50, then m $\overset{\frown}{DH}$ = __?__ .
14. If m∠GPE = 35, then m $\overset{\frown}{GE}$ = __?__ .
15. If m $\overset{\frown}{HG}$ = 60, then m∠HPG = __?__ .
16. If m∠DPH = 100 and m∠HPG = 45, then m $\overset{\frown}{DG}$ = __?__ .

Written Exercises

$\overline{CD}$ bisects central ∠AOB. Name:

A
1. Five minor arcs
2. Five major arcs
3. Two semicircles
4. Three pairs of congruent arcs

State the measure of the arc shown in red.

5.

7.

9.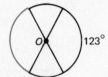

6.

8.

10.

11. At three o'clock, the measure of the angle formed by the hands of a clock is __?__ .
12. At five o'clock, the measure of the angle formed by the hands of a clock is __?__ .
13. Draw a circle. On it locate points *X*, *Y*, and *Z* in such a way that m $\overset{\frown}{XY}$ + m $\overset{\frown}{YZ}$ = m $\overset{\frown}{XZ}$ is a true statement.
14. Draw a circle. On it locate points *R*, *S*, and *T* in such a way that m $\overset{\frown}{RS}$ + m $\overset{\frown}{ST}$ = m $\overset{\frown}{RT}$ is a false statement.

15. Given: $\overline{AB}$ and $\overline{CD}$ are diameters.

    Prove: $\widehat{AD} \cong \widehat{BC}$

16. Given: $\overline{AB}$ and $\overline{CD}$ are diameters.

    Prove: $\overline{AC} \cong \overline{BD}$

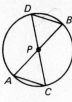

B 17. Given: $\overline{XY}$ is a diameter of $\odot O$;

    $m \angle X = j$

    Prove: $m \widehat{ZY} = 2j$

18. Given: $\overline{XY}$ is a diameter of $\odot O$;

    $m \widehat{XZ} = 2k$

    Prove: $m \angle X = 90 - k$

19. Prove Theorem 8-4.

    Hint: Show $m \widehat{AB} = m \widehat{CD}$.

20. Write a demonstration of Theorem 8-5.

C 21. Given: $\overline{AB}$ is a diameter of $\odot O$;

    $\overline{AX} \parallel \overline{OY}$

    Prove: $\widehat{XY} \cong \widehat{YB}$

22. Given: $\overline{AB}$ is a diameter of $\odot O$;

    $m \widehat{XY} = m \widehat{YB}$

    Prove: $\overline{AX} \parallel \overline{OY}$

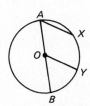

8-4 *Arcs and Chords*

In $\odot P$ there are two arcs, $\widehat{XY}$ and $\widehat{XZY}$, with endpoints X and Y. Unless specified otherwise, the expression the arc of chord $\overline{XY}$ will mean $\widehat{XY}$, the minor arc cut off by $\overline{XY}$.

THEOREM 8-6 In the same circle or in congruent circles, congruent chords have congruent arcs.

Given: $\odot O$ with $\overline{AB} \cong \overline{CD}$

Prove: $\widehat{AB} \cong \widehat{CD}$

For a proof see Exercises 1-6.

THEOREM 8-7 In the same circle or in congruent circles, congruent arcs have congruent chords.

The demonstration is left as Exercise 23.

When $\overset{\frown}{XM} \cong \overset{\frown}{YM}$, M is called the **midpoint** of $\overset{\frown}{XY}$. Any line or segment that contains M is said to **bisect** $\overset{\frown}{XY}$. The **center** of $\overset{\frown}{XY}$ is point O, the center of the circle that includes $\overset{\frown}{XY}$ as a subset.

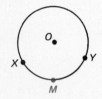

THEOREM 8-8 A diameter that is perpendicular to a chord bisects the chord and its two arcs.

Given: $\odot O$ with diameter $\overline{AB}$ and chord $\overline{XY}$; $\overline{AB} \perp \overline{XY}$

Prove: $\overline{XK} \cong \overline{YK}$; $\overset{\frown}{XB} \cong \overset{\frown}{YB}$; $\overset{\frown}{XA} \cong \overset{\frown}{YA}$

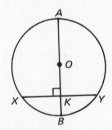 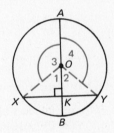

Proof:

STATEMENTS	REASONS
1. Draw $\overline{OX}$ and $\overline{OY}$.	1. Through any two points, there ___?___ .
2. $\overline{AB} \perp \overline{XY}$	2. Given
3. $\overline{OK} \cong \overline{OK}$	3. Congruence of segments is reflexive.
4. $\overline{OX} \cong \overline{OY}$	4. Radii of a $\odot$ are $\cong$.
5. $\triangle OKX \cong \triangle OKY$	5. HL Postulate
6. $\overline{XK} \cong \overline{YK}$; $\angle 1 \cong \angle 2$	6. Corr. parts of $\cong \triangle$ are $\cong$.
7. $\angle 3 \cong \angle 4$	7. If two $\angle$ are supp. to $\cong \angle$, ___?___ .
8. $\overset{\frown}{XB} \cong \overset{\frown}{YB}$; $\overset{\frown}{XA} \cong \overset{\frown}{YA}$	8. If two central $\angle$ are $\cong$, ___?___ .

The **distance** from a point to a line is defined to be the length of the segment drawn perpendicular to the line from the point. In the figure, $\overline{PR} \perp j$. Consequently, the distance from point P to line j is PR.

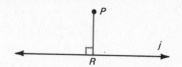

THEOREM 8-9 In the same circle or in congruent circles, if two chords are congruent, they are equally distant from the center.

Given: $\odot O$, with $\overline{AB} \cong \overline{CD}$;
$\overline{OX} \perp \overline{AB}$; $\overline{OY} \perp \overline{CD}$

Prove: $OX = OY$

For a condensed proof, see Exercises 17–22.

THEOREM 8-10 In the same circle or in congruent circles, if two chords are equally distant from the center, the chords are congruent.

The demonstration is left as Exercise 27.

Oral Exercises Refer to $\odot O$. State the theorem that supports the assertion.

1. If $\overline{RS} \cong \overline{TW}$, then $\overparen{RS} \cong \overparen{TW}$.
2. If $\overparen{RS} \cong \overparen{TW}$, then $\overline{RS} \cong \overline{TW}$.
3. If $\angle 1 \cong \angle 2$, then $\overparen{RS} \cong \overparen{TW}$.
4. If $\overparen{RS} \cong \overparen{TW}$, then $\angle 1 \cong \angle 2$.

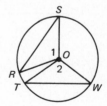

In $\odot P$, $\overline{JK} \perp \overline{CD}$.

5. $\overline{CM} \cong$ __?__
6. $\overline{JK}$ bisects __?__ , __?__ , and __?__ .
7. The midpoint of $\overparen{CD}$ is __?__ .
   The center of $\overparen{CD}$ is __?__ .
8. $\overparen{JC} \cong$ __?__

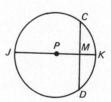

In ⊙O, $\overline{OH} \perp \overline{CD}$; OH = 3, CD = 8.

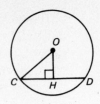

9. $\overline{CH} \cong$ __?__
10. Because CD = 8 and CH = DH, CH = __?__ .
11. $(OC)^2 = (CH)^2 + (OH)^2$, or $4^2 +$ __?__ ^{2}, or __?__
12. OC = __?__ (numerical value)

Written Exercises

Supply the reasons needed to complete the proof of Theorem 8-6.

Given: ⊙O with $\overline{AB} \cong \overline{CD}$

Prove: $\overparen{AB} \cong \overparen{CD}$

Proof:

	STATEMENTS		REASONS
A	1. Draw $\overline{OA}, \overline{OB}, \overline{OC},$ and $\overline{OD}$.	1.	__?__
	2. $\overline{OA} \cong \overline{OC}; \overline{OB} \cong \overline{OD}$	2.	__?__
	3. $\overline{AB} \cong \overline{CD}$	3.	__?__
	4. $\triangle AOB \cong \triangle COD$	4.	__?__
	5. $\angle AOB \cong \angle COD$	5.	__?__
	6. $\overparen{AB} \cong \overparen{CD}$	6.	__?__

Find the length indicated.

7.

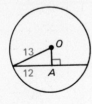

OA = __?__

9.

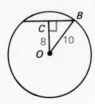

BC = __?__

11.

FG = 8; OF = 6;
OJ = __?__

8.

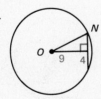

ON = __?__

10.

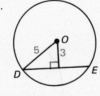

DE = __?__

12.

OR = 3; MK = 12;
OK = __?__

286 *GEOMETRY*

13. Given: $\odot O$; $\overline{OC} \perp \overline{AB}$, $m\,\widehat{KB} = m\,\widehat{BC}$
    Prove: $m\,\widehat{KB} = m\,\widehat{AC}$

14. Given: $\odot O$; $\overline{OC} \perp \overline{AB}$; $\widehat{KB} \cong \widehat{AC}$
    Prove: $\widehat{KB} \cong \widehat{BC}$

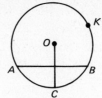

B 15. Given: Points R, S, T, and W on $\odot O$;
    $\overline{RS} \cong \overline{TW}$
    Prove: $\overline{RT} \cong \overline{SW}$

16. Given: Points R, S, T, and W on $\odot O$;
    $\widehat{RT} \cong \widehat{SW}$
    Prove: $\overline{RS} \cong \overline{TW}$

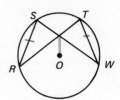

Supply the reasons for this condensed proof of Theorem 8-9.

Given: $\odot O$, with $\overline{AB} \cong \overline{CD}$;
       $\overline{OX} \perp \overline{AB}$; $\overline{OY} \perp \overline{CD}$

Prove: $OX = OY$

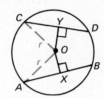

Proof:

STATEMENTS	REASONS
17. Draw $\overline{OA}$ and $\overline{OC}$.	17. _?_
18. $AX = \frac{1}{2}AB$; $CY = \frac{1}{2}CD$	18. _?_
19. $AB = CD$, and $\frac{1}{2}AB = \frac{1}{2}CD$	19. _?_
20. $AX = CY$	20. _?_
21. $(OX)^2 + (AX)^2 = r^2$, and $OX = \sqrt{r^2 - (AX)^2}$ $(OY)^2 + (CY)^2 = r^2$, and $OY = \sqrt{r^2 - (CY)^2}$	21. _?_
22. $OX = OY$	22. _?_

23. Prove Theorem 8-7.

24.

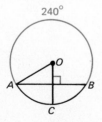

$AB = 16$. $OA = $ _?_

25.

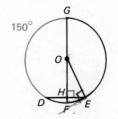

$OH = 6$. $FG = $ _?_

C 26. $\overset{\frown}{CD} \cong \overset{\frown}{FE}$; $OA = x - 1$;
$EF = 4x$; $GH = 4x + 2$.
$x = \underline{\quad?\quad}$

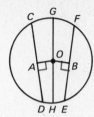

27. Write a demonstration of
Theorem 8-10.

28. Prove: If a chord of the larger of two concentric circles is tangent to the smaller circle, then the chord is bisected at the point of tangency.

29. Prove: If two minor arcs of a circle have unequal measures, then the arc with the greater measure has the longer chord.

Self-Test 1. Give the meaning of each of the following.
  a. circle   c. chord
  b. secant   d. line tangent to a circle

2. Sketch a nonregular pentagon inscribed in a circle. Sketch an isosceles triangle circumscribed about a circle.

Points A and B lie on ⊙O.

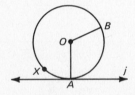

3. If $m \angle AOB = k$, then $m \overset{\frown}{AB} = \underline{\quad?\quad}$.
4. If line $j \perp \overline{OA}$, then j must be $\underline{\quad?\quad}$.
5. Does $m \overset{\frown}{AX} + m \overset{\frown}{XB} = m \overset{\frown}{AB}$?
6. If $m \overset{\frown}{AX} = 30$, then $m \overset{\frown}{XBA} = \underline{\quad?\quad}$.

Exs. 3–8

7. Suppose it is known that j is tangent to ⊙O at A. State the reason that supports the assertion that $\overline{OA} \perp j$.

8. Suppose it is known that $\overset{\frown}{CD} \cong \overset{\frown}{AB}$ in ⊙O. ($\overset{\frown}{CD}$ is not labeled in the drawing.) State the reason that supports the assertion that $\angle COD \cong \angle AOB$.

9. A 30 cm chord is drawn in a circle that has a 17 cm radius. Find the distance from the center of the circle to the chord.

10. Given: Points X, Y, Z, and W lie on ⊙P;
  $\overline{ZW} \perp \overline{XY}$
Prove: $\overline{XW} \cong \overline{YW}$

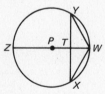

Check your answers with those printed at the back of the book.

Angles and Segments

Objectives

1. Solve problems and prove statements involving inscribed angles.
2. Solve problems and prove statements involving angles formed by secants and tangents.
3. Solve problems involving the lengths of chords, secant segments, and tangent segments.

8-5 *Inscribed Angles*

In each figure below, ∠1 is *inscribed* in the arc shown in red. Note that an angle can be inscribed in a major arc, a minor arc, and a semicircle.

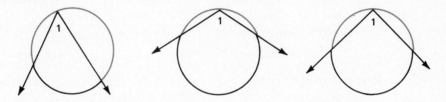

An inscribed angle is an angle whose vertex lies on a circle and whose sides contain chords of the circle.

In the figures below, the angles intercept the arcs shown in red. Note that some angles intercept two arcs.

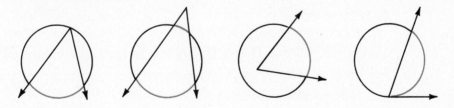

In the figure at the right, ∠X does not intercept $\overset{\frown}{RS}$, since side $\overrightarrow{XY}$ does not intersect the circle.

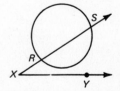

THEOREM 8-11 The measure of an inscribed angle is equal to half the measure of the intercepted arc.

Given: $\angle ABC$ inscribed in $\odot O$.　　Prove: $m\angle ABC = \frac{1}{2} m \overset{\frown}{AC}$

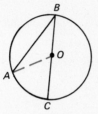 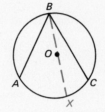 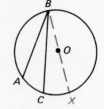

I. Point O lies on $\angle ABC$.

II. Point O lies in the interior of $\angle ABC$.

III. Point O lies in the exterior of $\angle ABC$.

Proof of Case I:

STATEMENTS	REASONS
1. Draw $\overline{OA}$.	1. Through two points there __?__ .
2. $\overline{OB} \cong \overline{OA}$	2. Radii of a $\odot$ are $\cong$.
3. $\angle A \cong \angle B$ and $m\angle A = m\angle B$	3. If two sides of a $\triangle$ are $\cong$, the __?__ .
4. $m\angle A + m\angle B = m\angle AOC$	4. The measure of an ext. $\angle$ of a $\triangle$ __?__ .
5. $m\angle B + m\angle B = m\angle AOC$	5. Substitution principle
6. $m\angle B = \frac{1}{2} m\angle AOC$	6. Division property of equality
7. $m \overset{\frown}{AC} = m\angle AOC$	7. The measure of a minor arc is __?__ .
8. $m\angle B = \frac{1}{2} m \overset{\frown}{AC}$	8. Substitution principle

The proofs of Cases **II** and **III** are left as Exercises 19 and 20.

COROLLARY **1** If two inscribed angles intercept congruent arcs, the angles are congruent.

COROLLARY 2 If a quadrilateral is inscribed in a circle, opposite angles are supplementary.

COROLLARY 3 An angle inscribed in a semicircle is a right angle.

Shown below are figures illustrating these three corollaries.

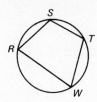

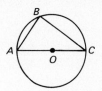

If $\overset{\frown}{DE} \cong \overset{\frown}{FG}$,
then $\angle 1 \cong \angle 2$.

If quad. *RSTW* is inscribed
in the circle, then $\angle R$ and
$\angle T$ are supp. and $\angle S$ and
$\angle W$ are supp.

If $\overset{\frown}{ABC}$ is a semicircle, then $\angle B$ is
a rt. $\angle$.

In the figure, $\overrightarrow{RS}$ is called a *tangent ray*. $\overrightarrow{TW}$ and
$\overrightarrow{UV}$ are called *secant rays*.

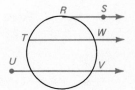

THEOREM 8-12 When a secant ray and a tangent ray are drawn from
a point on a circle, the measure of the angle formed
is equal to half the measure of the intercepted arc.

Given: $\odot O$ with secant ray $\overrightarrow{BA}$ **Prove:** $m \angle ABC = \frac{1}{2} m \overset{\frown}{AXB}$
and tangent ray $\overrightarrow{BC}$

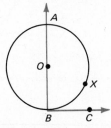

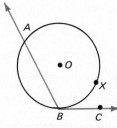

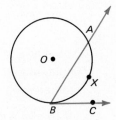

I. Point *O* lies on
$\angle ABC$.

II. Point *O* lies
in the interior
of $\angle ABC$.

III. Point *O* lies
in the exterior
of $\angle ABC$.

The proofs of the cases are left as Exercises 22, 23, and 24.

Points *A*, *B*, *C*, and *D* lie on the circle.

1. $m \overset{\frown}{AB} = 80$ $m\angle C = \underline{\quad?\quad}$ $m\angle D = \underline{\quad?\quad}$
2. $m\angle C = 42$ $m \overset{\frown}{AB} = \underline{\quad?\quad}$ $m\angle D = \underline{\quad?\quad}$
3. $m \overset{\frown}{CD} = 90$ $m\angle A = \underline{\quad?\quad}$ $m\angle B = \underline{\quad?\quad}$
4. $m\angle B = j$ $m \overset{\frown}{CD} = \underline{\quad?\quad}$ $m\angle A = \underline{\quad?\quad}$

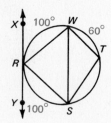

Points *R*, *S*, *T*, and *W* lie on the circle.
$\overleftrightarrow{XY}$ is a tangent at *R*.

5. $m \overset{\frown}{ST} = \underline{\quad?\quad}$ 8. $m\angle YRS = \underline{\quad?\quad}$
6. $m\angle RSW = \underline{\quad?\quad}$ 9. $m\angle WTS = \underline{\quad?\quad}$
7. $m\angle XRW = \underline{\quad?\quad}$ 10. $m\angle WRS = \underline{\quad?\quad}$

$\overline{JP}$ and $\overline{JM}$ are chords of $\odot O$. $\overline{JK}$ is a diameter.

1. $m \overset{\frown}{PM} = 40$; $m \overset{\frown}{JKM} = 210$
   $m \overset{\frown}{MK} = \underline{\quad?\quad}$; $m \overset{\frown}{JP} = \underline{\quad?\quad}$; $m\angle PJK = \underline{\quad?\quad}$
2. $m\angle PJK = 37$; $m \overset{\frown}{PM} = 41$
   $m \overset{\frown}{PK} = \underline{\quad?\quad}$; $m \overset{\frown}{MK} = \underline{\quad?\quad}$; $m\angle MJK = \underline{\quad?\quad}$

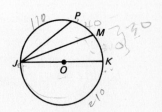

$\overline{XA}$, $\overline{AB}$, and $\overline{XB}$ are chords. $\overleftrightarrow{CD}$ is a tangent at *X*.

3. $m\angle AXD = 50$; $m\angle A = 60$
   $m\angle BXC = \underline{\quad?\quad}$; $m\angle B = \underline{\quad?\quad}$
4. $m\angle BXD = 116$; $m\angle AXD = 62$
   $m \overset{\frown}{BAX} = \underline{\quad?\quad}$; $m\angle B = \underline{\quad?\quad}$

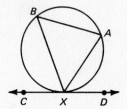

Quadrilateral *RSTW* is inscribed in $\odot O$. $\overline{WS}$ is a diameter. $\overleftrightarrow{TV}$ is a tangent.

5. $\angle WTS$ has measure $\underline{\quad?\quad}$. As a pair, $\angle TWS$ and $\angle TSW$ are $\underline{\quad?\quad}$ angles.
6. If $m \overset{\frown}{TS} = 100$, $m\angle SWT = \underline{\quad?\quad}$ and $m\angle STV = \underline{\quad?\quad}$.
7. If $m\angle RWS = 29$, $m \overset{\frown}{RS} = \underline{\quad?\quad}$ and $m \overset{\frown}{RW} = \underline{\quad?\quad}$.
8. If $m\angle STV = 51$, $m\angle TRS = \underline{\quad?\quad}$ and $m\angle SWT = \underline{\quad?\quad}$.

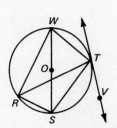

9. Given: $\overline{XY} \parallel \overline{ZW}$
   Prove: $\overset{\frown}{XZ} \cong \overset{\frown}{YW}$

10. Given: $m \overset{\frown}{XZ} = m \overset{\frown}{YW}$
    Prove: $\overline{XY} \parallel \overline{ZW}$

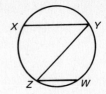

11. Given: $\overline{JA}$ and $\overline{JB}$ are tangent
    to $\odot O$ at A and B.
    Prove: $\overline{JA} \cong \overline{JB}$

12. Given: $\overline{JA}$ and $\overline{JB}$ are tangent
    to $\odot O$ at A and B;
    $m \overset{\frown}{AB} = 110$
    Prove: $m \angle J = 70$

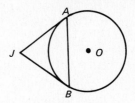

B 13. Given: $\triangle RST$ is inscribed in $\odot P$;
    $\overleftrightarrow{CD}$ is a tangent at T; $\overleftrightarrow{CD} \parallel \overline{RS}$
    Prove: $\overset{\frown}{RT} \cong \overset{\frown}{ST}$

14. Given: $\triangle RST$ is inscribed in $\odot P$;
    $\overleftrightarrow{CD}$ is a tangent at T; $\overline{RT} \cong \overline{ST}$
    Prove: $\overleftrightarrow{CD} \parallel \overline{RS}$

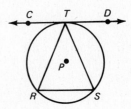

Exercises 15–17 deal with a quadrilateral *EFGH* inscribed in a circle.

15. If $m \angle E = 4x + 40$ and $m \angle G = 5x + 5$, then $x =$ ___?___ .

16. If $m \angle E = 7x + 20$, $m \angle F = 10x + 5$, and $m \angle G = 3x + 40$, then the numerical value of $m \angle F =$ ___?___ .

17. If $m \angle F = x^2 + 30$ and $m \angle H = 150 - 10x$, then $m \angle F =$ ___?___ or ___?___ .

18. Can a circle be circumscribed about a quadrilateral whose angles have measures 60, 80, 116, and 104? Explain your answer.

19. Prove Case **II** of Theorem 8-11.
    Hint: Draw $\overrightarrow{BO}$. $m \angle ABC = m \angle ABX + m \angle XBC$. Use Case **I**.

20. Prove Case **III** of Theorem 8-11.

21. Prove: The bisector of an inscribed angle divides the intercepted arc into two congruent arcs.

22. Prove: Case **I** of Theorem 8-12.
    Hint: Show that $m \angle ABC = 90$ and $m \overset{\frown}{AXB} = 180$.

C 23. Prove Case **II** of Theorem 8-12.

   Hint: Draw $\overrightarrow{BO}$. Use the Angle Addition Postulate, the Arc Addition Postulate, Case **I**, and Theorem 8-11.

24. Prove Case **III** of Theorem 8-12.

25. $\triangle RST$ is inscribed in $\odot O$. $m\angle R = 40$ and $m\angle S = 48$. Explain why points T and O must lie on opposite sides of $\overleftrightarrow{RS}$.

26. Vertices D, E, and F of quadrilateral $DEFG$ lie on a circle. $m\angle D = m\angle E = m\angle F = 91$. Explain why point G must lie in the exterior of the circle.

8-6 *Other Angles*

THEOREM 8-13 When two secants intersect in the interior of a circle, the measure of an angle formed is equal to half the sum of the measures of the arcs intercepted by that angle and its vertical angle.

Given: $\overleftrightarrow{XY}$ and $\overleftrightarrow{ZW}$ intersect in the interior of the $\odot$.

Prove: $m\angle 1 = \frac{1}{2}(m\,\widehat{XZ} + m\,\widehat{YW})$

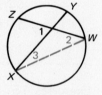

Proof:

STATEMENTS	REASONS
1. Draw $\overline{XW}$.	1. Through two points there __?__ .
2. $m\angle 1 = m\angle 2 + m\angle 3$	2. The measure of an ext. $\angle$ of a $\triangle$ is equal __?__ .
3. $m\angle 2 = \frac{1}{2}m\,\widehat{XZ}$; $m\angle 3 = \frac{1}{2}m\,\widehat{YW}$	3. The measure of an inscribed $\angle$ __?__ .
4. $m\angle 1 = \frac{1}{2}m\,\widehat{XZ} + \frac{1}{2}m\,\widehat{YW}$	4. Substitution principle
5. $m\angle 1 = \frac{1}{2}(m\,\widehat{XZ} + m\,\widehat{YW})$	5. Distributive property

THEOREM 8-14 When two secant rays, a secant ray and a tangent ray, or two tangent rays are drawn to a circle from an exterior point, the measure of the angle formed is equal to half the difference of the measures of the intercepted arcs.

I   Given: Secant rays $\overrightarrow{PA}$ and $\overrightarrow{PB}$

Prove: $m \angle P = \frac{1}{2}(m \ \overset{\frown}{AB} - m \ \overset{\frown}{CD})$

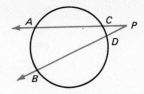

II   Given: Tangent $\overrightarrow{PT}$; secant $\overrightarrow{PB}$

Prove: $m \angle P = \frac{1}{2}(m \ \overset{\frown}{TB} - m \ \overset{\frown}{TD})$

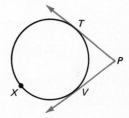

III   Given: Tangent rays $\overrightarrow{PT}$ and $\overrightarrow{PV}$

Prove: $m \angle P = \frac{1}{2}(m \ \overset{\frown}{TXV} - m \ \overset{\frown}{TV})$

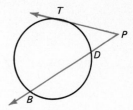

The proofs of the three cases are left as Exercises 25, 26, and 27.

Oral Exercises   Using the secants and tangents shown, state the measure of the numbered angle.

1.
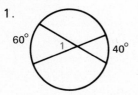

3.
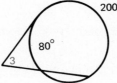

5.
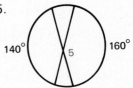

2.

4.

6.
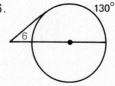

State an equation that you could use to find the numerical value of *x*.

7.
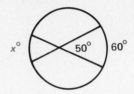
$x°$ 50°   60°

9.
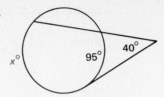
$x°$ 95°   40°

8.
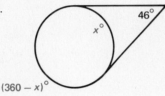
46°
$x°$
$(360 - x)°$

10.
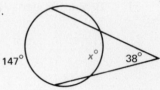
147° $x°$ 38°

Written Exercises

Points *T, U, V, W* and *X* lie on ⊙*O*.
$\overline{UX}$ is a diameter. $\overleftrightarrow{TZ}$ is a tangent.

$m \, \overarc{TX} = 50$

$m \, \overarc{XW} = 30$

$m \, \overarc{UV} = 20$

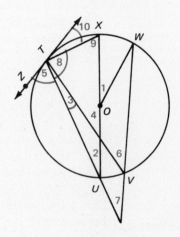

A   1–10. Copy the figure on your own paper so that you can write measures alongside arcs. Find the measure of each numbered angle.

$\overline{GH}$ and $\overline{JK}$ are chords of the ⊙.

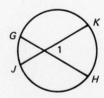

11. If $m \, \overarc{GJ} = 40$ and $m \, \overarc{HK} = 82$, $m\angle 1 = $ ___?___ .
12. If $m \, \overarc{GJ} = b$ and $m \, \overarc{HK} = b + c$, $m\angle 1 = $ ___?___ .
13. If $m\angle 1 = 60$ and $m \, \overarc{HK} = 80$, $m \, \overarc{GJ} = $ ___?___ .
14. If $m\angle 1 = c$ and $m \, \overarc{GJ} = t$, $m \, \overarc{HK} = $ ___?___ .

$\overline{PE}$ and $\overline{PF}$ are tangent segments.

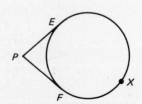

15. If $m \, \overarc{EF} = 100$, $m\angle P = $ ___?___ .
16. If $m \, \overarc{EXF} = 250$, $m\angle P = $ ___?___ .
17. If $m\angle P = 75$, $m \, \overarc{EF} = $ ___?___ .
18. If $m\angle P = 81$, $m \, \overarc{EXF} = $ ___?___ .

$\overline{AT}$ is a tangent segment and $\overrightarrow{AS}$ is a secant ray.

19. If $m\,\widehat{ST} = 100$ and $m\,\widehat{RT} = 70, m\angle A = \underline{\quad?\quad}$.
20. If $m\,\widehat{ST} = j$ and $m\,\widehat{RT} = k, m\angle A = \underline{\quad?\quad}$.
21. If $m\,\widehat{RNS} = 200$ and $m\,\widehat{RT} = 60, m\angle A = \underline{\quad?\quad}$.
22. If $m\,\widehat{RNS} = 205$ and $m\,\widehat{ST} = 105, m\angle A = \underline{\quad?\quad}$.

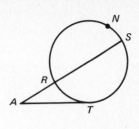

B 23. Given: $\overline{XY} \perp \overline{ZW}$
  Prove: $m\,\widehat{XW} + m\,\widehat{YZ} = 180$
24. Given: $\overline{XY} \perp \overline{ZW}$; $m\,\widehat{WY} = j$
  Prove: $m\,\widehat{XZ} = 180 - j$

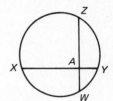

25. Prove Case **I** of Theorem 8-14.
  Hint: Draw $\overline{AD}$. $m\angle ADB = m\angle DAP + m\angle P$
26. Prove Case **II** of Theorem 8-14.
  Hint: Draw $\overline{DT}$. $m\angle P = m\angle TDB - m\angle PTD$
27. Prove Case **III** of Theorem 8-14.
  Hint: Draw $\overrightarrow{TV}$. Let W be a point that lies on $\overrightarrow{PV}$, but not on $\overline{PV}$. Then $m\angle P = m\angle WVT - m\angle PTV$.
28. Prove: When two tangent rays are drawn to a circle from an exterior point, the angle formed is supplementary to the angle formed by the radii drawn to the points of tangency.

EXAMPLE. $\overline{PX}$ and $\overline{PY}$ are tangents. $m\,\widehat{XY} > 90$.
  Make a deduction about $m\angle P$.

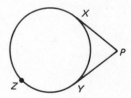

SOLUTION:
$$m\,\widehat{XY} > 90$$
$$m\,\widehat{XZY} < 270$$
$$-m\,\widehat{XY} < -90$$
$$m\,\widehat{XZY} - m\,\widehat{XY} < 180$$
$$\tfrac{1}{2}(m\,\widehat{XZY} - m\,\widehat{XY}) < 90$$
$$m\angle P < 90$$

$\overline{TA}$ and $\overline{TB}$ are tangents.

C 29. $m\,\widehat{AB} < 100$. Make a deduction about $m\angle T$.
30. $m\,\widehat{ASB} > 250$. Make a deduction about $m\angle T$.
31. $m\angle T > 60$. Make a deduction about $m\,\widehat{AB}$.
32. $m\angle T < j$. Make a deduction about $m\,\widehat{ASB}$.

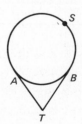

33. $\overline{RS}$ and $\overline{WT}$ are chords.
$m\ \widehat{WS} < 70.\ m\ \widehat{RT} \leq 100.$
Make a deduction about $m\angle RVW.$

34. $m\angle RVW > m\angle SVW.\ m\ \widehat{RW} = m\ \widehat{RT}.$
$m\ \widehat{WRT} \leq 250.$ Make a deduction
about $m\ \widehat{ST}.$

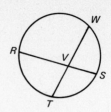

8-7 *Circles and Lengths of Segments*

To many people, it does not seem likely that the statement $a \cdot b = c \cdot d$ is a correct one. Nevertheless, the
statement can be proved.

THEOREM 8-15 When two chords intersect within a circle, the product
of the lengths of the segments of one chord is equal
to the product of the lengths of the segments of the
other.

Given: Chords $\overline{XY}$ and $\overline{ZW}$ intersecting
at K within a circle.

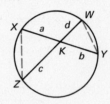

Prove: $a \cdot b = c \cdot d$

Proof:

STATEMENTS	REASONS
1. Draw $\overline{XZ}$ and $\overline{WY}$.	1. Through any __?__ .
2. $\angle X \cong \angle W;\ \angle Z \cong \angle Y$	2. If two inscribed ⩘ intercept __?__ .
3. $\triangle XKZ \sim \triangle WKY$	3. AA Postulate
4. $\dfrac{a}{d} = \dfrac{c}{b}$	4. Lengths of corr. sides of $\sim$ __?__ .
5. $a \cdot b = c \cdot d$	5. A property of proportions

If $\overleftrightarrow{AB}$ is tangent to $\odot O$ at point B, then
$\overline{AB}$ is a tangent segment from A to $\odot O$.

If point P lies in the exterior of $\odot O$, and
$\overleftrightarrow{PD}$ intersects the $\odot$ at C and D, $\overline{PD}$ is a
secant segment and $\overline{PC}$ is the external seg-
ment of $\overline{PD}$.

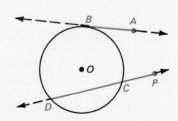

THEOREM 8-16 If two secants are drawn to a circle from an exterior point, the product of the lengths of one secant segment and its external segment is equal to the product of the lengths of the other secant segment and its external segment.

Given: A circle with secant segments $\overline{PX}$ and $\overline{PZ}$

Prove: $PX \cdot PY = PZ \cdot PW$

For a proof, see Exercises 1–6.

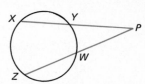

THEOREM 8-17 If a tangent and a secant are drawn to a circle from an exterior point, the square of the length of the tangent segment is equal to the product of the lengths of the secant segment and its external segment.

Given: A circle with tangent segment $\overline{PT}$ and secant segment $\overline{PX}$

Prove: $(PT)^2 = PX \cdot PY$

The proof is left as Exercise 23.

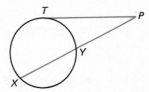

Oral Exercises Chords, secants, and tangents are shown. State an equation you could use to find x.

1.

2.
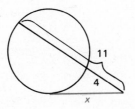

3.
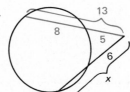

4.
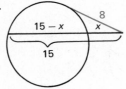

5.

6.

Written Exercises

Supply the reasons needed to complete the proof of Theorem 8-16.

Given: A circle with secant segments $\overline{PX}$ and $\overline{PZ}$

Prove: $PX \cdot PY = PZ \cdot PW$

Proof:

STATEMENTS	REASONS
A 1. Draw $\overline{XW}$ and $\overline{ZY}$.	1. ?
2. $\angle X \cong \angle Z$	2. ?
3. $\angle P \cong \angle P$	3. ?
4. $\triangle XPW \sim \triangle ZPY$	4. ?
5. $\dfrac{PX}{PZ} = \dfrac{PW}{PY}$	5. ?
6. $PX \cdot PY = PZ \cdot PW$	6. ?

Chords, secants, and tangents are shown. Find x.

7.

8.

9.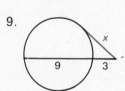

10.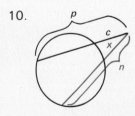

11.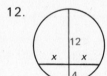

12.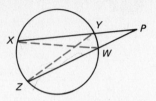

13.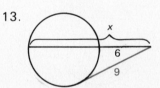

14.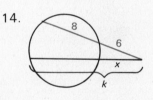

Quiz on
Secsions
8.5 8.7

Chords $\overline{RS}$ and $\overline{TZ}$ intersect at K.

EXAMPLE. $RK = 3$, $KS = 8$, $TZ = 10$. Find TK.

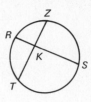

SOLUTION: Let $x = TK$.
Then $ZK = 10 - x$.

$$x(10 - x) = 3 \cdot 8$$
$$10x - x^2 = 24$$
$$x^2 - 10x + 24 = 0$$
$$(x - 6)(x - 4) = 0$$
$$x = 6 \text{ or } x = 4$$
$$TK = 6 \text{ or } TK = 4$$

B 15. $RK = 6$, $KS = 2$, $TZ = 7$. Find TK.
16. $RS = 8$, $TK = 8$, $KZ = 2$. Find RK.
17. $RK = 8$, $RS = 13$, $TZ = 14$. Find KZ.
18. $RK = 8$, $KS = 6$, $TK = 10$. Find TZ.

Secants $\overline{OA}$ and $\overline{OB}$ and tangent $\overline{OC}$ are drawn from point O.

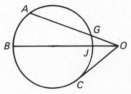

19. $OJ = 4$, $OC = 6$. Find BJ.
20. $OG = 4$, $GA = 8$, $JB = 13$. Find OJ.
21. $OJ = 5$, $JB = 11$, $GA = 16$. Find OA.
22. $JB = 5\sqrt{3}$, $OJ = 3\sqrt{3}$. Find OC.

C 23. Prove Theorem 8-17.
Hint: Draw $\overline{TX}$ and $\overline{TY}$.

24. Prove: If two coplanar circles intersect in two points, then the line joining those points bisects a common tangent segment.

25. Chords $\overline{AB}$ and $\overline{CD}$ meet requirements **a**, **b**, and **c**.

a. $\overline{AB}$ and $\overline{CD}$ intersect at K in the interior of a circle.
b. AK, KB, CK, and KD are integers.
c. $AB = 20$

List all possible values of $CK \cdot KD$.

26. Discuss the possibility of drawing a figure, roughly like the one shown, so that requirements **a**, **b**, and **c** are all satisfied:

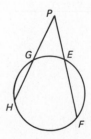

a. PE, EF, PG, and GH are integers.
b. The ratio of PE to EF is 2 to 3.
c. $PG = GH$

Self-Test

1. If $m \overset{\frown}{CD} = 50$, $m \angle 1 =$ ___?___.

2. If $m \overset{\frown}{CD} = 50$ and $m \overset{\frown}{AB} = 70$, $m \angle 2 =$ ___?___.

3. If $\overline{BD}$ is a diameter, $m \angle BAD =$ ___?___.

4. If $m \angle 2 = 55$ and $m \overset{\frown}{DC} = 45$, $m \overset{\frown}{AB} =$ ___?___.

5. If $AN = 8$, $NC = 6$, and $BN = 12$, then $ND =$ ___?___.

6. If $BN = 10$, $ND = 4$, and $AC = 13$, then $AN =$ ___?___ or ___?___.

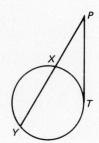

7. If $m \overset{\frown}{YT} = 140$ and $m \overset{\frown}{XT} = 80$, $m \angle P =$ ___?___.

8. If $m \angle P = 35$ and $m \overset{\frown}{YT} = 2 \cdot m \overset{\frown}{XT}$, then $m \overset{\frown}{XT} =$ ___?___.

9. If $PY = 18$ and $PX = 8$, then $PT =$ ___?___.

10. If $PT = 6$ and $XY = 5$, then $PX =$ ___?___.

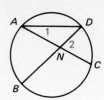

11. Prove the statement: If two inscribed angles intercept the same arc, the angles are congruent.

12. Given: Points R, S, and X lie on the circle; $\overline{RT}$ is a tangent segment; $m \angle T = 50$; $m \overset{\frown}{RX} = 100$

    Prove: $\triangle RST \sim \triangle XRS$

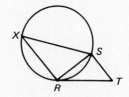

Check your answers with those printed at the back of the book.

CHAPTER SUMMARY

1. *Relationships expressed by formulas*

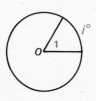 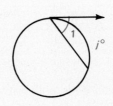 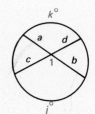

$m \angle 1 = j$ $m \angle 1 = \frac{1}{2}j$ $m \angle 1 = \frac{1}{2}j$ $m \angle 1 = \frac{1}{2}(j + k)$

$a \cdot b = c \cdot d$

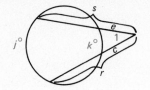

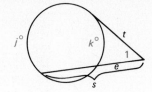

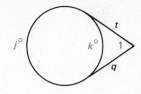

$$m\angle 1 = \tfrac{1}{2}(j - k)$$
$$s \cdot e = r \cdot c$$

$$m\angle 1 = \tfrac{1}{2}(j - k)$$
$$s \cdot e = t^2$$

$$m\angle 1 = \tfrac{1}{2}(j - k)$$
$$t = q$$

2. *Additional relationships*

A tangent to a circle is perpendicular to the radius drawn to the point of tangency.

In the same circle or in congruent circles, congruent central angles have congruent arcs, and conversely.

A diameter that is perpendicular to a chord bisects the chord and its two arcs.

Inscribed angles that intercept congruent arcs are congruent.

Opposite angles of an inscribed quadrilateral are supplementary.

An angle inscribed in a semicircle is a right angle.

CHAPTER TEST

Classify each statement as true or false.

1. When each side of a quadrilateral is tangent to a circle, the quadrilateral is inscribed in the circle.

2. When a central angle and an inscribed angle intercept the same arc, the angles are congruent.

3. A tangent to a circle is perpendicular to the radius drawn to the point of tangency.

4. If points R, S, and T lie on a circle and $\overset{\frown}{RS} \cap \overset{\frown}{ST} = S$, then $m\,\overset{\frown}{RS} + m\,\overset{\frown}{ST} = m\,\overset{\frown}{RST}$.

5. Opposite angles of an inscribed quadrilateral are supplementary.

6. If $\overline{AB}$ intersects $\odot O$ in just one point, $\overline{AB}$ must be tangent to the circle.

7. If one circle lies in the interior of a second circle, the circles must be concentric.

8. Many circles can be tangent to a given line at a given point on the line.

9. An angle inscribed in a semicircle is a right angle.

10. Congruent circles must lie in the same plane.

In Exercises 11–14, $\overline{AB}$ is a diameter of $\odot O$ and $\overleftrightarrow{XY}$ is tangent at point X. $m\ \widehat{BX} = 120$.

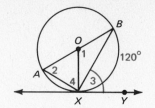

11. $m\angle 1 = $ __?__
12. $m\angle 2 = $ __?__
13. $m\angle 3 = $ __?__
14. $m\angle 4 = $ __?__

In Exercises 15 and 16, $\overline{RS}$ and $\overline{TW}$ are chords of the circle.

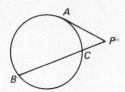

15. If $m\ \widehat{RT} = 50$ and $m\angle RNT = 42$, $m\ \widehat{WS} = $ __?__ .
16. If $RN = 6$, $NS = 8$, and $TN = 9$, $NW = $ __?__ .

In Exercises 17 and 18, $\overleftrightarrow{PA}$ is a tangent of the circle and $\overleftrightarrow{PB}$ is a secant.

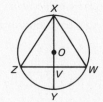

17. If $m\ \widehat{AC} = 76$ and $\widehat{AB} \cong \widehat{BC}$, then $m\angle P = $ __?__ .
18. If $PA = 6$ and $PC = 3$, then $PB = $ __?__ .

19. Given: Diameter $\overline{XY} \perp$ chord $\overline{ZW}$

    Prove: $\overline{XZ} \cong \overline{XW}$

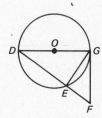

20. Given: $\overline{DG}$ is a diameter of $\odot O$;
    $\overleftrightarrow{DF}$ is a secant; $\overline{GE}$ is a
    chord; $\overleftrightarrow{GF}$ is a tangent.

    Prove: $\triangle DGF \sim \triangle GEF$

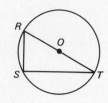

CHAPTER REVIEW

8-1 *Circles and Lines*

Circle O contains points R, S, and T.

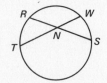

1. $\overline{OT}$ is called a __?__ RADIUS
2. $\overleftrightarrow{ST}$ is called a __?__ . CHORD
3. The longest chord shown is __?__ SEGMENT
4. $\triangle RST$ is _____ $\odot O$.

   (inscribed in, circumscribed about)

304 *GEOMETRY*

8-2 Tangents

$\overleftrightarrow{AB}$, $\overleftrightarrow{BC}$, and $\overleftrightarrow{AC}$ are tangent to $\odot P$.

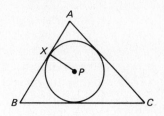

5. How many tangents can be drawn to $\odot P$ at point X?

6. How is $\overline{PX}$ related to $\overline{AB}$?

7. Can there be a line intersecting $\odot P$ in only one point that is not tangent to $\odot P$?

8-3 Arcs and Central Angles

8. The measure of a semicircle is __?__ .

9. Two circles are defined to be congruent when __?__ .

10. If $\angle ADB$ is a central angle, and $m\angle ADB = 52$, then $m\ \overset{\frown}{AB} = $ __?__ .

8-4 Arcs and Chords

In $\odot O$, diameter $\overline{RS}$ is perpendicular to chord $\overline{TQ}$ at X.

11. $\overset{\frown}{ST} \cong$ __?__   12. $\overset{\frown}{RQ} \cong$ __?__   13. $\overline{TX} \cong$ __?__

14. If two chords are equally distant from the center of a circle, __?__ .

8-5 Inscribed Angles

Points A, B, C, and D lie on the $\odot$.
$m\ \overset{\frown}{AD} = 80$; $m\ \overset{\frown}{DC} = 50$. $\overleftrightarrow{AE}$ is a tangent.

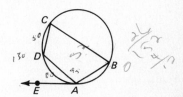

15. $m\angle B = $ __?__

16. $m\angle DAE = $ __?__

17. If $m\angle DAB = 95$, then $m\angle C = $ __?__ .

8-6 Other Angles

Points R, S, T, and U lie on the circle.
$m\ \overset{\frown}{RU} = 120$ and $m\ \overset{\frown}{ST} = 40$.

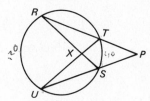

18. $m\angle RXU = $ __?__

19. $m\angle P = $ __?__

20. If $m\ \overset{\frown}{RT} = 103$, then $m\ \overset{\frown}{US} = $ __?__ .

8-7 Circles and Lengths of Segments

$\overline{EF}$ is a tangent segment, $\overline{EC}$ is a secant segment, and $\overline{AB}$ is a chord.

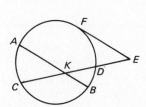

21. If $AK = 12$, $BK = 6$, and $CK = 9$, $DK = $ __?__ .

22. If $EC = 18$ and $ED = 8$, $FE = $ __?__ .

23. If $FE = 20$ and $DE = 10$, $CD = $ __?__ .

24. If $CK = 6$, $DK = 4$, $AB = 11$, and $AK > BK$, $AK = $ __?__ .

Problems Solved by Use of Auxiliary Lines

You may perhaps already know that some problems turn out to be much more difficult than they look. The key to a solution may lie in thinking of the right auxiliary line to draw. But there are cases where you might work many hours without finding the key. In this section we present two problems that are difficult enough even after you are handed the key. You may enjoy speculating about how long a time you might have needed to work before you thought of a way to draw a helpful auxiliary line.

The Butterfly

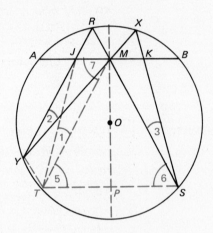

Given: Circle O with chord $\overline{AB}$;

    M is the midpoint of $\overline{AB}$;

    Chords $\overline{RS}$ and $\overline{XY}$ contain M;

    $\overline{RY}$ intersects $\overline{AB}$ at J;

    $\overline{XS}$ intersects $\overline{AB}$ at K.

Prove: $\overline{JM} \cong \overline{KM}$

Hints about a proof:

Let us agree that a preliminary theorem is available: If two opposite angles of a quadrilateral are supplementary, a circle can be circumscribed about the quadrilateral.

Through S draw a line parallel to $\overline{AB}$. Draw $\overline{TY}$, $\overline{TJ}$, $\overline{TM}$, and $\overleftrightarrow{OM}$.

By drawing $\overline{OA}$ and $\overline{OB}$ (not shown on the diagram), you can prove: $\triangle AMO \cong \triangle BMO$, $\angle AMO \cong \angle BMO$, and $\overleftrightarrow{OM} \perp \overline{AB}$.

Then $\overleftrightarrow{OM} \perp \overline{TS}$, and $\overleftrightarrow{OM}$ bisects $\overline{TS}$.

$\triangle MPT \cong \triangle MPS$, $\overline{TM} \cong \overline{SM}$, and $\angle 5 \cong \angle 6$.

But $\angle 5 \cong \angle 7$, so $\angle 6 \cong \angle 7$.

Because $\angle RYT$ is supplementary to $\angle 6$, $\angle RYT$ is supplementary to $\angle 7$. Consequently, a circle, not shown, can be circumscribed about quadrilateral $YTMJ$. $\angle 1$ and $\angle 2$ intercept the same arc in this circle, so $\angle 1 \cong \angle 2$.

But $\angle 3 \cong \angle 2$, so $\angle 1 \cong \angle 3$.

$\triangle TJM \cong \triangle SKM$ by the ASA Postulate, and $\overline{JM} \cong \overline{KM}$.

A Numerical Problem

Given: $m\angle TRS = m\angle TSR = 80$;
$\qquad m\angle YRS = 60$; $m\angle XSR = 50$

Find $m\angle XYR$.

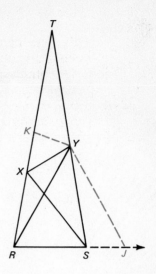

Hints: On $\overrightarrow{RS}$ take J so that $RJ = RY$.

On $\overrightarrow{RT}$ take K so that $RK = RY$.

Find, where possible, the measures of angles.

Note some isosceles triangles and an equilateral triangle.

Because $\triangle TKY \cong \triangle YSJ$, $\overline{KY} \cong \overline{SJ}$.

Also, $\overline{KX} \cong \overline{SJ}$.

Exercises

1. Write a proof for the Butterfly exercise.

2. Find $m\angle XYR$ in the numerical problem above.

3. In the figure, showing a circle with some chords: $AB = BC = CA = 10$; $CD = 11$.
Find the sum $AD + DB$.

Hint: On $\overline{CD}$ take point X such that $CX = AD$. Draw $\overline{XB}$.

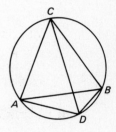

AREAS AND VOLUMES

Areas of Polygons

Objectives

1. Understand what is meant by "the area of a polygonal region" and the significance of the initial area postulates.
2. Recognize that any side of a triangle or parallelogram can be considered to be a base and that to any base there is a corresponding altitude.
3. Recognize that the formulas for the areas of parallelograms, triangles, trapezoids, and regular polygons can all be derived from the postulate for the area of a rectangle.
4. Compute the areas of triangles, parallelograms, and trapezoids.
5. Compute the apothem, radius, and area of special regular polygons.

9-1 *Areas of Rectangles*

Each diagram below represents a *polygonal region*.

  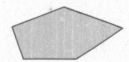

A polygonal region is the union of a polygon and its interior. Points that lie on the polygon or in its interior are points of the region.

In earlier chapters we accepted postulates which enabled us to express the lengths of segments and the measures of angles by positive numbers. The postulate that follows likewise associates positive numbers with polygonal regions.

POSTULATE 19   Corresponding to every polygonal region there is a unique positive number called the **area** of that region.

The area of a polygonal region is commonly referred to as the area of the polygon that bounds the region.

When the sides of a square are one unit long, the area of the square is one square unit. Thus, a square with sides 1 centimeter long has an area of 1 square centimeter, written 1 cm².

1 unit of length

1 square unit of area

The fact that congruent triangles have exactly the same size and shape suggests another area postulate.

POSTULATE 20 If two triangles are congruent, the regions they bound have the same area.

On the basis of the diagrams that follow, it seems reasonable to accept a third postulate about areas of polygonal regions.

  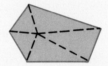 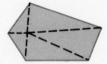

POSTULATE 21 (AREA ADDITION POSTULATE) A polygonal region can be separated into a finite number of non-overlapping regions, the sum of whose areas is equal to the area of the given region.

Any side of a rectangle or parallelogram can be considered to be a *base*. An *altitude* corresponding to a base is any perpendicular segment whose endpoints lie on the lines containing the base and the side opposite. Thus, in a rectangle if one side is selected as a base, either adjacent side is a corresponding altitude. In the figures below, each red segment is an altitude to the side marked base.

 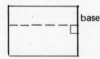 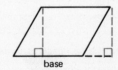 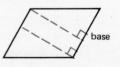

The letter *b* is used to denote the length of a base and *h* is used to denote the length of any altitude to that base.

The rectangle shown is 3 units long and 2 units wide. It is made up of six squares, each with area 1 square unit. We might conclude, then, that the area is 6 square units. This example suggests the following postulate.

POSTULATE 22   The area of a rectangle is equal to the product of the length of a base and the length of an altitude to that base. ($A = bh$)

THEOREM 9-1   The area of a square is equal to the square of the length of a side. ($A = s^2$)

When lengths are specified in terms of a particular unit, it is important to name the units of area. (See Example 1.)

EXAMPLE 1. Find the area of a rectangle with length 6 cm and width $2\frac{1}{2}$ cm.

SOLUTION: $A = bh$ $A = 6 \cdot 2\frac{1}{2}$ $A = 15$ (cm²)

EXAMPLE 2. A rectangle with length 8 has area 30. Find the width.

SOLUTION: $A = bh$ $30 = 8h$ $h = \frac{30}{8} = 3\frac{3}{4}$

Oral Exercises

1. Which of these numbers cannot be a measure of area?

        8   -3 $\frac{4}{7}$ $2\sqrt{6}$ $-\frac{3}{5}$

2. Which of these geometric figures do not have measures called their area?

        segment   triangle   angle   pentagon

3. If two triangles have equal areas, must they be congruent?

4. If two polygons have equal areas, must they have the same number of sides?

5. When given only the area of a rectangle, can you find its dimensions?

6. If the perimeter of a square is 1 cm, what is its area?

7. State the perimeter of a square whose area is $49k^2$.

8. When both the length and width of a rectangle are doubled, by what factor is the area multiplied?

In Exercises 1–8, find the area of a rectangle of base length b and altitude length h. (Where variables appear, $b > 0$ and $h > 0$.)

1. $b = 6$ cm $h = 4$ cm
2. $b = 3\frac{1}{2}$ cm $h = 8$ cm
3. $b = 4.8$ $h = 3.5$
4. $b = 5\sqrt{2}$ $h = 3\sqrt{2}$

5. $b = 5k$ $h = 3k$
6. $b = 2k + 1$ $h = k$
7. $b = t - 3$ $h = t + 3$
8. $b = 2x - 1$ $h = x + 1$

Exercises 9–12 refer to rectangles. Find the missing measure.

	b	h	A		b	h	A
9.	4 cm	?	24 cm²	11.	$2\sqrt{3}$	?	$12\sqrt{3}$
10.	?	$2\frac{1}{2}$ cm	48 cm²	12.	?	$.5k$	$.45k^2$

13. Find the area of a rectangle with length 6 cm and perimeter 20 cm.

14. What is the ratio of the areas of two squares if the lengths of their sides have the ratio $2:3$?

In Exercises 15 and 16 find the area of the shaded regions.

B 15.

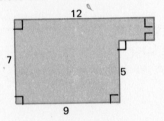

16.

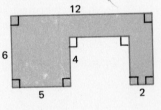

17. The lengths of the sides of a rectangle have the ratio $3:4$. The area is 300. Find the length and the width.

18. A walk 2 meters wide surrounds a rectangular grass plot 30 meters long and 10 meters wide. Find the area of the walk.

19. For what value of k will a square with side length $2k - 5$ have area 81?

20. The width of a rectangle is 5, and the length of a diagonal is 13. Find the area of the rectangle.

21. A square has diagonals of length 8 cm. Find the area.

22. A rectangle with side lengths $2x + 2$ and $x + 1$ has area 72. Find the length and the width of the rectangle.

C 23. Find the lengths of the sides of a rectangle of area 24 and perimeter 22.

24. If $2x^2 + 2x - 12$ represents the area of a polygon, what is the range of values for x?

25. If the length of a rectangle is increased by 25 percent, by what percent must the width be decreased if the area is to remain the same?

26. If rectangle $ABCD$ has area $36\sqrt{3}$, find the length and width.

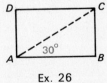

Ex. 26

9-2 *Areas of Parallelograms and Triangles*

Detailed formal proofs of most area theorems are lengthy and time consuming. For that reason, only a *Sketch of Proof* will accompany a theorem. From the Sketch of Proof shown, you should be able to recognize that a formal proof is possible.

THEOREM 9-2   The area of a parallelogram is equal to the product of the length of a base and the length of a corresponding altitude. $(A = bh)$

Sketch of Proof:

When corr. altitudes $\overline{BE}$ and $\overline{AF}$ are drawn in the given $\square ABCD$, rect. $ABEF$ and $\cong$ rt. $\triangle$ AFD and BEC are formed. By the Area Addition Postulate, Area of $\square ABCD =$ Area of rect. $ABEF$. Therefore, Area of $\square ABCD = bh$.

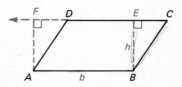

THEOREM 9-3   The area of a triangle is equal to one-half the product of the length of a base and the length of a corresponding altitude. $(A = \frac{1}{2}bh)$

Sketch of Proof:

Given $\triangle ABC$. When $\overline{CD} \parallel \overline{AB}$ and $\overline{BD} \parallel \overline{AC}$ are drawn, $\square ABDC$ with area bh is formed. Since Area of $\triangle ABC +$ Area of $\triangle DCB =$ Area of $\square ABDC$ and $\triangle ABC \cong \triangle DCB$, it follows that Area of $\triangle ABC = \frac{1}{2}$ Area of $\square ABDC$. Thus, Area of $\triangle ABC = \frac{1}{2}bh$.

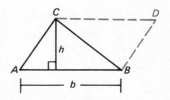

COROLLARY 1   The area of a rhombus is equal to one-half the product of the lengths of its diagonals. $(A = \frac{1}{2}d_1d_2)$

The *Sketch of Proof* is left as Exercise 23.

COROLLARY 2   The area of an equilateral triangle of side length s is equal to $\dfrac{s^2\sqrt{3}}{4}$. $\left(A = \dfrac{s^2\sqrt{3}}{4}\right)$

The *Sketch of Proof* is left as Exercise 24.

Recall that any side of a triangle can be taken as a base. There are three ways of expressing the area of the triangle shown.

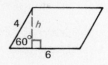

Area of $\triangle RST = \frac{1}{2}b_1h_1 = \frac{1}{2}b_2h_2 = \frac{1}{2}b_3h_3$

EXAMPLE 1. Find the area of the parallelogram shown.

SOLUTION: Draw an altitude forming a $30°$-$60°$-$90°$ $\triangle$.

$h = 2\sqrt{3}$
$A = bh = 6 \cdot 2\sqrt{3} = 12\sqrt{3}$

EXAMPLE 2. Find the length of a side of an equilateral triangle with area $9\sqrt{3}$.

SOLUTION:
$$A = \frac{s^2}{4}\sqrt{3} \qquad 9\sqrt{3} = \frac{s^2}{4}\sqrt{3}$$
$$9 = \frac{s^2}{4}$$
$$s^2 = 36$$
$$s = 6$$

Oral Exercises

In Exercises 1–3, name the altitude which corresponds to the given base of rt. $\triangle RST$.

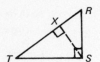

1. $\overline{ST}$ 2. $\overline{RS}$ 3. $\overline{RT}$

4. If two parallelograms have equal areas, must they have congruent bases and congruent altitudes?

5. Can you find the area of a parallelogram if you are given only the lengths of two adjacent sides?

Exercises 6–8 refer to the figure shown.

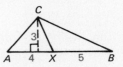

6. What is the area of $\triangle AXC$?
7. What is the area of $\triangle CXB$?
8. What is the area of $\triangle CAB$?

9. What is the area of a right triangle with legs having lengths a and b?

10. In a triangle, side t is longer than side s. Is the altitude to side s longer than the altitude to side t?

Written Exercises

Exercises 1–8 refer to a triangle with base length b, altitude length h, and area A. Supply the missing measure.

		b	h	A		b	h	A
A	1.	8	5	?	5.	$6k$	$4k$	?
	2.	4	?	12	6.	$4k$	?	$10k^2$
	3.	?	8	18	7.	?	$3b$	$15ab$
	4.	$3\sqrt{2}$	$2\sqrt{2}$	?	8.	$\sqrt{3}k$	?	$4\sqrt{6}k^2$

9. Find the area of a rhombus with diagonals whose lengths are 8 and 12.

10. A parallelogram of area 78 has one side of length 12. Find the length of an altitude to that side.

Exercises 11–16 refer to a right triangle with legs of length a and b and hypotenuse of length c. Find the area of the triangle.

B
11. $a = 8$ $b = 4$ 14. $a = 12$ $c = 13$
12. $a = 3\sqrt{2}$ $b = 6$ 15. $a = 4\sqrt{2}$ $c = 8$
13. $a = 4\sqrt{3}$ $b = 2\sqrt{3}$ 16. $b = 2\sqrt{3}$ $c = 5$

In Exercises 17–20, find the area of $\square ABCD$ for the given measures.

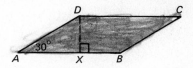

17. $AB = 12$ $AD = 8$
18. $AB = 10$ $AX = 4\sqrt{3}$
19. $AB = 10\sqrt{3}$ $AX = 6$
20. $AB = 8$ $AD = 6\sqrt{2}$

21. Find the area of an equilateral triangle with perimeter 24 cm.

22. Find the perimeter of an equilateral triangle with area $12\sqrt{3}$ cm².

23. Write a *Sketch of Proof* for Corollary 1. (*Hint:* Use the fact that diagonals form $\cong \triangle$.)

24. Write a *Sketch of Proof* for Corollary 2. (*Hint:* Use 30°-60°-90° triangle relationships.)

In Exercises 25–27, find the ratio of the area of $\triangle AXY$ to the area of $\triangle ACB$ when:

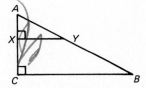

C
25. $AX = 2$ $XC = 4$ $XY = 3$
26. $AX = 2$ $XC = 3$ $CB = 10$
27. $XC = 4$ $XY = 6$ $CB = 14$

28. The lengths of the sides of a triangle are 6, 12, and 15. Find the ratio of the areas of the two triangles formed by the bisector of the largest angle.

29. Write a *Sketch of Proof* for this statement: The diagonals of a parallelogram form four triangles of equal area.

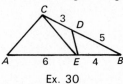

30. In the figure shown, find the ratio of the area of $\triangle CDE$ to the area of $\triangle ACB$.

Ex. 30

9-3 *Areas of Trapezoids*

Recall that an **altitude of a trapezoid** is a perpendicular segment from any point in one base to a point in the line containing the other base.

THEOREM 9-4 The area of a trapezoid is equal to one-half the product of the length of an altitude and the sum of the lengths of the bases. $A = \frac{1}{2}h(b_1 + b_2)$

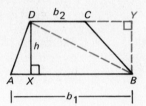

Sketch of Proof:

When the auxiliary segments shown are drawn, trap. *ABCD* is separated into $\triangle ABD$ and $\triangle DCB$, each with altitude of length h. Area of trap. *ABCD* = Area of $\triangle ABD$ + Area of $\triangle DCB$. Area of trap. $ABCD = \frac{1}{2}b_1h + \frac{1}{2}b_2h = \frac{1}{2}h(b_1 + b_2)$

EXAMPLE 1. Find the area of a trapezoid with bases 12 cm and 7 cm long and an altitude of length 5 cm.

SOLUTION: $A = \frac{1}{2}h(b_1 + b_2) = \frac{5}{2}(12 + 7) = \frac{95}{2} = 47\frac{1}{2}$ (cm²)

EXAMPLE 2. A trapezoid of area 150 has one base of length 18 and an altitude of length 12. Find the length of the other base.

SOLUTION: Let x represent the length of the other base.

$$A = \frac{1}{2}h(b_1 + b_2) \qquad 150 = \frac{1}{2} \cdot 12(18 + x)$$
$$150 = 108 + 6x$$
$$42 = 6x$$
$$7 = x$$

Oral Exercises

1. Can you find the area of a trapezoid when given only its perimeter?
2. Can the two legs of a trapezoid be considered to be the bases?
3. What is the length of the median of a trapezoid whose bases have lengths of 12 and 8?
4. Do the diagonals of a trapezoid form four triangles of equal area?
5. Does the median of a trapezoid form two trapezoids of equal area?
6. Does a segment joining the midpoints of the bases of a trapezoid form two trapezoids of equal area?

Written Exercises

Exercises 1–8 refer to trapezoids with base lengths b_1 and b_2, altitude length h, and area A. In each exercise supply the missing measure.

		b_1	b_2	h	A
A	1.	12 cm	4 cm	6 cm	?
	2.	8 m	5 m	3 m	?
	3.	7	3	?	40
	4.	12	8	?	44
	5.	?	3	3	12
	6.	$6k$	?	$4k$	$28k^2$
	7.	$5\sqrt{3}k$	$3\sqrt{3}k$	$\sqrt{3}k$	?
	8.	$5\sqrt{2}t$	?	$4t$	$14\sqrt{2}t^2$

9. Find the length of the median of a trapezoid if the bases have lengths of 6 and 10.

10. A trapezoid with median of length 6 has area 24. Find the length of the altitude.

In Exercises 11–16, find the area of the trapezoid shown.

B 11.

14.

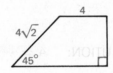

12.

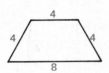

15.

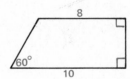

13.

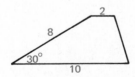

16.

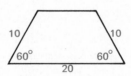

C 17. An isosceles trapezoid whose bases have lengths 12 and 16 is inscribed in a circle of radius 10. The center of the circle lies in the interior of the trapezoid. Find the area of the trapezoid.

18. Given trap. $ABCD$ with $\overline{AB} \parallel \overline{DC}$. If $AB = 30$, $AD = 10$, $m\angle A = 30$, and $m\angle B = 45$, find the area of trap. $ABCD$.

9-4 *Areas of Regular Polygons*

The theorems that follow establish the fact that within every regular polygon there is a unique point that is called the **center** of the polygon.

THEOREM 9-5   Any three noncollinear points lie on a circle.

Sketch of Proof:

Given noncollinear points A, B, and C. Draw $\triangle ABC$. Draw l_1 and l_2, the perpendicular bisectors of sides $\overline{AB}$ and $\overline{AC}$. Lines l_1 and l_2 intersect in some point O. (If $l_1 \parallel l_2$, then $\overline{AB} \parallel \overline{AC}$, which is impossible.)

Since $\triangle AOX \cong \triangle BOX$, $AO = BO$.
Since $\triangle AOY \cong \triangle COY$, $AO = CO$.
Thus, $AO = BO = CO$.

Therefore, a circle with center O and radius AO will pass through points A, B, and C.

THEOREM 9-6   A circle can be circumscribed about any regular polygon.

Sketch of Proof:

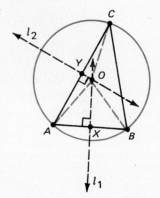

Given regular polygon $ABCDE$. . . . By Theorem 9-5, a circle with center O can be passed through vertices A, B, and C. Draw $\overline{OD}$ and radii $\overline{OA}$, $\overline{OB}$, and $\overline{OC}$.

$\overline{OB} \cong \overline{OC}$ (radii)

$\overline{AB} \cong \overline{DC}$ (sides of reg. polygon)

$\angle 1 \cong \angle 2$ since $\angle ABC \cong \angle BCD$ and $\angle 3 \cong \angle 4$

$\triangle AOB \cong \triangle DOC$ (SAS). Thus, $\overline{OA} \cong \overline{OD}$ (corr. parts of $\cong \triangle$)

Therefore, D must lie on $\odot O$. In like manner the remaining vertices taken in succession can be shown to lie on $\odot O$.

THEOREM 9-7   A circle can be inscribed in any regular polygon.

The *Sketch of Proof* is left as Exercise 15.

COROLLARY   The inscribed and circumscribed circles of a regular polygon have the same point as center.

The *Sketch of Proof* is left as Exercise 16.

Definitions

1. The center of a regular polygon is the common center of its inscribed and circumscribed circles.

2. The radius of a regular polygon is the distance from the center of the polygon to a vertex.

3. The apothem of a regular polygon is the distance from the center of the polygon to a side.

4. A central angle of a regular polygon is an angle formed by two radii drawn to consecutive vertices.

Center: O
Apothem: OM
Radius: OA, OC
Central Angle: ∠AOC

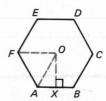

Center: O
Apothem: OX
Radius: OA, OF
Central Angle: ∠AOF

THEOREM 9-8   The area of a regular polygon is equal to one-half the product of the apothem and the perimeter.
$(A = \frac{1}{2}ap)$

Sketch of Proof:

Given regular *n*-gon *TUVW* . . . , apothem *a*, side length *s*, perimeter *p*, and area *A*. If all radii are drawn, *n* congruent △ are formed, each with area $\frac{1}{2}as$.

$A = n(\frac{1}{2}as) = \frac{1}{2}a(ns)$

But $ns = p$. Therefore, $A = \frac{1}{2}ap$.

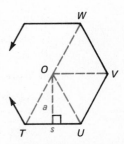

EXAMPLE 1. Find the radius and apothem of an equilateral triangle with sides of length 6.

SOLUTION: Use 30°-60°-90° △ relationships.

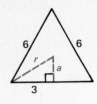

$$a = \frac{3}{\sqrt{3}} = \sqrt{3}$$

$$r = 2a = 2\sqrt{3}$$

EXAMPLE 2. Find the area of a regular hexagon with a 9-cm apothem.

SOLUTION: Use 30°-60°-90° △ relationships.

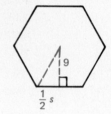

$$\tfrac{1}{2}s = \frac{9}{\sqrt{3}} = 3\sqrt{3}$$

$$s = 6\sqrt{3},\ p = 36\sqrt{3}$$

$$A = \tfrac{1}{2}ap = \tfrac{1}{2}\cdot 9\cdot 36\sqrt{3}$$

$$= 162\sqrt{3}\ (\text{cm}^2)$$

Oral Exercises

1. If a square has apothem 5, what is the length of a side?
2. If a polygon is inscribed in a circle, must the polygon be regular?
3. Can the apothem of a regular polygon be greater than the radius?
4. What is the area of a regular pentagon with side length k and apothem t?
5. What is the measure of a central angle of a regular decagon?
6. For what regular polygon is the radius equal to the length of a side?

Written Exercises

Exercises 1–8 refer to regular polygons with side length s, radius r, and apothem a. In each exercise find the missing measures.

		s	a	r
A	1. Square:	8	?	?
	2. Square:	?	3	?
	3. Square:	?	?	$4\sqrt{2}$
	4. Equilateral △:	12	?	?
	5. Equilateral △:	?	$\sqrt{3}$	?
	6. Equilateral △:	?	?	6
	7. Reg. Hexagon:	8	?	?
	8. Reg. Hexagon:	?	?	10

In each exercise find the area of the given polygon.

B 9. Equilateral triangle with radius $2\sqrt{3}$.

10. Square with apothem $4\sqrt{2}$.

11. Regular hexagon with side length 4.

12. Equilateral triangle with apothem $2\sqrt{3}$.

13. Regular hexagon with apothem 6.

14. Square inscribed in a circle of radius 5.

C 15. Write a *Sketch of Proof* for Theorem 9-7. (*Hint:* Draw the circle specified in Theorem 9-6 and consider the position of the midpoints of the sides.)

16. Write a *Sketch of Proof* for the Corollary to Theorem 9-7. (*Hint:* The inscribed circle is tangent to the sides of the polygon at their midpoints.)

Self-Test Classify the given statement as true or false.

1. If two triangles have equal areas, the triangles must be congruent.
2. If you are given the perimeter of a square, you can find its area.
3. The area of a right triangle is one-half the product of the lengths of the legs.
4. The apothem of a regular polygon is the distance from the center to a side.
5. The area of a polygon cannot be an irrational number.
6. If you know the area of a rectangle, you can compute the perimeter.

Find the area of the polygon shown.

7.

5
8

10.

4
4
7

8.

5
7

11.

6   6
6

9.

9
12

12.
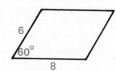
6
60°
8

13. The diagonals of a rhombus have lengths of 8 cm and 6 cm. Find the area of the rhombus.

14. Find the area of a regular hexagon whose perimeter is 18 cm.

Measuring Circles

Objectives

1. Recognize how the area and perimeter formulas for regular polygons relate to the area and circumference formulas for circles.
2. Recognize that π is an irrational number and state some approximations for π.
3. Compute the circumferences and areas of circles.
4. Compute arc lengths and the areas of sectors and segments of a circle.

9-5 *Circumferences of Circles*

Pictured below are four regular polygons inscribed in congruent circles.

Note that as the number of sides of the inscribed polygon is increased:

(a) The apothem increases, getting nearer in length to the radius of the circle.
(b) The perimeter increases, getting nearer to the perimeter of the circle.
(c) The area increases, getting nearer to the area of the circle.

By making the number of sides large enough, we could bring the apothem as close to the radius as we wish, the perimeter of the polygon as close to the perimeter of the circle as we wish, and the area of the polygon as close to the area of the circle as we wish. We describe the situation in the following language:

> The **circumference of a circle** (C) is the *limit* of the perimeters of the inscribed regular polygons.

> The **area of a circle** (A) is the *limit* of the areas of the inscribed regular polygons.

Now consider the ratio of the perimeter of an inscribed regular polygon to the length of a diameter. In the case of an equilateral triangle the ratio is $\frac{3}{2}\sqrt{3}$; in the case of a square the ratio equals $2\sqrt{2}$; and in the case of a regular hexagon the ratio equals 3. In each case the ratio is a constant.

This suggests that the ratio of the circumference of a circle to its diameter is also constant. The theorem that follows demonstrates that this is indeed the case.

THEOREM 9-9 For all circles the ratio of the circumference to the diameter is a constant.

Sketch of Proof:

Let C and C' denote the circumferences of the given circles O and O' with diameters d and d'. In $\odot O$ inscribe a regular n-gon of perimeter p_n and in $\odot O'$ a regular n-gon of perimeter p'_n.

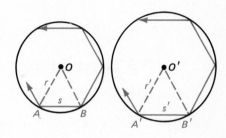

1. Ratio of perimeters of n-gons:
$$\frac{p_n}{p'_n} = \frac{ns}{ns'} = \frac{s}{s'}$$

2. Since $\triangle AOB \sim \triangle A'O'B'$, $\dfrac{s}{s'} = \dfrac{r}{r'}$.

3. Therefore, $\dfrac{p_n}{p'_n} = \dfrac{r}{r'} = \dfrac{d}{d'}$.

4. Now take n so large that p_n is as close to C as you please, and p'_n is as close to C' as you please. Then we may substitute $\dfrac{C}{C'}$ for $\dfrac{p_n}{p'_n}$ and we have $\dfrac{C}{C'} = \dfrac{d}{d'}$. Thus $\dfrac{C}{d} = \dfrac{C'}{d'}$.

Step 4 asserts that for any two circles, $\dfrac{C}{d}$ is a constant. The constant is an irrational number denoted by the Greek letter π (pi).

As early as the 3rd Century B.C. Archimedes arrived at the conclusion that π was a number between $3\frac{1}{7}$ and $3\frac{10}{71}$. With today's computers, approximations correct to thousands of places are possible. The most commonly used approximations of π are:

$$3.14 \qquad \tfrac{22}{7} \qquad 3.1416$$

Since $\dfrac{C}{d} = \pi$, it follows that $C = \pi d$ and $C = 2\pi r$.

COROLLARY The circumference of a circle is the product of 2π and the radius. $(C = 2\pi r)$

In computing a circumference, do not replace π by any of its decimal approximations unless instructed to do so.

EXAMPLE 1. Find the circumference of a circle with radius 6 cm.

SOLUTION: $C = 2\pi r = 2\pi \cdot 6 = 12\pi$ (cm)

EXAMPLE 2. Find correct to tenths the circumference of a circle with radius 4.2. Use $\pi \doteq 3.14$.

SOLUTION: $C = 2\pi r \doteq 2(3.14)(4.2) \doteq 26.376 \doteq 26.4$

In a circle the length of an arc with degree measure n is $\dfrac{n}{360}$ times the circumference of the circle.

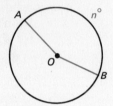

$$\text{length of } \overset{\frown}{AB} = \frac{n}{360} \cdot 2\pi r$$

EXAMPLE 3. In a circle of radius 8, find the length of an arc with degree measure 40.

SOLUTION: Length of arc $= \dfrac{40}{360}(2\pi r) = \dfrac{1}{9}(16\pi) = \dfrac{16\pi}{9}$

Oral Exercises

1. State the circumference of a circle with radius 5.
2. State the radius of a circle with circumference 2π.
3. If two circles have equal circumferences, must they be congruent?
4. Which is the more accurate approximation of π: 3.14 or 3.15?
5. If an arc of a circle has degree measure 60, what fractional part of the circumference is the length of the arc?
6. If the length of an arc is $\frac{1}{4}$ of the circumference, what is the degree measure of the arc?

Written Exercises

In Exercises 1–6, find the circumference of a circle in which:

A

1. $r = 9$ cm
2. $d = 10$ m
3. $r = 2\frac{1}{2}$
4. $d = 3\frac{1}{3}$
5. $r = 3k$
6. $d = \frac{5}{3}k$

324 *GEOMETRY*

In Exercises 7–12, find the radius of a circle whose circumference is:

even
even

7. 12π cm

8. 15π m

9. $4\sqrt{3}\pi$

10. $5\sqrt{2}\pi$

11. $8k\pi$

12. π

In Exercises 13–15, use $\pi \doteq 3.14$ and compute the circumference correct to tenths.

13. $r = 3.4$ cm

14. $d = 8.6$ m

15. $r = 12.1$

In Exercises 16–18, use $\pi \doteq 3.14$ and compute the radius correct to tenths.

16. $C = 10$

17. $C = 12.4$

18. $C = 27.5$

19. Do the circumferences of two circles have the same ratio as the radii?

20. How far will a wheel of radius 20 cm travel in 6 revolutions?

In Exercises 21–24, find the circumference of a circle circumscribed about:

B 21. A square with side length 8.

22. An equilateral triangle with side length 6.

23. A regular hexagon with side length 12.

24. A right triangle with legs of lengths 4 and 6.

25. In a circle of radius 12, what is the length of an 80° arc?

26. Find the radius of a circle in which a 45° arc has length 4π.

27. Given a regular hexagon with sides of length 12. Find the ratio of the circumferences of its inscribed and circumscribed circles.

28. In a circle of radius k cm, by how much is the circumference increased when the radius is increased by 1 cm?

C 29. Find the circumference of a circle inscribed in a rhombus with diagonals of lengths 12 and 16.

30. A circle inscribed in an equilateral triangle and a circle inscribed in a regular hexagon have equal circumferences. What is the ratio of the lengths of a side of the triangle and a side of the hexagon?

Challenge

Think of the earth as a perfect sphere. A band fits snugly around the earth at the equator. The band is then stretched one meter, and is placed so that its points are equidistant from the earth. Which of the following animals could crawl under the band—an ant, a mouse, a kitten, a large dog?

9-6 *Areas of Circles*

To find a formula for the area of a circle, we make use of the formula for the area of a regular polygon ($A = \frac{1}{2}ap$) stated in Theorem 9-8.

THEOREM 9-10 The area of a circle is equal to the product of π and the square of the radius of the circle. ($A = \pi r^2$)

Sketch of Proof:

Given $\odot O$ with radius r, circumference C, and area A. In $\odot O$ inscribe a regular n-gon with apothem a_n, perimeter p_n, and area A_n. By Theorem 9-8, $A_n = \frac{1}{2}a_n p_n$. Now take n so large that a_n is as close as you please to r, p_n is as close as you please to C, and A_n is as close as you please to A. Then, $A_n = \frac{1}{2}a_n p_n$ can be written $A = \frac{1}{2}rC$. Since $C = 2\pi r$, our formula becomes:

$$A = \tfrac{1}{2}r(2\pi r), \text{ or } A = \pi r^2$$

The shaded region is called a *sector* of $\odot O$. A sector of a circle is a region bounded by two radii and an arc of the circle. The unshaded region of $\odot O$ with $\overset{\frown}{AXB}$ is also a sector.

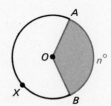

The area of a sector with arc of degree measure n is $\dfrac{n}{360}$ times the area of the circle.

$$\text{Area of Sector} = \frac{n}{360} \cdot \pi r^2$$

EXAMPLE 1. In a circle of radius 12, find the area of a sector whose arc has degree measure 150.

SOLUTION: $A = \frac{150}{360} \cdot \pi \cdot (12)^2 = \frac{5}{12} \cdot \pi \cdot 144 = 60\pi$

A **segment of a circle** is a region bounded by an arc of a circle and the chord of that arc. The area of the segment shown can be found by subtracting the area of $\triangle SOR$ from the area of the sector whose arc is $\overset{\frown}{SXR}$. The unshaded region of $\odot O$ is also a segment of $\odot O$.

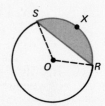

EXAMPLE 2. In a circle of radius 6 cm, find the area of a segment with arc of degree measure 90.

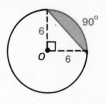

SOLUTION: Area of sector $= \frac{90}{360} \cdot \pi \cdot 6^2 = 9\pi$

Area of $\triangle = \frac{1}{2} \cdot 6 \cdot 6 = 18$

Area of segment $= 9\pi - 18$ (cm^2)

Oral Exercises

1. What is the area of a circle with radius 4 cm?
2. What is the radius of a circle with area 25π?
3. When the radius of a circle is doubled, how is the area affected?
4. What is the ratio of the areas of two circles with radii 2 and 3?
5. What is the ratio of the radii of two circles whose areas have the ratio $9:25$?
6. What part of the area of a circle is the area of a sector of degree measure 120?
7. Is a semicircle both a sector and a segment?
8. If the area of a sector is one-sixth of the area of the circle in which it lies, what is the degree measure of its arc?
9. What is the formula for the area of a circle in terms of its diameter?
10. What is the area of a circle in which the longest possible chord is 8 cm long?

Written Exercises

In Exercises 1–4 find the area of a circle in which:

A   1. $r = 4$ 2. $d = 10$ 3. $r = 3\sqrt{2}$ 4. $d = 6\sqrt{3}$

In Exercises 5–8 find the radius of a circle in which:

5. $A = 49\pi$ 6. $A = \frac{4}{9}\pi$ 7. $A = 12\pi$ 8. $A = 48\pi$

What is the ratio of the radii of two circles whose areas are in the ratio:

9. $4:81$ 10. $9:16$ 11. $3:4$ 12. $1:2$

13. Find the area of the region bounded by two concentric circles with radii 6 and 9.
14. Find the area of a sector with a 30° arc and 6 cm radius.
15. Find the area of a sector with a 60° arc and radius $3\sqrt{2}$.
16. In a circle of radius 10 cm, a sector has area 40π cm^2. Find the degree measure of the arc of the sector.

In Exercises 17–20 find the area of a circle:

B 17. Inscribed in an equilateral triangle of side 6 cm.

18. Circumscribed about a square with side 4 cm.

19. Circumscribed about an equilateral triangle with perimeter 36 meters.

20. Inscribed in a regular hexagon with side 12 cm.

21. A circle is circumscribed about a square of side length 4. Find the area of a segment bounded by a side and a minor arc.

22. What is the area of the smaller segment whose chord is 8 cm long in a circle with radius 8 cm?

23. Two circles have radii 6 cm and their centers are 6 cm apart. Find the area of the region common to both circles.

24. Find the area of that part of a circle lying between two parallel chords 6 cm apart and each 6 cm long.

In each figure find the area of the shaded region.

C 25.

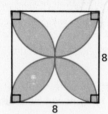

26.

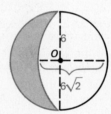

Self-Test Given $\odot O$ with radius 6 and $m\angle AOB = 60$.

1. Circumference of $\odot O$ = ___?___

2. Area of $\odot O$ = ___?___

3. Length of $\overset{\frown}{ACB}$ = ___?___

4. Length of $\overset{\frown}{ADB}$ = ___?___

5. Area of sector with arc $\overset{\frown}{ACB}$ = ___?___

6. Area of sector with arc $\overset{\frown}{ADB}$ = ___?___

7. A circle of circumference 10π has an area of ___?___ .

8. A circle of area 49π has a circumference of ___?___ .

9. The ratio of the areas of two circles with radii of 3 and 5 is ___?___ .

10. In a circle of area 81π, a sector of area 45π has an arc of degree measure ___?___ .

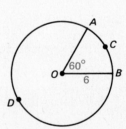

Check your answers with those printed at the back of the book.

Careers
Meteorology

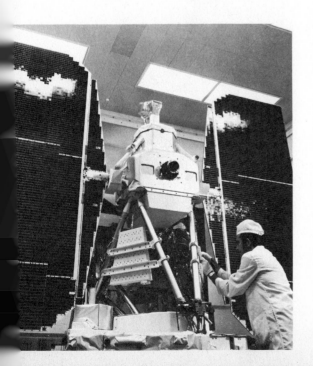

The primary concern of meteorologists is predicting weather. To make their predictions, meteorologists analyze up-to-the-minute data on air and water temperatures, air pressure, humidity, wind direction, and wind velocity. The accuracy of weather forecasting has been greatly improved by the development of orbiting weather satellites, which gather data previously unobtainable, and computers, which can perform rapid calculations on data gathered from observation stations all over the world. Meteorologists also trace the pattern of air currents in the upper atmosphere by tracking the course of weather balloons.

Weather prediction is possible because meteorologists have been able to translate the relationships among the factors affecting weather into mathematical terms. As these relationships are better understood, the accuracy of weather forecasting should continue to improve.

Solids

Objectives

1. Identify the parts of right prisms and pyramids.
2. Understand what is meant by a cubic unit of volume.
3. Compute the lateral area, total area, and volume of a right prism or pyramid.
4. Identify the parts of right circular cylinders and cones.
5. Compute the lateral area, total area, and volume of a right circular cylinder or cone.

9-7 *Right Prisms*

The three solids pictured below are prisms. In each, the bounding plane surfaces are called faces. The shaded faces are bases and the remaining faces are lateral faces. Bases lie in parallel planes and are congruent polygons. Lateral faces are parallelograms intersecting in parallel segments called lateral edges. Prisms I and II, in which all lateral faces are rectangles, are right prisms. Prism III is an oblique prism.

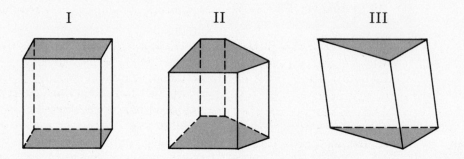

Prism I is a rectangular solid. Its six faces are rectangles. A rectangular solid in which all edges are congruent is a cube.

An altitude of a prism is a segment perpendicular to the planes of the bases and having an endpoint in each plane. In a right prism each lateral edge is an altitude. The length of an altitude is called the height (*h*) of the prism.

The Lateral Area (L.A.) of a prism is the sum of the areas of its lateral faces. The Total Area (T.A.) is the sum of the areas of all faces. Thus, where *B* denotes the area of a base:

$$\text{T.A.} = \text{L.A.} + 2B$$

The solid shown is a right prism with an n-sided base of perimeter p. The L.A. is the sum of the areas of n rectangles.

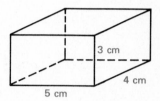

$$\text{L.A.} = s_1h + s_2h + s_3h + \cdots + s_nh$$
$$\text{L.A.} = \underbrace{(s_1 + s_2 + s_3 + \cdots + s_n)h}_{\text{perimeter}}$$

$$\text{L.A.} = ph \quad \text{and} \quad \text{T.A.} = ph + 2B$$

EXAMPLE 1. Find the lateral area and total area of the rectangular solid shown.

SOLUTION: $p = 18$ cm

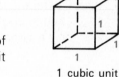

$$\text{L.A.} = ph = 18 \cdot 3 = 54 \text{ (cm}^2)$$
$$\text{T.A.} = \text{L.A.} + 2B = 54 + (2)(20) = 94 \text{ (cm}^2)$$

Volumes of solids are measured in terms of cubic units. A cube with all edges 1 linear unit long has a volume (V) of 1 cubic unit.

1 cubic unit

The right prism shown can be described as made up of 24 cubes, each with volume 1 cubic centimeter (1 cm³). It is said to have a volume of 24 (cm³). Each of the three layers contains $(4 \cdot 2)$ cubes. Note that $(4 \cdot 2) \cdot 3 = 24$. This suggests that the volume (V) of a right prism is the product of the number of units of area in the base (B) and the number of units of height (h). We assume this to be true for all right prisms.

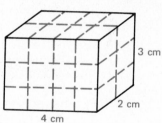

In any right prism: $V = Bh$

EXAMPLE 2. In the given right prism the bases are trapezoids. Find the volume of the prism.

SOLUTION: $V = Bh$

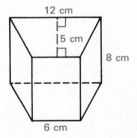

$$B = \tfrac{5}{2}(12 + 6) = 45 \text{ (cm}^2)$$
$$h = 8 \text{ cm}$$
$$V = 45 \cdot 8 = 360 \text{ (cm}^3)$$

Exercises 1–8 refer to the right prism shown.

1. The prism has __?__ faces.
2. The prism has __?__ lateral faces.
3. $\overline{DA}$ is a __?__ edge.
4. The length of $\overline{DF}$ is __?__ .
5. The perimeter of a base is __?__ .
6. The area of a base is __?__ .
7. The lateral area of the prism is __?__ .
8. The volume of the prism is __?__ .

9. Is each lateral edge of a right prism an altitude?
10. Must the bases of a right prism be congruent polygons?
11. Must the bases of a right prism be regular polygons?
12. What is the minimum number of faces a prism can have?

Written Exercises

Find the lateral area, the total area, and the volume of a cube with edges of length:

A 1. 3   2. 5   3. e 4. $2k$

Find the length of an edge of a cube in which the area of a face is:

5. 16 cm²   6. 49 cm²   7. 12 cm²   8. 32 cm²

9. Find the length of the edge of a cube with lateral area 36 cm².
10. Find the length of the edge of a cube with total area 48 cm².
11. The base of a right prism is a square with sides of length 4 cm. If the volume is 80 cm³, find the height.
12. When the edges of a cube are doubled in length, by what factor are the following multiplied?   (a) L.A.   (b) T.A.   (c) V

For the rectangular solid shown, find the L.A., the T.A., and the volume when:

B 13. $l = 6$ cm $w = 4$ cm $h = 3$ cm
14. $l = 8$ cm $w = 4\frac{1}{2}$ cm $h = 6$ cm
15. $l = 3\sqrt{2}$ cm $w = 2\sqrt{2}$ cm $h = 3$ cm

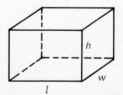

Find the volume and total area of a right prism of height 10 cm when the base is:

16. An equilateral triangle with sides of length 12 cm.
17. A rhombus with diagonals 6 cm and 8 cm long.
18. A regular hexagon with sides of length 8 cm.

C 19. Find the volume of a cube with diagonals of length $6\sqrt{3}$ cm.

20. A right prism with regular hexagons as bases has volume $96\sqrt{3}$ cm³. If all eighteen edges are congruent, find the length of an edge.

21. A rectangular tank with base dimensions of 120 cm and 80 cm is filled with water to a depth of 50 cm. The water rises $6\frac{2}{3}$ cm when a solid metal cube is submerged in the tank. Find the length of an edge of the cube.

22. If the length and width of a rectangular solid are each diminished by 20%, by what percent must the height be increased if the volume is to remain unchanged?

9-8 *Regular Pyramids*

A pyramid in which polygon *ABCDE* is the base and point *V* is the vertex is shown. The five triangular faces having *V* in common are lateral faces. The segments in which lateral faces intersect are lateral edges. The segment from *V* perpendicular to the base is the altitude and its length is the height (*h*) of the pyramid.

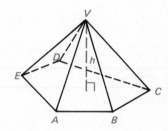

Our study of pyramids will be restricted to special pyramids called *regular pyramids*. In a regular pyramid the base is a regular polygon and all lateral edges are congruent. A regular pyramid has these additional properties:

(1) The altitude meets the base at the center of the bounding polygon.

(2) All lateral faces are congruent isosceles triangles. In each isosceles triangle the altitude from the vertex is a slant height and its length is denoted by l.

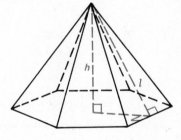

In a regular pyramid with slant height l and an *n*-sided base with perimeter p and area B:

$$\text{L.A.} = \tfrac{1}{2}pl \qquad \text{T.A.} = \tfrac{1}{2}pl + B$$

If you understand the meaning of the terms "lateral area" and "total area," you can compute both measures of a regular pyramid without thinking in terms of formulas.

In a formal deductive development of the properties of pyramids it is possible to establish the following formula for the volume of any pyramid:

Volume of Pyramid: $V = \frac{1}{3}Bh$

EXAMPLE. Given a regular square pyramid with base edges of length 10 cm and lateral edges of length 12 cm, find the:
(a) lateral area   (b) total area
(c) volume

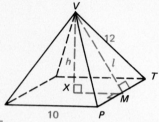

SOLUTION:

(a) In rt. $\triangle VMT$: $l = \sqrt{144 - 25} = \sqrt{119}$

$\qquad$ L.A. $= \frac{1}{2}(40)\sqrt{119} = 20\sqrt{119}$ (cm^2)

(b) T.A. $=$ L.A. $+ B = 20\sqrt{119} + 100$ (cm^2)

(c) In rt. $\triangle VXM$: $h = \sqrt{l^2 - 25} = \sqrt{119 - 25} = \sqrt{94}$

$\qquad V = \frac{1}{3}Bh = \frac{1}{3}(100)(\sqrt{94}) = \frac{100}{3}\sqrt{94}$ (cm^3)

Oral Exercises

1. How many lateral faces does a pentagonal pyramid have?
2. In a regular pyramid can the altitude be longer than the slant height?
3. In a regular pyramid can the slant height be longer than a lateral edge?
4. What is the minimum number of faces a pyramid can have?
5. Can the area of the base of a pyramid be greater than the L.A.?
6. Can the lateral faces of a square pyramid be equilateral triangles?
7. A regular square pyramid and a right prism have equal heights and bases of equal area. What is the ratio of their volumes?
8. What is the height of a regular pyramid with base area 10 cm^2 if its volume is 20 cm^3?

Written Exercises

Find the lateral area of a regular pyramid with a slant height 12 cm long if the base is:

A
1. A square with sides of length 10 cm.
2. An equilateral triangle with sides of length 7 cm.
3. A pentagon with sides of length 6 cm.
4. A hexagon with sides of length 8 cm.

5. Find the volume of a regular square pyramid with base area 24 cm^2 and height 8 cm.
6. Find the length of the altitude of a regular square pyramid if the length of a base edge is 4 cm and the volume is 32 cm^3.

7. A regular triangular pyramid has a volume of 15 cm³ and base edges of length 6 cm. Find the length of the altitude.

8. In a regular triangular pyramid the length of a base edge is 12 cm. If the length of a lateral edge is 10 cm, find the length of the slant height.

B 9. Find the total area of a regular hexagonal pyramid with base edges 12 cm long and a height of 6 cm.

10. Find the total area of a regular triangular pyramid in which all six edges are 4 cm long.

11. A regular hexagonal pyramid has height 8 cm and base edges of length 6 cm. Find the volume of the pyramid.

12. A regular square pyramid with base perimeter 40 cm has a lateral edge of length 13 cm. Find the total area.

C 13. Find the volume of a regular triangular pyramid in which all edges are 6 cm long.

14. Given a regular square pyramid of height $2k$ and base edge length $2k$. At a distance of k from the vertex a plane is passed parallel to the base. Find the volumes of the two solids into which the plane divides the given pyramid.

9-9 *Right Circular Cylinders and Cones*

Both cylinders shown are **circular cylinders**. In each, the circular regions are **bases** and the segment $\overline{OO'}$ is the **axis** of the cylinder. An **altitude** is any perpendicular segment from a point in one base to a point in the plane of the other base. The length of an altitude is the **height** (h) of the cylinder.

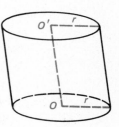

A cylinder such as the one at the right, in which the axis is also an altitude, is a *right circular cylinder*.

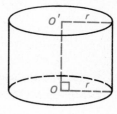

In the discussion and problems that follow, the word "cylinder" will always refer only to a right circular cylinder.

Recall our three formulas for a right prism:

$$\text{L.A.} = ph \qquad \text{T.A.} = ph + 2B \qquad V = Bh$$

All three formulas also apply to cylinders. Since the bases of a cylinder are circles, $p = 2\pi r$ and $B = \pi r^2$. When these substitutions are made, the following formulas for a cylinder are obtained.

$$\text{L.A.} = 2\pi rh \qquad \text{T.A.} = 2\pi rh + 2\pi r^2 \qquad V = \pi r^2 h$$

Suppose you removed the ends of a cylindrical tin can and then unrolled the curved surface. You would then have a rectangular region and two circular regions as shown below. Do you see how the L.A. and T.A. formulas for cylinders relate to this illustration?

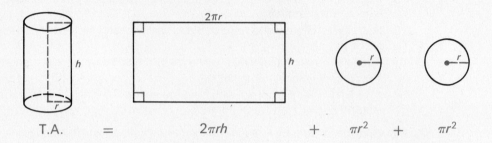

T.A.   = $2\pi rh$ + πr^2 + πr^2

In solving the example that follows, the special formulas for cylinders are used. You may prefer to work directly from the more general forms that apply both to right prisms and cylinders.

EXAMPLE 1. A cylinder has a 5 cm radius and 6 cm height. Find:
    (a) Lateral Area
    (b) Total Area
    (c) Volume

SOLUTION: (a) L.A. $= 2\pi rh = 2\pi(5)(6) = 60\pi$ (cm^2)
           (b) T.A. $= 2\pi rh + 2\pi r^2 = 60\pi + 2\pi(5)^2 = 110\pi$ (cm^2)
           (c) $V = \pi r^2 h = \pi(5)^2 \cdot 6 = 150\pi$ (cm^3)

The cone shown has *axis* $\overline{TO}$ perpendicular to the *circular base* at its center O. It is a **right circular cone** and the axis is also the *altitude*. All segments that join the *vertex* (T) to a point on the circle that bounds the base are **slant heights** and are congruent segments. The length of a slant height is denoted by l.

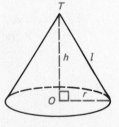

In the discussion and exercises that follow, the word "cone" will refer only to a right circular cone.

Just as the formulas for right prisms can be applied to right circular cylinders, the formulas for regular pyramids can also be applied to right circular cones.

$$\text{L.A.} = \tfrac{1}{2}pl \qquad \text{T.A.} = \tfrac{1}{2}pl + B \qquad V = \tfrac{1}{3}Bh$$

Since a cone has a circular base, $p = 2\pi r$ and $B = \pi r^2$. Substituting in the above formulas results in special formulas for cones.

$$\text{L.A.} = \pi r l \qquad \text{T.A.} = \underline{\pi r l + \pi r^2} \qquad V = \tfrac{1}{3}\pi r^2 h$$

EXAMPLE 2. A cone has a radius of 6 cm and an
altitude of 9 cm. Find:
    (a) Lateral Area
    (b) Total Area
    (c) Volume

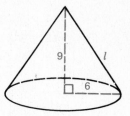

SOLUTION:
    (a) $l = \sqrt{(6)^2 + (9)^2} = \sqrt{117} = 3\sqrt{13}$
        $\text{L.A.} = \pi r l = \pi(6)(3\sqrt{13}) = 18\sqrt{13}\pi \ (\text{cm}^2)$
    (b) $\text{T.A.} = \pi r l + \pi r^2 = 18\sqrt{13}\pi + 36\pi \ (\text{cm}^2)$
    (c) $V = \tfrac{1}{3}\pi r^2 h = \tfrac{1}{3}\pi(6)^2(9) = 108\pi \ (\text{cm}^3)$

Written Exercises

In Exercises 1–4, two measures of a *cylinder* are given. Supply the two remaining measures.

	r	h	L.A.	V
A 1.	4	3	?	?
2.	5	6	?	?
3.	5	?	20π	?
4.	4	?	?	96π

In Exercises 5–8, two measures of a *cone* are given. Supply the three remaining measures.

	r	h	l	T.A.	V
5.	3	4	?	?	?
6.	5	?	13	?	?
7.	?	$2\sqrt{5}$	6	?	?
8.	3	?	?	?	27π

B 9. A cone of radius 3 cm has total area 24π cm². Find the volume of the cone.
10. A cone of radius 3 cm and a cylinder of radius 4 cm have equal volumes. Find the ratio of the height of the cone to that of the cylinder.
11. The total area of a cylinder is 110π cm² and the height is 6 cm. Find the radius of the cylinder.
12. A solid metal cylinder of radius 6 cm and height 18 cm is melted down and recast as a cone of radius 9 cm. Find the height of the cone.

Self-Test   Exercises 1–6 refer to the regular pyramid shown.

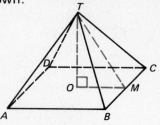

1. The pyramid has __?__ lateral faces.
2. $\overline{TO}$ is the __?__ of the pyramid.
3. $\overline{TM}$ is the __?__ of the pyramid.
4. Square $ABCD$ is the __?__ of the pyramid.
5. $\overline{TB}$ is a __?__ edge of the pyramid.
6. The ratio of OM to AB is __?__ .

7. Find the lateral area, total area, and volume of a cube with edges of length 6 cm.
8. Find the volume of a cone that has a radius of 8 cm and a height of 6 cm.
9. Find the total area of a cylinder that has a radius of 4 cm and a height of 6 cm.
10. Find the lateral area of a cone that has a radius of 4 cm and a height of 6 cm.

Check your answers with those printed at the back of the book.

CHAPTER SUMMARY

1. Corresponding to every polygonal region there is a unique positive number called the area of the region. Regions bounded by congruent triangles have equal areas. Any given polygonal region can be separated into a finite number of non-overlapping regions, the sum of whose areas is equal to the area of the given region.

2. Formulas for areas of polygons:

   Rectangle: $A = bh$ Rhombus: $A = \frac{1}{2}d_1 d_2$

   Square: $A = s^2$ Equilateral Triangle: $A = \dfrac{s^2\sqrt{3}}{4}$

   Parallelogram: $A = bh$ Trapezoid: $A = \frac{1}{2}h(b_1 + b_2)$

   Triangle: $A = \frac{1}{2}bh$ Regular Polygon: $A = \frac{1}{2}ap$

3. A circle can be circumscribed about and inscribed in any regular polygon.

4. The ratio of the circumference to the diameter of any circle is the number π.

5. Formulas for circles:

   $C = 2\pi r$ Length of $\overarc{AB} = \dfrac{n}{360} \cdot 2\pi r$

   $A = \pi r^2$ Area of Sector $= \dfrac{n}{360} \cdot \pi r^2$

338 *GEOMETRY*

6. Area and volume formulas for solids:

Right Prism	Regular Pyramid
L.A. $= ph$	L.A. $= \frac{1}{2}pl$
T.A. $= ph + 2B$	T.A. $= \frac{1}{2}pl + B$
$V = Bh$	$V = \frac{1}{3}Bh$

Right Circular Cylinder	Right Circular Cone
L.A. $= 2\pi rh$	L.A. $= \pi rl$
T.A. $= 2\pi rh + 2\pi r^2$	T.A. $= \pi rl + \pi r^2$
$V = \pi r^2 h$	$V = \frac{1}{3}\pi r^2 h$

CHAPTER TEST

Find the area of the figure described.

1. Square: perimeter 20 cm
2. Rectangle: length 8 cm, width 6 cm
3. Circle: radius 7 cm
4. Circle: circumference 12π cm
5. Right Triangle: legs of length 8 cm and $4\sqrt{3}$ cm
6. Trapezoid: base lengths 14 cm and 6 cm; altitude length 5 cm
7. Rhombus: diagonals of lengths 10 cm and 8 cm
8. Isosceles Triangle: base length 8 cm; legs of length 5 cm
9. Equilateral Triangle: perimeter 18 cm
10. Sector of Circle: radius 6 cm; arc measure 90

Find the volume of the solid described.

11. Right Prism
    $B = 20$ cm^2 $h = 5$ cm
12. Regular Pyramid
    $B = 15$ cm^2 $h = 4$ cm
13. Right Circular Cylinder
    $r = 5$ cm $h = 6$ cm
14. Right Circular Cone
    $r = 6$ cm $h = 8$ cm

A right circular cone has radius 6 cm and slant height length 10 cm.

15. Find the lateral area.
16. Find the total area.
17. Find the height.
18. Find the volume.
19. A sector of a circle has a 45° arc and area 8π cm^2. Find the radius of the sector.
20. A cone of radius 4 cm has total area 36π cm^2. Find the volume.
21. The base of a regular pyramid is a square with sides 10 cm long. Each lateral edge is 13 cm long. Find the total area of the pyramid.
22. A segment of a circle has a 120° arc and a chord of length $8\sqrt{3}$ cm. Find the area of the segment.

CHAPTER REVIEW

9-1 *Areas of Rectangles*

1. Find the area of a rectangle 10 cm long and 4 cm wide.
2. Find the area of a square whose side is $3\sqrt{2}$ cm long.
3. Find the perimeter of a square whose area is 25 cm².

9-2 *Areas of Parallelograms and Triangles*

Find the area of the parallelogram and triangles shown.

4.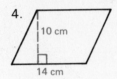
10 cm
14 cm

5.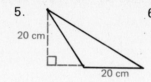
20 cm
20 cm

6.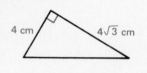
4 cm
$4\sqrt{3}$ cm

9-3 *Areas of Trapezoids*

Find the area of each trapezoid shown.

7.
6 cm
7 cm
14 cm

8.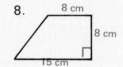
8 cm
8 cm
15 cm

9.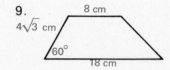
8 cm
$4\sqrt{3}$ cm
60°
18 cm

9-4 *Areas of Regular Polygons*

Given a regular polygon with perimeter p, apothem a, and radius k.

10. The radius of the polygon's inscribed circle is __?__ .
11. The radius of the polygon's circumscribed circle is __?__ .
12. The area of the polygon is __?__ .

9-5 *Circumferences of Circles*

13. For all circles the ratio of the __?__ to the __?__ is the number π.
14. A circle with radius 10 cm has circumference __?__ cm.
15. A circle with circumference 12π cm has radius __?__ cm.
16. In a circle with radius 9 cm, a 40° arc is __?__ cm long.

9-6 *Areas of Circles*

17. A circle with radius 9 cm has area __?__ cm².
18. A circle with area 14π cm² has radius __?__ cm.
19. In a circle with radius 6 cm a sector with 60° arc has area __?__ cm².
20. If the ratio of the radii of two circles is 3:5, the ratio of the areas of the two circles is __?__ .

9-7 *Right Prisms*

21. A right prism whose base is a hexagon has __?__ lateral faces.
22. A cube with edges 10 cm long has total area __?__ cm².
23. A right prism with base area 8 cm² and volume 24 cm³ has height __?__ cm.
24. Two cubes with edge lengths in the ratio 1:2 have volumes in the ratio __?__ .

9-8 *Regular Pyramids*

In the regular square pyramid shown:

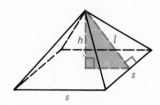

25. L.A. = __?__
26. T.A. = __?__
27. $V =$ __?__
28. $\sqrt{h^2 + \left(\dfrac{s}{2}\right)^2} =$ __?__

9-9 *Right Circular Cylinders and Cones*

29. A cylinder of radius 4 cm and height 6 cm has lateral area __?__ cm².
30. A cylinder of radius 5 cm and height 8 cm has volume __?__ cm³.
31. A cone of radius 3 cm and height 4 cm has total area __?__ cm².
32. A cone of radius 6 cm and height 9 cm has volume __?__ cm³.

programming in BASIC

In this chapter you have learned many formulas which are used to calculate area and volume. Each formula can be changed into other related ones by using procedures you learned in algebra. For example, the formula for the area of a trapezoid is:

$$A = \tfrac{1}{2}h(b_1 + b_2)$$

This equation can be transformed by multiplying both sides by 2 and then dividing by $(b_1 + b_2)$:

$$h = \frac{2A}{(b_1 + b_2)}$$

Starting with the original formula and multiplying both sides by 2, and then dividing by h, we get

$$b_1 + b_2 = \frac{2A}{h},$$

from which we find:

$$b_1 = \frac{2A}{h} - b_2 \quad \text{and} \quad b_2 = \frac{2A}{h} - b_1$$

These four formulas are included in the following computer program which computes the value of A, h, b_1, or b_2, if the values of the other three are given.

```
10    PRINT "SOLUTION FOR MISSING NUMBERS";
15    PRINT "RELATED TO A TRAPEZOID WHERE"
20    PRINT "B1 AND B2 ARE THE BASES, H IS";
25    PRINT "THE HEIGHT, AND A IS THE AREA."
30    PRINT
40    PRINT "TYPE B1,B2,H, AND A;"
45    PRINT "TYPE O FOR ANY MISSING VALUE."
50    INPUT B1,B2,H,A
60    IF A=0 THEN 160
70    IF H=0 THEN 190
80    IF B1=0 THEN 220
90    IF B2=0 THEN 250
100   PRINT "THERE IS NO MISSING VALUE."
110   IF A=.5*H*(B1+B2) THEN 140
120   PRINT "THE VALUE FOR THE AREA";
125   PRINT "DOES NOT AGREE WITH THE OTHER VALUES."
130   GOTO 30
140   PRINT "THE AREA AGREES WITH THE OTHER VALUES."
150   GOTO 30
160   LET A=.5*H*(B1+B2)
170   PRINT "THE AREA IS ";A
180   GOTO 30
190   LET H=2*A/(B1+B2)
200   PRINT "THE ALTITUDE IS ";H
210   GOTO 30
220   LET B1=2*A/H-B2
230   PRINT "THE MISSING BASE IS ";B1
240   GOTO 30
250   LET B2=2*A/H-B1
260   PRINT "THE MISSING BASE IS ";B2
270   GOTO 30
280   END
```

Exercises

1. Type and RUN the program. Use as input 5,7,3,0. This will ask for the area when the bases are 5 and 7 and the height is 3. Then use as input 5,7,0,18 which will find the height of the same trapezoid. Then use as input 5,0,3,18 and 0,7,3,18. In so doing we have checked that all our formulas are correct.

2. Select any of the other formulas in this chapter and write a similar program. Be careful when you solve the formula for the other variables. Have the computer check your work as we did in Exercise 1.

Similar Figures/Plane and Solid

The term *similar polygons* was defined in Chapter 6. A formal definition of *similar solids* involves terms with which you are not familiar and thus will not be attempted here. Similar solids can be described as solids that have the same shape but not necessarily the same size. In similar solids whose faces are bounded by polygons, corresponding faces are similar polygons, and the lengths of all pairs of corresponding edges have the same ratio.

The following theorems state ratio relationships that you may already have deduced on the basis of your solutions to certain earlier exercises.

extra for experts

THEOREM A The areas of two similar polygons have the same ratio as the squares of the lengths of any pair of corresponding sides.

THEOREM B The lateral and total areas of two similar solids have the same ratio as the squares of the lengths of any pair of corresponding segments.

THEOREM C The volumes of two similar solids have the same ratio as the cubes of the lengths of any pair of corresponding segments.

Pictured below are two *similar regular square* pyramids. Two of several proportions you could state about these solids, based on the above theorems, are:

$$(1) \quad \frac{\text{L.A. of I}}{\text{L.A. of II}} = \frac{t^2}{(t')^2} \qquad\qquad (2) \quad \frac{V \text{ of I}}{V \text{ of II}} = \frac{t^3}{(t')^3}$$

I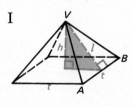

II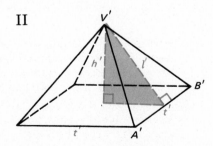

It is not difficult to show that, in the case of these particular similar solids, both stated ratios are correct.

I 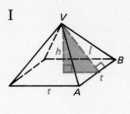   II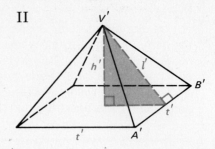

(1) $\dfrac{\text{L.A. of } \mathbf{I}}{\text{L.A. of } \mathbf{II}} = \dfrac{\frac{1}{2}(4t)l}{\frac{1}{2}(4t')l'} = \dfrac{tl}{t'l'} = \dfrac{t}{t'} \cdot \dfrac{l}{l'}$

Since $\triangle VAB \sim \triangle V'A'B'$, $\dfrac{l}{l'} = \dfrac{t}{t'}$.

Therefore, $\dfrac{\text{L.A. of } \mathbf{I}}{\text{L.A. of } \mathbf{II}} = \dfrac{t}{t'} \cdot \dfrac{t}{t'} = \dfrac{t^2}{(t')^2}$.

(2) $\dfrac{V \text{ of } \mathbf{I}}{V \text{ of } \mathbf{II}} = \dfrac{\frac{1}{3}t^2 h}{\frac{1}{3}(t')^2 h'} = \dfrac{t^2 h}{(t')^2 h'} = \dfrac{t^2}{(t')^2} \cdot \dfrac{h}{h'}$

Since the shaded $\triangle$ are similar, $\dfrac{h}{h'} = \dfrac{\frac{1}{2}t}{\frac{1}{2}t'} = \dfrac{t}{t'}$.

Therefore, $\dfrac{V \text{ of } \mathbf{I}}{V \text{ of } \mathbf{II}} = \dfrac{t^2}{(t')^2} \cdot \dfrac{t}{t'} = \dfrac{t^3}{(t')^3}$.

Any two circles are said to be similar. Therefore, the areas of any two circles have the same ratio as the squares of their radii or the squares of their diameters. (See Exercise 21 for the proof.)

Similarly, any two spheres are similar. In this section we shall use the formulas for the surface area and the volume of a sphere:

$$A = 4\pi r^2 \qquad \text{and} \qquad V = \tfrac{4}{3}\pi r^3$$

For any two spheres, the surface areas have the same ratio as the squares of their radii or the squares of their diameters. Also, the volumes of any two spheres have the same ratio as the cubes of their radii or the cubes of their diameters. (See Exercises 22 and 23 for the proofs.)

EXAMPLE. The surface area of two spheres are in the ratio $2:9$. Find the ratio of their radii.

SOLUTION:

$$\frac{4\pi r_1^2}{4\pi r_2^2} = \frac{2}{9}$$

$$\frac{r_1^2}{r_2^2} = \frac{2}{9}$$

$$\frac{r_1}{r_2} = \sqrt{\frac{2}{9}} = \frac{\sqrt{2}}{3}$$

Exercises

State the ratio of the areas of two similar polygons for which the ratio of the lengths of a pair of corresponding sides is:

1. $2:3$ 2. $3:5$ 3. $\sqrt{2}:6$ 4. $\sqrt{5}:\sqrt{15}$

State the ratio of the radii of two circles, if the ratio of their areas is:

5. $9:25$ 6. $49:81$ 7. $3:4$ 8. $9:13$

Given two similar cones. If the lengths of a pair of corresponding edges have the given ratio, state the ratio of the total areas and the ratio of the volumes.

9. $2:3$ 10. $3:4$ 11. $\sqrt{2}:2$ 12. $1:\sqrt{3}$

Two similar regular triangular pyramids have total areas of 10 cm^2 and 40 cm^2. Find the volume of the larger pyramid if the volume of the smaller pyramid is:

13. 5 cm^3 14. 18 cm^3 15. $\frac{3}{4}$ cm^3 16. $\frac{5}{4}$ cm^3

If the volumes of two spheres have the ratio $8:27$, find the surface area of the smaller sphere when the surface area of the larger sphere is:

17. 63 cm^2 18. 24 cm^2 19. $\frac{1}{4}$ cm^2 20. 1 cm^2

21. Prove that the areas of two circles have the same ratio as the squares of their radii or the squares of their diameters.
22. Prove that the surface areas of two spheres have the same ratio as the squares of their radii or the squares of their diameters.
23. Prove that the volumes of two spheres have the same ratio as the cubes of their radii or the cubes of their diameters.

CUMULATIVE REVIEW: CHAPTERS 7–9

True–False Exercises

A 1. A line that intersects a circle must lie in the plane of the circle.

2. A line that intersects a circle in two points must lie in the plane of the circle.

3. The formula for the volume of a right circular cone is $V = \frac{1}{3}\pi r^2 h$.

4. If the sides of a triangle have lengths 11, 60, and 61, the triangle must be a right triangle.

5. If two circles intersect in two points, the circles must be coplanar.

6. If two circles intersect in two points, the circles must be congruent.

7. If two triangles are congruent, they must have equal areas.

8. If two triangles have equal areas, the triangles must be congruent.

9. A line that contains an interior point of a sphere must intersect the sphere in two points.

10. The area of a circle is greater than the area of any polygon that is inscribed in the circle.

B 11. If a ray that is not tangent to a circle intersects the circle, then the ray must intersect the circle in two points.

12. If each side of an equilateral triangle has length 10, then each altitude has length $5\sqrt{3}$.

13. If an inscribed angle intercepts a minor arc, then the measure of the angle must be less than 45.

14. If a triangle is inscribed in a circle, then the triangle must be an acute triangle or a right triangle.

15. The ratio of the length of a diagonal of a square to the length of a side of the square is $\sqrt{2}:1$.

16. If each side of a rhombus is 10 cm long, then the area of the rhombus must be at least 50 cm^2.

17. In a given circle, the chord of a 120° arc is less than twice as long as the chord of a 60° arc.

18. If the measures of the angles of a triangle are in the ratio $1:2:3$, then the lengths of the sides are in the ratio $1:2:3$.

19. A triangle with sides of lengths $\sqrt{k}$, $\sqrt{2k}$, and $\sqrt{3k}$ must be a right triangle.

20. If the radius of a right circular cylinder is $3c$ and the altitude is $5k$, then the total area is equal to $6\pi c(3c + 5k)$.

Area Exercises

State the area of the figure described.

A 1. A right triangle whose legs have lengths 6 and 8.

2. A rectangle with a side 12 cm long and a diagonal 15 cm long.

3. A circle whose diameter is 8.

4. A trapezoid whose bases have lengths 9 and 13 and whose altitude has length 6.

5. A circle whose circumference is 20π.

B 6. An equilateral triangle each of whose sides has length 18.

7. A rhombus whose diagonals have lengths 8 and 12.

8. A square whose perimeter is 28.8.

9. A 20° sector of a circle whose radius is 6.

10. A regular hexagon whose perimeter is 300.

Completion Exercises

$\overline{AH}$ is a tangent segment in the figure shown.

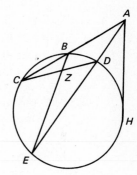

A 1. If $m\widehat{BEH} = 260$ and $m\widehat{DH} = 70$,
then $m\widehat{BD} = \underline{\quad?\quad}$.

2. If $m\widehat{CE} = 80$, then $m\angle CDE = \underline{\quad?\quad}$.

3. If $m\widehat{CE} = 80$ and $m\widehat{BD} = 30$,
then $m\angle CZE = \underline{\quad?\quad}$.

4. If $m\widehat{EH} = 120$ and $m\widehat{DH} = 60$,
then $m\angle EAH = \underline{\quad?\quad}$.

5. If $m\angle E = 21$, then $m\widehat{BD} = \underline{\quad?\quad}$.

6. If $CZ = 8$, $ZD = 6$, and $BZ = 3$,
then $ZE = \underline{\quad?\quad}$.

7. If $AB = 10$, $BC = 8$, and $AD = 8$,
then $DE = \underline{\quad?\quad}$.

8. If $AH = 12$ and $DE = 10$, then $AE = \underline{\quad?\quad}$.

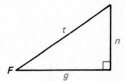

B 9. $\sin F = \dfrac{?}{?}$ 11. $t^2 - n^2 = \underline{\quad?\quad}$

10. $\tan F = \dfrac{?}{?}$ 12. If $\cos F = \dfrac{\sqrt{3}}{2}$, $m\angle F = \underline{\quad?\quad}$.

13. If $t = 20$ and $\dfrac{n}{g} = \dfrac{3}{4}$, then $g = \underline{\quad?\quad}$.

The edges of a rectangular solid have lengths 12, 4, and 3.

14. The total area of the solid is $\underline{\quad?\quad}$.

15. The volume of the solid is $\underline{\quad?\quad}$.

16. The length of a diagonal of the solid is $\underline{\quad?\quad}$.

C 17. Each edge of the base of a regular square pyramid has length 8. If the length of the altitude of the pyramid is 20, then the length of a lateral edge is $\underline{\quad?\quad}$.

18. If each of the eight edges of a regular square pyramid has length 6, then the volume of the pyramid is $\underline{\quad?\quad}$.

19. If the radius of a right circular cone is 4 and the length of the altitude is 3, then the total area of the cone is $\underline{\quad?\quad}$.

20. In a right triangle, an altitude is drawn from the vertex of the right angle. If the altitude divides the hypotenuse into segments having lengths 9 and 16, the area of the triangle is $\underline{\quad?\quad}$.

10

CONSTRUCTIONS AND LOCI

The Basic Constructions

Objectives

1. Perform the fifteen basic constructions.
2. Apply the basic constructions in original construction exercises.

10-1 *Meaning of Construction*

Since the days of the early Greek mathematicians, the study of *constructions* has been an important part of geometry. The ancient Greeks established the ground rules for *constructing* a geometric figure and for *drawing* a geometric figure. In a drawing, you are free to use any instrument you choose. In *constructing a geometric figure,* however, you are limited to two instruments, a *compass* and a *straightedge*. You do not use a protractor to measure angles or a ruler to measure lengths. Although you may use a ruler as a straightedge, you must remember that the marks on the ruler are not part of the straightedge.

In the construction of a geometric figure:

1. The straightedge is used only to draw lines, rays, or segments.

2. The compass is used only to draw circles or arcs of circles.

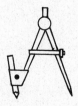

Three basic constructions follow. Study them carefully so that you will understand that a complete solution to a construction problem consists of the following six parts.

1. A statement of the required construction
2. A statement, in terms of a figure, of what is given
3. A statement of what is to be constructed
4. The *Construction* (figure)
5. An *Explanation* of the construction
6. A *Justification* of the construction

CONSTRUCTION 1   Given a segment, construct a segment congruent to the given segment.

Given: $\overline{XY}$

To Construct: A segment congruent to $\overline{XY}$

Construction:

Explanation:
1. Using a straightedge, draw a line. Call it l.
2. Select any point on l and call it A.
3. Using a compass, with X as center and radius XY, construct an arc intersecting $\overline{XY}$ at Y. (The arc is a check on the accuracy of your measurement.)
4. With A as center and radius XY, construct an arc intersecting line l. Label the point of intersection B.

$\overline{AB}$ is the desired segment.

Justification: Since $AB = XY$, $\overline{AB} \cong \overline{XY}$.

CONSTRUCTION 2　Given an angle, construct an angle congruent to the given angle.

Given: ∠ABC

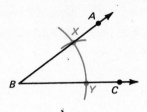

To Construct: An angle congruent to ∠ABC

Construction:

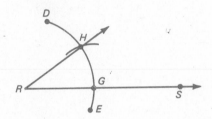

Explanation:

1. Draw a ray. Label it $\overrightarrow{RS}$.

2. With B as center and any convenient radius, construct an arc intersecting $\overrightarrow{BA}$ and $\overrightarrow{BC}$. Label the points of intersection X and Y.

3. With the same radius used in Step 2 and with R as center, construct $\overset{\frown}{DE}$ intersecting $\overrightarrow{RS}$. Label the point of intersection G.

4. With Y as center and radius YX, construct an arc intersecting $\overrightarrow{BA}$.

5. With G as center and radius YX, construct an arc intersecting $\overset{\frown}{DE}$. Label the point of intersection H.

6. Draw $\overrightarrow{RH}$.

∠HRG is the desired angle.

Justification:

When $\overline{XY}$ and $\overline{HG}$ are drawn, △XBY ≅ △HRG (SSS Postulate). Hence ∠HRG ≅ ∠ABC.

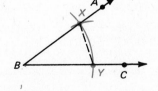
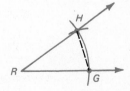

CONSTRUCTION 3 Given an angle, construct the ray that bisects the angle.

Given: ∠ABC

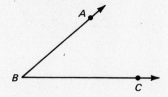

To Construct: The ray that bisects ∠ABC

Construction:

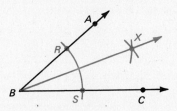

Explanation:

1. With B as center and any convenient radius, construct an arc intersecting $\overrightarrow{BA}$ and $\overrightarrow{BC}$. Label the points of intersection R and S.

2. With points R and S as centers and a radius greater than $\frac{1}{2}RS$, construct arcs intersecting in the interior of ∠ABC. Label the point of intersection X.

3. Draw $\overrightarrow{BX}$.

$\overrightarrow{BX}$ is the desired ray.

Justification:

When $\overline{RX}$ and $\overline{SX}$ are drawn, △BRX ≅ △BSX (SSS Postulate). Hence ∠RBX ≅ ∠SBX, and it follows, by definition, that $\overrightarrow{BX}$ is an angle bisector.

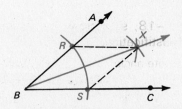

In most of the work in this chapter, you will be asked to write only the first four parts of a complete solution, as listed on page 350. You should be prepared, however, to explain and justify each construction.

Exercises 1–4 refer to the construction of the ray that bisects $\angle RST$.

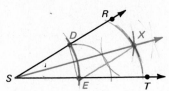

1. The center for $\overset{\frown}{DE}$ is point ___?___ .
2. Points D and E are the centers of two arcs that intersect in point ___?___ .
3. DX _____?_____ EX
   $(<, =, >)$
4. EX _____?_____ $\frac{1}{2}DE$
   $(<, =, >)$

5. What instruments may be used in a construction problem?
6. How does a ruler differ from a straightedge?
7. If you are given a right angle, how can you construct an angle with measure 45?
8. If you are given an angle with measure x $(x < 90)$, how can you construct an angle with measure $2x$?

In Exercises 1–6, copy the two given segments on your paper. Construct a segment having the indicated length. You need not write an explanation or justification.

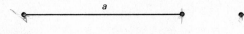

A

1. $a + b$
2. $a - b$
3. $a + 2b$
4. $2b - a$
5. $3b - a$
6. $2a - 2b$

In Exercises 7–18, show your construction. You need not write an explanation or justification.

7. Draw an acute angle. Call it $\angle ABC$. Construct an angle congruent to $\angle ABC$.
8. Draw an obtuse angle. Call it $\angle RST$. Construct an angle congruent to $\angle RST$.
9. Draw an acute angle. Construct the bisector of the angle.
10. Draw an obtuse angle. Construct the bisector of the angle.

EXAMPLE. Given $\angle R$ and $\angle S$. Construct an angle whose measure is equal to $m\angle R + m\angle S$.

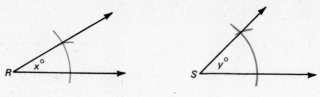

SOLUTION:

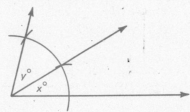

B   11. Draw an acute angle. Let y represent its measure. Construct an angle with measure $2y$.

12. Draw two acute angles. Let x and y represent the measures of the angles. Construct an angle with measure $x + y$.

13. Draw an obtuse angle and an acute angle. Construct an angle whose measure is equal to the difference of the measures of the given angles.

14. Draw two acute angles. Let r and s represent the measures of the angles. Construct an angle with measure $\frac{1}{2}(r + s)$.

15. Draw an obtuse angle. Let x represent the measure of the angle. Construct an angle with measure $\frac{1}{4}x$.

16. Draw an acute angle, $\angle A$, and a line l. At a point R on l, construct the supplement of $\angle A$.

C   17. Draw an acute angle. Let x represent the measure of the angle. Construct an angle with measure $\dfrac{360 - x}{4}$.

18. Draw an obtuse angle. Let y represent the measure of the angle. Construct an angle with measure $\dfrac{540 - 3y}{2}$.

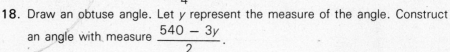

Challenge

A triangle is circumscribed about a circle whose radius is 50. One side of the triangle is divided by its point of tangency into segments whose lengths are 85 and 86. Find the length of the shortest side of the triangle.

10-2 *Parallel Lines and Perpendicular Lines*

The following constructions show how to construct parallel lines and perpendicular lines.

CONSTRUCTION 4 Given a point on a line in a plane, construct a line perpendicular to the given line at the given point.

Given: Point R on line l

To Construct: A line perpendicular to l at point R

Construction:

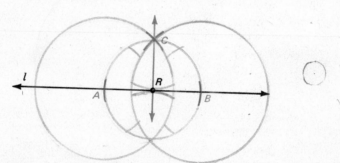

Explanation:

1. With R as center and a convenient radius, construct two arcs intersecting l. Label the points of intersection A and B.

2. With A and B as centers and any radius greater than $\frac{1}{2}AB$, construct a pair of intersecting arcs. Label the point of intersection C.

3. Draw $\overleftrightarrow{CR}$.

$\overleftrightarrow{CR}$ is the desired line.

Justification:

When $\overline{AC}$ and $\overline{BC}$ are drawn, $\triangle ARC \cong \triangle BRC$ (SSS Postulate). Hence $\angle ARC \cong \angle BRC$. Then $\overleftrightarrow{CR} \perp l$, because if two lines meet to form congruent adjacent angles, the lines are $\perp$.

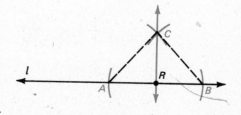

CONSTRUCTION 5 Given a point outside a line, construct a perpendicular to the line from the point.

Given: Point S not on line t

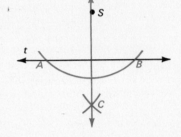

To Construct: A line through S which is perpendicular to t

Construction and Explanation:

1. With S as center and a convenient radius, construct an arc intersecting t in two points. Label the points A and B.

2. With A and B as centers and any radius greater than $\frac{1}{2}AB$, construct a pair of arcs that intersect at some point other than S. Label the point of intersection C.

3. Draw $\overleftrightarrow{SC}$.

$\overleftrightarrow{SC}$ is the desired line.

The Justification is left as Exercise 25.

CONSTRUCTION 6 Given a segment, construct a perpendicular bisector of the segment.

Given: $\overline{DE}$

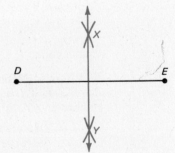

To Construct: A perpendicular bisector of $\overline{DE}$

Construction and Explanation:

1. With a radius greater than $\frac{1}{2}DE$, construct two arcs having D as center and two arcs having E as center. Label the points of intersection X and Y.

2. Draw $\overleftrightarrow{XY}$.

$\overleftrightarrow{XY}$ is the desired line.

The Justification is left as Exercise 26.

CONSTRUCTION 7 Given a point outside a line, construct a line parallel to the given line through the given point.

Given: Point A not on line t

To Construct: A line through A parallel to t

Construction and Explanation:

1. Through A draw any line intersecting t. Label the point of intersection X.
2. Construct an angle, $\angle 2$, with vertex at point A such that $\angle 1$ and $\angle 2$ are corresponding angles and $\angle 2 \cong \angle 1$. Let Y be any point on the new side of $\angle 2$.
3. Draw $\overleftrightarrow{AY}$.

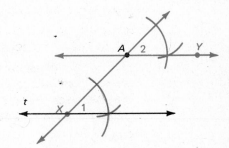

$\overleftrightarrow{AY}$ is the desired parallel.

Justification:

$\overleftrightarrow{AY}$ is parallel to t, because when two lines are cut by a transversal so that corresponding angles are congruent, the two lines are parallel.

Oral Exercises Exercises 1–3 refer to the figure shown.

1. In constructing a line from point S that is perpendicular to l, the center of the first arc drawn is point __?__ .

2. In constructing a line perpendicular to $\overleftrightarrow{AB}$ at point A, the center of the first arc drawn is point __?__ .

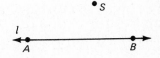

3. In constructing the perpendicular bisector of $\overline{AB}$, the radius of the arcs should be _____?_____ $\frac{1}{2}AB$.
$(<, =, >)$

4. Explain how to construct a segment whose length is one-fourth that of a given segment.

5. Explain how to construct a line parallel to a given line by constructing only perpendicular lines.

6. Explain how to construct the altitude of △ABC that contains vertex A.

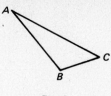

Ex. 6

Written Exercises

In each exercise draw a figure similar to, but larger than, the one shown. Do the indicated construction. Clearly show all arcs and lines used. You need not write an explanation or justification.

A 1. A line perpendicular to *l* at *D*

5. A line through *C* perpendicular to $\overleftrightarrow{AB}$

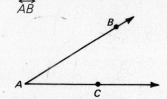

2. A line through *A* perpendicular to *t*

6. A line perpendicular to $\overline{RS}$ at *R*

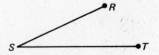

3. A perpendicular bisector of $\overline{RS}$

7. A line through *D* parallel to $\overleftrightarrow{FE}$

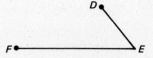

4. A line through *T* parallel to *l*

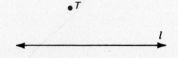

8. A line through *R* parallel to $\overleftrightarrow{ST}$

B **9.** A line perpendicular to $\overline{AC}$ at A

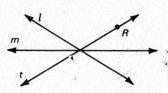

15. A line through R parallel to $\overleftrightarrow{ST}$

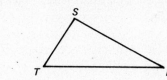

10. A line through R parallel to l

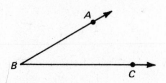

16. A line through X perpendicular to $\overleftrightarrow{YZ}$

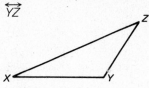

11. A complement of $\angle ABC$

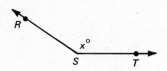

17. A square with sides of length x

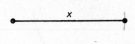

12. An angle with measure $x - 90$

18. A rectangle with sides of length x and y

13. An angle with measure 45

) - 2 4

19. Parallelogram $ABCD$

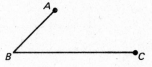

14. An angle with measure 135

20. Parallelogram $RSTW$

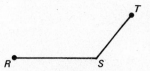

21. The bisectors of the angles of $\triangle ABC$

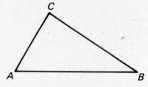

22. The perpendicular bisectors of the sides of $\triangle MNO$

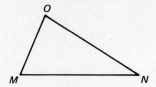

23. A square with perimeter y

24. An isosceles right triangle with a hypotenuse of length x

25. Write, in paragraph form, a justification for Construction 5.
26. Write, in paragraph form, a justification for Construction 6.

10-3 *Constructions and Circles*

The construction problems in this section represent a few of the many constructions dealing with circles.

CONSTRUCTION 8   Given an arc of a circle, construct the midpoint of the arc.

Given: $\overset{\frown}{RS}$ of a circle

To Construct: The midpoint of $\overset{\frown}{RS}$

Construction:

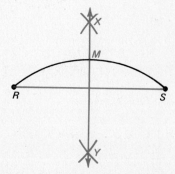

Explanation:

1. Draw $\overline{RS}$.

2. Construct the perpendicular bisector of $\overline{RS}$. Let M be the intersection of the perpendicular bisector and $\overparen{RS}$.

M is the desired midpoint.

The Justification is left as Exercise 18.

CONSTRUCTION 9 Given a point on a circle, construct the tangent to the circle at the given point.

Given: Point X on $\odot O$

To Construct: A tangent to $\odot O$ at X

Construction:

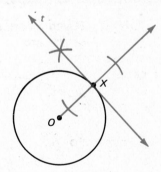

Explanation:

1. Draw $\overrightarrow{OX}$.

2. Construct a line perpendicular to $\overrightarrow{OX}$ at point X. Call the line t.

Line t is the desired tangent.

Justification: t is $\perp$ to a radius at its outer endpoint. Hence t is tangent to $\odot O$.

CONSTRUCTION 10 Given a point outside a circle, construct the tangents to the circle from the point.

Given: Point R and $\odot O$

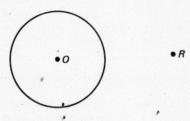

To Construct: The tangents to $\odot O$ from R

Construction:

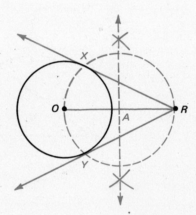

Explanation:

1. Draw $\overline{OR}$.

2. Construct the perpendicular bisector of $\overline{OR}$. Label the midpoint of $\overline{OR}$ point A.

3. With A as center and radius AO, construct a circle. Label the points of intersection with $\odot O$ points X and Y.

4. Draw $\overrightarrow{RX}$ and $\overrightarrow{RY}$.

$\overrightarrow{RX}$ and $\overrightarrow{RY}$ are the desired tangents.

Justification: If $\overrightarrow{OX}$ and $\overrightarrow{OY}$ are drawn, $\angle OXR$ and $\angle OYR$ are right angles since each is inscribed in a semicircle. Since $\overrightarrow{RX}$ and $\overrightarrow{RY}$ are perpendicular to radii of $\odot O$ at their outer endpoints, $\overrightarrow{RX}$ and $\overrightarrow{RY}$ are tangent to $\odot O$.

CONSTRUCTION 11

Given a triangle, circumscribe a circle about the triangle.

Given: △ABC

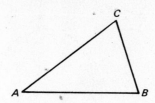

To Construct: A circle passing through A, B, and C

Construction:

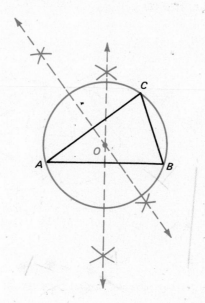

Explanation:

1. Construct the perpendicular bisectors of any two sides of △ABC ($\overline{AB}$ and $\overline{AC}$ in the figure shown). Let O be the point of intersection of the perpendicular bisectors.

2. With O as center and OA as radius, construct a circle.

Circle O is the desired circle.

The Justification is left as Exercise 19.

CONSTRUCTION 12 Given a triangle, inscribe a circle in the triangle.

Given: △RST

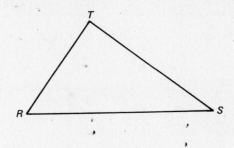

To Construct: A circle tangent to $\overline{RS}$, $\overline{RT}$, and $\overline{ST}$

Construction:

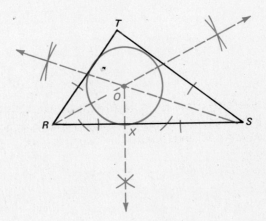

Explanation:

1. Construct the bisectors of any two angles of △RST (∠R and ∠S in the figure shown). Let O be the point of intersection of the bisectors.

2. Construct a perpendicular to $\overline{RS}$ from O. Label the point of intersection X.

3. With O as center and OX as radius, construct a circle.

Circle O is the desired circle.

The Justification is left as Exercise 20.

Classify each statement as true or false.

1. Given any triangle, it is possible to inscribe a circle in the triangle.
2. Given any triangle, it is possible to circumscribe a circle about the triangle.
3. If point A lies in the exterior of $\odot O$, then there exist two lines through A that are tangent to $\odot O$.
4. If point B lies on $\odot O$, then there exist two lines through B that are tangent to $\odot O$.
5. The center of the inscribed circle of a triangle must lie in the interior of the triangle.
6. The center of the circumscribed circle of a triangle must lie in the interior of the triangle.
   Hint: Think of an obtuse triangle.
7. The hypotenuse of a right triangle is a diameter of the circle circumscribed about the triangle.
8. Given an arc of a circle, it is possible by construction to locate the center of the circle.

In each exercise draw a figure similar to, but larger than, the one shown. Do the indicated construction. Clearly show all arcs and lines used. You need not write an explanation or justification.

A

1. The midpoint of $\overgroup{DE}$

3. A line tangent to $\odot O$ at P

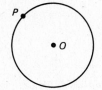

2. The midpoint of $\overgroup{ABC}$

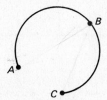

4. A line through R tangent to $\odot O$

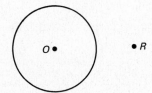

5. A circle circumscribed about △RST

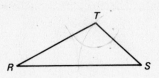

6. A circle inscribed in △ABC

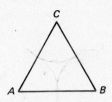

7. A circle inscribed in △DEF

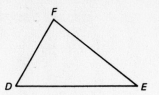

8. A right triangle inscribed in ⊙O with one vertex at X

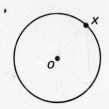

B **9.** A square circumscribed about ⊙O

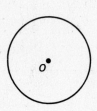

11. A tangent to ⊙O that is perpendicular to t

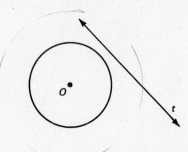

10. A tangent to ⊙O that is parallel to l

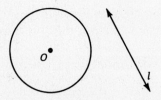

12. A circle with radius AB that is internally tangent to ⊙O at Z

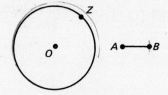

C **13.** Two tangents to ⊙*O* that form an angle whose measure is 60

14. A tangent to ⊙*O* that makes a 45° angle with *m*

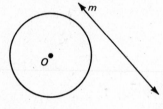

15. In ⊙*O* inscribe an equilateral △ with one vertex at *X*.

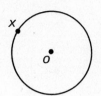

16. A line that is a common external tangent to ⊙*O* and ⊙*O'*

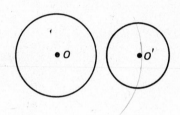

17. Circumscribe about ⊙*O* an isosceles trapezoid with a base whose length equals *AB*.

18. Write, in paragraph form, a justification for Construction 8.
Hint: Draw chords $\overline{RM}$ and $\overline{SM}$.

19. Write, in paragraph form, a justification for Construction 11.
Hint: Draw $\overline{OA}$, $\overline{OB}$, and $\overline{OC}$. Use congruent triangles to show that *B* and *C* lie on ⊙*O*.

20. Write, in paragraph form, a justification for Construction 12.
Hint: Show that ⊙*O* with radius *OX* must be tangent to $\overleftrightarrow{RS}$, $\overleftrightarrow{ST}$, and $\overleftrightarrow{RT}$.

10-4 *Special Segments*

Certain special segments can be constructed by using the properties of similar triangles.

CONSTRUCTION 13 Given a segment, divide the segment into any given number of congruent segments. (3 shown)

Given: $\overline{AB}$

To Construct: Points X and Y on $\overline{AB}$ such that $\overline{AX} \cong \overline{XY} \cong \overline{YB}$

Construction:

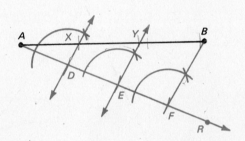

Explanation:

1. With A as endpoint, draw any ray not collinear with $\overline{AB}$. On the ray, label a point R.
2. Starting with A as center and any convenient radius, construct three congruent segments on $\overrightarrow{AR}$. Label the points D, E, and F.
3. Draw $\overline{FB}$.
4. Construct lines through D and E that are parallel to $\overline{FB}$. Label the points of intersection on $\overline{AB}$ X and Y.

$\overline{AX}$, $\overline{XY}$, and $\overline{YB}$ are the desired segments.

Justification: If parallel lines cut off congruent segments on one transversal, they cut off congruent segments on every transversal. Since $\overline{AD} \cong \overline{DE} \cong \overline{EF}$, $\overline{AX} \cong \overline{XY} \cong \overline{YB}$.

CONSTRUCTION 14
Given three segments, construct a fourth segment such that the lengths of the four segments are in proportion.

Given: Segments with lengths a, b, c

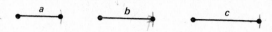

To Construct: A segment of length x such that $\dfrac{a}{b} = \dfrac{c}{x}$

Construction:

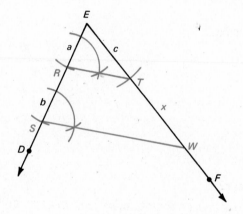

Explanation:

1. Draw an angle DEF.
2. On $\overrightarrow{ED}$, mark off $ER = a$ and $RS = b$.
3. On $\overrightarrow{EF}$, mark off $ET = c$.
4. Draw $\overline{RT}$.
5. Construct a line through S that is parallel to $\overline{RT}$. Label the point of intersection with $\overrightarrow{EF}$ point W.

$\overline{TW}$ is the desired segment of length x.

Justification: In $\triangle ESW$, $\overline{RT}$ is parallel to $\overline{SW}$. Hence $\dfrac{a}{b} = \dfrac{c}{x}$.

CONSTRUCTION 15 Given two segments, construct a segment whose length is the geometric mean between the lengths of the given segments.

Given: Segments with lengths a and b

To Construct: A segment of length x such that $\dfrac{a}{x} = \dfrac{x}{b}$ $(x = \sqrt{ab})$

Construction:

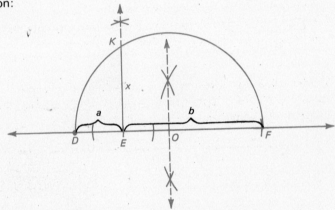

Explanation:

1. Draw a line and mark off $DE = a$ and $EF = b$.
2. Construct the perpendicular bisector of $\overline{DF}$. Label the midpoint O.
3. With O as center and radius OF, draw a semicircle.
4. At point E, construct a line perpendicular to $\overleftrightarrow{DE}$. Label the point of intersection with the semicircle K.

$\overline{EK}$ is the desired segment of length x.

Justification: If $\overline{DK}$ and $\overline{FK}$ are drawn, $\triangle DKF$ is a right triangle. Since $\triangle DEK \sim \triangle KEF$, $\dfrac{DE}{KE} = \dfrac{KE}{FE}$ or $\dfrac{a}{x} = \dfrac{x}{b}$.

State whether the given statements are equivalent.

1. $\dfrac{x}{r} = \dfrac{s}{t}$ and $\dfrac{x}{s} = \dfrac{r}{t}$

2. $\dfrac{a}{x} = \dfrac{x}{b}$ and $x = a\sqrt{b}$

3. $ax = bc$ and $\dfrac{a}{b} = \dfrac{c}{x}$

4. $x = \dfrac{a^2}{b}$ and $\dfrac{b}{a} = \dfrac{a}{x}$

5. $x = \sqrt{2ab}$ and $\dfrac{2a}{x} = \dfrac{x}{b}$

6. $x = \dfrac{ab}{c}$ and $\dfrac{a}{c} = \dfrac{b}{x}$

A

In Exercises 1–4, begin each exercise by drawing a segment whose length is about 12 cm. Label its endpoints A and B.

1. Divide $\overline{AB}$ into three congruent segments.
2. Divide $\overline{AB}$ into four congruent segments.
3. Divide $\overline{AB}$ into two segments whose lengths have the ratio 2:3.
4. Construct a segment whose length is $\frac{5}{6}AB$.

On your paper, draw three segments with lengths approximately equal to those shown. Use these lengths in Exercises 5–12 to construct a segment of length x.

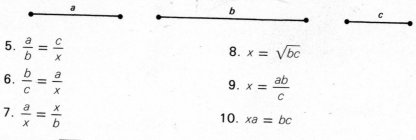

5. $\dfrac{a}{b} = \dfrac{c}{x}$

6. $\dfrac{b}{c} = \dfrac{a}{x}$

7. $\dfrac{a}{x} = \dfrac{x}{b}$

8. $x = \sqrt{bc}$

9. $x = \dfrac{ab}{c}$

10. $xa = bc$

B 11. $x = \sqrt{2ac}$

12. $x = 2\sqrt{ac}$

On your paper, draw three segments with lengths approximately equal to those shown. Use your lengths in Exercises 13–17.

13. Construct an equilateral triangle with perimeter a.
14. Divide a segment of length a into two segments with lengths in the ratio b:c.
15. Construct a segment, with length x, such that $x^2 = b(b + c)$.
16. Construct a segment, with length x, such that $xb = \frac{1}{3}ac$.
17. Construct a segment, with length x, such that $6x = a + 2b$.

18. On your paper draw a triangle similar to, but larger than, the one shown. Find, by construction, the point M on side $\overline{RS}$ so that $RM:MS = RT:TS$.

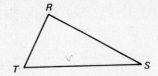

C 19. Draw a segment about 16 cm long. Label the endpoints C and D. Construct a triangle whose perimeter is equal to CD and whose sides have lengths in the ratio $2:2:3$.

20. On your paper draw a figure similar to, but larger than, the one shown. Locate, by construction, a point X on $\overleftrightarrow{CD}$ such that $\angle AXC \cong \angle BXD$.

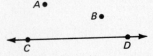

21. Through any given point R in the interior of a given angle, construct a segment, $\overline{AB}$, such that A and B lie on the angle and $AR:RB = 1:2$.

22. Given a circle with chord $\overline{DE}$. Locate a point X on $\overarc{DE}$ such that $XD:XE = 1:2$.

Self-Test In Exercises 1–6, draw a figure similar to, but larger than, the one shown. Do the indicated construction.

1. An altitude from C

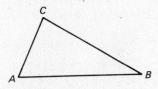

2. A perpendicular bisector of $\overline{RT}$

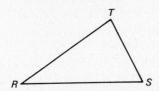

3. The center of the circle inscribed in $\triangle DEF$

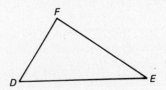

4. A tangent to $\odot O$ at A

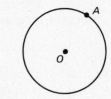

5. A line through D parallel to l

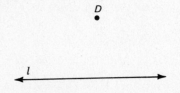

6. A segment whose length is $\frac{1}{3}AB$

Careers

Architecture

Before a building can be constructed, a lot of "behind the scene" preparation must take place. A team of architects, engineers, and technicians confer at each stage of the planning process.

First, the architects and the customer discuss the practical and aesthetic considerations of the proposed building. The decisions reached are incorporated into the initial design plans of the building.

Next, the architects calculate such things as the durability of the construction materials, the building specifications, and the cost estimates. Consulting engineers assist in the preparation of the plans for the electrical, heating, and plumbing systems. This information is used to develop detailed sketches and models.

Finally, technicians and architects translate the specifications into final plans. Design layouts are drawn (using, among other instruments, compasses and protractors), detailing instructions and dimensions for each part of the building.

The dramatic effect of creative architecture is exemplified in the picture shown above of the Sydney Opera House in Sydney, Australia.

Locus

Objectives

1. Describe the locus that satisfies a given condition.
2. Describe the locus that satisfies more than one given condition.
3. Apply the concept of locus in the solution of a construction exercise.

10-5 *Describing a Locus*

The solutions to some construction problems use the idea of *locus*. Roughly, the word means location or place. A locus is a figure; it is the set of all points, and only those points, that satisfy a given condition.

Consider the following problem:

In a plane, what is the locus of points 1 cm from a given line l in that plane?

To help find the locus we draw a line l and then draw a number of points that are 1 cm from l.

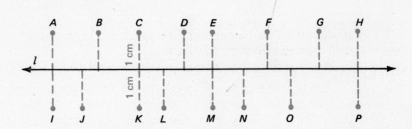

To specify the locus, we must consider all points such as *A, B, C, . . .* As soon as we can visualize the location of all the points, we draw (construct only when specifically told to do so) the geometric figure that contains the points.

We then identify the locus by naming the geometric figure that the points form and describing the position of that figure.

A satisfactory answer to the problem above is:

The locus is a pair of lines parallel to, and 1 cm from, l.

If the phrase "in a plane" were deleted from our locus problem, the drawing and description would change as follows.

Figure:

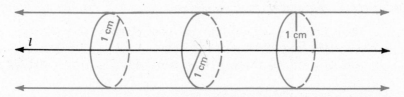

Description: The locus is a cylindrical surface with a 1 cm radius and with axis *l*.

You should always think in terms of three dimensions unless the problem restricts the locus to two dimensions.

A solution to a locus problem consists of two parts:
1. A figure showing the locus.
2. A statement that names the locus and describes its position.

EXAMPLE 1. What is the locus of points equidistant from two parallel lines *l* and *m*, and in their plane?

SOLUTION:

a. *Figure:*

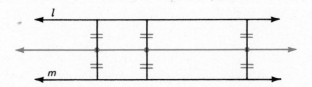

b. *Description:* The locus is a line lying in the plane of *l* and *m*, parallel to *l* and *m*, and midway between them.

EXAMPLE 2. In a plane, what is the locus of points 2 cm from a fixed point O in that plane?

SOLUTION:

a. *Figure:*

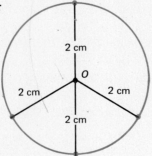

b. *Description:* The locus is a circle with O as center and radius of 2 cm.

EXAMPLE 3. What is the locus of points 2 cm from a fixed point O?

SOLUTION:

a. *Figure:*

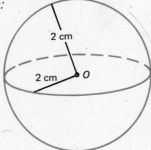

b. *Description:* The locus is a sphere with O as center and radius of 2 cm.

Oral Exercises

1. What are the two parts of a solution to a locus problem?
2. What should be included in the verbal part of the solution to a locus problem?
3. What determines whether you should think in terms of two dimensions or three dimensions?
4. Describe the locus of the outer end of the minute hand on a clock as the time changes from 9:00 A.M. to 10:00 A.M.
5. Describe the locus of the outer end of the hour hand on a clock as the time changes from 1:00 P.M. to 7:00 P.M.
6. Describe the locus of points equidistant from the floor and ceiling of your classroom.
7. Describe the locus of points in your classroom that are 1 meter from the floor.
8. Describe the locus of points in your classroom that are 1 meter from a fixed point on the floor of the room.

Written Exercises

In Exercises 1–14, draw a figure that shows the locus and write a description of the locus.

A

1. In a plane, what is the locus of points 3 cm from a fixed point R in that plane?
2. What is the locus of points 3 cm from a fixed point T?
3. In a plane, what is the locus of points equidistant from two fixed points A and B in that plane?
4. What is the locus of points equidistant from two fixed points?
5. What is the locus of points that lie in the interior of an angle and are equidistant from the sides of the angle?
6. In a plane, what is the locus of points equidistant from two intersecting lines in that plane?
7. In a plane, what is the locus of points 2 cm from a given line t in that plane?
8. What is the locus of points 2 cm from a fixed line l?
9. What is the locus of points equidistant from two parallel lines?
10. In the plane of a square, what is the locus of points equidistant from the four vertices of the square?
11. What is the locus of points equidistant from the four vertices of a square?
12. What is the locus of the centers of all circles that are tangent to each of two parallel lines?
13. A given circle has center O and a radius of 3 cm. What is the locus of the midpoints of all radii of the circle?
14. Given two concentric circles with radii of 2 cm and 4 cm. What is the locus of points in the plane of the two circles and equidistant from them?

B

15. Construct two perpendicular lines l and t. Construct the locus of points that are in the plane of l and t and are equidistant from l and t.
16. Given $\odot O$ with radius k. Construct the locus of points that are in the interior of the circle and $\dfrac{k}{2}$ units from a fixed diameter of the circle.
17. Given $\overline{AB}$. In a plane, construct the locus of the vertices of isosceles triangles that have $\overline{AB}$ as a base.
18. Given point A on line l. In a plane, construct the locus of the centers of all circles that are tangent to l at A.

C

19. Describe the locus of the midpoints of all the chords of $\odot O$ that pass through a fixed point X in the interior of the circle.
20. Given $\odot O$ with radius r. A second circle, with radius t $(t < r)$, moves inside $\odot O$ so that it always is tangent to $\odot O$. Describe the path followed by the center of the moving circle.
21. Given a segment, $\overline{RS}$. In a plane, construct the locus of points X such that $\angle RXS$ is a right angle.
22. Given a segment, $\overline{CD}$. In a plane, construct the locus of the vertices E of $\triangle CDE$ such that $m \angle CED = 75$.

10-6 *Loci*

The plural of locus is *loci* (**lo**-sigh). In this section we shall consider intersections of loci.

To find such intersections, we proceed as follows:

1. Draw the separate loci.
2. Study all possible relative positions of the separate loci.
3. Describe the points, if any, that lie on the intersection of the loci.

EXAMPLE 1. Given two parallel lines *s* and *t* and a point *A* all in one plane. Find the locus of points in the plane that are equidistant from *s* and *t* and are at a given distance *d* from *A*.

SOLUTION: The first locus is line *l* parallel to *s* and *t* and midway between them.

The second locus is a circle with center *A* and radius *d*.

All points that lie on *l* and on ⊙*A* satisfy the conditions of the problem. There are three different relative positions for *l* and the circle.

Possibility 1

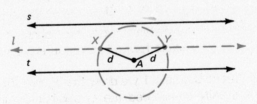

The locus is the set consisting of points *X* and *Y* determined by the intersection of secant *l* with ⊙*A*.

Possibility 2

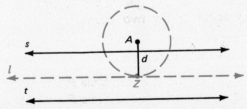

The locus is point *Z* determined by the intersection of tangent *l* and ⊙*A*.

Possibility 3

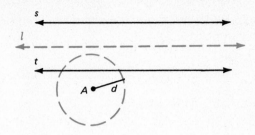

The locus is the empty set.

EXAMPLE 2. Describe the locus of points that are equidistant from two given points *D* and *E* and are at a distance *k* from a given point *P*.

SOLUTION: The first locus is plane *X* that is a perpendicular bisector of $\overline{DE}$.

The second locus is a sphere with center *P* and radius *k*.

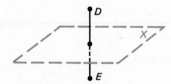

Possibility 1 If the distance from *P* to plane *X* is greater than *k*, the locus is the empty set.

Possibility 2 If the distance from *P* to plane *X* is equal to *k*, the locus is the point of tangency of plane *X* with sphere *P*.

Possibility 3 If the distance from *P* to plane *X* is less than *k*, the locus is the circle formed by the intersection of plane *X* and sphere *P*.

Note that in Example 1 we drew the figure for each possibility. In Example 2, we mentally considered the possibilities. You may use either method.

Oral Exercises

In Exercises 1–8, the geometric figures named are coplanar. Describe the intersection of the two figures.

1. Two parallel lines
2. Two intersecting lines
3. A secant and a circle
4. A tangent and a circle

5. Circle *O* with radius 2 and circle *P* with radius 4 when *OP* = 6
6. Circle *O* with radius 3 and circle *P* with radius 4 when *OP* = 5
7. Circle *O* with radius 2 and circle *P* with radius 5 when *OP* = 8
8. Circle *O* with radius 4 and circle *P* with radius 6 when *OP* = 1

Exercises 9–14 are three dimensional. Describe the intersections that are possible.

9. Two lines
10. A line and a plane
11. Two spheres

12. A plane and a sphere
13. A line and a sphere
14. Two parallel lines and a sphere

Written Exercises

A

1. Points A and B lie in plane X. Describe the locus of points in X that are 2 cm from A and 5 cm from B.

2. $\overline{AB}$ and point R lie in plane M. Describe the locus of points in M that are equidistant from A and B, and are 3 cm from R.

3. Two intersecting lines lie in plane R. Describe the locus of points in R that are equidistant from the two lines and are 2 cm from the point of intersection of the lines.

4. Points A, B, and C lie in plane Y. Describe the locus of points in Y that are equidistant from A, B, and C.

5. Plane W contains parallel lines l and m; a line t lies in plane W. Describe the locus of points in W that are 1 cm from t and equidistant from l and m.

6. Point A lies in the interior of $\angle RST$. Describe the locus of points in the interior of $\angle RST$ that are equidistant from the sides of the angle and are 1 cm from A.

B

7. Point B is 2 cm from plane X. Describe the locus of points in X that are 4 cm from B.

8. Point C lies in plane Y. Describe the locus of points 2 cm from Y and 3 cm from C.

9. Given points R, S, and T. Find the locus of points equidistant from R and S, and 4 cm from T.

10. Given two parallel planes X and Y and a point A. Find the locus of points equidistant from X and Y, and 3 cm from A.

C

11. Point X is 13 cm from points R, S, and T. $RS = 6$, $ST = 8$, and $RT = 10$. M is the midpoint of $\overline{RT}$. $XM =$ __?__

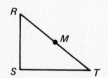

12. $\odot O$ is tangent to $\overrightarrow{DE}$ and $\overrightarrow{DF}$. Construct two circles, each one tangent to $\odot O$, to $\overrightarrow{DE}$, and to $\overrightarrow{DF}$.

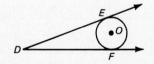

13. Given △ABC. Construct a circle in the exterior of the triangle that is tangent to $\overline{BC}$, $\overrightarrow{AC}$, and $\overrightarrow{AB}$.

14. Given △ABC. Construct circles A, B, and C such that each circle is tangent externally to the other two.

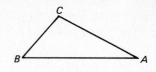

10-7 *Constructions and Loci*

In many cases the solution to a construction problem depends on finding a point that satisfies more than one condition. A knowledge of loci helps in discovering where the required point is located.

EXAMPLE 1. Given $\overline{AB}$, $\overline{BC}$, and $\overline{AC}$. Construct a triangle whose sides have lengths x, y, and z.

EXPLANATION: A sketch of the triangle is drawn to aid in discovering how to do the construction. Note that C must be z units from A and y units from B. Hence C will lie on the intersection of two circles, one with center A and radius z, the other with center B and radius y. We draw a working line, construct $\overline{AB}$, and construct point C as shown in the figure.

SKETCH

SOLUTION:

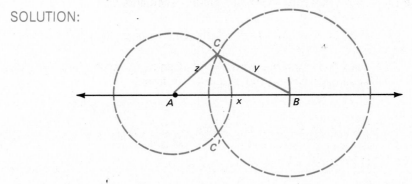

The problem called for the construction of a triangle, and hence only one triangle is shown. A second triangle, using vertices A, B, and C', also meets the given conditions.

EXAMPLE 2.   Given $\overline{RS}$, $\overline{RT}$, and $\overline{TW}$. Construct a triangle RST so that $\overline{TW}$ is the altitude from T.

R———x———S   R———y———T   T———z———W

EXPLANATION: Point T must satisfy two conditions: it must be y units from R and z units from $\overleftrightarrow{RS}$. All points y units from R lie on a circle with center R and radius y. All points z units from $\overleftrightarrow{RS}$ lie on two parallel lines, each z units from $\overleftrightarrow{RS}$.

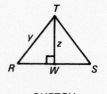

SKETCH

SOLUTION:

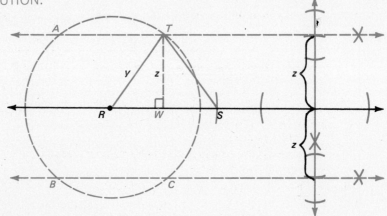

Points A, B, and C could also be used for vertex T. Hence there are three more triangles that meet the given conditions.

Oral Exercises

1. Given any three segments, can you always construct a triangle with sides congruent to those segments?

2. Is it possible to construct a triangle whose sides have lengths of 2 cm, 3 cm, and 4 cm?

3. Is it possible to construct a triangle whose sides have lengths of 3 cm, 4 cm, and 8 cm?

4. Given $\overline{AB}$, how many right triangles can you construct that have $\overline{AB}$ as a leg?

5. Gene constructed a right triangle with two given segments as legs. Julie also constructed a right triangle with the given segments as legs. How are the two triangles related?

6. Given $\overline{XY}$, is it possible to construct an equilateral triangle with an altitude congruent to $\overline{XY}$?

7. Given $\overline{AB}$, $\overline{BC}$, and $\overline{BM}$, is it always possible to construct a triangle with two sides congruent to $\overline{AB}$ and $\overline{BC}$, and an altitude congruent to $\overline{BM}$?

8. Given $\overline{RS}$ and $\overline{ST}$, can you always construct a right triangle with $\overline{RS}$ as a leg and $\overline{ST}$ as the hypotenuse?

Written Exercises

On your paper, draw segments and angles approximately like those shown. Use those segments and angles for Exercises 1–14.

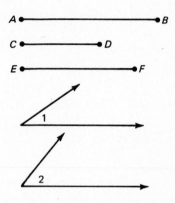

A

1. Construct a triangle with sides congruent to $\overline{AB}$, $\overline{CD}$, and $\overline{EF}$.

2. Construct a right triangle with legs congruent to $\overline{CD}$ and $\overline{EF}$.

3. Construct a right triangle with a leg congruent to $\overline{CD}$ and the hypotenuse congruent to $\overline{AB}$.

4. Construct a right triangle with a leg congruent to $\overline{AB}$ and the altitude to the hypotenuse congruent to $\overline{CD}$.

5. Construct a right triangle with the hypotenuse congruent to $\overline{CD}$ and an acute angle congruent to $\angle 1$.

6. Construct a rhombus with an angle congruent to $\angle 2$ and sides congruent to $\overline{EF}$.

B

7. Construct a right triangle with an angle congruent to $\angle 1$ and the altitude to the hypotenuse congruent to $\overline{CD}$.

8. Construct an isosceles triangle with a base angle congruent to $\angle 2$ and the altitude to the base congruent to $\overline{EF}$.

9. Construct an isosceles triangle with a base congruent to $\overline{AB}$ and the radius of the circumscribed circle congruent to $\overline{CD}$.

10. Construct an isosceles triangle with a leg congruent to $\overline{AB}$ and the altitude to that leg congruent to $\overline{CD}$.

11. Construct an equilateral triangle with a radius of the inscribed circle congruent to $\overline{EF}$.

12. Construct an equilateral triangle with a radius of the circumscribed circle congruent to $\overline{CD}$.

13. Construct a right triangle such that the altitude to the hypotenuse divides the hypotenuse into segments congruent to $\overline{CD}$ and $\overline{AB}$.

14. Construct a right triangle with the altitude and the median to the hypotenuse congruent to $\overline{CD}$ and $\overline{EF}$ respectively. (*Hint:* How does the length of the median compare to the length of the hypotenuse?)

C **15.** On your paper, draw a figure like the one shown. Construct a circle tangent to line l and also tangent to $\odot O$ at P.

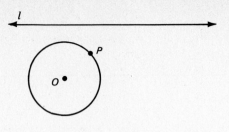

16. On your paper, draw a figure like the one shown. Construct a circle tangent to $\odot R$ and also tangent to line t at X.

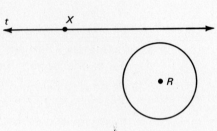

17. Construct a quadrilateral $RSTW$ so that $\overline{RS} \cong \overline{AB}$, $\overline{ST} \cong \overline{CD}$, $\overline{TW} \cong \overline{EF}$, $\angle R \cong \angle 1$, and $\angle W \cong \angle 2$. Use segments and angles approximately congruent to the ones shown.

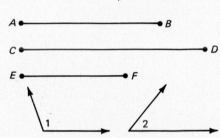

Self-Test In Exercises 1–8 write a description of the locus of points that satisfy the given condition(s).

1. In a plane, d units from a point A in the plane
2. 5 cm from a point E
3. Equidistant from two parallel planes
4. In a plane, equidistant from two intersecting lines in the plane
5. A given distance k from a line l
6. In a plane, equidistant from two points R and S in the plane
7. Equidistant from the vertices of a triangle
8. Equidistant from the sides of a triangle

9. Given points X and Y. Find the locus of points 2 cm from X and 5 cm from Y. Describe all possibilities.
10. Given $\overline{AB}$ and $\overline{CD}$ with $AB > CD$. Is it always possible to construct a right triangle with a hypotenuse congruent to $\overline{AB}$ and a leg congruent to $\overline{CD}$?

CHAPTER SUMMARY

1. The only instruments that may be used in constructions are a compass and a straightedge.

2. Basic Constructions
   (1) A segment congruent to a given segment.
   (2) An angle congruent to a given angle.
   (3) The bisector of a given angle.
   (4) A line perpendicular to a given line at a given point on the line.
   (5) A line perpendicular to a given line from a given point not on the line.
   (6) The perpendicular bisector of a given segment.
   (7) A line parallel to a given line through a given point not on the line.
   (8) The midpoint of a given arc.
   (9) A tangent to a given circle at a given point on the circle.
   (10) A tangent to a given circle from a given external point.
   (11) Circumscribing a circle about a given triangle.
   (12) Inscribing a circle in a given triangle.
   (13) Dividing a given segment into any number of congruent segments.
   (14) A segment of length x such that $\dfrac{a}{b} = \dfrac{c}{x}$, where a, b, and c are the lengths of three given segments.
   (15) A segment whose length is the geometric mean between the lengths of two given segments.

3. A locus of points is the set of those points, and only those points, that satisfy a given condition.

4. The set of points that satisfy more than one condition is found by considering the various possible intersections of the loci for the separate conditions.

CHAPTER TEST

In Exercises 1–8, draw on your paper a figure similar to, but larger than, the one shown. Do the indicated construction. You need not write an explanation or justification.

1. Construct a segment whose length is $\frac{1}{2}AB$.

2. Construct the altitude from vertex E.

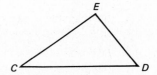

3. Construct a line through H that is parallel to $\overleftrightarrow{FG}$.

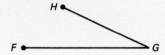

4. Construct the center of the circle inscribed in $\triangle SKL$.

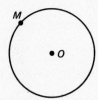

5. Construct a line through M that is tangent to $\odot O$.

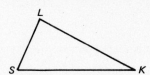

6. Divide $\overline{NP}$ into three congruent segments.

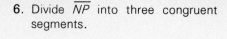

7. Construct a segment of length x such that $\dfrac{a}{x} = \dfrac{x}{b}$.

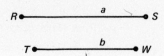

8. Construct a right $\triangle XYZ$ such that leg $\overline{YZ}$ is congruent to $\overline{VW}$ and $\angle X$ is congruent to $\angle U$.

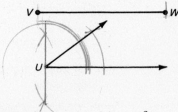

9. In a plane, the locus of points 5 cm from a fixed point A is a __?__ .

10. In space, the locus of points 5 cm from a fixed point A is a __?__ .

11. Describe the locus of points in the plane of $\triangle EFG$ that are equidistant from the three, vertices of the triangle.

12. Describe the locus of the midpoints of all radii of a given circle whose radius is 6 cm.

Make a "ruler" like the one shown to use in Exercises 13 and 14.

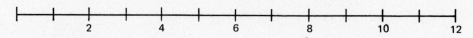

13. Given points A and B such that $AB = 8$ units. Construct, in a plane, the locus of points equidistant from A and B and 5 units from point A.

14. Given a point R on a line l. Construct, in a plane, the locus of points 3 units from line l and 4 units from point R.

CHAPTER REVIEW

In Exercises 1–15, draw on your paper a figure similar to, but larger than, the one shown. Do the indicated construction. You need not write an explanation or justification.

10-1 *Meaning of Construction*

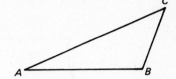

1. Draw a line. On the line construct a segment whose length is equal to 2(*AB*). Label your answer $\overline{RS}$.
2. Construct an angle congruent to ∠*A*.
3. Construct the bisector of ∠*B*.

10-2 *Parallel Lines and Perpendicular Lines*

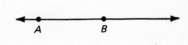

4. Construct a line perpendicular to $\overleftrightarrow{AB}$ at *A*.
5. Construct a line perpendicular to $\overleftrightarrow{AB}$ from *C*.
6. Construct the perpendicular bisector of $\overline{AB}$.
7. Construct a line parallel to $\overleftrightarrow{AB}$ through *C*.

10-3 *Constructions and Circles*

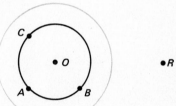

8. Construct the midpoint of $\overset{\frown}{AB}$.
9. Construct the tangent to ⊙*O* at point *C*.
10. Construct a tangent to ⊙*O* from point *R*.
11. Draw an acute triangle. Find, by construction, the center of the circle circumscribed about the triangle.
12. Draw an obtuse triangle. Find, by construction, the center of the circle inscribed in the triangle.

10-4 *Special Segments*

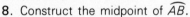
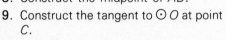

13. Construct a segment with length $\frac{1}{3}a$.
14. Construct a segment of length *x* such that $\frac{a}{b} = \frac{c}{x}$.
15. Construct a segment whose length is the geometric mean between *b* and *c*. Label your answer *x*.

10-5 *Describing a Locus*

16. In a plane, what is the locus of points 3 cm from a given point *R*?
17. What is the locus of points equidistant from two given parallel planes?
18. In the plane of a square, what is the locus of points equidistant from the four vertices of the square?

10-6 *Loci*

19. Given, in plane X, point A and line l. What is the locus of points in X that are 2 cm from A and are 3 cm from line l?

20. Given two parallel planes, X and Y, and a point D. What is the locus of points equidistant from X and Y and also 2 meters from point D?

10-7 *Constructions and Loci*

21. Draw three segments that are approximately congruent to the three shown. Construct a $\triangle RST$ such that $\overline{RS} \cong \overline{CD}$, $\overline{RT} \cong \overline{EF}$, and the altitude from vertex R is congruent to $\overline{AB}$.

22. Draw a segment and an angle that are approximately congruent to the ones shown. Construct a right $\triangle KEA$ such that $\overline{KE}$, the hypotenuse, is congruent to $\overline{XY}$ and $\angle K \cong \angle Z$.

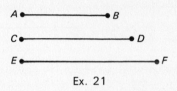

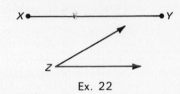

Ex. 21   Ex. 22

extra
for
experts

In the work on locus in this chapter, we merely made statements about loci. To *prove* that a locus we name is actually the correct one, we must establish two things.

1. *Any point* on the locus named satisfies the given conditions.

2. *Any point* that satisfies the given conditions lies on the locus named.

Thus we must prove that a statement and its converse are both true.

EXAMPLE. Prove: In a plane, the locus of points equidistant from points A and B is the perpendicular bisector of $\overline{AB}$.

In Part **I** we must prove that any point on the perpendicular bisector of $\overline{AB}$ is equidistant from A and B.

Given: l is a $\perp$ bisector of $\overline{AB}$;
    P is any point on l.

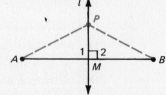

Prove: $PA = PB$

Proof:

STATEMENTS	REASONS
1. Draw $\overline{PA}$ and $\overline{PB}$.	1. Between two points __?__.
2. l is a $\perp$ bisector of $\overline{AB}$.	2. Given
3. $\angle 1$ and $\angle 2$ are rt. $\angle$s.	3. __?__
4. $\triangle AMP$ and $\triangle BMP$ are rt. $\triangle$s.	4. __?__
5. $\overline{AM} \cong \overline{BM}$	5. __?__
6. $\overline{PM} \cong \overline{PM}$	6. __?__
7. $\triangle AMP \cong \triangle BMP$	7. LL Theorem
8. $\overline{PA} \cong \overline{PB}$	8. Corr. parts of $\cong \triangle$s are $\cong$.
9. $PA = PB$	9. Def. of $\cong$ segments

In Part II, we must prove that any point that is equidistant from A and B lies on the perpendicular bisector of $\overline{AB}$.

Given: $XA = XB$

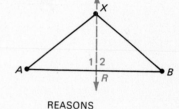

Prove: X lies on the $\perp$ bisector of $\overline{AB}$.

Proof:

STATEMENTS	REASONS
1. Draw a line through X that is $\perp$ to $\overline{AB}$. Label the point of intersection R.	1. Through a point not on a line __?__.
2. $\angle 1$ and $\angle 2$ are rt. $\angle$s.	2. __?__
3. $\triangle ARX$ and $\triangle BRX$ are rt. $\triangle$s.	3. __?__
4. $XA = XB$	4. __?__
5. $\overline{XA} \cong \overline{XB}$	5. Def. of $\cong$ segments
6. $\overline{XR} \cong \overline{XR}$	6. __?__
7. $\triangle ARX \cong \triangle BRX$	7. HL Postulate
8. $\overline{AR} \cong \overline{BR}$	8. __?__
9. $\overline{XR}$ is the $\perp$ bisector of $\overline{AB}$.	9. Def. of a $\perp$ bisector

Exercises

Prove the following locus theorems.

1. In the plane of an angle, the locus of points in the interior of the angle and equidistant from the sides of the angle is a ray that bisects the angle.
2. In a plane, the locus of the vertex of the right angle of a right triangle with a given fixed segment as the hypotenuse is a circle with the given segment as diameter.

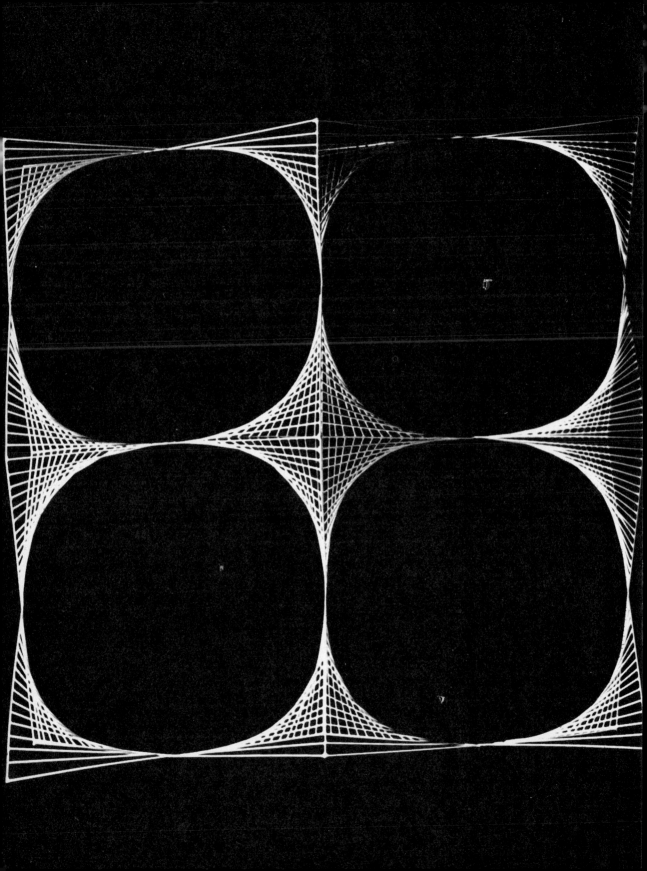

COORDINATE GEOMETRY

The Coordinate Plane

Objectives

1. Specify points in the coordinate plane by means of their coordinates.
2. Represent vertical and horizontal lines in the coordinate plane by means of equations.
3. Represent coordinates and certain algebraic equations as points and lines in the plane.
4. State and apply the distance formula.

11-1 Location in the Plane

In Chapter 1 you represented numbers by points on a line. In this chapter you will represent *ordered pairs* of numbers by points in a plane. A pair of numbers is an ordered pair when the order in which they are named has significance. Thus $(9, -5)$ and $(-5, 9)$ are different ordered pairs.

In the diagram at the right, point A is called the graph of the ordered pair $(1, 3)$. Notice that the first number of the ordered pair is 1 and that A is 1 unit to the right of the black vertical line. The second number is 3, and A is 3 units above the black horizontal line. Do you see that points B, C, and D are the graphs of the ordered pairs $(-2, 1)$, $(-\frac{1}{2}, -2)$, and $(2, -3)$?

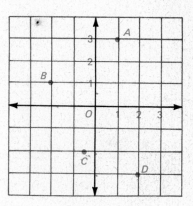

To plot points in a plane, you use two number lines, as just indicated. The first one, usually horizontal, is called the *x*-axis. A second number line, perpendicular to the first one at the zero-point, is called the *y*-axis. The point of intersection, *O*, is called the origin. The two lines, called coordinate axes (ax-eez), separate the plane into four regions called quadrants, which are numbered as shown.

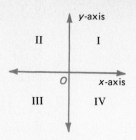

On the number line, there is a graph corresponding to any real number. Thus on the number line shown, the point *A* is the graph of −1. Can you see, however, that on the coordinate axes, the graph of $x = -1$ is a vertical line one unit to the left of the *y*-axis? All vertical lines are represented by equations of the form $x = a$; all horizontal lines, by $y = b$. The equation of the *y*-axis is $x = 0$. What is the equation of the *x*-axis?

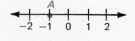

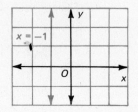

You can now find the equation of any horizontal or vertical line.

EXAMPLE. Write the equation of the given line.

SOLUTION: The line is horizontal and is 2 units above the *x*-axis, so the equation of the line is $y = 2$.

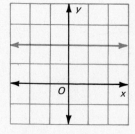

Now consider the intersection of the vertical line whose equation is $x = -1$ and the horizontal line whose equation is $y = 2$. The two lines intersect in exactly one point, *A*, denoted by (−1, 2). The numbers −1 and 2 are the coordinates of point *A*. In particular, −1 is called the *x*-coordinate of point *A*, and 2 is called the *y*-coordinate.

Besides indicating the coordinates of points *A*, *B*, and *C*, the diagram shown provides this additional information: The *distance* between *A* and *B* is 3, the distance between *A* and *C* is 4, and ∠*CAB* is a right angle.

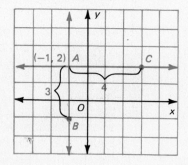

For every point in the plane there is a unique ordered pair of real numbers, and vice versa. This one-to-one correspondence between the set of points in the plane and the set of ordered pairs of real numbers is called a **coordinate system.**

Oral Exercises

1. State whether the graph in the coordinate plane is a vertical line, a horizontal line, or neither.
   a. $x = 3$
   b. $y = \pi$
   c. $(3, 2)$
   d. $y = -7000$
   e. $(27, 0)$
   f. $x = c$

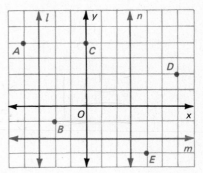

2. Give the equation for:
   a. line l
   b. line m
   c. line n

3. State the coordinates of each labeled point in the graph shown.

4. Give the coordinates for the intersection of lines:
   a. l and m
   b. m and n
   c. l and n
   d. l and the x-axis

Written Exercises

A

1. Graph the following points on one set of axes:
   $A(1, 1)$; $B(-3, 0)$; $C(-4, -1)$; $D(3, -2)$

2. Graph the following points on one set of axes:
   $E(2, 0)$; $F(2, -3)$; $G(-2, 3)$; $H(0, -4)$

3. Write the coordinates of each labeled point in the figure.

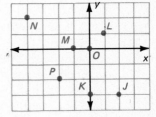

Ex. 3

4. Graph the following lines on one set of axes.
   a. Line l with equation $x = 5$
   b. Line m with equation $y = 2$
   c. Line n with equation $x = -2$
   d. Line p with equation $y = -\frac{3}{2}$

5. Using your work for Exercise 4, give the coordinates of the intersection of the following lines.
   a. l and m
   b. m and n
   c. l and p
   d. n and p

6. Graph the points $R(-2, -3)$; $S(4, -3)$; $T(4, 5)$. Then find RS and ST.

In Exercises 7–10, plot the points and find the distance between them.

7. (5, 4) and (9, 4)

8. (2, −4) and (2, 3)

9. (3, −4) and (0, −4)

10. (−3, 4) and (−3, −1)

Draw a graph and then write the answer.

B 11. Three of the vertices of a square are points (3, 4), (3, 7), and (6, 4). State the coordinates of the fourth vertex.

12. Three of the vertices of a rectangle are points (−3, −3), (2, 5), and (2, −3). State the coordinates of the fourth vertex.

13. Three vertices of an isosceles trapezoid are points (−3, −1), (7, −1), and (−1, 5). Can the origin be the fourth vertex?

14. Two vertices of a square are points (4, −1) and (4, 7). State the coordinates of two possible pairs of points for the other two vertices.

Three coordinate axes are needed to locate points in space. Think of the y-axis and the z-axis as lying in the plane of the paper and of the x-axis as being perpendicular to the plane of the paper, with the positive direction toward you.

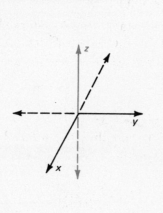

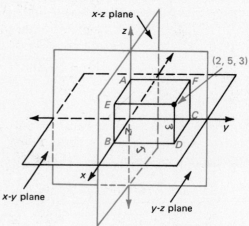

Each point is located by an ordered triple of numbers. The point (2, 5, 3) lies 2 units in "front" of the y-z plane, 5 units to the right of the x-z plane, and 3 units above the x-y plane. This point is the intersection of the three planes x = 2, y = 5, and z = 3.

C 15. Give the coordinates of points A, B, C, D, E, and F.

16. On which axis does each of the following points lie?
a. (3, 0, 0)   b. (0, 0, −5)   c. (0, 4, 0)

17. On which plane does each of the following points lie?
a. (0, 2, 5)   b. (−3, 4, 0)   c. (−1, 0, 0)

18. Five vertices of a rectangular solid are points (2, 2, 7), (2, 2, 0), (3, 1, 0), (3, 1, 7), and (2, 1, 0). State the coordinates of the other three vertices.

11-2 *The Distance Formula*

In the previous section you learned how to find the distance between points on horizontal and vertical lines. To find the distance between two points which do not lie on a horizontal or vertical line, you need only complete a right triangle and use the Pythagorean Theorem.

EXAMPLE 1. Find the distance between points $A(-3, 2)$ and $B(1, -2)$.

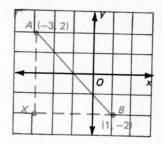

SOLUTION: Draw the horizontal and vertical segments shown. The coordinates of X are $(-3, -2)$. Then $AX = XB = 4$ and $(AB)^2 = 4^2 + 4^2 = 32$. Thus $AB = \sqrt{32}$ or $4\sqrt{2}$.

EXAMPLE 2. Compute the distance d between the points $(-2, -1)$ and $(4, 3)$ without graphing the points.

SOLUTION: Picture a right triangle mentally. The length of the horizontal leg is $|4 - (-2)|$, or 6. The length of the vertical leg is $|3 - (-1)|$, or 4. Then $d^2 = 6^2 + 4^2$, and $d = \sqrt{52}$, or $2\sqrt{13}$.

A general formula for the distance between two points $P_1(x_1, y_1)$ and $P_2(x_2, y_2)$ may be derived by completing the right triangle $P_1P_2P_3$ as shown. Note that the coordinates of P_3 are (x_2, y_1).

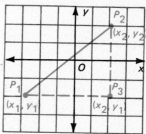

By the Ruler Postulate (Section 1-4):

$$P_1P_3 = |x_2 - x_1|; \quad P_2P_3 = |y_2 - y_1|$$

$$\begin{aligned}(P_1P_2)^2 &= (P_1P_3)^2 + (P_2P_3)^2 \\ &= |x_2 - x_1|^2 + |y_2 - y_1|^2 \\ &= (x_2 - x_1)^2 + (y_2 - y_1)^2\end{aligned}$$

THEOREM 11-1 The distance d between two points (x_1, y_1) and (x_2, y_2) is:

$$d = \sqrt{(x_2 - x_1)^2 + (y_2 - y_1)^2}$$

EXAMPLE 3. Find the distance between points $(5, 0)$ and $(1, -3)$.

SOLUTION 1: Let P_1 be point $(5, 0)$. Then $x_1 = 5$ and $y_1 = 0$.
Let P_2 be point $(1, -3)$. Then $x_2 = 1$ and $y_2 = -3$.

$$d = \sqrt{(x_2 - x_1)^2 + (y_2 - y_1)^2}$$
$$d = \sqrt{(1 - 5)^2 + (-3 - 0)^2}$$
$$d = \sqrt{16 + 9} = \sqrt{25} = 5$$

SOLUTION 2: Visualize horizontal and vertical sides to complete a right triangle.
The vertical side is 3 units long. The horizontal side is 4 units long.
Then $d^2 = 4^2 + 3^2$
$\qquad\quad = 16 + 9 = 25$
$\qquad d = 5$

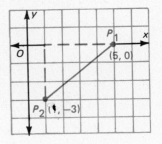

Oral Exercises

1. P_1 is point $(\underline{\ ?\ }, \underline{\ ?\ })$; $x_1 = \underline{\ ?\ }$; $y_1 = \underline{\ ?\ }$.
2. P_2 is point $(\underline{\ ?\ }, \underline{\ ?\ })$; $x_2 = \underline{\ ?\ }$; $y_2 = \underline{\ ?\ }$.
3. Find the value of $|x_2 - x_1|$ and $(x_2 - x_1)^2$.
4. Find the value of $|y_2 - y_1|$ and $(y_2 - y_1)^2$.
5. Find the distance $P_1 P_2$.
6. What is the distance between P_1 and the x-axis? P_1 and the y-axis?
7. Find the distance OP_1.
8. What is the distance between P_2 and the x-axis? P_2 and the y-axis?
9. Find the distance OP_2.
10. Is the distance between two points ever a negative number?

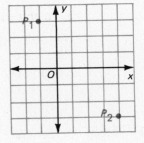

Written Exercises

In Exercises 1–10, find the distance between the given points. Express your answers in simplest radical form.

A

1. $(0, 0)$ and $(5, 10)$
2. $(-2, -4)$ and $(3, 8)$
3. $(2, 1)$ and $(5, 1)$
4. $(2, 1)$ and $(4, 0)$
5. $(6, 3)$ and $(6, -2)$
6. $(5, 0)$ and $(0, 5)$
7. (a, b) and $(0, 0)$
8. (a, b) and $(2, 3)$
9. $(-1, -5)$ and (c, d)
10. (a, b) and (c, d)

11. The distance between $(0, 0)$ and $(0, 1)$ is $\underline{\ ?\ }$.
12. The distance between $(0, 0)$ and $(0, \underline{\ ?\ })$ is 9. (Give two possible answers.)

Exercises 13–18 refer to the diagram at right.

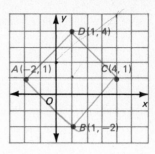

B 13. Find AD and CD. Is $\triangle ACD$ isosceles?
14. Is quadrilateral $ABCD$ equilateral?
15. Find AC.
16. Use the converse of the Pythagorean Theorem to show that $\triangle ADC$ is a right triangle.
17. What kind of figure is quadrilateral $ABCD$? Why?
18. Does $OC = OD$?

Show by comparing lengths of segments that the statements are true.

19. The triangle whose vertices are points $A(1, 1)$, $B(4, 5)$, and $C(0, 2)$ is isosceles.
20. The triangle whose vertices are points $R(3, 0)$, $S(1, -6)$, and $T(4, -7)$ is not equilateral.
21. The quadrilateral with vertices $A(4, 3)$, $B(4, 8)$, $C(7, 17)$, and $D(7, 12)$ has two pairs of congruent opposite sides.
22. The diagonals of a quadrilateral with vertices $K(2, 3)$, $L(-1, 4)$, $M(-2, -1)$, and $N(3, 0)$ are congruent.

Find the distance between the given points in space.

C 23. The origin and $(4, 0, 0)$
24. The origin and $(3, 4, 0)$
25. The origin and $(3, 4, 12)$
26. $(2, 3, 4)$ and $(7, 4, 3)$
27. $(0, 0, 0)$ and (x, y, z)
28. (x_1, y_1, z_1) and (x_2, y_2, z_2)

Self-Test In Exercises 1–4, state the coordinates of each point.

1. The intersection of lines l and m
2. The origin
3. Point P
4. Point R

In Exercises 5–8, state an equation to represent each line.

5. Line m 7. The x-axis
6. Line l 8. The y-axis

Exs. 1–10

9. Find PR.
10. Is $\triangle OPR$ isosceles?
11. Graph the following points using one set of axes.
   a. $(4, -3)$ b. $(-\frac{1}{2}, 2)$ c. $(0, 1)$
12. Graph the following lines using one set of axes.
   a. $x = 3$ b. $y = -1$

Segments and Lines

Objectives

1. Use the midpoint formula to find the coordinates of the midpoint or endpoint of a segment.
2. Find the slope of the line containing two given points.
3. Determine whether two lines are parallel, perpendicular, or neither.
4. Graph the line specified by a given equation.
5. Write an equation of a line when given either two points on the line or one point and the slope of the line.
6. Use an algebraic method to determine the intersection of two lines.

11-3 *The Midpoint Formula*

Suppose you want to find the coordinates of the midpoint of a segment with endpoints $(3, 0)$ and $(1, 1)$.

By making a careful drawing on a grid, you can verify that the coordinates of the midpoint M are $(2, \frac{1}{2})$.

> Note that the x-coordinate of M is the average of 3 and 1.
> Note that the y-coordinate of M is the average of 0 and 1.

Using the averaging technique for points $(-6, 3)$ and $(0, -1)$, we find that the midpoint of the segment joining these points has x-coordinate -3 and y-coordinate 1. Again you can verify this result by making a drawing on a grid.

Our two examples suggest that the segment joining points (x_1, y_1) and (x_2, y_2) has midpoint $\left(\dfrac{x_1 + x_2}{2}, \dfrac{y_1 + y_2}{2} \right)$. To see that the formula is correct, consider first a horizontal number line. Take a segment whose endpoints have coordinates x_1 and x_2, with $x_1 < x_2$. Remember that neither x_1 nor x_2 is necessarily positive.

$$P_1P_2 = x_2 - x_1$$
$$P_1M = \tfrac{1}{2}(x_2 - x_1)$$

The coordinate of M is $x_1 + \frac{1}{2}(x_2 - x_1)$, or $\dfrac{x_1 + x_2}{2}$.

A vertical segment whose endpoints have coordinates y_1 and y_2 has, by similar reasoning, a midpoint with coordinate $\dfrac{y_1 + y_2}{2}$.

Now consider a segment with endpoints $P_1(x_1, y_1)$ and $P_2(x_2, y_2)$. To determine the coordinates of the midpoint M, draw the horizontal and vertical segments shown.

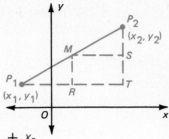

Then T has the coordinates (x_2, y_1). Since $\overline{MR} \parallel \overline{P_2T}$, $\triangle P_1MR \sim \triangle P_1P_2T$. Then, since $P_1M = \frac{1}{2}P_1P_2$, $P_1R = \frac{1}{2}P_1T$.

R, the midpoint of $\overline{P_1T}$, has x-coordinate $\dfrac{x_1 + x_2}{2}$.

Therefore M has x-coordinate $\dfrac{x_1 + x_2}{2}$.

By similar reasoning, M has y-coordinate $\dfrac{y_1 + y_2}{2}$.

THEOREM 11-2 The coordinates of the midpoint of the segment joining the points (x_1, y_1) and (x_2, y_2) are

$$\left(\frac{x_1 + x_2}{2}, \frac{y_1 + y_2}{2} \right).$$

Oral Exercises

Use the midpoint formula to find the midpoint of the segment joining the given points.

1. $(2, 0)$ and $(8, 0)$
2. $(1, 8)$ and $(3, 10)$
3. $(2, 3)$ and $(-1, -5)$
4. $(-6, -2)$ and $(-4, -1)$
5. $(-6, 1)$ and $(3, 7)$
6. $(9, 8)$ and $(-3, 4)$
7. $(0.5, 1)$ and $(4.5, 7)$
8. $(-1, 2.6)$ and $(5, 4.6)$
9. (a, b) and $(6, -5)$
10. (a, b) and (c, d)

Written Exercises

Use the midpoint formula to find the midpoint of the segment joining the given points. Check Exercises 1–4 by plotting the points.

A

1. $(2, 2)$ and $(2, 4)$
2. $(4, -6)$ and $(0, 0)$
3. $(-1, \frac{1}{2})$ and $(-3, 3\frac{1}{2})$
4. $(2, 1)$ and $(2, -1)$
5. $(3, -4)$ and $(-3, 4)$
6. $(\frac{1}{4}, 9)$ and $(\frac{7}{4}, 11)$
7. $(a, 0)$ and $(0, b)$
8. (a, b) and $(a + 2b, 2a - b)$

In Exercises 9–12, you are given the coordinates of the midpoint M and one endpoint E_1 of a segment. Determine the coordinates of the second endpoint E_2 either by using the midpoint formula or by plotting the points on a graph.

B   9. $E_1(0, 0)$; $M(2, 3)$ 11. $E_1(r, -3)$; $M(-4, -4)$

     10. $E_1(5, -1)$; $M(-3, 7)$ 12. $E_1(c, d)$; $M(e, f)$

In Exercises 13–20, the coordinates of the vertices of a quadrilateral are $O(0, 0)$ $A(6, 0)$ $B(4, 4)$, and $C(2, 6)$.

13. Find M_1, the midpoint of $\overline{OA}$.

14. Find M_2, the midpoint of $\overline{AB}$.

15. Find M_1M_2.

16. Find M_3, the midpoint of $\overline{BC}$.

17. Find M_4, the midpoint of $\overline{OC}$.

18. Find M_3M_4.

19. Is $M_1M_2 = M_3M_4$? Is $M_1M_4 = M_2M_3$?

20. What kind of quadrilateral is $M_1M_2M_3M_4$?

21. Given $E(2, 4)$ and $G(6, 10)$, find the coordinates of F, the midpoint of $\overline{EG}$. Use the distance formula to show that $EF = FG$.

22. Repeat Exercise 21, using $E(p, q)$ and $G(r, s)$.

In Exercises 23–28, state the midpoint of the segment joining the given points.

C   23. The origin and $(2, 6, 4)$ 26. $(-5, 3, -7)$ and $(2, -4, -3)$

     24. The origin and $(-4, 3, -7)$ 27. $(2a, 2b, 4c)$ and $(2d, 2e, 0)$

     25. $(3, 4, 2)$ and $(5, 0, 4)$ 28. (x_1, y_1, z_1) and (x_2, y_2, z_2)

29. If $M(2, 3, 4)$ is the midpoint of $\overline{OP}$ and O is the origin, find the coordinates of P.

30. If $N(3, 1, 0)$ is the midpoint of $\overline{LS}$ and L is point $(-3, 2, 4)$, find the coordinates of S.

11-4 *The Slope of a Line*

In the diagram at the right, it looks as if line l is *steeper* than line k. The mathematical definition of *slope* confirms this observation and provides a method for measurement of steepness.

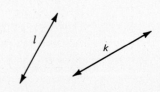

The **slope** m **of a line** passing through any two points (x_1, y_1) and (x_2, y_2), where $x_1 \neq x_2$, is defined as follows:

$$m = \frac{y_2 - y_1}{x_2 - x_1}$$

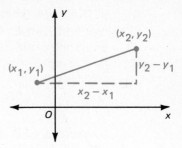

Slopes are numbers, and can be positive, negative, or zero.

EXAMPLE. Determine the slope of the line passing through points $(-1, 2)$ and $(4, 5)$.

SOLUTION 1: Let $(-1, 2)$ be (x_1, y_1) and $(4, 5)$ be (x_2, y_2).

$$m = \frac{y_2 - y_1}{x_2 - x_1} = \frac{5 - 2}{4 - (-1)} = \frac{3}{5}$$

SOLUTION 2: Let $(4, 5)$ be (x_1, y_1) and $(-1, 2)$ be (x_2, y_2).

$$m = \frac{y_2 - y_1}{x_2 - x_1} = \frac{2 - 5}{-1 - 4} = \frac{-3}{-5} = \frac{3}{5}$$

The two solutions in the example show that either of the two given points can be chosen as (x_1, y_1).

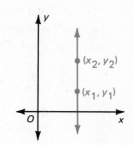

Notice that when x_1 and x_2 are equal, the denominator of the expression $\frac{y_2 - y_1}{x_2 - x_1}$ is 0 and the expression is meaningless. Vertical lines (lines parallel to the y-axis) have no slope. The slope of such lines is not defined.

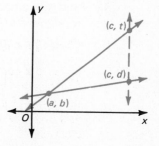

Note that two distinct nonvertical lines through the same point (a, b) must have different slopes. For if one line contains point (c, d) then the other line, being distinct, cannot contain point (c, d). On the second line, at the point whose x-coordinate is c, the y-coordinate must be some number t which is different from d. Then the slopes $\frac{d - b}{c - a}$ and $\frac{t - b}{c - a}$ are unequal.

When you look at the graph of a line, you can tell whether the slope is positive, negative, zero, or not defined. Notice in the two figures at the left below, that when a line slants upward as you read from left to right, $y_2 - y_1 > 0, x_2 - x_1 > 0$, and the slope is a positive number. In the other two figures the line slants downward as you read from left to right. Then $y_2 - y_1 < 0, x_2 - x_1 > 0$, and the slope is a negative number.

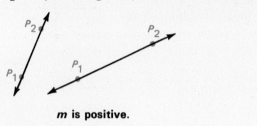

m is positive.

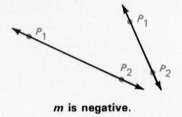

m is negative.

Oral Exercises

1. For each line shown, tell whether the slope appears to be positive, negative, zero, or not defined.

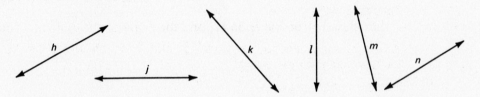

In Exercises 2–7, state the value of $y_2 - y_1$ and $x_2 - x_1$.

2. $P_1(0, 0)$; $P_2(3, 8)$

3. $P_1(0, 0)$; $P_2(2, -7)$

4. $P_1(5, 1)$; $P_2(-4, 1)$

5. $P_1(-6, -3)$; $P_2(2, 1)$

6. $P_1(7, 8)$; $P_2(7, 9)$

7. $P_1(a, b)$; $P_2(c, d)$

Written Exercises

Find the slope of the line containing the points named. If the line has no slope, write *Slope not defined*.

A

1. $(5, 2)$ and $(2, 8)$

2. $(\frac{1}{2}, \frac{1}{5})$ and $(\frac{1}{2}, \frac{3}{5})$

3. $(-4, -1)$ and $(0, 9)$

4. $(7, -3)$ and $(-4, -3)$

5. $(-8, 0)$ and $(-2, 9)$

6. $(\frac{1}{4}, -1)$ and $(\frac{3}{4}, 1)$

B

7. (p, q) and $(0, 0)$

8. $(r, 0)$ and $(0, r)$

9. $(0, a)$ and $(b, 0)$

10. (c, d) and (e, f)

11. (a, b) and $(a + b, c + b)$

12. $(j + 2k, k)$ and $(k, 2k - j)$

In Exercises 13–16, use the slope formula to find the missing coordinate.

13. Points $(2, 4)$ and $(5, \underline{})$ lie on a line whose slope is $\frac{7}{3}$.
14. Points $(\underline{}, 3)$ and $(-2, -5)$ lie on a line whose slope is 4.
15. Points $(0, 0)$ and $(1, \underline{})$ lie on a line whose slope is c.
16. Points (a, b) and $(c, \underline{})$ lie on a line whose slope is m.

17. Given a quadrilateral with vertices $A(0, 0)$, $B(6, 0)$, $C(4, 4)$, and $D(2, 6)$ find:
    a. The coordinates of the midpoints of the sides.
    b. The slopes of the lines passing through consecutive midpoints.
18. Given points $E(-3, 2)$, $F(1, 4)$, $G(5, 5)$, and $H(9, 7)$.

    a. Find the slope of $\overleftrightarrow{EF}$, the slope of $\overleftrightarrow{GH}$, and the slope of $\overleftrightarrow{EH}$.
    b. Are the four points collinear? Verify your answer by plotting the points.

11-5 *Parallel and Perpendicular Lines*

A careful look at a graph of two nonvertical parallel lines suggests that the lines have equal slopes. When the lines are both parallel to the x-axis, then each has slope zero, and the slopes are equal. Any other nonvertical parallel lines must intersect the x-axis, and you can prove their slopes equal in the following way:

Let the slope of line l_1 be m_1 and the slope of line l_2 be m_2, with $l_1 \parallel l_2$. From points B and S, taken on l_1 and l_2 as shown, draw $\overline{BC}$ and $\overrightarrow{ST}$ perpendicular to the x-axis.

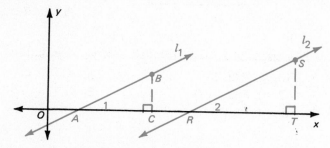

Then, AC is the difference of the x-coordinates of A and B, and CB is the difference of the y-coordinates.

$\dfrac{BC}{AC} = m_1$. Similarly, $\dfrac{ST}{RT} = m_2$.

$\triangle ACB \sim \triangle RTS$, since $\angle 1 \cong \angle 2$ (corr. $\underline{\&}$) and $\angle C \cong \angle T$ (rt. $\underline{\&}$).

$\dfrac{BC}{ST} = \dfrac{AC}{RT}$, since lengths of corresponding sides of $\sim\underline{\&}$ are in proportion.

$\dfrac{BC}{AC} = \dfrac{ST}{RT}$, and $m_1 = m_2$ by the Substitution Principle.

Conversely, when $m_1 = m_2$, you can show that $l_1 \parallel l_2$. This is true since a line through R and parallel to l_1 must have slope m_1, and it is not possible for two distinct lines through the same point to have equal slopes.

THEOREM 11-3 Two nonvertical lines are parallel if and only if they have equal slopes.

You will recall that the phrase *if and only if* permits one theorem to include both a statement and its converse. Theorem 11-3 could be replaced by two theorems:

> If two nonvertical lines are parallel, they have equal slopes.
> If two nonvertical lines have equal slopes, they are parallel.

The slopes of two perpendicular lines, neither one a vertical line, are also related in a particular way. The product of the slopes is -1. The proof of the theorem which follows is omitted.

THEOREM 11-4 Two nonvertical lines are perpendicular if and only if the slope of one line is the negative reciprocal of the slope of the other line.

$$m_1 = -\frac{1}{m_2}, \qquad \text{or} \qquad m_1 \cdot m_2 = -1$$

Oral Exercises

1. State two theorems that are combined in Theorem 11-4.
2. Line l has slope $\frac{1}{2}$. Any line parallel to l has slope __?__ . Any line perpendicular to l has slope __?__ .
3. Line s has slope $-\frac{3}{5}$. Any line parallel to s has slope __?__ . Any line perpendicular to s has slope __?__ .
4. Line p has slope 4. Any line parallel to p has slope __?__ . Any line perpendicular to p has slope __?__ .

In Exercises 5-8, state whether lines with the given slopes are parallel, perpendicular, or neither.

5. $m_1 = \frac{1}{4}$; $m_2 = 0.25$
6. $m_1 = -3$; $m_2 = \frac{1}{3}$
7. $m_1 = 5$; $m_2 = -5$
8. $m_1 = 0$; m_2 is not defined.

Written Exercises

1. Lines p and q are parallel. The slope of p is 5, and the slope of q is $\dfrac{10}{v}$. Find the value of v.

2. Lines r and s are perpendicular. The slope r is 4, and the slope of s is $\dfrac{w}{2}$. Find the value of w.

In Exercises 3–6, determine which sides, if any, of quadrilateral $ABCD$ are parallel or perpendicular.

EXAMPLE. $A(0, -2)$; $B(4, 0)$; $C(3, 2)$; $D(1, 1)$

SOLUTION: slope of $\overline{AB} = \dfrac{0 - (-2)}{4 - 0} = \dfrac{1}{2}$; slope of $\overline{BC} = \dfrac{2 - 0}{3 - 4} = -2$

slope of $\overline{CD} = \dfrac{1 - 2}{1 - 3} = \dfrac{1}{2}$; slope of $\overline{AD} = \dfrac{1 - (-2)}{1 - 0} = 3$

$\overline{AB} \parallel \overline{CD}$, since each segment has slope $\frac{1}{2}$.

$\overline{AB} \perp \overline{BC}$, and $\overline{CD} \perp \overline{BC}$, since in each case $\frac{1}{2}(-2) = -1$.

3. $A(0, 0)$; $B(6, -2)$; $C(7, 1)$; $D(1, 3)$
4. $A(0, -4)$; $B(2, -3)$; $C(1, -1)$; $D(-2, 0)$
5. $A(-3, -1)$; $B(3, 1)$; $C(1, 3)$; $D(-2, 2)$
6. $A(1, 1)$; $B(6, 1)$; $C(4, 3)$; $D(1, 3)$

For each triangle EFG find the slope of each side and each altitude.

7. $E(0, 0)$; $F(3, -1)$; $G(1, 2)$ 8. $E(0, 0)$; $F(3, 0)$; $G(0, 2)$

Is quadrilateral $JKLM$ a special kind of quadrilateral?

9. $J(0, 0)$; $K(4, 2)$; $L(2, 3)$; $M(0, 2)$
10. $J(4, -2)$; $K(5, 0)$; $L(1, 1)$; $M(0, -3)$

Are the diagonals of quadrilateral $RSTW$ perpendicular?

11. $R(0, 0)$; $S(4, 3)$; $T(1, 7)$; $W(-3, 4)$
12. $R(0, 0)$; $S(4, 3)$; $T(0, 6)$; $W(-4, 3)$

Find the value of d such that $\angle ABC$ is a right angle.

13. $A(d, 5)$; $B(-5, d)$; $C(-3, -2)$ 14. $A(4, d)$; $B(d, 1)$; $C(1, -3)$

Is the quadrilateral formed by joining the midpoints of the sides of quadrilateral $OABC$ a parallelogram?

15. $O(0, 0)$; $A(6, 0)$; $B(4, 4)$; $C(2, 6)$
16. $O(0, 0)$; $A(2a, 0)$; $B(2b, 2c)$; $C(2d, 2e)$

11-6 *The Equation of a Line*

The following theorem provides a way to represent all lines in the coordinate plane. The proof is omitted.

THEOREM 11-5 The graph of any equation that can be written in the form $ax + by = c$, a and b not both 0, is a line.

If you are given an equation in this form, you can easily plot the line.

EXAMPLE 1. Graph $2x + 3y = 6$.

SOLUTION: When $x = 0$, by substitution, $2(0) + 3y = 6$ and $y = 2$. The point $(0, 2)$ lies on the line. When $y = 0$, by substitution, $2x + 3(0) = 6$ and $x = 3$. The point $(3, 0)$ lies on the line. Plot the two

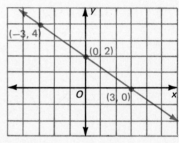

points and draw the line. As a check, you may find a third point on the line. When $x = -3$, $2(-3) + 3y = 6$ and $y = 4$. Thus the point $(-3, 4)$ also lies on the line.

It can be proved that the converse of Theorem 11-5 is also true. That is, given any line, you can write an equation in the form $ax + by = c$ for that line. There are times, however, when equations written in other forms have advantages.

EXAMPLE 2. Find an equation for the line passing through the point $(3, 5)$ and having slope -2.

SOLUTION: Let point $(3, 5)$ be P_1. Let any other point (x, y) of the line be P_2. The slope of $\overleftrightarrow{P_1P_2}$ may be expressed as $\dfrac{y - 5}{x - 3}$. The slope is given as -2. Therefore:

$$\frac{y - 5}{x - 3} = -2, \text{ or}$$

$$y - 5 = -2(x - 3)$$

The last equation in Example 2 is said to be in *point-slope* form. By inspection of an equation in this form, you can find the slope and the coordinates of a point on the line. For example, the line with equation $y + 7 = 4(x - 2)$ has slope 4 and contains the point $(2, -7)$.

THEOREM 11-6 An equation of the line passing through the point (x_1, y_1) and having slope m is $y - y_1 = m(x - x_1)$.

Theorem 11-6 can be proved by following the method of Example 2, using (x_1, y_1) in place of $(3, 5)$ and m in place of -2.

COROLLARY An equation of the line containing points (x_1, y_1) and (x_2, y_2) is $y - y_1 = m(x - x_1)$, where $m = \dfrac{y_2 - y_1}{x_2 - x_1}$ and $x_2 \neq x_1$.

EXAMPLE 3. Find an equation of the line containing points $(-4, 2)$ and $(3, 5)$.

SOLUTION: The slope of the line is $\dfrac{5 - 2}{3 - (-4)} = \dfrac{3}{7}$.

An equation of the line through point $(-4, 2)$ with slope $\dfrac{3}{7}$ is:

$$y - 2 = \frac{3}{7}(x + 4)$$

When the equation of a line is given in point-slope form, you can quickly plot two points and draw the graph of the line.

EXAMPLE 4. Graph $y + 2 = \frac{3}{2}(x - 1)$.

SOLUTION: One point on the line is $(1, -2)$, and the slope of the line is $\frac{3}{2}$. Plot the point $(1, -2)$. Since the slope is $\frac{3}{2}$, a second point is located 3 units up and 2 units to the right. Plot the second point and draw the line.

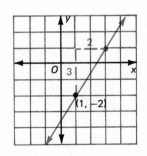

Suppose you are given the equations of two lines and are asked to find the coordinates of the point at which they intersect. One method is to graph each line and estimate the coordinates of the point of intersection. A more accurate method is to solve the pair of equations algebraically. Note that the point of intersection has coordinates that satisfy *both* equations. You can find these coordinates either by the substitution method or by the addition or subtraction method.

EXAMPLE 5. Find, by an algebraic method, the point of intersection of $x + 2y = 15$ and $y = 3x - 3$.

SOLUTION 1: $\begin{cases} x + 2y = 15 \\ \quad\quad y = 3x - 3 \end{cases}$

$$x + 2(3x - 3) = 15 \text{ (substituting } 3x - 3 \text{ for } y)$$
$$7x - 6 = 15$$
$$x = 3$$
$$y = 3(3) - 3 = 6$$

The point of intersection is (3, 6).

SOLUTION 2: $\begin{cases} x + 2y = 15 \\ \quad\quad y = 3x - 3 \end{cases}$

$\begin{cases} x + 2y = 15 \\ 3x - y = \quad 3 \end{cases}$

$\begin{cases} \quad x + 2y = 15 \\ 6x - 2y = \quad 6 \end{cases}$
$$7x \quad\quad\quad = 21 \text{ (adding)}$$
$$x = 3$$
$$y = 3(3) - 3 = 6$$

The point of intersection is (3, 6).

Oral Exercises In Exercises 1–6, state the slope of the line and name one point on the line.

1. $y - 2 = \frac{2}{3}(x - 3)$

2. $y + 5 = 8(x - 1)$

3. $y - 1 = x + 10$

4. $y = -(x - 3)$

5. $y = x$

6. $y - c = \frac{a}{b}(x - d)$

In Exercises 7–12, state two points on the line.

EXAMPLE. $x + 2y = 6$

SOLUTION: When $x = 0$, $2y = 6$ and $y = 3$. One point is $(0, 3)$.
When $y = 0$, $x = 6$. A second point is $(6, 0)$.

7. $5x + 4y = 20$ 9. $y = 3x - 6$ 11. $y = -x$
8. $2x - y = 4$ 10. $2x - 3y = 12$ 12. $y = 2$

Written Exercises

Plot the graph of each equation.

A 1. $2x + y = 4$ 3. $4x + 3y = 12$ 5. $y = -2(x - 2)$
2. $y = x - 1$ 4. $y - 2 = \frac{1}{2}(x - 1)$ 6. $y + 1 = \frac{1}{3}x$

State an equation of the line passing through point P and having slope m.

7. $P(2, 3)$; $m = 1$ 9. $P(0, 0)$; $m = \frac{2}{3}$
8. $P(5, -1)$; $m = -\frac{1}{2}$ 10. $P(-1, 2)$; $m = 0$

State an equation of the line containing the given points.

11. $(2, 1)$ and $(6, 5)$ 13. $(-1, -3)$ and $(2, 1)$
12. $(0, 0)$ and $(2, 4)$ 14. $(-3, -4)$ and $(7, -4)$

Use an algebraic method to find the intersection of the given lines.

15. $x + y = 5$; $x - y = 1$
16. $3x - y = 7$; $5x + 3y = 35$
17. $y - 1 = \frac{2}{3}(x + 9)$; $y = 7$
18. $y - 2 = 2(x - 1)$; $y + 8 = 3(x + 1)$

B 19. $4x + y = 7$; $x = a$
20. $ax + by = c$; $y = 2x$

State an equation of the line meeting the given conditions.

21. The line passing through point $(3, 2)$ and parallel to a line whose slope is 2.
22. The line passing through point $(3, 2)$ and perpendicular to a line with slope 2.
23. The line with slope $\frac{2}{3}$ and passing through the midpoint of the segment joining points $(-1, 6)$ and $(-7, -4)$.
24. The line which is the perpendicular bisector of the segment joining points $(2, 4)$ and $(6, 10)$.
25. The line parallel to the line with equation $y = \frac{3}{5}(x - 1)$ and passing through the origin.
26. The line perpendicular to the line with equation $y = \frac{3}{5}(x - 1)$ and passing through point $(-2, 1)$.

In Exercises 27–30, $\triangle ABC$ has vertices $A(-4, 2)$, $B(6, 8)$, and $C(4, -2)$.

C 27. State an equation of the line passing through the midpoints of $\overline{AB}$ and $\overline{AC}$. Then show that the line is parallel to $\overline{BC}$.

28. The three medians of a triangle intersect in one point. Find the coordinates of the point in which the medians of $\triangle ABC$ intersect.

29. Show that the point determined in Exercise 28 divides each median into two segments whose lengths are in the ratio $1:2$.

30. The three altitudes of a triangle intersect in one point. Find the coordinates of the point in which the altitudes of $\triangle ABC$ intersect.

Self-Test   Use the midpoint formula to find the midpoint of the segment joining the given points.

1. $(0, 7)$ and $(-6, -1)$

2. (a, b) and $(3, -3)$

You are given the coordinates of one endpoint E_1 and the midpoint M of a segment. Find the coordinates of the second endpoint.

3. $E_1(8, 3)$; $M(-2, 5)$

4. $E_1(-1, -1)$; $M(s, s)$

Find the slope of the line containing the points named.

5. $(6, 8)$ and $(2, -10)$

6. $(3.2, g)$ and $(-1.3, g)$

7. Given points $A(3, -9)$; $B(-2, 3)$; $C(10, 8)$; and $D(15, -4)$, state which sides of quadrilateral $ABCD$ are parallel or perpendicular.

Plot the graph of each equation.

8. $y = -\frac{1}{2}(x + 5)$

9. $4x - y = 8$

Write an equation for each line described.

10. The line passes through the points $(7, -4)$ and $(-3, -9)$.

11. The line passes through the point $(1, 2)$ and has slope $\frac{1}{8}$.

12. Using an algebraic method, find the intersection of the lines with equations $2x + y = 2$ and $y = x + 8$.

Check your answers with those printed in the back of the book.

410 *GEOMETRY*

Careers

Navigation

The principal aim of a navigator is to determine the safest and most direct route for a ship or airplane. Geometric concepts play an important role in the instruments and methods used in navigation.

A transparent plotter is a protractor and straightedge used to measure angles and distances and to draw course lines on a chart. A sextant determines the angle of elevation from the horizon to a star, and by applying trigonometric ratios, a pilot can quickly calculate distances.

Celestial navigation utilizes the planets and the stars to determine position. All points on the earth's surface and all of the astronomical bodies are considered to lie within an immense sphere whose center coincides with the center of the earth. A three-dimensional coordinate system enables the accurate location of a craft.

Radar and radio have dramatically changed navigational methods. Using new methods, a pilot is now able to guide a craft even when visibility is poor.

Proofs Using Coordinate Geometry

Objectives

1. Determine an advantageous placement of a given polygon on the coordinate axes, and assign coordinates to the vertices of the polygon.
2. Given the coordinates of the vertices of a polygon, determine whether any sides of the polygon are parallel or perpendicular.
3. Use coordinate geometry methods to prove properties of polygons.

11-7 *Organizing Coordinate Proofs*

Some theorems which are quite difficult to prove using our earlier methods are considerably easier to prove using coordinate geometry methods. In any coordinate proof, you must translate the geometric elements of your problem into algebraic elements. A key to this translation is the placement of the coordinate axes with respect to a given figure.

You have already seen that the location of a line or triangle with respect to the coordinate axes is an important factor in determining the complexity of the algebraic work involved. The following examples investigate desirable placements of certain plane figures with respect to the coordinate axes.

EXAMPLE 1. Which placement of the rectangle seems most advantageous?

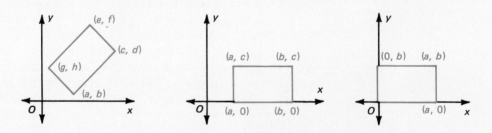

SOLUTION: Note that in the third diagram, fewer letters are needed than in any other diagram. The third diagram also illustrates many of the properties of a rectangle more clearly than the other two diagrams. Therefore, the placement of the rectangle in the third diagram is generally the most advantageous.

When locating a figure on the coordinate axes:

1. Try to locate a key point at the origin (for example, a vertex or the midpoint of a segment).
2. It is often useful to locate a segment on the x-axis.

Your choice of placement will depend on what you want to prove, and on the best way to simplify your algebraic calculations.

EXAMPLE 2.   Given isosceles △RST with $\overline{RS} \cong \overline{RT}$, locate the triangle in a convenient way on the coordinate axes, and assign coordinates to points R, S, and T.

SOLUTION 1: Let $\overline{ST}$ be located on the x-axis with the origin at the midpoint of $\overline{ST}$. Let T have coordinates (a, 0) where a is any real number. Then S has coordinates (−a, 0), since S is the same distance from the origin as T, but in the opposite direction. Let R have coordinates (0, b),

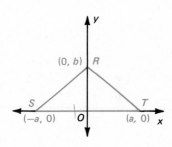

where b is any real number; R must lie on the y-axis, since the altitude from the vertex of an isosceles triangle intersects the base at its midpoint.

SOLUTION 2: Let $\overline{ST}$ be located on the x-axis with point S at (0, 0). Then let T have coordinates (2a, 0), where a is any real number. (The choice of 2a rather than a avoids fractions for the coordinates of R.) R has the same x-coordinate as the midpoint of $\overline{ST}$. So the coordinates of R are (a, b), where b is any real number.

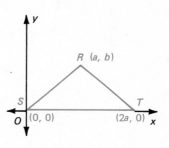

When setting up coordinate geometry proofs, you should use the more obvious properties of a figure in assigning coordinates to points. Try to express the coordinates of points by using as few letters as possible. That will make your calculations easier. However, when you do this, you must be able to justify your choice of coordinates.

State which placement of the figure named seems most advantageous.

1. A rectangle

a. 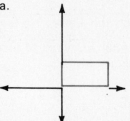   b. 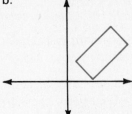   c.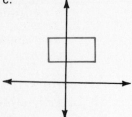

2. An equilateral triangle

a. 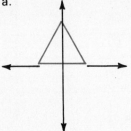   b. 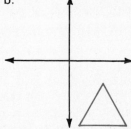   c.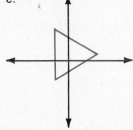

3. An isosceles triangle

a. 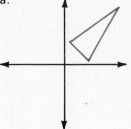   b. 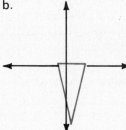   c.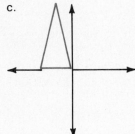

4. An isosceles trapezoid

a. 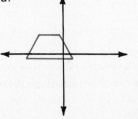   b. 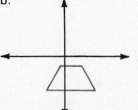   c.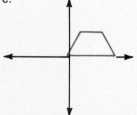

Square *OABC* is placed on the coordinate axes as shown.

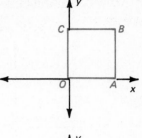

5. If *A* is point (*a*, 0), state the coordinates of the other three vertices.

6. If *C* is point (0, 2*b*), state the coordinates of the other three vertices.

Isosceles trapezoid *ABCD* is placed on the coordinate axes so that $\overline{AB}$ lies on the *x*-axis and *O* is the midpoint of $\overline{AB}$.

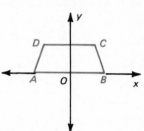

7. If *A* has coordinates (−*a*, 0) and *C* has coordinates (*b*, *c*), state the coordinates of *B* and *D*.

8. If *B* has coordinates (3*k*, 0) and *C* has coordinates (2*k*, 2*k*), state the coordinates of *A* and *D*.

Written Exercises

In Exercises 1–4, graph and label a figure using the information given. Then answer the questions.

EXAMPLE. The *x*-axis contains the base, $\overline{AB}$, of an equilateral triangle *ABC*, with the midpoint of the base at the origin. If vertex *A* has coordinates (−*p*, 0), find the coordinates of *B* and *C* in terms of *p*.

SOLUTION: The *x*-coordinate of *B* is *p*, since *OB* = *OA* = *p*. *B* has coordinates (*p*, 0). Since $\overline{OC}$ is the altitude of $\triangle ABC$, $\triangle OCB$ is a 30°-60°-90° rt. $\triangle$. Therefore $OC = \dfrac{AB}{2}\sqrt{3} = \dfrac{2p}{2}\sqrt{3} = p\sqrt{3}$. Thus point *C* has coordinates $(0, p\sqrt{3})$.

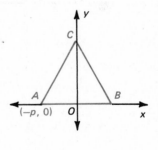

A

1. Two sides of a rectangle lie on the coordinate axes. If (0, *a*) and (*b*, 0) are the coordinates of two vertices, find the coordinates of the other two vertices.

2. The base of a square lies on the *x*-axis with the midpoint of the base at the origin. If the lower right vertex has coordinates (*k*, 0), what are the coordinates of the other three vertices?

3. The lower base of a trapezoid lies on the x-axis and has endpoints with coordinates $(0, 0)$ and $(a, 0)$. One endpoint of the upper base has coordinates (b, c). What is the y-coordinate of the other endpoint of the upper base?

4. An equilateral triangle has one vertex at the origin and its base along the x-axis. If the coordinates of a second vertex are $(2a, 0)$, find the coordinates of the third vertex. (Two answers are possible.)

Determine perpendicular or parallel sides of quadrilateral *ABCD*.

5. $A(0, 0)$; $B(a, 0)$; $C(b, c)$; $D(d, c)$
6. $A(0, 0)$; $B(-a, 0)$; $C(-b, c)$; $D(0, d)$
7. $A(a, b)$; $B(a, -b)$; $C(-a, -b)$; $D(-a, b)$
8. $A(0, 0)$; $B(a, 0)$; $C(a - b, c)$; $D(b, c)$

B 9. The base of an isosceles triangle is parallel to the x-axis, with an endpoint of the base located on the y-axis. If the endpoints of the base have coordinates $(0, k)$ and $(2l, k)$, what is the x-coordinate of the vertex?

10. The base of an isosceles triangle is a vertical segment parallel to the y-axis, and the x-axis does not intersect the triangle. If the lower endpoint of the base is labeled (c, d), what is the x-coordinate of the upper endpoint of the base? If the y-coordinate of the upper endpoint is $5d$, what is the y-coordinate of the vertex of the isosceles triangle?

11. The coordinates of three consecutive vertices of a parallelogram are (a, b), $(0, 0)$, and $(c, 0)$. The numbers a, b, and c are all positive.
    a. What is the y-coordinate of the fourth vertex?
    b. How many units to the right of the y-axis is the point with coordinates (a, b)?
    c. How many units to the right of a vertical line through the point with coordinates $(c, 0)$ must the fourth vertex lie?
    d. What, in terms of the other letters, is the x-coordinate of the fourth vertex?

12. Three consecutive vertices of an isosceles trapezoid are (a, b), $(0, 0)$, and $(c, 0)$. The numbers a, b, and c are all positive.
    a. What is the y-coordinate of the fourth vertex?
    b. How many units to the right of the y-axis is vertex (a, b)?
    c. How many units to the left of a vertical line through the point with coordinates $(c, 0)$ must the fourth vertex lie?
    d. What, in terms of the other letters, is the x-coordinate of the fourth vertex?

EXAMPLE. Prove: In a plane, two lines perpendicular to the same line are parallel to each other.

Proof: 1. Let r and s be given lines both perpendicular to some line t.
2. Place the given lines so that no line is parallel to an axis.
3. Let m be the slope of t. $(m \neq 0)$
4. Then r and s must each have slope $-\dfrac{1}{m}$.
5. Therefore $r \parallel s$, since lines having equal slopes are parallel.

13. Prove: In a plane, two lines parallel to the same line are parallel to each other.

14. Prove: A line lying in the plane of two parallel lines and perpendicular to one of them is perpendicular to the other.

C 15. Using no geometric properties of a parallelogram other than those given by the definition, prove that a parallelogram with vertices (a, b), $(0, 0)$ and $(c, 0)$ has point $(a + c, b)$ as its fourth vertex.

16. Prove that an isosceles trapezoid with consecutive vertices (a, b), $(0, 0)$ and $(c, 0)$ has point $(c - a, b)$ as its fourth vertex.

11-8 *Proofs of Properties of Polygons*

You can use the distance and midpoint formulas and the properties of parallel and perpendicular lines to prove many facts about polygons. In every coordinate proof, place the given polygon on the coordinate axes in such a way that your algebraic work will be simple and direct.

EXAMPLE 1. Prove: The segment joining the midpoints of two sides of a triangle is parallel to the third side and its length is half the length of the third side.

Proof: Given $\triangle ABC$ with R and S the midpoints of $\overline{AC}$ and $\overline{BC}$, respectively. Let $\overline{AB}$ lie on the x-axis, let A be the origin, and let the coordinates of B and C be as shown below.

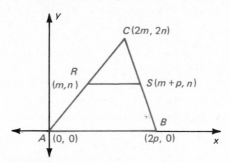

By the midpoint formula, R is the point (m, n) and S is the point $(m + p, n)$. Thus the slope of $\overline{RS}$ is $\dfrac{n - n}{m + p - m} = \dfrac{0}{p} = 0$. Similarly, the slope of $\overline{AB}$ is 0. Therefore, $\overline{RS} \parallel \overline{AB}$.

By the distance formula, $RS = p$ and $AB = 2p$. Therefore, $RS = \frac{1}{2}AB$.

Note: This proves Theorem 5-11.

EXAMPLE 2. Prove: The median of a trapezoid is parallel to the bases and its length is equal to half the sum of the lengths of the bases.

Proof: Given trapezoid $DEFG$ with median $\overline{MN}$. By definition, M and N are the midpoints of $\overline{DG}$ and $\overline{EF}$. Let point D be the origin, let $\overline{DE}$ lie on the x-axis, and let the coordinates of E, F, and G be as shown.

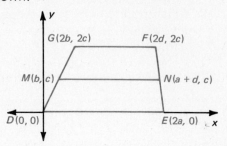

By the midpoint formula, M is the point (b, c) and N is the point $(a + d, c)$. The slope of $\overline{MN}$ is $\dfrac{c - c}{a + d - b} = 0$.

Similarly, the slope of $\overline{DE}$ is 0. Therefore, $\overline{MN} \parallel \overline{DE}$. Similarly, you can prove $\overline{MN} \parallel \overline{GF}$.

By the distance formula, $MN = a + d - b$ and $DE + GF = (2a) + (2d - 2b) = 2(a + d - b)$. Thus, $MN = \frac{1}{2}(DE + GF)$.

Note: This proves Theorem 5-10.

Oral Exercises

Vertices of $\square WXYZ$ have the coordinates shown.

1. What are the coordinates of the midpoint of $\overline{WY}$? of $\overline{XZ}$?

2. Since the midpoint of $\overline{WY}$ is the same as the midpoint of $\overline{XZ}$, $\overline{WY}$ and $\overline{XZ}$ __?__ each other.

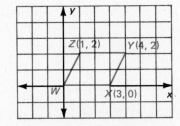

In the trapezoid shown, $\overline{ML} \parallel \overline{JK}$.

3. What are the coordinates of the midpoint of $\overline{JK}$? of $\overline{ML}$?

4. Do the midpoints of $\overline{JK}$ and $\overline{ML}$ lie on a line parallel to the y-axis?

5. What are the coordinates of the midpoint of $\overline{JM}$? of $\overline{KL}$?

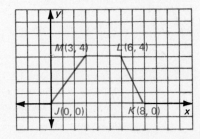

Written Exercises

Begin each proof by telling how you are placing the polygon named with respect to the coordinate axes.

A
1. Prove: The diagonals of a rectangle are congruent.
2. Prove: The diagonals of a parallelogram bisect each other. (*Hint:* Show that the midpoints of the diagonals are the same point.)

B
3. Prove: The midpoint of the hypotenuse of a right triangle is equidistant from the three vertices.
4. Prove: The segments joining the midpoints of the opposite sides of a quadrilateral bisect each other.
5. Prove: The diagonals of an isosceles trapezoid are congruent.
6. Prove: In an isosceles triangle, two medians are congruent.

C
7. Prove: The length of the segment joining the midpoints of the diagonals of a trapezoid is equal to half the difference of the lengths of the bases.
8. Prove: The union of the three segments joining, in pairs, the midpoints of the sides of an isosceles triangle is an isosceles triangle.
9. Prove: The union of the segments joining, in order, the midpoints of the sides of an isosceles trapezoid is a rhombus.
10. Prove: The medians of a triangle meet in a point, and this point separates each median into segments whose lengths have the ratio 1:2.

Self-Test

1. Which placement of the rhombus seems most advantageous?

a.
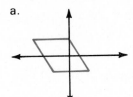

b.
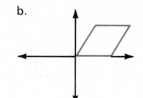

c.
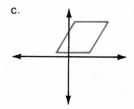

2. The base of a rectangle lies on the x-axis with the midpoint of the base at the origin. If $(a, 0)$ and (a, b) are the coordinates of two vertices of the rectangle, find the coordinates of the other two vertices.
3. The base of an equilateral triangle lies on the x-axis with one vertex at the origin. If the midpoint of the base has coordinates $(a, 0)$, find the coordinates of the other two vertices. (Two answers are possible.)
4. Three consecutive vertices of a parallelogram are $(0, a)$; $(0, 0)$; and (b, c). The numbers a, b, and c are all positive. State the coordinates of the fourth vertex.
5. Given points $E(4, 5)$; $F(-4, 1)$; $G(-2, -3)$; and $H(6, 1)$, prove that quadrilateral $EFGH$ is a rectangle.
6. Prove: The sum of the squares of the lengths of the four sides of a parallelogram is equal to the sum of the squares of the lengths of the diagonals.

CHAPTER SUMMARY

1. You can represent ordered pairs of numbers by points in a coordinate plane. The one-to-one correspondence between the set of points in the plane and the set of ordered pairs of real numbers is called a coordinate system.

2. Points in the coordinate plane are located with respect to the x- and y-axes. These axes intersect in a point called the origin, and divide the coordinate plane into four quadrants. For any ordered pair (a, b), a is the x-coordinate and b is the y-coordinate.

3. In the coordinate plane, the distance between any two points (x_1, y_1) and (x_2, y_2) is $\sqrt{(x_2 - x_1)^2 + (y_2 - y_1)^2}$. The midpoint of the segment joining any two points (x_1, y_1) and (x_2, y_2) has the coordinates $\left(\dfrac{x_1 + x_2}{2}, \dfrac{y_1 + y_2}{2}\right)$.

4. The slope of any nonvertical line passing through any two points (x_1, y_1) and (x_2, y_2) is defined as $\dfrac{y_2 - y_1}{x_2 - x_1}$. The slope of a horizontal line is zero. The slope of a vertical line is not defined.

5. Two nonvertical lines with slopes m_1 and m_2:
   a. Are parallel if and only if $m_1 = m_2$.
   b. Are perpendicular if and only if $m_1 = -\dfrac{1}{m_2}$, or $m_1 \cdot m_2 = -1$.

6. The graph of any equation that can be written in the form $ax + by = c$, a and b not both 0, is a line. An equation of the line passing through the point (x_1, y_1) and having slope m is $y - y_1 = m(x - x_1)$.

7. When setting up coordinate geometry proofs:
   a. Locate the figure in an advantageous position with respect to the axes.
   b. Use the known properties of a figure in assigning coordinates to points.

8. Many theorems can be proved by coordinate geometry. In developing proofs you often apply the distance formula, the midpoint formula, and the slope properties of parallel and perpendicular lines.

9. The following facts concerning the coordinates of the vertices of certain special polygons are useful.
   a. If the x-axis contains the base of an isosceles triangle, one endpoint of the base is $(0, 0)$, and the vertex is (a, b), then the third vertex is $(2a, 0)$.
   b. If three consecutive vertices of a parallelogram are (b, c), $(0, 0)$, and $(a, 0)$, then the fourth vertex is $(a + b, c)$.
   c. If the x-axis contains the longer base of an isosceles trapezoid and three consecutive vertices are (b, c), $(0, 0)$, and $(a, 0)$, then the fourth vertex is $(a - b, c)$.

CHAPTER TEST

In Exercises 1–4, complete each statement with one of the following words: *Always, Sometimes,* or *Never.*

1. The graph of (a, b) is __?__ the same as the graph of (b, a).
2. A distance is __?__ a negative number.
3. The slope of a line is __?__ less than zero.
4. In a plane, two lines that have different slopes __?__ intersect.

Complete the following statements.

5. The graph of the equation $y = 17$ is a line parallel to the __?__-axis.
6. The distance between points $(-1, 7)$ and $(3, 10)$ is __?__.
7. The midpoint of the segment joining points $(12, 8)$ and $(2, -6)$ is point $(\underline{\,?\,}, \underline{\,?\,})$.
8. The slope of the line passing through points $(5, 0)$ and $(7, 4)$ is __?__.

What kind of special quadrilateral is quadrilateral *JKLM*?

9. $J(3, -2)$; $K(7, 0)$; $L(5, 4)$; $M(1, 2)$
10. $J(1, -2)$; $K(4, 2)$; $L(0, 3)$; $M(-3, -1)$

11. Write an equation of the line passing through the point $(6, -5)$ and perpendicular to a line whose slope is 3.
12. Write an equation of the line passing through point $(-4, 6)$ and parallel to the line with equation $y - 2 = 3(x + 1)$.

Find the point of intersection of the lines with the given equations.

13. $9x - y = 22$; $7x - y = 18$ 14. $5x - 2y = 14$; $3x - 2y = 10$

15. Quadrilateral *RSTU* is an isosceles trapezoid located on the coordinate axes as shown. Determine the coordinates of points *T* and *U* if the midpoint of the base of the trapezoid is at the origin.

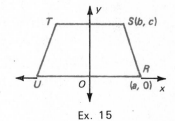

Ex. 15

16. Sketch a parallelogram placed conveniently on the coordinate axes. Assign coordinates to the four vertices in terms of as few letters as possible.

17. Prove: A line bisecting one side of a triangle and parallel to a second side bisects the third side. (Use the given figure and the indicated placement of axes.)

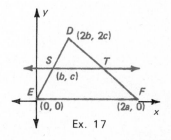

Ex. 17

18. Prove: The median of a trapezoid is parallel to the base of the trapezoid.

CHAPTER REVIEW

11-1 *Location in the Plane*

1. In the ordered pair of numbers (7, 12), 7 is the ___?___-coordinate and 12 is the ___?___-coordinate.
2. The y-coordinate of a point tells the distance from that point to the ___?___-axis.
3. Graph the following points using one set of axes: $A(1, 2)$; $B(-2, 0)$; $C(0, 0)$; $D(0, 4)$; and $E(3, 2)$.
4. State whether the graph is a vertical line, a horizontal line, or neither.
   a. $x = 7$ c. (3, 0)
   b. $y = 0$ d. $y = c, c \neq 0$

11-2 *The Distance Formula*

5. The distance between the points (x_1, y_1) and (x_2, y_2) is given by the formula $d = $ ___?___ .
6. The distance between the points (a, b) and (c, d) is ___?___ .

Find the distance between the given points. Express your answers in simplest radical form.

7. (0, 0) and (3, 4)   9. (2, 3) and $(-1, -5)$
8. $(-5, 2)$ and $(3, -1)$ 10. (b, c) and (7, 11)

11-3 *The Midpoint Formula*

11. The midpoint of the segment joining points (0, 0) and $(12, -9)$ is point (___?___, ___?___).
12. The midpoint of the segment joining points $(-4, 7)$ and $(6, -1)$ is point (___?___, ___?___).
13. The midpoint of the segment joining points (x_1, y_1) and (x_2, y_2) is point (___?___, ___?___).
14. Point (2, 1) is the midpoint of $\overline{MN}$. If M is point $(-3, -1)$, N is point (___?___, ___?___).

11-4 *The Slope of a Line*

15. When the slope of a line is 0, the line must be parallel to the ___?___-axis.
16. The slope formula does not apply to any line which is parallel to the ___?___-axis.

In Exercises 17–20, find the slope of the line containing the given points. If the line has no slope, write *Slope not defined*.

17. (1, 3) and (7, 6)   19. (2, 8) and (2, 17)
18. (0, 0) and $(3, -1)$ 20. $(-11, 4)$ and (5, 4)

11-5 *Parallel and Perpendicular Lines*

21. When the slopes of two lines are equal, the lines are __?__ .
22. When the slope of one line is the negative reciprocal of the slope of another line, the lines are __?__ .

In Exercises 23 and 24, determine which sides, if any, of quadrilateral *ABCD* are parallel or perpendicular.

23. $A(6, -4)$; $B(10, 4)$; $C(2, 8)$; $D(-6, 2)$
24. $A(-4, -2)$; $B(1, -3)$; $C(8, 2)$; $D(3, 2)$

11-6 *The Equation of a Line*

25. An equation of the line passing through point $(5, 8)$ and having slope -2 is __?__ .
26. An equation of the line containing point (x_1, y_1) and having slope m is __?__ .
27. An equation of a line containing points $(4, 1)$ and $(6, 9)$ is __?__ .
28. An equation of the line passing through point $(6, -5)$ and perpendicular to a line with slope 3 is __?__ .
29. Graph the line specified by the equation $y + 2 = 3(x - 1)$.
30. The point of intersection of the lines with equations $4x - 3y = 11$ and $5x + 11y = -1$ is __?__ .

11-7 *Organizing Coordinate Proofs*

31. Draw a sketch showing a nonadvantageous placement of a rectangle with respect to the coordinate axes.
32. Draw two different sketches of advantageous placements of an isosceles trapezoid with respect to the coordinate axes. Label the vertices in each.
33. The base of an equilateral triangle lies on the *x*-axis, with its midpoint located at the origin. If the coordinates of one vertex are $(a, 0)$, then the coordinates of the other vertices are $(\underline{\ ?\ }, \underline{\ ?\ })$ and $(\underline{\ ?\ }, \underline{\ ?\ })$.
34. Two sides of a square are parallel to the *x*-axis and one side lies on the *y*-axis. If the vertices of the lower side are $(0, a)$ and (b, a), then the coordinates of the other two vertices are $(\underline{\ ?\ }, \underline{\ ?\ })$ and $(\underline{\ ?\ }, \underline{\ ?\ })$.

11-8 *Proofs of Properties of Polygons*

35. In a coordinate proof, in order to prove two lines parallel, you can show that the slopes of the lines are __?__ .
36. In a coordinate proof, in order to prove the diagonals of a rhombus perpendicular, you can show that the slope of one diagonal is __?__ .
37. Prove: The lengths of the diagonals of a square are equal.
38. Prove: The length of the median of a trapezoid is equal to half the sum of the lengths of the bases.

programming in BASIC

Suppose you have a square dart board which looks like this.

The area of the board is 1 square meter, and the area of the quarter circle is $\frac{\pi}{4}$ (approximately 0.7854) square meters. If a lot of darts were thrown at random at the board, the ratio of the number of darts falling within the quarter circle to the number of all those striking the board should approximate 0.7854:1. You could try this experiment yourself, if you built a dart board and threw a dart, say, 1000 times. Most people would think that seems too much like work.

Using coordinate geometry, you can have the computer do the experiment for you. Orient the square on the coordinate axes and assign coordinates to the vertices of the square as shown in the figure. If you have the computer assign random numbers between 0 and 1 to x and to y, then it can calculate the value of z using the Pythagorean Theorem. By comparing z with 1, the computer can determine whether point (x, y) is located within the quarter circle. It can quickly do this up to, say, 400 times.

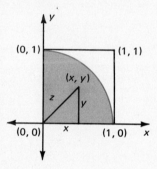

This is the program:

```
10   PRINT "SIMULATION—EXPERIMENTAL VALUE FOR PI"
20   PRINT
30   PRINT "HOW MANY DARTS ARE TO BE THROWN";
40   INPUT D
50   PRINT
60   PRINT "THE EXPERIMENTAL VALUE FOR PI IS";
70   LET N=0
80   FOR I=1 TO D
90   LET X=RND(0)
100  LET Y=RND(0)
110  LET Z=SQR(X*X+Y*Y)
120  IF Z>=1 THEN 140
130  LET N=N+1
140  NEXT I
150  LET R=4*N/D
160  PRINT R
170  END
```

Line Number	Instruction to the Computer
90, 100	Assign random numbers between 0 and 1 to X and to Y, respectively. (The number 0 is used, not the letter O.)
110	Compute $\sqrt{X^2 + Y^2}$ and let Z take that value.
120	If $Z \geq 1$ (the point is located on or outside the quarter circle), branch to line 140.
130	(Counter for the number of points which are located within the quarter circle)
150	Compute the ratio of the number of points within the quarter circle to the total number of points. Multiply this ratio by 4 (to obtain the experimental value for π).

Exercises

1. Type the program, LIST, and RUN. Do it several times, using different numbers of darts.

2. Consider a different figure on our dart board. The graph of the equation $y = x^2$ is a parabola. On our 1 meter board, the area below the parabola is one third square meter. Change the above program to find this area experimentally. You will need to count the number of points for which $y < x^2$.

3. Change the program to find the area of the shaded region experimentally. (*Hint:* Orient the dart board on the coordinate axes and determine an equation of the line which bounds the shaded region.)

12

TRANSFORMATIONS

Some Basic Mappings

Objectives

1. Recognize and use the terms mapping, image, preimage, congruence mapping, isometry, and transformation.
2. Locate congruent segments and angles in congruence mappings.
3. Locate images of figures under reflections and under half-turns.
4. Recognize the properties of reflections and half-turns.

12-1 *Mappings and Congruence Mappings*

In earlier chapters you studied congruence of segments, of angles, and of triangles. In this chapter you will study congruence of these figures, and of others, from a point of view that involves "movement."

To decide, informally, whether two figures are congruent, you can see whether a tracing of one figure fits over the other figure.

EXAMPLE 1. Determine informally, by tracing, whether $\triangle ABC \cong \triangle MXD$.

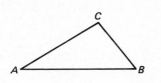

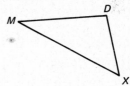

SOLUTION:

Trace $\triangle ABC$.

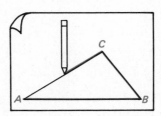

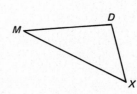

(Continued on page 428)

Move the tracing to see if it will fit over △MXD.

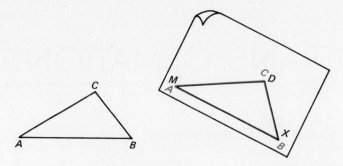

The tracing fits. Thus △ABC ≅ △MXD.

The movement above illustrates the idea of **mapping**. For the mapping above, we say:

△ABC → △MXD   Triangle ABC is mapped into triangle MXD.

We also say:

ABC → MXD   ABC is mapped into MXD.

Under this mapping, △MXD is called the **image** of △ABC. △ABC is the **preimage** of △MXD. The image of point B is point X. The preimage of $\overline{MD}$ is $\overline{AC}$.

The mapping ABC → MXD can be indicated in other correct ways, ACB → MDX, for instance. Do you see that ACB → MXD does not correctly describe the mapping?

EXAMPLE 2. Determine informally, by tracing, whether the quadrilaterals are congruent.

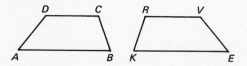

SOLUTION: (You should carry out the steps.)

a. Make a tracing of quad. ABCD.
b. Move the tracing to see if it will fit over quad. EKRV.

You should note that quad. ABCD will fit over quad. EKRV only if you flip the tracing. The quadrilaterals are congruent.

Two of the ways to indicate the mapping in Example 2 are:

Quad. *ABCD* → Quad. *EKRV*   *CBAD* → *RKEV*

When a mapping is such that a figure and its image are congruent, we call the mapping a congruence mapping, or an isometry (eye-**som**-e-tree). In Example 2, above, *ABCD* → *EKRV* is a congruence mapping, or an isometry.

The mapping *DEF* → *RST* is clearly not an isometry. It is a particular kind of *transformation*, however. Note that each point of △*DEF* is mapped into a point such that the coordinates of the image point are twice as great as those of the preimage point.

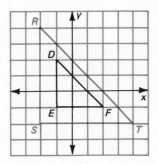

A transformation of the plane is a mapping such that:

(1) Each point of the plane has exactly one image.

(2) For each point of the plane there is exactly one preimage.

Oral Exercises

In Exercises 1–10, use the mapping △*ABC* → △*XYZ*. Complete the statements.

1. *A* → ___?___
2. ___?___ → *Z*
3. ___?___ → $\overline{XY}$
4. ∠*A* → ___?___
5. $\overline{AC}$ → ___?___
6. The image of *B* is ___?___ .
7. The image of ∠*B* is ___?___ .
8. The image of $\overline{AB}$ is ___?___ .
9. The preimage of *Y* is ___?___ .
10. The preimage of $\overline{YZ}$ is ___?___ .

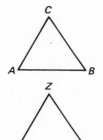

11. For a given transformation, how many images does each point have?
12. A certain mapping is such that two different points map into point *P*. Is that mapping a transformation?

In each exercise two figures are congruent. State a congruence mapping.

EXAMPLE.

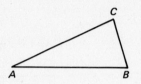 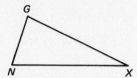

SOLUTION: Triangle *ABC* maps into triangle *XNG*, or *ABC* maps into *XNG*. (There are other correct ways to state the congruence mapping.)

13.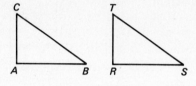

15.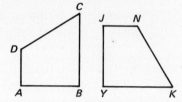

14.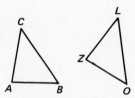

16.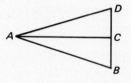

In Exercises 1–12, the isometry $\triangle XMZ \rightarrow \triangle YMZ$ is given. Complete the statements.

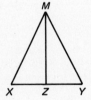

1. $\overline{XZ} \rightarrow$ __?__
2. $\angle XMZ \rightarrow$ __?__
3. __?__ $\rightarrow Y$
4. $\overline{MZ} \rightarrow$ __?__

5. The image of X is __?__.
6. The preimage of $\angle Y$ is __?__.
7. The preimage of $\overline{YM}$ is __?__.
8. The image of $\overline{MZ}$ is __?__.

9. Because $\triangle XMZ \rightarrow \triangle YMZ$ is an isometry, $\overline{XZ} \cong$ __?__.
10. The given isometry can also be called a __?__ mapping.
11. One point that maps into itself is __?__.
12. One segment is its own preimage. That segment is __?__.

A mapping is given. Complete the second statement so that you specify the same mapping.

13. $\triangle DEF \rightarrow \triangle XYZ$ $EFD \rightarrow$?

14. Quad. $RSTU \rightarrow$ quad. $JKCD$ Quad. $TURS \rightarrow$?

15. Each figure shown is congruent to exactly one other figure. Complete the congruence mappings.

$ABC \rightarrow$? $\triangle DFE \rightarrow$? $YML \rightarrow$?

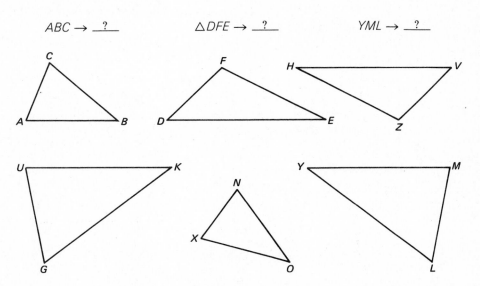

16. Refer to Exercise 15. If you checked the congruence mappings by tracing, in which case would you have to flip the tracing?

There is a congruence mapping for the figure shown. Do not draw in your book, but think of $\overline{RW}$, $\overline{XS}$, $\overline{WT}$, and $\overline{VS}$ as being part of the figure. Complete the statements.

B 17. $\angle X \cong$?

18. $\angle RSW \cong \angle$?

19. $\overline{RS} \cong$?

20. $XW =$?

21. $\overline{XS} \cong$?

22. $RW =$?

23. $\angle$? $\cong \angle WTS$

24. $\angle$? $\cong \angle VST$

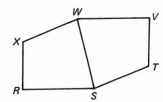

The pentagons shown are congruent. Do not draw in your book, but think of such segments as $\overline{HK}$ as being part of the figure. Complete the statements.

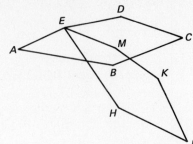

C   25. An isometry: $HJKME \rightarrow$ _?_
    26. An isometry: $MKJHE \rightarrow$ _?_
    27. $m\angle KME = m\angle$ _?_
    28. $HK =$ _?_
    29. $\triangle HJK \cong \triangle$ _?_
    30. $m\angle HME = m\angle$ _?_
    31. An isometry: $HKME \rightarrow$ _?_
    32. $\angle MHK \cong \angle$ _?_

12-2 *Reflections*

Suppose you put a drop of paint on a sheet of paper, fold the paper over, press the two halves together, and then unfold the sheet of paper. Speaking informally, you can describe the two blots as being congruent. One blot looks like a mirror image of the other.

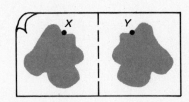

This suggests a mapping that can be described mathematically. The key idea is this: If $\overline{XY}$ were drawn, the line of fold would be the perpendicular bisector of $\overline{XY}$. In the discussion that follows, we will transfer the idea of this mapping to the points in a plane.

A reflection in the line j maps every point P into a point P' such that:

(1) If P does not lie on j, then j is the perpendicular bisector of $\overline{PP'}$.

(2) If P lies on j, then P' is the same point as P.

Under reflection in line j:

R is mapped into R'.
S is mapped into S' (same point).
R' is mapped into R.
$\overline{RT}$ is mapped into $\overline{R'T'}$.

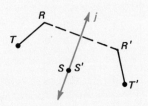

To abbreviate *reflection in line j,* we write M_j. The line *j* is called the *mirror* of the reflection. To abbreviate the statement *Point P is mapped, under reflection in line j, into point P',* we write:

$$P \xrightarrow{\ M_j\ } P'$$

The symbol $\xrightarrow{\ M_j\ }$ is used for sets of points, too. For instance, $\overline{AB} \xrightarrow{\ M_j\ } \overline{A'B'}$ is read: $\overline{AB}$ is mapped, under reflection in line *j*, into $\overline{A'B'}$.

Reflection in a line is a congruence mapping.

To show this, we must first show that every segment maps, under reflection in a line, into a segment congruent to the given segment. Given $\overline{AB} \xrightarrow{\ M_j\ } \overline{A'B'}$, we wish to prove $\overline{AB} \cong \overline{A'B'}$.

Case 1. A and B both lie on *j*. Then every point on $\overline{AB}$ maps into itself, and $\overline{AB} \cong \overline{A'B'}$.

Case 2. A lies on *j*, but B does not. Since *j* is the perpendicular bisector of $\overline{BB'}$, $\triangle AXB \cong \triangle A'XB'$ by the LL Theorem, and $\overline{AB} \cong \overline{A'B'}$.

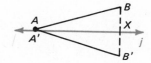

Case 3. A and B lie on the same side of *j*. $\triangle AYX \cong \triangle A'YX$ as in Case 2. Then $\overline{AX} \cong \overline{A'X}$, and $\angle 1 \cong \angle 2$. $\angle 3 \cong \angle 4$. $\triangle AXB \cong \triangle A'XB'$, and $\overline{AB} \cong \overline{A'B'}$.

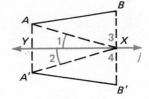

Case 4. A and B lie on opposite sides of *j*. As in Case 2, $\overline{AZ} \cong \overline{A'Z}$ and $\overline{ZB} \cong \overline{ZB'}$. Then $\overline{AB} \cong \overline{A'B'}$.

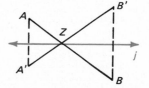

It can also be shown that, under a reflection, angles map into congruent angles and triangles into congruent triangles. See Exercises 25 and 26.

Name the image, under reflection in line k, of the figure named.

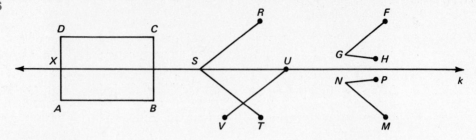

1. Point A
2. Point D
3. Point X
4. $\overline{DC}$

5. $\overline{DX}$
6. Point S
7. $\overline{SR}$
8. $\overline{SU}$

9. $\angle RSU$
10. $\angle RST$
11. $\overline{GF}$
12. $\angle PNM$

For each of the abbreviations, find and read the matching phrase or sentence.

13. M_k

14. M_j

15. $P \xrightarrow{M_k} P'$

16. $\overline{CD} \xrightarrow{M_k} \overline{C'D'}$

17. $\overrightarrow{RS} \xrightarrow{M_k} \overrightarrow{R'S'}$

18. $\triangle ABC \xrightarrow{M_k} \triangle A'B'C'$

a. Reflection in line k

b. $\overline{CD}$ is mapped, under reflection in line k, into $\overline{C'D'}$.

c. $\triangle ABC$ is mapped, under reflection in line k, into $\triangle A'B'C'$.

d. Reflection in line j

e. P is mapped, under reflection in line k, into P'.

f. $\overrightarrow{RS}$ is mapped, under reflection in line k, into $\overrightarrow{R'S'}$.

19. State whether each letter maps, under reflection in line m, into an image that looks the same as the original letter.

20. Repeat Exercise 19, but reflect each letter in line n.

Written Exercises

Copy the figure on squared paper. Then draw, on the same squared paper, the image under reflection in line k.

A 1.

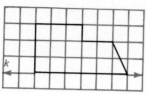

3.

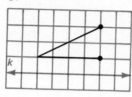

5.

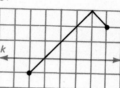

2.

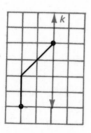

4.

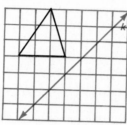

6.

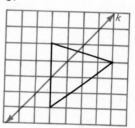

In Exercises 7–12, state the coordinates of the image of the given point under reflection in the mirror named. Copy and complete the table.

Reflection in:

		x-axis	y-axis	Line $y = x$
7.	A	$(2, -4)$		$(4, 2)$
8.	B		$(-4, 0)$	
9.	C			
10.	D			
11.	E			
12.	O			

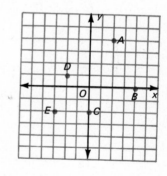

Write the statement in words.

13. $A \xrightarrow{M_k} A'$

14. $\overline{RS} \xrightarrow{M_j} \overline{R'S'}$

15. $AXC \xrightarrow{M_j} A'X'C'$

16. $\overleftrightarrow{BC} \xrightarrow{M_j} \overleftrightarrow{B'C'}$

Copy the figure shown. Make a straightedge and compass construction.

B **17.** Find the image, under reflection in line t, of A.

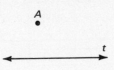

18. Find the image, under reflection in line m, of B.

19. Find the mirror k, given
$$Z \xrightarrow{M_k} Z'.$$

Z' •

Z •

20. Find the mirror j, given
$$R \xrightarrow{M_j} R'.$$

R •

• R'

Exercises 21–24 refer to reflection in a line m. Classify each statement as true or false.

21. Two parallel lines map into two parallel lines.

22. Two perpendicular lines map into two perpendicular lines.

23. A line t perpendicular to the mirror m maps into line t itself.

24. Every line s maps into a line parallel to s.

C **25.** Given: $ABC \xrightarrow{M_j} A'B'C'$

Explain why $\triangle ABC$ is congruent to $\triangle A'B'C'$. (*Hint:* Recall that a segment maps, under reflection, into a congruent segment.)

26. Given: $RST \xrightarrow{M_k} R'S'T'$

Explain why $\angle RST$ is congruent to $\angle R'S'T'$. (*Hint:* Draw $\overline{RT}$ and $\overline{R'T'}$.)

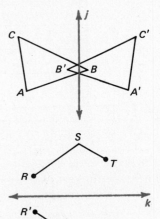

27. Given: $A \xrightarrow{M_j} A'$. Copy the figure. Using only a straightedge, locate X' such that $X \xrightarrow{M_j} X'$.

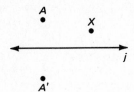

28. Copy the figure. Use straightedge and compass to construct a point Y on line k such that $\angle BYM \cong \angle CYN$. (*Hint:* Find C' such that $C \xrightarrow{M_k} C'$.)

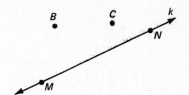

12-3 *Half-Turns*

Begin with $\triangle ABC$ and point O. Draw any line through O, and use this line as a reference line.

Trace point O, the reference line, and $\triangle ABC$.

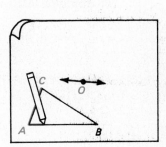

Turn the tracing, keeping the copy of point O over point O, until the copy of the reference line again lies over the reference line.

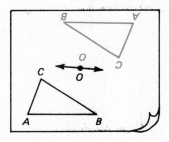

The movement described above suggests a mapping that can be defined in simple mathematical terms. Notice that if the segment joining C and its image were drawn, point O would be the midpoint of that segment.

A **half-turn** about point O maps every point P into a point P' such that:

(1) If P is different from O, then O is the midpoint of $\overline{PP'}$.

(2) If P is the point O, then P' is the same point as P.

Under a half-turn about point O:

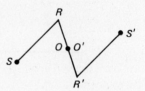

R is mapped into R'.
O is mapped into O', which is O.
$\overline{RS}$ is mapped into $\overline{R'S'}$.
$\overline{R'O'}$ is mapped into $\overline{RO}$.

For *a half-turn about point O* we write H_O. The point O is called the *center* of the half-turn. To abbreviate the statement *Point P is mapped, under a half-turn about point O, into point P',* we write:

$$P \xrightarrow{\ H_O\ } P'$$

In Section 12-2 you saw that reflection in a line is a congruence mapping, or isometry. A half-turn about a point is also an isometry.

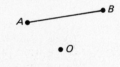

First we show that, when $\overline{AB} \xrightarrow{\ H_O\ } \overline{A'B'}$, then $\overline{AB} \cong \overline{A'B'}$.

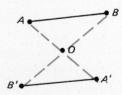

Draw $\overline{AA'}$ and $\overline{BB'}$. By definition of half-turn, point O is the midpoint of $\overline{AA'}$ and of $\overline{BB'}$. $\triangle AOB \cong \triangle A'OB'$ by the SAS Postulate, and $\overline{AB} \cong \overline{A'B'}$.

It can also be shown that, under a half-turn, any $\triangle RST$ maps into a congruent $\triangle R'S'T'$. (See Exercise 22.) Consequently, any $\angle RST$ maps into a congruent $\angle R'S'T'$.

A half-turn about a point is a congruence mapping.

Name the image, under a half-turn about point *O*, of the figure named.

1. Point *A*
2. Point *N*
3. Point *X*
4. Point *O*
5. $\overline{RV}$
6. $\overleftrightarrow{CD}$

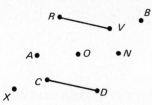

For each of the abbreviations, find and read the matching phrase or sentence.

7. H_O

8. H_P

9. M_j

10. $X \xrightarrow{H_O} X'$

11. $X \xrightarrow{M_j} X'$

12. $XYZ \xrightarrow{H_O} X'Y'Z'$

a. A half-turn about point *O*

b. *X* is mapped, under a half-turn about point *O*, into *X'*.

c. A reflection in line *j*

d. A half-turn about point *P*

e. *XYZ* is mapped, under a half-turn about point *O*, into *X'Y'Z'*.

f. *X* is mapped, under reflection in line *j*, into *X'*.

Copy the figure on squared paper. Then draw, on the same squared paper, the image under a half-turn about point *O*. (When copying the figures, allow room for the images.)

A

1.

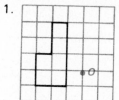

3.

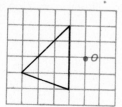

5.

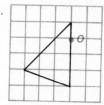

2.

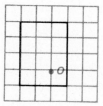

4.

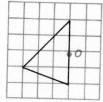

6.

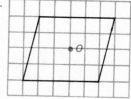

Write the statement in words.

7. $A \xrightarrow{H_O} A'$

8. $\overleftrightarrow{AB} \xrightarrow{H_O} \overleftrightarrow{A'B'}$

9. $\overline{CD} \xrightarrow{H_O} \overline{DC}$

10. $RST \xrightarrow{H_P} R'S'T'$

In Exercises 11–14, O denotes the origin and H_O denotes a half-turn about the origin. Copy and complete each statement. (Use graph paper if you wish.)

11. $(5, 1) \xrightarrow{H_O} \underline{\ ?\ }$

12. $(-3, 2) \xrightarrow{H_O} \underline{\ ?\ }$

13. $(0, -4) \xrightarrow{H_O} \underline{\ ?\ }$

14. $(j, k) \xrightarrow{H_O} \underline{\ ?\ }$

In Exercises 15–18, P denotes point $(2, -4)$. Copy and complete each statement.

B 15. $(-5, 4) \xrightarrow{H_P} \underline{\ ?\ }$

16. $(5, 5) \xrightarrow{H_P} \underline{\ ?\ }$

17. $(2, -4) \xrightarrow{H_P} \underline{\ ?\ }$

18. $(-3, -3) \xrightarrow{H_P} \underline{\ ?\ }$

19. Copy the figure. Use a straightedge and compass to construct P' such that $P \xrightarrow{H_O} P'$.

20. Copy the figure. Use straightedge and compass to construct point O such that $X \xrightarrow{H_O} X'$.

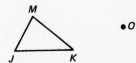

21. Copy the figure. Construct and label the image, under a half-turn about point O, of $\triangle JKM$.

22. Given: $RST \xrightarrow{H_O} R'S'T'$
Explain why $\triangle RST$ is congruent to $\triangle R'S'T'$. (*Hint:* Recall that every segment maps, under a half-turn, into a congruent segment.)

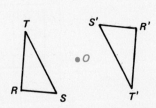

C 23. Given: $\overleftrightarrow{AB}$ does not contain point O; $AB \xrightarrow{H_0} A'B'$.
Prove: $\overleftrightarrow{AB} \parallel \overleftrightarrow{A'B'}$

24. Given: $\overline{AB}$ contains point O; $\overline{AB} \xrightarrow{H_0} \overline{A'B'}$.
Describe the relationship of $\overleftrightarrow{AB}$ and $\overleftrightarrow{A'B'}$.

25. Copy the figure. Construct polygon $A'B'C'D'E'F'$ such that:
$ABCDEF \xrightarrow{H_0} A'B'C'D'E'F'$.

26. Copy the figure. Construct two segments each of which has one endpoint on line l, has one endpoint on $\triangle RST$, and has X as its midpoint.

(*Hint:* First construct $\triangle R'S'T'$ such that $RST \xrightarrow{H_X} R'S'T'$.)

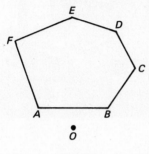

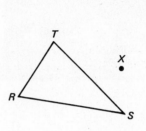

Ex. 25   Ex. 26

Self-Test In Exercises 1–3, use the mapping $RST \rightarrow R'S'T'$.

1. The image of R is __?__ .
2. The preimage of $\overline{R'T'}$ is __?__ .
3. If the mapping is an isometry, $\angle RTS \cong \angle$ __?__ .

4. Is reflection in a line a congruence mapping?
5. Is a half-turn about a point a congruence mapping?
6. Under a transformation, every point of the plane has exactly one __?__ , and every image has exactly one __?__ .

Make judgments based on the appearance of the figure.

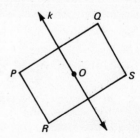

7. $P \xrightarrow{M_k}$ __?__   10. $\overline{PQ} \xrightarrow{M_k}$ __?__

8. $P \xrightarrow{H_0}$ __?__   11. $\overline{PR} \xrightarrow{H_0}$ __?__

9. $S \xrightarrow{H_0}$ __?__   12. $O \xrightarrow{M_k}$ __?__

Careers

Chemistry

We rely on products of chemical research every day though we seldom realize how many hours chemists worked to develop products such as plastics, synthetic fibers, and antibiotics.

Chemists investigate the properties and composition of matter and try to put this knowledge to practical use. They design and conduct laboratory experiments, and describe their results in reports which may be published in scientific journals. Scientific knowledge is advanced by this interchange of ideas among chemists and scientists in related fields.

Geometric models such as the one shown at the left help chemists understand the structure and behavior of atoms and molecules. For example, models are useful in illustrating any points and lines of symmetry that exist in a molecule. The concepts of symmetry you will study in this chapter have important applications in chemistry and other physical sciences.

Mappings and Compositions of Mappings

Objectives

1. Recognize and use the terms self-congruence, identity self-congruence, line of symmetry, point of symmetry, dilation, and composition.
2. Locate images of figures under rotations, under translations, under dilations, and under compositions of mappings.
3. Recognize the properties of figures under rotations and under translations.
4. Use the fact that every rotation and translation can be expressed as a composition of reflections.

12-4 *Self-Congruence and Symmetry*

Recall that congruence of triangles is reflexive. For any triangle *ABC*:

$$\triangle ABC \cong \triangle ABC$$

A congruence of this type is called an identity self-congruence.

Every isosceles triangle has a second self-congruence in addition to the identity self-congruence. For the isosceles triangle *XZY* we have two congruences:

$$\triangle XZY \cong \triangle XZY \qquad \triangle XZY \cong \triangle YZX$$

Both of these congruences are self-congruences. In each case, a figure is congruent to itself.

Related to the identity self-congruence $\triangle XZY \cong \triangle XZY$ is the identity mapping:

$$XZY \to XZY$$

Under an identity mapping, every point is mapped into itself.

Related to the self-congruence $\triangle XZY \cong \triangle YZX$, there is a particular mapping. Let *j* be the line that contains point *Z* and is perpendicular to $\overline{XY}$. If *j* is a line of reflection, we have:

$$XZY \xrightarrow{M_j} YZX$$

Line *j* is called a *line of symmetry* for $\triangle XZY$. When reflection of a figure in some line leads to a self-congruence, the line is called a line of symmetry for the figure.

Whenever a figure is mapped, under a half-turn about some point O, into itself, then O is called a point of symmetry for the figure. Point O is a point of symmetry for the polygon shown.

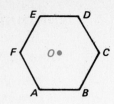

$$ABCDEF \xrightarrow{H_O} DEFABC$$

Symmetry lines and points provide a basis for alternate definitions of some polygons.

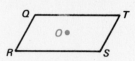

An isosceles triangle is a triangle with a line of symmetry.

A parallelogram is a quadrilateral with a point of symmetry.

Because $AXB \xrightarrow{M_j} BXA$:

$\overline{AX} \cong \overline{BX}$

$\angle A \cong \angle B$

j bisects $\angle AXB$.

j is the $\perp$ bis. of $\overline{AB}$.

Because $RSTQ \xrightarrow{H_O} TQRS$:

$\overline{RS} \cong \overline{TQ}$; $\overline{ST} \cong \overline{QR}$

$\overline{QT} \parallel \overline{RS}$; $\overline{RQ} \parallel \overline{ST}$

$\angle R \cong \angle T$; $\angle S \cong \angle Q$

$\overline{RT}$ and $\overline{SQ}$, not pictured, bisect each other at O.

Oral Exercises

In Exercises 1–5, refer to the figures below.

a. 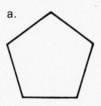   b. 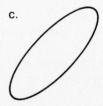   c.   d.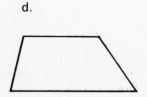

1. For which figures could a horizontal line of symmetry be drawn?
2. For which figures could a vertical line of symmetry be drawn?
3. For which figures could a line of symmetry, neither horizontal nor vertical, be drawn?
4. How many lines of symmetry could be drawn for Figure **b**? for Figure **c**?
5. For which figures could a point of symmetry be located?

Classify each statement as true or false.

6. $\triangle ABC \cong \triangle CBA$

7. $\triangle ABC \cong \triangle BAC$

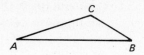

8. The congruence $\triangle RST \cong \triangle TSR$ is an identity self-congruence.
9. The congruence $\triangle SRT \cong \triangle SRT$ is an identity self-congruence.
10. The mapping $RST \rightarrow RTS$ is an identity mapping.
11. Under an identity mapping, every point is mapped into itself.

Written Exercises

Copy the line k and the figure shown on squared paper. Then complete the figure in such a way that k is a line of symmetry.

EXAMPLE.

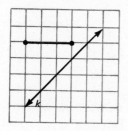

SOLUTION:

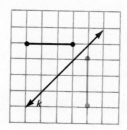

A 1.

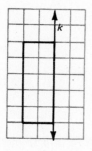

3.

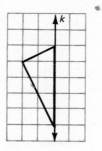

5.

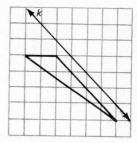

2.

4.

6.

Copy the point O and the figure shown on squared paper. Then complete the figure in such a way that O is a point of symmetry.

7.

8.

9.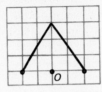

10.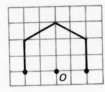

11.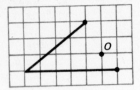

12.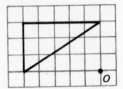

In △ABC, AC = BC. State whether the mapping is a self-congruence.

B 13. ACB → BCA
14. ABC → CBA
15. BCA → BCA
16. Which mapping, in Exercises 13–15, is an identity self-congruence?

Draw a figure if there is one that meets the conditions. Otherwise, write *Not possible*.

17. A trapezoid with no line of symmetry
18. A trapezoid with exactly one line of symmetry
19. A trapezoid with a point of symmetry
20. A parallelogram with four lines of symmetry
21. A parallelogram with two points of symmetry
22. A parallelogram with exactly one line of symmetry
23. A polygon with exactly five lines of symmetry
24. A polygon with exactly six lines of symmetry

The coordinates of the vertices of a quadrilateral are given.
a. State the equations of all lines of symmetry, if there are any.
b. State the coordinates of a point of symmetry, if there is one.

C 25. (3, 2); (−3, 2); (−3, −2); (3, −2)
26. (1, 1); (−5, 1); (−5, −3); (1, −3)
27. (2, 5); (−2, 2); (−2, −3); (2, 0)
28. (2, 3); (0, 0); (4, 1); (6, 4)

Consider the meaning of symmetry of three-dimensional figures.

29. How many planes of symmetry does a rectangular solid have?
30. How many lines of symmetry does a rectangular solid have?
31. How many lines of symmetry does a right circular cone have?
32. How many points of symmetry does a rectangular solid have? A right circular cone?

12-5 *Composition of Mappings*

One mapping can be followed by another.

EXAMPLE

Given $\triangle ABC$, line j, and point O. Draw a figure showing $\triangle A'B'C'$, where $ABC \xrightarrow{M_j} A'B'C'$.

Then draw $\triangle A''B''C''$, where $A'B'C' \xrightarrow{H_O} A''B''C''$.

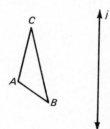

SOLUTION:

Draw the image, under reflection in line j, of $\triangle ABC$. To do this, locate A' so that j is the $\perp$ bis. of $\overline{AA'}$, and so on.

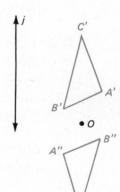

Now draw the image, under a half-turn about point O, of $\triangle A'B'C'$. To do this, locate A'' so that O is the midpoint of $\overline{A'A''}$, and so on.

The sequence of mappings in the example can be denoted by:

$$ABC \xrightarrow{M_j} A'B'C' \xrightarrow{H_O} A''B''C''$$

ABC is mapped, under reflection in line j, into $A'B'C'$; and $A'B'C'$ is mapped, under a half-turn about point O, into $A''B''C''$.

A shorter way to indicate the sequence of mappings uses the idea of *composition* and the symbol ∘. The mapping M_j followed by the mapping H_0 can be denoted by

$$M_j \circ H_0$$

read   *M sub j followed by H sub O,*

or   *reflection in line j composition half-turn about point O.*

For the example shown above, we can write

$$ABC \xrightarrow{M_j \circ H_0} A''B''C''$$

read *ABC maps, under M sub j followed by H sub O, into A''B''C''.*

Under the *composite mapping,* above:

The image of point A is point A''.

The preimage of $\overline{A''B''}$ is $\overline{AB}$, and so on.

A natural question to consider is the following: Do the composite mappings $M_j \circ H_0$ and $H_0 \circ M_j$ yield the same images? To see that the answer is *No, not necessarily,* simply check the two mappings below of a single point P.

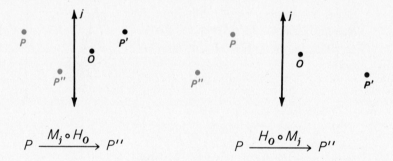

$$P \xrightarrow{M_j \circ H_0} P'' \qquad\qquad P \xrightarrow{H_0 \circ M_j} P''$$

There are cases where $M_j \circ H_0$ and $H_0 \circ M_j$ yield the same images. See Exercise 29.

When two mappings yield, for every point R, the same image point R' we call the mappings *equal.* In Exercise 30 you will be asked to show that:

Every half-turn about a point is equal to the composition of two reflections.

In Exercises 1–8, make judgments based on the appearance of the figure.

1. The image of B, under reflection in line k, is ___?___ .
2. The image of C, under reflection in line j, is ___?___ .
3. The image of B, under reflection in line k followed by reflection in line j, is ___?___ .
4. The image of D, under a half-turn about point O, is ___?___ .
5. The image of B, under reflection in line j, is ___?___ .
6. The image of D, under a half-turn about point O followed by reflection in line j, is ___?___ .
7. The image of A, under reflection in line k followed by a half-turn about point O, is ___?___ .
8. The image of A, under reflection in line k followed by reflection in line k, is ___?___ .

Read each expression. Then explain the meaning.

EXAMPLE. $H_O \circ H_P$

SOLUTION: H sub O followed by H sub P. A half-turn about point O followed by a half-turn about point P.

9. $H_O \circ M_j$
10. $H_P \circ H_O$

11. $H_P \circ H_P$
12. $M_k \circ M_j$

In the figure for Exercises 1–8, $ABC \xrightarrow{\ M_k\ } A'B'C'$.

A
1. $A \xrightarrow{\ M_k\ }$ ___?___
2. $\overline{BC} \xrightarrow{\ M_k\ }$ ___?___
3. $C' \xrightarrow{\ M_k\ }$ ___?___
4. $A'B' \xrightarrow{\ M_k\ }$ ___?___
5. $B \xrightarrow{\ M_k\ }$ ___?___ $\xrightarrow{\ M_k\ }$ ___?___
6. $B \xrightarrow{\ M_k \circ M_k\ }$ ___?___
7. $\triangle ABC \xrightarrow{\ M_k\ }$ ___?___ $\xrightarrow{\ M_k\ }$ ___?___
8. $\triangle ABC \xrightarrow{\ M_k \circ M_k\ }$ ___?___

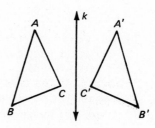

Complete the statement when possible. If the image is not shown in the figure write *Not shown*.

9. $V \xrightarrow{H_O} \underline{\quad?\quad}$

10. $Y \xrightarrow{H_O} \underline{\quad?\quad}$

11. $X \xrightarrow{H_O} \underline{\quad?\quad}$

12. $X \xrightarrow{H_P} \underline{\quad?\quad}$

13. $Z \xrightarrow{H_P \circ H_O} \underline{\quad?\quad}$

14. $V \xrightarrow{H_O \circ H_P} \underline{\quad?\quad}$

15. $Z \xrightarrow{H_P \circ H_P} \underline{\quad?\quad}$

16. $Y \xrightarrow{H_O \circ H_O} \underline{\quad?\quad}$

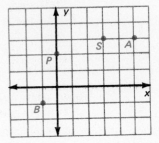

State the coordinates of point T.

B

17. $A \xrightarrow{M_x \circ M_y} T$

18. $A \xrightarrow{M_x \circ H_P} T$

19. $A \xrightarrow{H_S \circ M_x} T$

20. $A \xrightarrow{H_P \circ M_x} T$

21. $B \xrightarrow{H_P \circ H_S} T$

22. $B \xrightarrow{H_S \circ H_P} T$

23. $B \xrightarrow{M_y \circ H_S} T$

24. $B \xrightarrow{H_S \circ M_y} T$

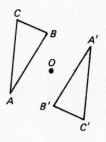

The mapping $ABC \xrightarrow{H_O} A'B'C'$ is given. Complete the statements.

25. $A \xrightarrow{H_O \circ H_O} \underline{\quad?\quad}$

26. $\overline{AB} \xrightarrow{H_O \circ H_O} \underline{\quad?\quad}$

27. $ABC \xrightarrow{H_O \circ H_O} \underline{\quad?\quad}$

28. The composite mapping $H_O \circ H_O$ is an $\underline{\quad?\quad}$ mapping.

C 29. Show that when line j contains point O, the image of any point A under the composite mapping $M_j \circ H_O$ is the same as the image of A under the composite mapping $H_O \circ M_j$.
Hint: Set up a coordinate system. For the *x*-axis, use line j. For the *y*-axis, use the line perpendicular to j at O.

30. Show that for any half-turn H_O there exist reflections M_j and M_k such that $H_O = M_j \circ M_k$.
Hint: Set up a coordinate system. For the *x*-axis, take any line through O. For the *y*-axis, use the line perpendicular to the *x*-axis at O. Let P be any point (c, d). Consider the image of P under H_O and the image of P under $M_j \circ M_k$ where j is the *x*-axis and k is the *y*-axis.

12-6 *Rotations*

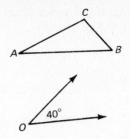

Begin with △ABC and a 40°
angle that has vertex O.

Make a tracing of the triangle
and the angle.

Rotate the tracing about point O,
through the 40° angle.

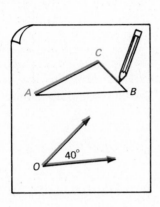

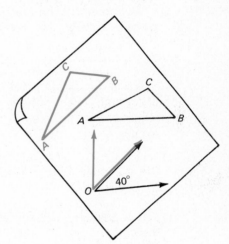

The movement described above suggests a mapping called a *rotation*. The rotation was a counterclockwise rotation, a rotation through 40°. If the rotation had been clockwise, using the same angle, it would be called a rotation through −40°. For example, rotate the black square about point A through −120° and the black square moves into the red one.

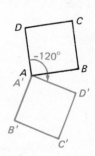

We shall allow rotations of 180°, −200°, and so on. Do you see that a rotation through 385° yields the same image as a rotation through 25°?

A name often used for angle measure is α (the Greek letter "alpha"). In the definition that follows, $0 < \alpha < 180$. The definition can be extended to account for other values of α.

A rotation about point O *through* $\alpha°$ maps every point P into an image point P' such that:

(1) If P is different from O, then $OP' = OP$ and $m\angle P'OP = \alpha$.
(2) If P is the point O, then P' is the same point as P.

For *a rotation about point* O *through* $\alpha°$ we write $R_{O,\alpha}$. Point O is the *center* of the rotation.

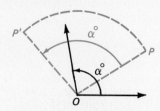

To abbreviate the statement *Point P is mapped, under a rotation about point O through* $\alpha°$, *into point P'*, we write:

$$P \xrightarrow{\;R_{O,\alpha}\;} P'$$

A half-turn about point O can be considered to be a rotation about point O through $180°$. Recall that a half-turn is equal to the composition of reflections in two lines. A related fact, which we state without proof, is the following:

> Every rotation about point O through $\alpha°$ is equal to the composition of two reflections.

It is also true, whenever two lines j and k intersect in a point O, that the composition of reflection in j and reflection in k is equal to a rotation about point O. See Exercises 20–24.

Oral Exercises

State another name for each rotation.

EXAMPLE. $R_{O,30}$ SOLUTION: $R_{O,390}$

(Many other answers, $R_{O,-330}$ for instance, are also correct.)

1. $R_{O,375}$ 3. $R_{O,340}$ 5. $R_{O,-20}$
2. $R_{O,10}$ 4. $R_{O,-350}$ 6. $R_{O,-180}$

State a rotation equal to the given composition.

EXAMPLE. $R_{O,20} \circ R_{O,40}$ SOLUTION: $R_{O,60}$

7. $R_{O,50} \circ R_{O,30}$ 9. $R_{O,90} \circ R_{O,-30}$ 11. $R_{O,-90} \circ R_{O,100}$
8. $R_{O,90} \circ R_{O,60}$ 10. $R_{O,-30} \circ R_{O,-10}$ 12. $R_{O,60} \circ R_{O,-80}$

Written Exercises

Point *A* is mapped, under rotation about point *O* through the number of degrees specified below, into point *A'*. State the coordinates of *A'*.

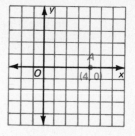

A

1. 90°
2. 180°
3. 270°
4. −90°
5. 540°
6. 720°

Point *B* is mapped, under rotation about point *O* through the number of degrees specified below, into point *B'*. State the coordinates of *B'*.

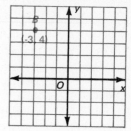

7. 90°
8. −90°
9. 180°
10. 450°

Regular hexagon *ABCDEF* has center *O*. If there is a rotation about point *O* for the mapping indicated, determine the angle of rotation. If there is no rotation meeting the given condition, write *Not a rotation*.

EXAMPLE. *ABCDEF → BCDEFA*   SOLUTION: A 60° angle

11. *ABCDEF → CDEFAB*
12. *ABCDEF → DEFABC*
13. *ABCDEF → FABCDE*
14. *ABCDEF → EFABCD*
15. *ABCDEF → ABFCED*
16. *ABCDEF → ABCDEF*

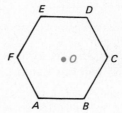

Copy the figure on squared paper. Draw the image of the figure, under the rotation specified.

B

17. $R_{O,90}$

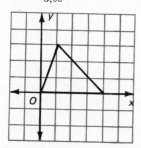

18. $R_{O,-90}$

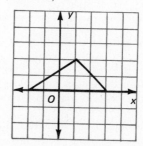

19. $R_{O,135}$

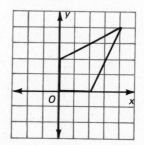

In Exercises 20–24, it is given that $A \xrightarrow{M_j} B$ and $B \xrightarrow{M_k} C$. It is to be shown that there is a rotation that maps A into C.

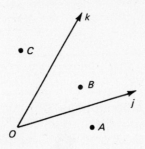 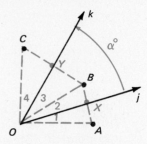

20. Draw $\overline{OA}$, $\overline{OB}$, $\overline{OC}$, $\overline{AB}$, and $\overline{BC}$. Because $A \xrightarrow{M_j} B$, j is the $\perp$ bis. of $\overline{AB}$, $\triangle OXA \cong \triangle \underline{\quad?\quad}$, and $m\angle 1 = m\angle \underline{\quad?\quad}$.

21. Because $B \xrightarrow{M_k} C$, k is the $\perp$ bis. of $\overline{BC}$, $\triangle OYB \cong \triangle \underline{\quad?\quad}$, and $m\angle 3 = m\angle \underline{\quad?\quad}$.

22. Because $m\angle 1 + m\angle 2 + m\angle 3 + m\angle 4 = 2(m\angle 2 + m\angle 3)$, and $m\angle 2 + m\angle 3 = \alpha$, $m\angle AOC = \underline{\quad?\quad}$.

23. Because $\overline{OA} \cong \overline{OB}$ and $\overline{OB} \cong \overline{OC}$, $\overline{OA} \cong \overline{OC}$. Then $A \xrightarrow{R_{O,2\alpha}} \underline{\quad?\quad}$.

24. Since $A \xrightarrow{M_j \circ M_k} \underline{\quad?\quad}$, a rotation equal to $M_j \circ M_k$ is $R_{\underline{?}, \underline{?}}$.

Exercises 25 and 26 illustrate problems that would be extremely difficult to solve without using properties of mappings.

C 25. Point P, line l, and $\odot O$ are given. You are to construct an equilateral triangle with one vertex at point P, one vertex on line l, and one vertex on $\odot O$. Carry out the construction step-by-step.

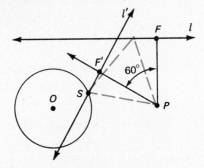

Construct $\overline{PF} \perp l$.

Construct a ray so that a 60° angle is formed at P. On this ray take $PF' = PF$.

Construct a line $l' \perp$ to $\overline{PF'}$ at F'.

Just as $R_{P,60}$ maps F into F', it maps every other point of l into a point of l'. In particular, there is some point of l that is mapped into point S. $\overline{PS}$ is one side of the desired triangle. Complete the construction.

26. Given three parallel lines. Construct an equilateral triangle with one vertex on each line.

12-7 Translations

Begin with △ABC and $\overleftrightarrow{XX'}$.

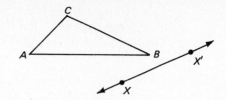

Make a tracing of △ABC and $\overline{XX'}$.

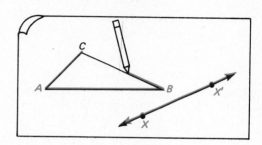

Slide the tracing, keeping the tracing of $\overline{XX'}$ over $\overleftrightarrow{XX'}$, until the tracing of X lies over X'.

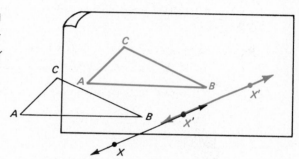

The movement suggests something that could be called a *slide* or a *glide*. The name commonly used, however, is *translation*. Notice, in the last diagram, that the segment joining point B and its image would be parallel to and congruent to the given segment $\overline{XX'}$. This relationship is used in the definition that follows.

A **translation** that maps point X into point X' maps every point P into a point P' such that:

(1) If P does not lie on $\overleftrightarrow{XX'}$, then PXX'P' is a parallelogram.

(2) If P lies on $\overleftrightarrow{XX'}$, then there is a segment $\overline{YY'}$ such that both XYY'X' and PYY'P' are parallelograms.

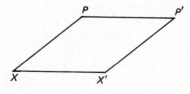
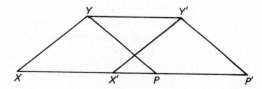

For *the translation that maps X into X'* we write $T_{XX'}$. This symbol may be read simply *translation XX'*.

To abbreviate the statement *Point P is mapped, under the translation XX', into point P'*, we write:

$$P \xrightarrow{\ T_{XX'}\ } P'$$

In Section 12-6 you saw that every rotation is equal to the composition of two reflections. The mirrors used were intersecting lines. Now, using parallel lines for the mirrors, you can show (see Exercise 28) that:

> Every translation is equal to the composition of two reflections.

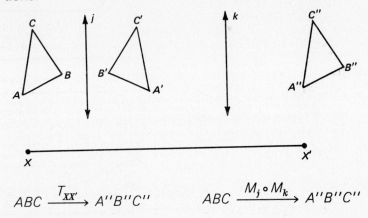

$$ABC \xrightarrow{\ T_{XX'}\ } A''B''C'' \qquad ABC \xrightarrow{\ M_j \circ M_k\ } A''B''C''$$

Recall that every reflection is a congruence mapping. Thus you can conclude that every translation is a congruence mapping, or an isometry.

Oral Exercises State whether the diagram illustrates a reflection, a rotation, or a translation.

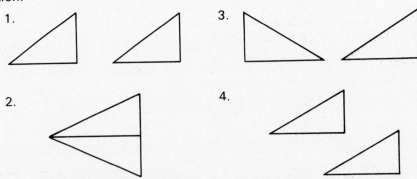

1.

3.

2.

4.

5.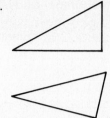

6.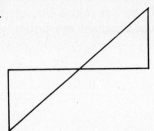

Points are mapped under the translation $T_{ZZ'}$. State the coordinates of the image of the point named.

7. O

8. A

9. B

10. C

11. D

12. E

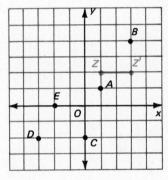

Written Exercises

Points are mapped under the translation $T_{WW'}$. Find the coordinates of the image of the point named.

A

1. O

2. A

3. B

4. C

5. D

6. E

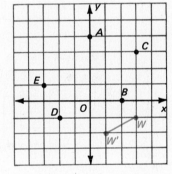

The figure includes five congruent squares. Complete each statement.

7. $A \xrightarrow{T_{XZ}} \underline{\ ?\ }$

8. $\overline{AB} \xrightarrow{T_{CG}} \underline{\ ?\ }$

9. $ABFE \xrightarrow{T_{XY}} \underline{\ ?\ }$

10. $ABFE \xrightarrow{T_{YZ}} \underline{\ ?\ }$

11. $BCGF \xrightarrow{T_{ZY}} \underline{\ ?\ }$

12. $ABFE \xrightarrow{T_{AF}} \underline{\ ?\ }$

13. $ABFE \xrightarrow{M_{\overleftrightarrow{EF}}} \underline{\ ?\ }$

14. $ABFE \xrightarrow{H_F} \underline{\ ?\ }$

15. $CDHG \xrightarrow{T_{FX}} \underline{\ ?\ }$

16. $CDHG \xrightarrow{T_{ZX}} \underline{\ ?\ }$

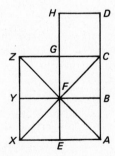

Copy the figure on squared paper. Draw the image, under the mapping specified, of the figure.

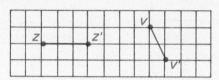

B 17. $T_{ZZ'}$

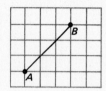

20. $T_{ZZ'} \circ T_{VV'}$

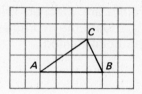

18. $T_{Z'Z}$

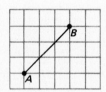

21. $T_{VV'} \circ T_{ZZ'}$

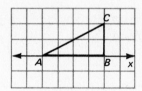

19. $T_{VV'}$

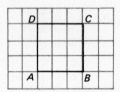

22. $M_X \circ T_{Z'Z}$

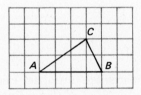

23. Given: $P \xrightarrow{T_{XX'}} P'$
Copy the figure and locate P' by construction.

24. Given: $AB \xrightarrow{T_{XX'}} A'B'$
Copy the figure and locate B' by construction.

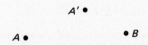

C **25.** Given: $\overline{XX'}$; $\overline{ZZ'}$; point A; $A \xrightarrow{T_{XX'} \circ T_{ZZ'}} B$
Copy the figure and locate B by construction.

26. Use the same figure and construction you completed in Exercise 25. It is now given that
$A \xrightarrow{T_{ZZ'} \circ T_{XX'}} C$. Locate C by construction.

27. If your constructions in Exercises 25 and 26 were accurate, points B and C should be the same point. State a theorem suggested by the constructions.

28. Given: $P \xrightarrow{T_{XX'}} P'$. Complete the explanation that there are lines j and k such that $P \xrightarrow{M_j \circ M_k} P'$.

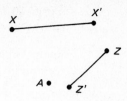
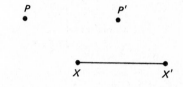

Let XX' equal $2d$. Draw any two lines j and k, perpendicular to $\overline{XX'}$, d units apart. Then j and k are perpendicular to $\overleftrightarrow{PP'}$.

Let $PQ = e$. On $\overrightarrow{PP'}$ take V such that $QV = e$. Then $P \xrightarrow{M_j} V$. (To complete the explanation you need to show that $V \xrightarrow{M_k} P'$ and that $P \xrightarrow{M_j \circ M_k} P'$.)

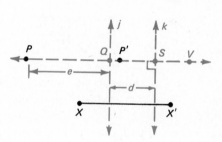

Challenge

Copy the figure. Construct a segment $\overline{ZW}$ such that Z lies on $\odot P$, W lies on $\odot Q$, and $\overline{ZW}$ is congruent and parallel to $\overline{XY}$.
Hint: Construct the image, under T_{XY}, of $\odot P$.

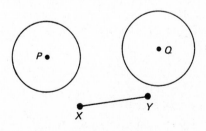

12-8 *Dilations*

Thus far the only kind of mappings we have studied are isometries, or congruence mappings. In this section, we shall study a special transformation that is related to similarity.

Begin with $\triangle ABC$ and point O.

Let A' lie on $\overrightarrow{OA}$ so that $OA' = 2(OA)$.
Let B' lie on $\overrightarrow{OB}$ so that $OB' = 2(OB)$.
Let C' lie on $\overrightarrow{OC}$ so that $OC' = 2(OC)$.

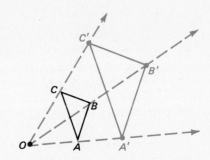

The transformation, $ABC \rightarrow A'B'C'$, described above is called a *dilation* with *center* O and *scale factor* 2.

A dilation with center O and scale factor k ($k > 0$) is a mapping such that:

(1) If P is different from O, then P' lies on $\overrightarrow{OP}$ and $OP' = k(OP)$.
(2) If P is the point O, then P' is the same point as P.

If $k > 1$, the dilation is called an expansion. If $0 < k < 1$, the dilation is a contraction. If $k = 1$, the dilation is the identity mapping. We use the notation:

$$P \xrightarrow{\ D_{O,k}\ } P'$$

EXAMPLE

Given point O and $\triangle RST$, find the image of $\triangle RST$ under the contraction with center O and scale factor $\frac{2}{3}$.

SOLUTION:

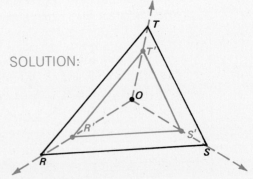

It can be shown that a dilation maps any line into a parallel line. See Exercises 27 and 28. Also, any angle is mapped into a congruent angle. See Exercise 29. A dilation with scale factor k maps any line segment $\overline{AB}$ into an image $\overline{A'B'}$ such that $A'B' = k(AB)$. See Exercise 30. Thus a dilation maps any polygon into a similar polygon.

State the coordinates of the image of the given point under a dilation with center O and given scale factor k.

1. $A; k = 2$
2. $A; k = 3$
3. $A; k = \frac{1}{3}$
4. $B; k = 2$

5. $B; k = \frac{1}{3}$
6. $C; k = 2$
7. $C; k = 0.5$
8. $O; k = 2$

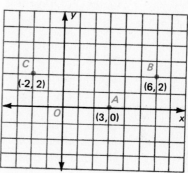

State the coordinates of the image of the given point under a dilation with center A and given scale factor k.

9. $O; k = 2$
10. $O; k = \frac{1}{2}$
11. $B; k = 2$
12. $B; k = \frac{1}{3}$

13. $B; k = 1$
14. $C; k = 2$
15. $C; k = 0.2$
16. $C; k = \frac{1}{2}$

Exs. 1–16

17. A dilation with scale factor $\frac{1}{5}$ is called a(n) __?__ .
18. A dilation with scale factor 3.5 is called a(n) __?__ .

Find the coordinates of the image of the given point under a dilation with center O and given scale factor k.

A

1. $A; k = 3$
2. $A; k = \frac{3}{2}$
3. $B; k = 0.5$

4. $B; k = 3$
5. $C; k = \frac{1}{4}$
6. $C; k = 1$

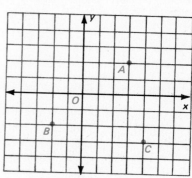

Find the coordinates of the image of the given point under a dilation with center B and given scale factor k.

7. $O; k = 4$
8. $O; k = \frac{1}{2}$
9. $A; k = \frac{1}{2}$

10. $B; k = 0.5$
11. $C; k = \frac{1}{2}$
12. $C; k = 1.5$

Exs. 1–12

Find the scale factor of the dilation with center (0, 0) which maps the given point into the image given. Is the dilation an expansion or a contraction?

13. $(2, 3) \to (6, 9)$
14. $(-4, -2) \to (-2, -1)$
15. $(16, -8) \to (4, -2)$

16. $(-6, 9) \to (-4, 6)$
17. $(-4, -8) \to (-10, -20)$
18. $(7, 21) \to (3, 9)$

Draw, in black, the polygon having the given vertices. Plot, in red, the image of each vertex under a dilation with center (0, 0) and with scale factor 2. Draw the image polygon in red.

B 19. $A(-1, 1)$; $B(0, -1)$; $C(2, 2)$
20. $A(2, 2)$; $B(-1, -3)$; $C(2.5, 0)$
21. $A(2, -1)$; $B(-4, -2)$; $C(-1, -4)$; $D(1, -3)$
22. $A(-2, 2)$; $B(-1, -1)$; $C(2, 1)$; $D(2, 2)$

Draw, in black, the polygon having the given vertices. Plot, in red, the image of each vertex under a dilation with center (0, 0) and scale factor $\frac{1}{2}$. Draw the image polygon in red.

23. $A(-4, 4)$; $B(0, -4)$; $C(8, 8)$
24. $A(3, 2)$; $B(-1, 2)$; $C(1, -2)$
25. $A(5, 5)$; $B(-5, 5)$; $C(-5, -5)$; $D(5, -5)$
26. $A(-2, -3)$; $B(4, 3)$; $C(0, 4)$; $D(-3, 1)$

C 27. Prove that a dilation maps any vertical line j into j or a line parallel to j.
28. Prove that a dilation maps any nonvertical line k into k or a line parallel to k.
29. Prove that a dilation maps any $\angle ABC$ into an angle congruent to $\angle ABC$.
   Hint: Let $\angle A'B'C'$ be the image angle. Draw $\overleftrightarrow{BB'}$ and treat it as a transversal.
30. Prove that a dilation with scale factor k maps any line segment, $\overline{AB}$, into $\overline{A'B'}$ such that $A'B' = k(AB)$.

Self-Test In $\triangle DXF$, $\overline{DX} \cong \overline{FX}$.

1. Complete the identity self-congruence: $\triangle DXF \cong \triangle \underline{\ ?\ }$.
2. Complete a self-congruence other than the identity self-congruence: $\triangle DXF \cong \triangle \underline{\ ?\ }$.
3. $\triangle DXF$ has a line of symmetry. That line passes through point $\underline{\ ?\ }$.

Find the coordinates of point K.

4. $A \xrightarrow{T_{WZ}} K$ 8. $A \xrightarrow{M_y \circ M_x} K$

5. $B \xrightarrow{D_{O,2}} K$ 9. $C \xrightarrow{R_{B,-90} \circ T_{WZ}} K$

6. $C \xrightarrow{R_{O,180}} K$ 10. $B \xrightarrow{M_y \circ H_O} K$

7. $Z \xrightarrow{R_{A,-90}} K$ 11. $C \xrightarrow{T_{ZW} \circ D_{O,3}} K$

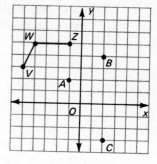

Exs. 4–13

Find the coordinates of the image of the given point under a dilation with center O and given scale factor k.

12. $(1, 2)$; $k = 3$ 13. $(4, 2)$; $k = \frac{1}{2}$

14. Each rotation is equal to the composition of two __?__. Each translation is equal to the composition of two __?__.

CHAPTER SUMMARY

1. The basic isometries, or congruence mappings, are:

   Reflection in a line j M_j
   Half-turn about a point O H_O
   Rotation about point O through α° $R_{O,\alpha}$
   Translation XX' $T_{XX'}$

2. Every half-turn, rotation, and translation is equal to the composition of two reflections.

3. A figure may have one or more lines of symmetry, and it may have a point of symmetry.

4. Dilations are transformations, but most dilations are not isometries. A dilation with center O and scale factor k is denoted by $D_{O,k}$.

CHAPTER TEST

In Exercises 1–4, use the mapping $\triangle ABC \rightarrow \triangle RST$.

1. The image of C is __?__.
2. The preimage of $\overline{ST}$ is __?__.
3. If the mapping is an isometry, then $\angle BAC \cong \angle$ __?__.
4. If the mapping is an isometry, then it is a __?__ mapping.

State whether the mapping $\angle ABC \rightarrow \angle DEF$ can be regarded as a reflection, a half-turn, a rotation, a translation, or none of these.

5.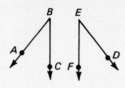

8.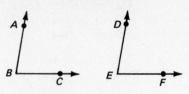

6.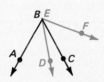

9.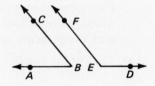

7.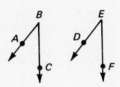

10.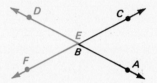

Points E, F, G, and K are the midpoints of the sides of rectangle $ABCD$. Classify each statement as true or false.

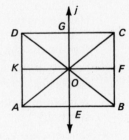

11. $\overleftrightarrow{KF}$ is a line of symmetry.

12. $\overleftrightarrow{BD}$ is a line of symmetry.

13. G is a point of symmetry.

14. O is a point of symmetry.

15. $E \xrightarrow{R_{O,90}} F$

18. $\triangle KOD \xrightarrow{H_O} \triangle FOB$

16. $K \xrightarrow{R_{O,135}} B$

19. $\triangle KOD \xrightarrow{T_{GC}} \triangle GOC$

17. $\triangle KOD \xrightarrow{M_j} \triangle FOC$

20. $\triangle AOE \xrightarrow{M_j \circ T_{OD}} \triangle ODK$

Point O is the origin and point A is point $(4, 6)$.

21. If $A \xrightarrow{D_{O,3}} B$, then B is point (__?__ , __?__).

22. If $O \xrightarrow{D_{A,\frac{1}{2}}} C$, then C is point (__?__ , __?__).

12-1 *Mappings and Congruence Mappings*

The isometry $\triangle ABC \rightarrow \triangle ABD$ is given.

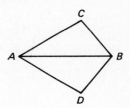

1. $\overline{AC} \rightarrow$ ___?___
2. The preimage of $\angle BAD$ is ___?___ .
3. One segment that maps into itself is ___?___ .
4. The isometry is also called a ___?___ mapping.

12-2 *Reflections*

Copy the figure on squared paper. Then draw the image, under reflection in line *k*.

5.

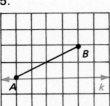

6.

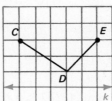

7.

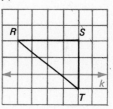

12-3 *Half-Turns*

P denotes point (3, 0). State the coordinates of the image.

8. $(5, 0) \xrightarrow{H_P}$ ___?___

9. $(3, 4) \xrightarrow{H_P}$ ___?___

10. $(6, 6) \xrightarrow{H_P}$ ___?___

12-4 *Self-Congruence and Symmetry*

11. Complete the identity self-congruence:
Square $ABCD \cong$ ___?___

12. Complete a self-congruence other than the identity self-congruence:
Square $ABCD \cong$ ___?___

13. How many lines of symmetry can be drawn for the square?

14. How many points of symmetry can be found for the figure?

12-5 *Composition of Mappings*

Given: $\triangle ABC \xrightarrow{H_O} \triangle RST$; $\triangle RST \xrightarrow{M_j} \triangle XYZ$

15. $A \xrightarrow{H_O \circ M_j}$ __?__

16. __?__ $\xrightarrow{H_O \circ M_j} \overline{XY}$

17. $\angle ABC \xrightarrow{H_O \circ H_O}$ __?__

12-6 *Rotations*

18. $A \xrightarrow{R_{O,-\alpha}}$ __?__

19. $C \xrightarrow{R_{O,2\alpha}}$ __?__

20. $\overline{BC} \xrightarrow{R_{O,\alpha}}$ __?__

21. $\overline{OA} \xrightarrow{R_{O,-2\alpha}}$ __?__

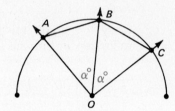

12-7 *Translations*

Quadrilateral *ABCD* is a parallelogram; $\overline{AB} \parallel \overline{XX'}$; $\overline{AB} \cong \overline{XX'}$

22. $A \xrightarrow{T_{XX'}}$ __?__

23. $\overline{AD} \xrightarrow{T_{XX'}}$ __?__

24. $D \xrightarrow{T_{AB}}$ __?__

25. $A \xrightarrow{T_{XX'} \circ T_{CD}}$ __?__

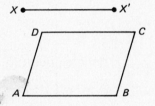

26. When a translation is expressed as a composition of two reflections, the lines of reflection _____?_____ .
                         (intersect, are parallel)

12-8 *Dilations*

State the coordinates of the image.

27. $A \xrightarrow{D_{O,2}}$ __?__

28. $A \xrightarrow{D_{B,2}}$ __?__

29. $B \xrightarrow{D_{O,\frac{1}{3}}}$ __?__

30. $B \xrightarrow{D_{O,6} \circ D_{O,\frac{1}{2}}}$ __?__

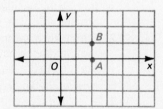

programming in BASIC

The computer can provide a means of graphing polygons and their images under various transformations. The program below graphs the vertices of a polygon (located in the first quadrant) and then graphs the image of the vertices under the expansion $P(x, y) \rightarrow P'(2x, 2y)$. The polygon can have up to ten vertices.

```
10  DIM X[10],Y[10],A[10],B[10]
20  PRINT "HOW MANY VERTICES";
30  INPUT N
40  FOR I=1 TO N
50  INPUT X[I],Y[I]
60  LET A[I]=2*X[I]
70  LET B[I]=2*Y[I]
80  NEXT I
90  PRINT
100 FOR I=9 TO 1 STEP -1
110 PRINT "!";
120 FOR J=1 TO N
130 IF Y[J] <> I THEN 150
140 PRINT TAB(2*X[J]);"*";
150 NEXT J
160 PRINT
170 NEXT I
180 FOR I=1 TO 9
190 PRINT "- ";
200 NEXT I
210 PRINT
220 PRINT
230 PRINT
240 FOR I=12 TO 1 STEP -1
250 PRINT "!";
260 FOR J=1 TO N
270 IF B[J] <> I THEN 290
280 PRINT TAB(2*A[J]);"+";
290 NEXT J
300 PRINT
310 NEXT I
320 FOR I=1 TO 14
330 PRINT "- ";
340 NEXT I
350 END
```

Note that one FOR-NEXT loop (lines 120 to 150) is completely contained within another (lines 100 to 170). This arrangement is called *nested loops*. For each value of I, the value of J changes from 1 to N to check whether any point has a *y*-coordinate equal to that value of I.

The terminal carriage cannot back-space on a given line. Therefore, if two or more vertices of the polygon have the same *y*-coordinate, input these points in increasing order of *x*-coordinates (for example, input consecutive coordinates in counter-clockwise order starting from the top left-hand vertex).

In line 140, the instruction TAB(2*X[J]) moves the terminal carriage to space 2·X[J], much in the same way the tab on a typewriter does. The *x*-coordinate must be multiplied by 2, since the *y*-units are about twice as great as the *x*-units; in this way the grid will be nearly square.

Here is a RUN of the program:

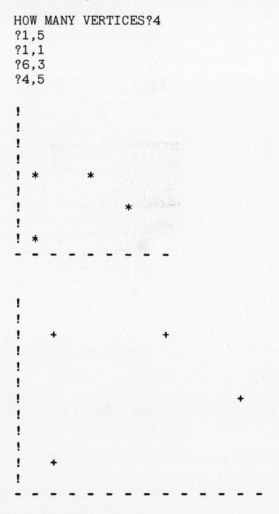

```
HOW MANY VERTICES?4
?1,5
?1,1
?6,3
?4,5
```

The length of the x-axis and y-axis may have to be increased if the polygon you wish to plot is larger than the one above. In this case, just increase the bounds for I in lines 100, 180, 240, and 320.

Exercises

1. RUN the program several times using different polygons. Does it appear that the image of an isosceles trapezoid under an expansion is also an isosceles trapezoid?
2. Change lines 60 and 70 in the program to translate the vertices of a polygon by the mapping $P(x, y) \rightarrow P'(x + 3, y + 1)$. Then RUN the program several times using different polygons.
3. A horizontal stretching is a nonisometric transformation specified by the mapping $P(x, y) \rightarrow P'(kx, y)$ where $k > 1$. Change lines 60 and 70 in the program to graph the vertices of a polygon and the image of the vertices under the stretching $P(x, y) \rightarrow P'(3x, y)$.

extra for experts

Glide Reflections

One particular mapping often treated as a basic isometry is the *glide reflection*. In the diagram below triangle ABC is mapped, under a particular glide reflection, into triangle $A'B'C'$.

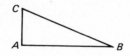

It is evident that the mapping is not a reflection, a half-turn, a rotation, a translation, or a dilation. The mapping is just what the name suggests: a glide (translation) followed by a reflection.

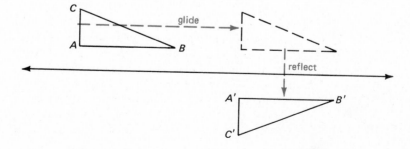

A glide reflection $G_{XX'}$ (G sub XX') is equal to the composite mapping $T_{XX'} \circ M_{\overleftrightarrow{XX'}}$.

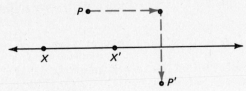

1. Given: $\triangle ABC \xrightarrow{\; G_{XX'} \;} \triangle A'B'C'$. Copy the figure below. Draw $\triangle A'B'C'$ carefully. (You need not construct.)

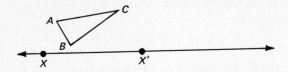

2. $G_{XX'}$ is defined to be $T_{XX'} \circ M_{\overleftrightarrow{XX'}}$. Explain that $G_{XX'}$ is also equal to $M_{\overleftrightarrow{XX'}} \circ T_{XX'}$. *Hint:* Set up a coordinate system. Let $\overleftrightarrow{XX'}$ be the x-axis. Let the line perpendicular to $\overleftrightarrow{XX'}$ at X be the y-axis. Take any point P.

Show that the image of P under $M_{\overleftrightarrow{XX'}} \circ T_{XX'}$ is the same as the image of P under $T_{XX'} \circ M_{\overleftrightarrow{XX'}}$.

CUMULATIVE REVIEW: CHAPTERS 7–12

True–False Exercises

Write T or F to indicate your answer.

A
1. If two right triangles are similar, they must also be congruent.
2. If two circles are externally tangent, each circle contains some points that lie in the exterior of the other circle.
3. The lateral area of a cone must be greater than the area of the base of the cone.
4. If quadrilateral $ABCD$ is a convex polygon, then the area of $\triangle ABC$ + the area of $\triangle CDA$ = the area of quad. $ABCD$.
5. A segment of a circle is the same as a minor arc of the circle.
6. An altitude of a right prism is parallel to the lateral edges of the prism.
7. Each leg of a right triangle is also an altitude of the triangle.
8. The area of any polygon circumscribed about a circle is greater than the area of the circle.
9. The number 31.4 is a frequently used approximation of π.
10. Every prism has a square base.
11. The distance between points (c, d) and (e, f) equals $\sqrt{(c - e)^2 + (d - f)^2}$.
12. The line $2x + 3y = 12$ has a positive slope.
13. If two parallel lines have slopes h and k, then $h = k$.
14. If the mapping $ABC \rightarrow RST$ is an isometry, then $\overline{AB} \cong \overline{RS}$.
15. If $P \xrightarrow{M_k} P'$, and point P lies on line k, then P and P' are different points.
16. The composition of any two translations is also a translation.

B
17. If the length of a diagonal of the base of a rectangular solid is greater than 20, then the length of a diagonal of the solid must be greater than $20\sqrt{2}$.
18. It is possible to inscribe, in a circle with a 10 cm radius, a triangle whose area is less than 1 cm².
19. In a right triangle, the altitude drawn to the hypotenuse is the longest of the three altitudes of the triangle.
20. The measure of any angle inscribed in a circle must be less than 170.
21. If the longest and shortest sides of a triangle are 10 cm and 7 cm long, respectively, then the area of the triangle must be less than 35 cm².
22. A circle with area $\frac{81}{4}\pi$ has circumference 9π.
23. The area of a trapezoid is equal to half the product of the length of the altitude and the average of the lengths of the bases.
24. A triangle whose sides have lengths 1, 1.875, and $2\frac{1}{8}$ is a right triangle.

Always, Sometimes, or Never Exercises

A   Write A, S, or N to indicate your answer.

1. The lengths of the sides of a right triangle are __?__ in the ratio $1:1:\sqrt{2}$.
2. A radius of a circle is __?__ a chord of the circle.
3. If $\odot A$ and $\odot B$ are both tangent to $\odot C$, then $\odot A$ is __?__ tangent to $\odot B$.
4. An angle formed by two secants to a circle from a point in the exterior of the circle is __?__ an acute angle.
5. A lateral edge of a regular pyramid is __?__ longer than the altitude of the pyramid.
6. A line that intersects a sphere in exactly one point is __?__ a secant of the sphere.
7. If the sides of a triangle have lengths r, s, and t, then it is __?__ true that $r^2 > s^2 + t^2$.
8. A line perpendicular to a radius of a circle is __?__ tangent to the circle.
9. In a circle, two noncongruent chords are __?__ equally distant from the center of the circle.
10. Given a triangle, it is __?__ possible to circumscribe a circle about the triangle.
11. Two coplanar lines with equal slopes __?__ intersect.
12. Lines with slopes $\frac{2}{5}$ and $-\frac{2}{5}$ respectively are __?__ perpendicular.
13. The distance between points $(c, 5)$ and $(k, 5)$ __?__ equals $|k - c|$.
14. Under rotation about point O, point O is __?__ mapped into point O.
15. Transformations are __?__ isometries.
16. A scalene triangle __?__ has a self-congruence other than the identity self-congruence.

B   17. For real numbers a and b it is __?__ true that $\sqrt{a^2 + b^2} = a + b$.
18. If $\overline{RS}$ is a chord of $\odot O$, $\overleftrightarrow{XY}$ lies in the plane of $\odot O$, and $\overleftrightarrow{XY}$ is a perpendicular bisector of $\overline{RS}$, then $\overleftrightarrow{XY}$ __?__ contains a diameter of $\odot O$.
19. If $\angle C$ of $\triangle RCJ$ is a right angle, then tan $\angle RJC$ is __?__ less than 1.
20. When a chord that is not a diameter intersects a diameter at a point in the interior of a circle, the product of the lengths of the segments of the chord is __?__ less than the product of the lengths of the segments of the diameter.
21. When a triangle and a rectangle have equal areas, the perimeter of the triangle is __?__ less than the perimeter of the rectangle.
22. If the longest and shortest sides of a triangle have lengths in the ratio $2:1$, the triangle is __?__ a 30°–60°–90° triangle.
23. If a line in the plane of a parallelogram is not a diagonal, but contains the point of intersection of the diagonals, that line __?__ divides the parallelogram into two quadrilaterals that have equal areas.
24. The locus of points that are equally distant from two lines is __?__ a pair of planes.

Multiple-Choice Exercises

Write the letter that indicates the best answer.

A

1. The area of rectangle $RSTQ$ equals:

   a. $RS \cdot TQ$ **b.** $RS \cdot ST$ **c.** $RT \cdot SQ$ **d.** none of these

2. In a plane, the locus of points a given distance from a given line is:

   a. a rectangle **b.** a point **c.** a line **d.** a pair of lines

3. If the area of a square is 50, the length of each diagonal of the square is:

   a. $10\sqrt{2}$ **b.** $5\sqrt{2}$ **c.** 10 **d.** 5

4. The geometric mean between 20 and 45 is:

   a. 30 **b.** 65 **c.** $32\frac{1}{2}$ **d.** $\sqrt{65}$

5. For every acute angle X:

   a. $\sin X < 1$ **b.** $\sin X > 1$ **c.** $\sin X > \tan X$ **d.** $\sin X < \cos X$

6. A line that contains a point in the exterior of a circle intersects the circle in:

   a. no points **b.** 1 point **c.** 2 points **d.** cannot tell

7. If C and d represent the circumference and diameter of a circle, then:

   a. $d = \pi C$ **b.** $\dfrac{C}{d} = \pi$ **c.** $\dfrac{d}{C} = \pi$ **d.** none of these

8. In a $30°$–$60°$–$90°$ triangle, the ratio of the length of the longer leg to the length of the shorter leg is:

   a. $\dfrac{\sqrt{3}}{1}$ **b.** $\dfrac{\sqrt{2}}{1}$ **c.** $\dfrac{2}{1}$ **d.** none of these

9. The median to the hypotenuse of a right triangle divides the triangle into two triangles that are both:

   a. acute **b.** obtuse **c.** scalene **d.** isosceles

10. Expressed in simplest radical form, $\sqrt{\dfrac{5}{12}}$ equals:

    a. $\dfrac{\sqrt{60}}{12}$ **b.** $5\sqrt{60}$ **c.** $\dfrac{\sqrt{15}}{6}$ **d.** $6\sqrt{15}$

11. The slope of the line $y - 6 = \frac{2}{3}(x + 5)$ is:

    a. $\frac{2}{3}$ **b.** $\frac{3}{2}$ **c.** $\frac{5}{6}$ **d.** $-\frac{5}{6}$

12. If R is point $(-2, 4)$ and if $S(3, 0)$ is the midpoint of $\overline{RT}$, then T is point:

    a. $(8, -4)$ **b.** $(\frac{1}{2}, 2)$ **c.** $(5, 8)$ **d.** $(-5, 8)$

B

13. If R is point $(1, -3)$ and T is point $(11, 5)$, then the diagonals of parallelogram $RSTQ$ meet at point:

    a. $(6, 4)$ **b.** $(6, 1)$ **c.** $(10, -8)$ **d.** cannot tell

14. Of the transformations listed, the one that is not an isometry is:

    a. half-turn **b.** dilation **c.** rotation **d.** reflection

15. If A is point $(3, 4)$, g is the x-axis, and $A \xrightarrow{M_g} A'$, then A' is the point:

    a. $(-3, -4)$ **b.** $(4, 3)$ **c.** $(3, -4)$ **d.** $(-3, 4)$

16. The composite transformation $R_{A,990} \circ H_A$ equals:

    a. $R_{A,-990}$ **b.** $R_{A,270}$ **c.** $H_A \circ R_{A,90}$ **d.** 2

17. If the lengths of two sides of an acute triangle are 7 and 9, the length of the third side may be:

    a. $\sqrt{130}$ **b.** 11   **c.** 12   **d.** none of these

18. If R, S, and T are distinct points on a circle, then it *cannot* be true that:

    a. $\overset{\frown}{RS} \cup \overset{\frown}{ST} = \overset{\frown}{RT}$ **c.** $\overset{\frown}{RS} \cap \overset{\frown}{ST} = S$

    b. $\overset{\frown}{RS} \cup \overset{\frown}{ST} = \overset{\frown}{ST}$ **d.** $\overset{\frown}{RS} \cap \overset{\frown}{ST} = \emptyset$

19. The ratio of the area of a circle to the circumference of the circle is:

    a. π **b.** $\dfrac{2}{r}$ **c.** $\dfrac{r}{2}$ **d.** none of these

20. If $\overline{RGT}$, $m\angle RXT = 90$, and $\overline{XG} \perp \overline{RT}$, then:

    a. $\dfrac{RX}{XG} = \dfrac{RG}{GT}$ **c.** $\triangle RGX \sim \triangle RTX$

    b. $RX \cdot XT = (XG)^2$ **d.** $\triangle RGX \sim \triangle XGT$

Matching Exercises

Write the numbers from 1 to 16 on your paper. Beside each number write the letter that identifies the matching expression.

A

1. Distance between two points
2. Area of a trapezoid
3. Total area of a cube
4. Volume of a pyramid
5. Area of a circle
6. Total area of a cylinder
7. Volume of a cube
8. Length of a diagonal of a rectangular solid
9. Total area of a cone
10. Area of a parallelogram
11. Length of a diagonal of a cube
12. Slope of a line
13. Circumference of a circle
14. Area of an equilateral triangle
15. Volume of a cylinder
16. Lateral area of a cylinder

a. $2\pi rh$

b. bh

c. $6s^2$

d. $2\pi r$

e. $\frac{1}{3}Bh$

f. $s\sqrt{3}$

g. $\sqrt{l^2 + w^2 + h^2}$

h. $\sqrt{(x_2 - x_1)^2 + (y_2 - y_1)^2}$

i. $2\pi rh + 2\pi r^2$

j. e^3

k. $\dfrac{s^2}{4}\sqrt{3}$

l. $\frac{1}{2}h(b_1 + b_2)$

m. $\pi r^2 h$

n. πr^2

o. $\pi rl + \pi r^2$

p. $\dfrac{y_2 - y_1}{x_2 - x_1}$

Completion Exercises

Write the correct expression on your paper. In the figure for Exercises 1–10: $\overline{RS}$ is tangent to the circle at S; $\overline{TV} \parallel \overline{RS}$; $m\widehat{SV} = 160$; $m\widehat{WU} = 50$

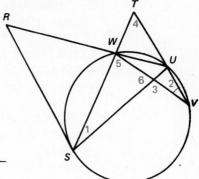

A

1. $m\angle 1 = \underline{\ ?\ }$
2. $m\angle 2 = \underline{\ ?\ }$
3. $m\angle 3 = \underline{\ ?\ }$
4. $m\angle 4 = \underline{\ ?\ }$
5. $m\angle 5 = \underline{\ ?\ }$
6. $m\angle 6 = \underline{\ ?\ }$
7. $m\,\widehat{SU} = \underline{\ ?\ }$
8. $m\,\widehat{SW} = \underline{\ ?\ }$
9. $m\angle RSW = \underline{\ ?\ }$
10. $m\angle R = \underline{\ ?\ }$

11. If the origin is the midpoint of the segment that joins points $(3, -5)$ and (s, t), then $s = \underline{\ ?\ }$.
12. The distance between points $(0, 2)$ and $(-3, 6)$ is $\underline{\ ?\ }$.
13. The slopes of two lines are g and k. If the lines are parallel, then $\underline{\ ?\ }$.
14. If $RST \rightarrow XYZ$, then the image of $\overline{RS}$ is $\underline{\ ?\ }$.
15. If $RST \rightarrow XYZ$ is a congruence mapping, then $\angle\underline{\ ?\ } \cong \angle XZY$.
16. If P and P' are different points and $P \xrightarrow{M_j} P'$, then line j is the $\underline{\ ?\ }$ of $\overline{PP'}$.

B

17. If $\odot P$ has diameter 10, and X is a point in the interior of the circle, then $XP \underline{\ ?\ } 5$.
    $(<, =, >)$
18. Angle of elevation is defined to be the acute angle formed by a line of sight and a $\underline{\ ?\ }$ line.
19. A triangle whose sides have lengths 12, 16, and 20 must be a $\underline{\ ?\ }$ triangle.
20. If A is an acute angle and $\tan A = \frac{5}{5}$, then $m\angle A = \underline{\ ?\ }$.

In Exercises 21 and 22, $\overline{RS}$ is a tangent and $\overline{RY}$ is a secant.

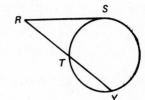

21. If $RS = 6$ and $RT = 4$, then $RY = \underline{\ ?\ }$.
22. If $RT = 49$ and $TY = 51$, then $RS = \underline{\ ?\ }$.

In Exercises 23 and 24, $\overline{AB}$ and $\overline{CD}$ are chords.

23. If $AX = 10$, $BX = 4$, and $CX = 5$, then $DX = \underline{\ ?\ }$.
24. If $AX = 12$, $BX = 6$, $CD = 17$, and $CX < DX$, then $CX = \underline{\ ?\ }$.

C   25. Point Z lies on $\overset{\frown}{AB}$ of $\odot O$. If $\angle AOB$ is an acute angle, then $m \angle AZB > \underline{\quad?\quad}$.

26. If the legs of a right triangle have lengths 2 and 7, then the sine of the smallest angle of the triangle equals $\underline{\quad?\quad}$.

27. If the lengths of the sides of a triangle are k, v, and n, and if $k^2 < v^2 - n^2$, then the triangle is a(n) $\underline{\quad?\quad}$ triangle.

28. If $\overline{RS}$ and $\overline{TP}$ are chords of $\odot O$, and if $RS > TP$, then $m \angle ROS \underline{\quad?\quad} m \angle TOP$.

29. The legs of a right triangle have lengths 6 and 8. In a similar right triangle, whose hypotenuse has length 50, the perimeter equals $\underline{\quad?\quad}$.

30. In a regular square pyramid with a base edge 14 cm long and an altitude 9 cm long, the lateral area equals $\underline{\quad?\quad}$ cm^2.

31. A cube with a diagonal $7\sqrt{3}$ cm long has a volume of $\underline{\quad?\quad}$ cm^3.

32. If an isosceles right triangle has an area equal to the area of a 10 by 12 rectangle, then the hypotenuse of the triangle has length $\underline{\quad?\quad}$.

Construction Exercises

On your paper draw an angle and two segments like those shown. Use $\angle T$ and lengths c and d in your constructions.

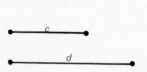 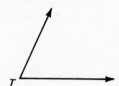

A   1. Construct an angle congruent to $\angle T$.

2. Construct a segment whose length equals $2c + d$.

3. Construct a right triangle whose legs have lengths c and d.

4. Construct a right triangle in which the hypotenuse has length d and one leg has length c.

5. Draw a scalene triangle. Circumscribe a circle about the triangle.

B   6. Construct an isosceles triangle in which each base angle is congruent to $\angle T$ and the altitude to the base has length d.

7. Construct a circle whose area equals $\pi(c^2 + d^2)$.

8. Construct a segment whose length equals $\sqrt{2cd}$.

9. Draw a circle, $\odot O$, with radius c. Take any point P such that $OP = d$. Construct a tangent to $\odot O$ from point P.

10. Construct a segment with length x such that $\dfrac{c}{d} = \dfrac{d}{x}$.

EXAMINATIONS

CHAPTER 1

Indicate the best answer by writing the appropriate letter.

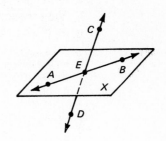

1. Plane X contains:
   a. $\overleftrightarrow{CD}$ b. $\overleftrightarrow{EC}$ c. $\overrightarrow{AB}$ d. point D

2. In mathematics, basic assumptions are called:
   a. theorems   b. postulates   c. conditionals   d. deductions

3. The distance between points D and E is expressed by:
   a. $\overline{DE}$ b. $\overleftrightarrow{DE}$ c. DE d. $\overrightarrow{DE}$

4. If points A, B, and C are noncollinear, a simple name for $\overleftrightarrow{AB} \cap \overline{BC}$ is:
   a. $\overrightarrow{AB}$ b. $\overline{AC}$ c. $\overleftrightarrow{AC}$ d. point B

5. On the number line, the distance between two points with coordinates 3 and -5 is:
   a. 2   b. 8   c. -2 d. -8

6. If point T lies on $\overrightarrow{EB}$ but not on $\overline{EB}$, then the correct order of points B, E, and T is:
   a. $\overline{EBT}$ b. $\overline{BET}$ c. $\overline{BTE}$ d. unknown

7. The statement "If $AB = DF$ and $DF = RS$, then $AB = RS$" illustrates that the equality of numbers is:
   a. reflexive   b. symmetric   c. transitive   d. associative

8. For all real numbers r and s, if $r < s$ and $t > 0$, then:
   a. $rt = st$ b. $r + t > s + t$ c. $rt > st$ d. $rt < st$

9. In the conditional "If s, then t," s is called the:
   a. hypothesis   b. conclusion   c. deduction   d. converse

10. If point A lies outside line t, the number of planes that contain point A and line t is:
    a. 0   b. exactly 1   c. unlimited   d. unknown

11. On the number line, point D has coordinate 4 and point E has coordinate 12. Point X lies on $\overrightarrow{ED}$ and $EX = 5$. The coordinate of X is:
    a. -1 b. 7   c. 17   d. 9

12. The converse of the conditional "If q, then r" is:
    a. If r, then q b. r, if q c. When q, then r d. r, only if q

CHAPTER 2

Indicate the best answer by writing the appropriate letter.

1. The vertex of $\angle RST$ is point:
   a. R b. S c. T d. unknown

2. In the plane figure shown, $\angle 1$ and $\angle 2$ are:
   a. vertical ∡
   b. obtuse ∡
   c. adjacent ∡
   d. supplementary ∡

3. The number of angles in the figure shown is:
   a. 3   b. 4   c. 5   d. 6

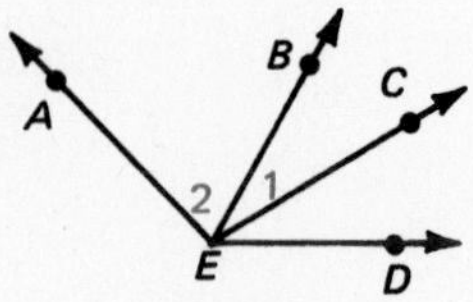

4. In the plane figure shown, $m\angle AEC + m\angle CED$ equals:
   a. $m\angle AED$ b. $m\angle DEB$ c. $m\angle BEC$ d. $m\angle AEB$

Exs. 2–5

5. If $\overrightarrow{EC}$ bisects $\angle DEB$ and $m\angle DEC = 28$, then $m\angle CEB$ equals:
   a. 28   b. 56   c. $m\angle DEB$ d. unknown

6. If $m\angle 1 = 30$ and $m\angle 2 = 60$, then $\angle 1$ and $\angle 2$ are:
   a. vertical ∡
   b. supplementary ∡
   c. complementary ∡
   d. adjacent ∡

7. If $m\angle 1 = 3x$, $m\angle 2 = 7x$, and $\angle 1$ is a supplement of $\angle 2$, then x equals:
   a. 9   b. 18   c. 90   d. 180

8. If the exterior sides of two adjacent angles lie in perpendicular lines, the angles are:
   a. congruent   b. obtuse   c. supplementary   d. complementary

9. If $\angle 1$ is complementary to $\angle 3$, and $\angle 2$ is complementary to $\angle 3$, then:
   a. $m\angle 1 = m\angle 3$
   b. $m\angle 1 > m\angle 3$
   c. $m\angle 1 = m\angle 2$
   d. $m\angle 1 > m\angle 2$

10. The statement "If $\angle A \cong \angle B$, then $\angle B \cong \angle A$" illustrates that congruence of angles is:
    a. reflexive   b. symmetric   c. transitive   d. associative

11. $\angle T$ and $\angle A$ are vertical angles. If $m\angle T = 2x + 8$ and $m\angle A = x + 22$, then x equals:
    a. 50   b. 20   c. 30   d. 14

12. The left column of a two-column proof is labeled:
    a. statements   b. reasons   c. given   d. prove

CHAPTER 3

Indicate the best answer by writing the appropriate letter.

1. If t and l are skew lines, then:
   a. t and l are coplanar
   b. $t \cup l = \emptyset$
   c. $t \cap l = \emptyset$
   d. $t \parallel l$

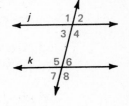

2. If $j \parallel k$, then $\angle 5$ is congruent to:
   a. $\angle 7$ b. $\angle 3$ c. $\angle 2$ d. $\angle 1$

3. If $j \parallel k$ and $m\angle 1 = 100$, then $\angle 6$ is:
   a. acute   b. right   c. obtuse   d. unknown

4. The number of obtuse angles in an obtuse triangle is:
   a. 0   b. 1   c. 2   d. 3

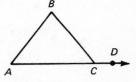

5. If $m\angle A = 50$ and $m\angle B = 80$, then $m\angle BCD$ equals:
   a. 30   b. 100   c. 130   d. unknown

6. The sum of the measures of the interior angles of a convex octagon equals:
   a. 900   b. 1080   c. 360   d. 720

7. The sum of the measures of the exterior angles of a convex pentagon, one angle at each vertex, equals:
   a. 180   b. 360   c. 540   d. 720

8. The total number of diagonals that can be drawn from one vertex of a hexagon is:
   a. 3   b. 4   c. 5   d. 6

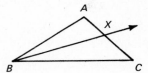

9. In $\triangle ABC$, $\overrightarrow{BX}$ bisects $\angle ABC$, $m\angle A = 110$, and $m\angle C = 40$. $m\angle ABX$ equals:
   a. 30   b. 25   c. 20   d. 15

10. If the measure of each interior angle of a regular polygon is 150, the polygon has:
    a. 8 sides   b. 10 sides   c. 12 sides   d. 14 sides

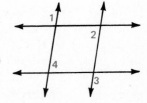

11. If $m\angle 1 = 100$, $m\angle 2 = 80$, and $m\angle 3 = 100$, then $m\angle 4$ equals:
    a. 100   b. 80   c. 70   d. 60

CHAPTER 4

Indicate the best answer by writing the appropriate letter.

1. In $\triangle RST$, the angle included between $\overline{RS}$ and $\overline{ST}$ is:
   a. $\angle R$ b. $\angle S$ c. $\angle T$ d. $\angle SRT$

2. $\triangle ABC \cong \triangle RST$, then:
   a. $\triangle ACB \cong \triangle STR$ b. $\triangle CAB \cong \triangle TSR$ c. $\triangle BAC \cong \triangle STR$
   d. $\triangle BAC \cong \triangle SRT$

3. If $\triangle DEF \cong \triangle PRS$, then:
   a. $\overline{DF} \cong \overline{PS}$ b. $\overline{EF} \cong \overline{PR}$ c. $\angle E \cong \angle S$ d. $\angle F \cong \angle R$

4. There is no congruence method that is abbreviated by:
   a. ASA   b. SSA   c. HL   d. HA

In Exercises 5–10, select the method that can
be used to prove $\triangle ABC \cong \triangle EDC$.

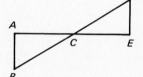

Exs. 5–10

5. Given: $\overline{AC} \cong \overline{EC}$; $\overline{BC} \cong \overline{DC}$
   a. SSS   b. ASA   c. SAS   d. AAS

6. Given: $\angle A \cong \angle E$; $\overline{AC} \cong \overline{EC}$
   a. LA   b. SAS   c. SSS   d. ASA

7. Given: $\angle B \cong \angle D$; $\overline{AC} \cong \overline{EC}$
   a. AAS   b. SAS   c. SSS   d. ASA

8. Given: $\angle A$ and $\angle E$ are rt. $\angle$s; $\overline{AC} \cong \overline{EC}$
   a. LL   b. HL   c. LA   d. HA

9. Given: $\angle A$ and $\angle E$ are rt. $\angle$s; $\overline{BC} \cong \overline{DC}$
   a. LL   b. HA   c. LA   d. HL

10. Given: $\angle A$ and $\angle E$ are rt. $\angle$s; $\overline{AB} \cong \overline{ED}$
    a. LL   b. HL   c. SAS   d. AAS

11. The measure of one base angle of an isosceles triangle is 52. The measure
    of the vertex angle is:
    a. 64   b. 128   c. 76   d. 104

12. In isosceles $\triangle DEF$, $DE = DF$. If $DE = 2x + 14$, $DF = 5x - 1$, and
    $EF = 2x + 3$, the perimeter of $\triangle DEF$ is:
    a. 5   b. 37   c. 48   d. 61

CHAPTER 5

Indicate the best answer by writing the appropriate letter.

1. If quadrilateral *RSTW* is a parallelogram and *ST* = 16, then *WT* is equal to:
   a. 16   b. *WR*   c. *RT*   d. unknown

2. If quadrilateral *ABCD* is a parallelogram and $m \angle A$ = 80, then $m \angle C$ is equal to:
   a. $m \angle B$ b. 100   c. 80   d. $m \angle D$

3. If quadrilateral *EFGH* is a parallelogram, then:
   a. $\angle HEG \cong \angle FEG$ c. $\triangle HEG \cong \triangle FGE$
   b. *HG* = *FG*   d. $\angle FGE \cong \angle FEG$

In Exercises 4–8, information is given about a quadrilateral *ABCD*. In each exercise select the word that best describes the quadrilateral.

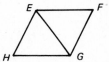

4. Given: $\overline{AB} \parallel \overline{CD}$; *AB* = *CD*
   a. parallelogram   b. rectangle   c. rhombus   d. square

5. Given: *AB* = *CD*; *BC* = *AD*; $m \angle A$ = 90
   a. parallelogram   b. rectangle   c. rhombus   d. square

6. Given: $\overline{AC}$ and $\overline{BD}$ bisect each other; $\overline{AC} \perp \overline{BD}$; *AC* = *BD*
   a. paralleogram   b. rectangle   c. rhombus   d. square

7. Given: $\overline{AB} \parallel \overline{CD}$; $\overline{AD} \parallel \overline{BC}$; *AC* = *BC*
   a. parallelogram   b. rectangle   c. rhombus   d. square

8. Given: $\overline{AC}$ and $\overline{BD}$ bisect each other; *AB* = *BC*
   a. parallelogram   b. rectangle   c. rhombus   d. square

9. The lengths of the bases of a trapezoid are 16 and 24. The length of the median is:
   a. 8   b. 40   c. 30   d. 20

10. In $\triangle OMN$, points *E* and *B* are the midpoints of $\overline{OM}$ and $\overline{ON}$. If *OE* = 5, *OB* = 7, and *EB* = 8, then the perimeter of $\triangle OMN$ equals:
    a. 40   b. 32   c. 20   d. 16

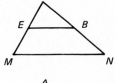

11. In $\triangle ABC$, $m \angle A$ = 50 and $m \angle ACD$ = 120. The longest side of $\triangle ABC$ is:
    a. $\overline{AB}$ b. $\overline{BC}$ c. $\overline{AC}$ d. unknown

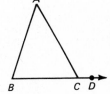

12. In $\triangle XYZ$, *XY* = 6 and *YZ* = 10. Then:
    a. *XZ* > 16   c. *XZ* < 4
    b. *XZ* > 10   d. *XZ* > 4

CHAPTER 6

Indicate the best answer by writing the appropriate letter.

1. The ratio of 12 to 20 written in reduced form is:
   a. 4:5   b. 5:3   c. 3:5   d. 2:3

2. If 5:8 = 10:x, then x equals:
   a. 16   b. 12   c. 6   d. 4

3. The proportion $\dfrac{5}{13} = \dfrac{x}{11}$ is equivalent to:

   a. $\dfrac{5}{x} = \dfrac{11}{13}$ b. $\dfrac{13}{11} = \dfrac{x}{5}$ c. $\dfrac{x}{13} = \dfrac{11}{5}$ d. $\dfrac{11}{x} = \dfrac{13}{5}$

4. If $\triangle DEF \sim \triangle PMR$, then $\triangle FDE$ is similar to:
   a. $\triangle MRP$ b. $\triangle MPR$ c. $\triangle RMP$ d. $\triangle RPM$

5. If $\triangle ABC \sim \triangle MNO$, then:

   a. $\angle A \cong \angle N$ b. $\dfrac{AB}{BC} = \dfrac{MN}{MO}$ c. $\angle B \cong \angle N$ d. $\dfrac{BC}{NO} = \dfrac{AC}{MN}$

6. If quad. *WXYZ* is similar to quad. *PRST*, then $\overline{XY}$ corresponds to:
   a. $\overline{RS}$ b. $\overline{PR}$ c. $\overline{RT}$ d. $\overline{PT}$

7. If $\triangle ABC \sim \triangle DEF$, then the ratio of $m\angle B$ to $m\angle E$ is:
   a. $m\angle A : m\angle F$ b. 1:1   c. $AB:DE$ d. unknown

8. In $\triangle DFC$, $\overline{EB} \parallel \overline{FC}$. If $DE = 4$, $DB = 6$, and $EF = 6$, then BC equals:
   a. 4   b. 6   c. 8   d. 9

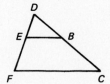

9. In $\triangle RST$, $\overline{KA} \parallel \overline{RS}$. If $TK = 6$, $KA = 6$, and $KR = 3$, then RS equals:
   a. 3   b. 6   c. 9   d. 12

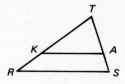

10. In $\triangle PRS$, $\overline{PX}$ bisects $\angle RPS$. If $SX = 4$, $XR = 3$, and $PR = 10$, then SP equals:
    a. $7\frac{1}{2}$ b. $13\frac{1}{3}$ c. 15   d. unknown

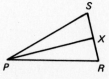

11. If the lengths of the corresponding sides of two similar polygons have the ratio 1:1, the polygons must be:
    a. congruent   b. regular   c. equilateral   d. equiangular

12. A 48-centimeter segment is divided into three parts whose lengths have the ratio 2:3:3. The length, in centimeters, of the shortest segment is:
    a. 6   b. 12   c. 16   d. 18

CHAPTER 7

Indicate the best answer by writing the appropriate letter.

1. The geometric mean between 3 and 12 is:
   a. 2   b. 4   c. 6   d. 8

2. Expressed in simplified form, $\sqrt{48}$ is equivalent to:
   a. $\sqrt{48}$ b. $2\sqrt{12}$ c. $3\sqrt{4}$ d. $4\sqrt{3}$

Exercises 3–5 refer to $\triangle ABC$ with $m\angle ABC = 90$, and $\overline{BD} \perp \overline{AC}$.

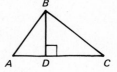

3. $\triangle ABD$ is similar to:
   a. $\triangle BCD$ b. $\triangle CBD$ c. $\triangle ABC$ d. $\triangle CAB$

4. BC is the geometric mean between AC and:
   a. AB b. BD c. DC d. AD

5. If $AB = 10$ and $BD = 8$, then AD equals:
   a. 4   b. 6   c. 8   d. 10

6. If the length of the shorter leg of a 30°–60°–90° $\triangle$ is 4, then the length of the hypotenuse is:
   a. 2   b. $4\sqrt{3}$ c. $4\sqrt{2}$ d. 8

7. If the length of the sides of a triangle are 3, 4, and 6, the triangle is:
   a. a 30°–60°–90° $\triangle$ c. a rt. $\triangle$
   b. a 45°–45°–90° $\triangle$ d. not a rt. $\triangle$

8. If the length of the hypotenuse of a 45°–45°–90° $\triangle$ is 8, then the length of a leg is:
   a. $8\sqrt{2}$ b. $4\sqrt{2}$ c. 4   d. $4\sqrt{3}$

9. If the dimensions of a rectangular solid are 3, 4, and 5, then the length of a diagonal of the solid is:
   a. 5   b. $5\sqrt{3}$ c. $\sqrt{34}$ d. $5\sqrt{2}$

10. In $\triangle RST$, $m\angle S = 90$. Tan R is equal to:
    a. $\dfrac{TS}{RS}$ b. $\dfrac{RS}{TS}$ c. $\dfrac{TS}{RT}$ d. $\dfrac{RS}{RT}$

11. In $\triangle RST$, $m\angle S = 90$. Sin T is equal to:
    a. $\dfrac{ST}{RT}$ b. $\dfrac{RS}{ST}$ c. $\dfrac{RS}{RT}$ d. $\dfrac{RT}{RS}$

12. In $\triangle JKM$, $m\angle K = 90$. If $\sin 25° \doteq .42$, $\cos 25° \doteq .91$ and $\tan 25° \doteq .47$, then x, correct to one decimal, is:
    a. 9.1   b. 4.7   c. 2.5   d. 4.2

CHAPTER 8

Indicate the best answer by writing the appropriate letter.

1. If two circles are externally tangent, the maximum number of common tangents that can be drawn to the circles is:
   a. 1   b. 2   c. 3   d. 4

2. If points *A* and *B* lie on a circle, then $\overleftrightarrow{AB}$ is a:
   a. chord   b. secant   c. radius   d. tangent

3. A major arc of circle *R* is:

   a. $\overarc{DEF}$ b. $\overarc{ED}$ c. $\overarc{DGF}$ d. $\overarc{ED}$

   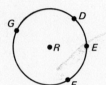

4. In circle *R*, $m\,\overarc{GD} + m\,\overarc{DF}$ equals:

   a. $m\,\overarc{DEF}$ b. $m\,\overarc{GDE}$ c. $m\,\overarc{GFD}$ d. $m\,\overarc{GDF}$

Exercises 5–7 refer to circle *O* with $m\,\overarc{AB} = 100$ and $m\,\overarc{AD} = 110$.

5. The measure of $\angle ABC$ is:
   a. 100   b. 90   c. 80   d. 70

6. The measure of $\angle A$ is:
   a. 40   b. 50   c. 60   d. 80

7. The measure of $\angle AXD$ is:
   a. 85   b. 90   c. 95   d. 100

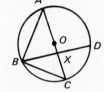

Exercises 8–10 refer to circle *S*.

8. If $m\,\overarc{FG} = 80$ and $m\,\overarc{EC} = 44$, then $m\angle D$ equals:
   a. 62   b. 36   c. 22   d. 18

9. If $CX = 4, XG = 6$ and $XH = 3$, then XF equals:
   a. 12   b. 8   c. 4.5   d. 2

10. If $DE = 6$, $EF = 8$, and $DC = 5$, then DG equals:
    a. 9.6   b. 11.8   c. 16.8   d. 18

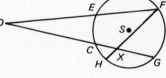

11. Quadrilateral *WXYZ* is inscribed in circle *P*. If $m\angle X = 80$ and $m\,\overarc{XW} = 105$, then $m\,\overarc{XY}$ equals:
    a. 95   b. 100   c. 105   d. 110

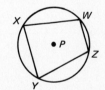

12. $\overleftrightarrow{CD}$ is tangent to circle *R* at point *B*, and $\overline{RE} \perp \overline{AB}$. If $AB = 6\sqrt{3}$ and $RE = 6$, then $m\angle ABC$ equals:
    a. 105   b. 110   c. 115   d. 120

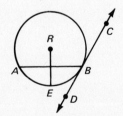

CHAPTER 9

Indicate the best answer by writing the appropriate letter.

1. A central angle of a regular polygon cannot have a measure of:
   a. 30   b. 40   c. 50   d. 60

2. When given the perimeter, you can always find the area of a:
   a. triangle   b. square   c. parallelogram   d. rhombus

3. If a pyramid has a base with n sides, the total number of faces of the pyramid is:
   a. $n - 1$ b. n c. $n + 1$ d. $2n$

4. If the area of a square is 18, the length of each diagonal is:
   a. $3\sqrt{2}$ b. $6\sqrt{2}$ c. $3\sqrt{3}$ d. 6

5. In a circle of radius 2 cm, a sector of area $\dfrac{4\pi}{5}$ cm^2 has an arc with degree measure:
   a. 30   b. 60   c. 72   d. 90

6. If the ratio of the volume of two cubes is $8:27$, the ratio of their total areas is:
   a. $2:3$ b. $4:9$ c. $8:27$ d. $16:81$

7. An isosceles triangle with base length 8 and perimeter 20 has an area of:
   a. 12   b. 16   c. $8\sqrt{5}$ d. $16\sqrt{5}$

8. Two sides of a triangle have lengths of 6 and 10. If their included angle has a measure of 60, the area of the triangle is:
   a. 15   b. 30   c. $15\sqrt{3}$ d. $30\sqrt{3}$

9. A trapezoid with area 24 and bases of length 4 and 12 has an altitude of length:
   a. 3   b. 6   c. 8   d. 12

10. If a cone and a cylinder each have a radius of 4 cm and a height of 3 cm, the ratio of their lateral areas is:
    a. $2:3$ b. $3:4$ c. $4:5$ d. $5:6$

CHAPTER 10

Indicate the best answer by writing the appropriate letter.

1. If A is a point in the exterior of a circle, then the total number of tangents that can be constructed through A to the circle is:
   a. 0   b. 1   c. 2   d. 3

2. The center of the circle inscribed in a scalene triangle is the point of intersection of the:
   a. altitudes   c. $\angle$ bisectors
   b. medians   d. $\perp$ bisectors of sides

3. The center of the circle circumscribed about a scalene triangle is the point of intersection of the:
   a. altitudes   c. $\angle$ bisectors
   b. medians   d. $\perp$ bisectors of sides

4. Given two segments whose lengths are r and s, with $r > s$. It is not possible to construct a segment of length x such that:
   a. $x = \frac{1}{5}r$ b. $x = s - r$ c. $x = \sqrt{rs}$ d. $x = 2s + r$

5. In a plane, the locus of points b units from a fixed point A is a:
   a. circle   b. line   c. point   d. ray

6. The locus of points equidistant from two parallel planes is:
   a. a point   b. a line   c. one plane   d. two planes

7. In a plane, the locus of points equidistant from the sides of an angle is a:
   a. point   b. ray   c. plane   d. segment

8. The locus of points equidistant from two fixed points is:
   a. a plane   b. two points   c. one point   d. a circle

9. In a plane, the locus of points t units from a fixed line l is:
   a. a circle   b. a plane   c. one line   d. two lines

10. In a circle, the locus of the midpoints of all chords that are parallel to a fixed diameter is a:
    a. circle   b. line   c. ray   d. segment

11. It is not possible for the intersection of a sphere and a plane to be:
    a. a point   b. the null set   c. a line   d. a circle

12. The locus of points equidistant from the vertices of a triangle is:
    a. another triangle   c. a circle
    b. a line   d. a ray

CHAPTER 11

Indicate the best answer by writing the appropriate letter.

1. The graph of $x = 2y + 1$ is:
   - **a.** a horizontal line
   - **b.** a vertical line
   - **c.** a line neither horizontal nor vertical
   - **d.** not a line

2. For any point (x, y), $|y|$ represents the distance from the point to:
   - **a.** the x-axis
   - **b.** the y-axis
   - **c.** the origin
   - **d.** point $(-x, -y)$

3. The distance between $(3, 1)$ and $(-2, 1)$ is:
   - **a.** 5
   - **b.** -5
   - **c.** 1
   - **d.** 0

4. Three vertices of a square are $(-2, 5)$, $(1, -2)$, and $(3, 3)$. The fourth vertex is:
   - **a.** $(6, -4)$
   - **b.** $(-4, 0)$
   - **c.** $(-3, -1)$
   - **d.** $(0, -4)$

5. The quadrilateral with vertices $(2, 3)$, $(-4, -5)$, $(-4, -15)$ and $(2, -7)$ is a:
   - **a.** trapezoid
   - **b.** parallelogram
   - **c.** rhombus
   - **d.** rectangle

6. The midpoint of $\overline{AB}$ is $(3, 4)$. If the coordinates of B are $(6, 6)$, then the coordinates of A are:
   - **a.** $(9, 10)$
   - **b.** $(4.5, 5)$
   - **c.** $(0, 2)$
   - **d.** $(9, 8)$

7. An equation of a line for which slope is not defined is:
   - **a.** $y = x$
   - **b.** $y = 0$
   - **c.** $y = -x$
   - **d.** $x = 5$

8. One point on a line with slope $\frac{2}{3}$ is $(6, 1)$. If the y-coordinate of another point on the line is 5, the x-coordinate of that point is:
   - **a.** -3
   - **b.** 12
   - **c.** $\frac{1}{3}$
   - **d.** 30

9. Lines j and k are perpendicular. The slope of j is 6, and the slope of k is $\frac{x}{3}$. The value of x is:
   - **a.** $-\frac{1}{2}$
   - **b.** $\frac{1}{2}$
   - **c.** 2
   - **d.** -2

10. The lines with equations $2x + 5y = 11$ and $4x - 10y = 2$ intersect at:
    - **a.** $(1, 1)$
    - **b.** $(1, 3)$
    - **c.** $(3, -1)$
    - **d.** $(3, 1)$

11. Points $(a, 0)$ and $(-a, 0)$ are two of the vertices of an equilateral triangle. The third vertex, which lies on the positive y-axis, is point:
    - **a.** $(0, a)$
    - **b.** $(0, 2a)$
    - **c.** $(0, a\sqrt{3})$
    - **d.** $(a\sqrt{3}, 0)$

12. If three consecutive vertices of a rhombus are (b, c), $(0, 0)$, and $(\sqrt{b^2 + c^2}, 0)$, with $b > 0$, then the x-coordinate of the fourth vertex is:
    - **a.** c
    - **b.** $\sqrt{b^2 + c^2}$
    - **c.** $b + \sqrt{b^2 + c^2}$
    - **d.** unknown

Indicate the best answer by writing the appropriate letter.

1. If the mapping $\square ABCD \rightarrow \square JKLM$ is an isometry, then:
   a. $\angle DAB \cong \angle JKL$
   b. $\overline{AC} \cong \overline{JL}$
   c. $C \rightarrow M$
   d. $\overline{CD} \cong \overline{MJ}$

2. The reflection of the line $y = x$ in the x-axis is the line:
   a. $x - y = 0$ b. $y = 0$ c. $y = -x$ d. $y = -2$

3. A transformation that maps the point $(-2, 1)$ into $(2, 1)$ is a reflection in:
   a. the x-axis   b. the line $y = x$ c. the y-axis   d. the origin

4. If M denotes the point $(1, 2)$, then $(-1, 3) \xrightarrow{H_M}$
   a. $(3, 1)$
   b. $(1, -3)$
   c. $(-1, -2)$
   d. $(3, -1)$

5. A quadrilateral with four lines of symmetry is a:
   a. parallelogram
   b. rectangle
   c. rhombus
   d. square

6. For nonequilateral $\triangle ABC$, where $\overline{AC} \cong \overline{BC}$, a statement which is *not* true is:
   a. $\triangle ABC \cong \triangle BAC$
   b. $\triangle ABC \cong \triangle BCA$
   c. $\triangle BCA \cong \triangle ACB$
   d. $\triangle ABC \cong \triangle ABC$

Exercises 7–10 refer to the diagram at the right.

7. $J \xrightarrow{M_x \circ H_O}$
   a. J b. K c. L d. M

8. $J \xrightarrow{M_y \circ M_x}$
   a. J b. K c. L d. M

9. $\triangle LMJ \xrightarrow{R_{O,90}}$
   a. $\triangle JKL$ b. $\triangle KLM$ c. $\triangle LMJ$ d. $\triangle MJK$

10. $J \xrightarrow{T_{KK'}}$
    a. K b. O c. K' d. unknown

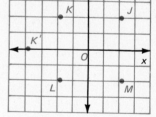

11. The image of point A $(2, 4)$ under a dilation with center $(0, 0)$ and scale factor 2 is:
    a. $(4, 2)$ b. $(-2, -4)$ c. $(4, 8)$ d. $(8, 4)$

12. The image of point Y $(3, 6)$ under a dilation with center $(3, 6)$ and scale factor $\frac{1}{3}$ is:
    a. $(1, 2)$ b. $(3, 6)$ c. $(0, 0)$ d. $(-3, -6)$

POSTULATES

POSTULATE 1   A line contains at least two points; a plane contains at least three points not all in one line; space contains at least four points not all in one plane.

POSTULATE 2   Through any two points there is exactly one line.

POSTULATE 3   Through any three points not on one line there is exactly one plane.

POSTULATE 4   If two points lie in a plane, then the line joining the points lies in that plane.

POSTULATE 5   If two planes intersect, then their intersection is a line.

POSTULATE 6   For any two points there is a unique positive number called the distance between the points.

POSTULATE 7
(THE RULER
POSTULATE)
The points on a line can be paired with the real numbers in such a way that:
1. Any desired point is paired with zero;
2. The distance between any two points is equal to the absolute value of the difference of the numbers paired with the points.

POSTULATE 8   For every angle there is a unique number between 0 and 180 called the measure of the angle.

POSTULATE 9
(PROTRACTOR
POSTULATE)
The set of rays which have a common endpoint O in the edge of a half-plane, and which lie in the half-plane or its edge, can be paired with the numbers between 0 and 180, inclusive, in such a way that:
1. One of the rays in the edge is paired with 0, and the other is paired with 180;
2. If $\overrightarrow{OA}$ is paired with x and $\overrightarrow{OB}$ with y, then $m\angle AOB = |x - y|$.

POSTULATE 10
(ANGLE
ADDITION
POSTULATE)
If point B lies in the interior of $\angle AOC$, then $m\angle AOB + m\angle BOC = m\angle AOC$.

POSTULATE 11	If two parallel lines are cut by a transversal, corresponding angles are congruent.
POSTULATE 12	If two lines are cut by a transversal so that corresponding angles are congruent, the lines are parallel.
POSTULATE 13 (SSS POSTULATE)	If three sides of one triangle are congruent to the corresponding parts of another triangle, the triangles are congruent.
POSTULATE 14 (SAS POSTULATE)	If two sides and the included angle of one triangle are congruent to the corresponding parts of another triangle, the triangles are congruent.
POSTULATE 15 (HL POSTULATE)	If the hypotenuse and a leg of one right triangle are congruent to the corresponding parts of another right triangle, the triangles are congruent.
POSTULATE 16 (ASA POSTULATE)	If two angles and the included side of one triangle are congruent to the corresponding parts of another triangle, the triangles are congruent.
POSTULATE 17 (AA POSTULATE)	If two angles of one triangle are congruent to two angles of another triangle, the triangles are similar.
POSTULATE 18 (ARC ADDITION POSTULATE)	If the intersection of arcs $\overset{\frown}{AX}$ and $\overset{\frown}{XB}$ of a circle is the single point X, then $m\ \overset{\frown}{AX} + m\ \overset{\frown}{XB} = m\ \overset{\frown}{AXB}$.
POSTULATE 19	Corresponding to every polygonal region there is a unique positive number called the area of that region.
POSTULATE 20	If two triangles are congruent, the regions they bound have the same area.
POSTULATE 21 (AREA-ADDITION POSTULATE)	A polygonal region can be separated into a finite number of non-overlapping regions, the sum of whose areas is equal to the area of the given region.
POSTULATE 22	The area of a rectangle is equal to the product of the length of a base and the length of an altitude to that base. ($A = bh$)

THEOREMS

Elements of Geometry

1-1 If two lines intersect, they intersect in exactly one point.

1-2 If a point lies outside a line, exactly one plane contains the line and the point.

1-3 If two lines intersect, exactly one plane contains both lines.

1-4 On a ray there is exactly one point at a given distance d from the endpoint of the ray.

1-5 A segment has exactly one midpoint.

Angles; Perpendicular Lines

2-1 If the exterior sides of two adjacent angles lie in a line, then the angles are supplementary.

2-2 In a half-plane, through the endpoint of a ray that lies in the edge of the half-plane, there is exactly one other ray such that the angle formed by the two rays has a given measure.

2-3 An angle has exactly one bisector.

2-4 All right angles are congruent.

2-5 If two lines are perpendicular, they form congruent adjacent angles.

2-6 If two lines form congruent adjacent angles, the lines are perpendicular.

2-7 If the exterior sides of two adjacent acute angles lie in perpendicular lines, the angles are complementary.

2-8 In a plane, through a given point on a line, there is exactly one perpendicular to the line.

2-9 If two angles are complementary to the same angle, they are congruent to each other.

2-10 If two angles are complementary to two congruent angles, they are congruent to each other.

2-11 If two angles are supplementary to the same angle, they are congruent to each other.

2-12 If two angles are supplementary to two congruent angles, they are congruent to each other.

2-13   Vertical angles are congruent.

2-14   Congruence of segments is reflexive, symmetric, and transitive.

2-15   Congruence of angles is reflexive, symmetric, and transitive.

Parallel Lines and Planes

3-1   If two parallel lines are cut by a transversal, alternate interior angles are congruent.

3-2   If a transversal is perpendicular to one of two parallel lines, it is perpendicular to the other one also.

3-3   If two lines are cut by a transversal so that the alternate interior angles are congruent, the lines are parallel.

3-4   In a plane, if two lines are perpendicular to a third line, they are parallel to each other.

3-5   Through a point outside a line, exactly one parallel can be drawn to the line.

3-6   Through a point outside a line, exactly one perpendicular can be drawn to that line.

3-7   The sum of the measures of the angles of a triangle is 180.

       COROLLARY 1   If two angles of one triangle are congruent to two angles of another triangle, the third angles are congruent.

       COROLLARY 2   Each angle of an equiangular triangle has measure 60.

       COROLLARY 3   In a triangle, there can be at most one right angle or obtuse angle.

       COROLLARY 4   The acute angles of a right triangle are complementary.

3-8   The measure of an exterior angle of a triangle is equal to the sum of the measures of the two remote interior angles.

Congruent Triangles

4-1   Congruence of triangles is reflexive, symmetric, and transitive.

4-2
(LL
THEOREM)   If two legs of one right triangle are congruent to the corresponding parts of another right triangle, the triangles are congruent.

4-3
(AAS
THEOREM)   If two angles and a not-included side of one triangle are congruent to the corresponding parts of another triangle, the triangles are congruent.

4-4 (HA THEOREM)	If the hypotenuse and an acute angle of one right triangle are congruent to the corresponding parts of another right triangle, the triangles are congruent.

4-5
(LA
THEOREM)   If a leg and an acute angle of one right triangle are congruent to the corresponding parts of another right triangle, the triangles are congruent.

4-6   If two sides of a triangle are congruent, the angles opposite those sides are congruent.

COROLLARY 1   An equilateral triangle is also equiangular.

COROLLARY 2   Each angle of an equilateral triangle has measure 60.

4-7   If two angles of a triangle are congruent, the sides opposite those angles are congruent.

COROLLARY   An equiangular triangle is also equilateral.

Applying Congruent Triangles

5-1   A diagonal of a parallelogram separates the parallelogram into two congruent triangles.

COROLLARY 1   Opposite sides of a parallelogram are congruent.

COROLLARY 2   Opposite angles of a parallelogram are congruent.

5-2   The diagonals of a parallelogram bisect each other.

5-3   If two sides of a quadrilateral are congruent and parallel, the quadrilateral is a parallelogram.

5-4   If both pairs of opposite sides of a quadrilateral are congruent, the quadrilateral is a parallelogram.

5-5   If the diagonals of a quadrilateral bisect each other, the quadrilateral is a parallelogram.

5-6   If three parallel lines cut off congruent segments on one transversal, they cut off congruent segments on every transversal.

5-7   The diagonals of a rectangle are congruent.

5-8   The diagonals of a rhombus are perpendicular.

5-9   Each diagonal of a rhombus bisects a pair of opposite angles.

5-10   The median of a trapezoid is parallel to the bases and has a length equal to half the sum of the lengths of the bases.

5-11　The segment joining the midpoints of two sides of a triangle is parallel to the third side and its length is half the length of the third side.

5-12　If one side of a triangle is longer than a second side, then the angle opposite the first side is larger than the angle opposite the second side.

5-13　If one angle of a triangle is larger than a second angle, then the side opposite the first angle is longer than the side opposite the second angle.

COROLLARY 1　The perpendicular segment from a point to a line is the shortest segment from the point to the line.

COROLLARY 2　The perpendicular segment from a point to a plane is the shortest segment from the point to the plane.

5-14　The sum of the lengths of any two sides of a triangle is greater than the length of the third side.

5-15　If two sides of one triangle are congruent to two sides of another triangle, but the included angle of the first triangle is larger than the included angle of the second, then the third side of the first triangle is longer than the third side of the second.

5-16　If two sides of one triangle are congruent to two sides of another triangle, but the third side of the first triangle is longer than the third side of the second, then the included angle of the first triangle is larger than the included angle of the second.

Similar Polygons

6-1　Similarity of polygons is reflexive, symmetric, and transitive.

6-2　If two polygons are similar, the ratio of their perimeters equals the ratio of the lengths of any pair of corresponding sides.

6-3　If an angle of one triangle is congruent to an angle of another triangle and the lengths of the sides including those angles are proportional, the triangles are similar.

6-4　If a line is parallel to one side of a triangle and intersects the other two sides, it divides them proportionally.

COROLLARY　If three parallel lines intersect two transversals, they divide them proportionally.

6-5　If a ray bisects an angle of a triangle, it divides the opposite side into segments whose lengths are proportional to the lengths of the other two sides.

Right Triangles

7-1   If the altitude is drawn to the hypotenuse of a right triangle, the two triangles formed are similar to the given triangle and to each other.

COROLLARY   If the altitude is drawn to the hypotenuse of a right triangle, the length of a leg of the right triangle is the geometric mean between the length of the hypotenuse and the length of the segment of the hypotenuse adjacent to that leg.

7-2   In any right triangle the square of the length of the hypotenuse is equal to the sum of the squares of the lengths of the legs.

7-3   If the sum of the squares of the lengths of two sides of a triangle is equal to the square of the length of the third side, the triangle is a right triangle.

7-4   If each acute angle of a right triangle has measure 45, the hypotenuse is $\sqrt{2}$ times as long as a leg.

7-5   If the acute angles of a right triangle have measures 30 and 60:

(a) The hypotenuse is twice as long as the shorter leg.

(b) The longer leg is $\sqrt{3}$ times as long as the shorter leg.

Circles

8-1   A line that lies in the plane of a circle and contains an interior point of the circle intersects the circle in two points.

8-2   A tangent to a circle is perpendicular to the radius drawn to the point of tangency.

8-3   A line that lies in the plane of a circle and is perpendicular to a radius at its outer endpoint is tangent to the circle.

8-4   In the same circle or in congruent circles, if two central angles are congruent, their arcs are congruent.

8-5   In the same circle or in congruent circles, if two minor arcs are congruent, their central angles are congruent.

8-6   In the same circle or in congruent circles, congruent chords have congruent arcs.

8-7   In the same circle or in congruent circles, congruent arcs have congruent chords.

8-8   A diameter that is perpendicular to a chord bisects the chord and its two arcs.

8-9   In the same circle or in congruent circles, if two chords are congruent, they are equally distant from the center.

8-10   In the same circle or in congruent circles, if two chords are equally distant from the center, the chords are congruent.

8-11   The measure of an inscribed angle is equal to half the measure of the intercepted arc.

     COROLLARY 1   If two inscribed angles intercept congruent arcs, the angles are congruent.

     COROLLARY 2   If a quadrilateral is inscribed in a circle, opposite angles are supplementary.

     COROLLARY 3   An angle inscribed in a semicircle is a right angle.

8-12   When a secant ray and a tangent ray are drawn from a point on a circle, the measure of the angle formed is equal to half the measure of the intercepted arc.

8-13   When two secants intersect in the interior of a circle, the measure of an angle formed is equal to half the sum of the measures of the arcs intercepted by that angle and its vertical angle.

8-14   When two secant rays, a secant ray and a tangent ray, or two tangent rays are drawn to a circle from an exterior point, the measure of the angle formed is equal to half the difference of the measures of the intercepted arcs.

8-15   When two chords intersect within a circle, the product of the lengths of the segments of one chord is equal to the product of the lengths of the segments of the other.

8-16   If two secants are drawn to a circle from an exterior point, the product of the lengths of one secant segment and its external segment is equal to the product of the lengths of the other secant segment and its external segment.

8-17

     If a tangent and a secant are drawn to a circle from an exterior point, the square of the length of the tangent segment is equal to the product of the lengths of the secant segment and its external segment.

Areas and Volumes

9-1   The area of a square is equal to the square of the length of a side. ($A = s^2$)

9-2   The area of a parallelogram is equal to the product of the length of a base and the length of a corresponding altitude. ($A = bh$)

9-3   The area of a triangle is equal to one-half the product of the length of a base and the length of a corresponding altitude. ($A = \frac{1}{2}bh$)

     COROLLARY 1   The area of a rhombus is equal to one-half the product of the lengths of its diagonals. ($A = \frac{1}{2}d_1 d_2$)

COROLLARY 2 The area of an equilateral triangle of side length s is equal to $\dfrac{s^2\sqrt{3}}{4}$. $\left(A = \dfrac{s^2\sqrt{3}}{4}\right)$

9-4 The area of a trapezoid is equal to one-half the product of the length of an altitude and the sum of the lengths of the bases. $A = \frac{1}{2}h(b_1 + b_2)$

9-5 Any three noncollinear points lie on a circle.

9-6 A circle can be circumscribed about any regular polygon.

9-7 A circle can be inscribed in any regular polygon.

COROLLARY The inscribed and circumscribed circles of a regular polygon have the same point as center.

9-8 The area of a regular polygon is equal to one-half the product of the apothem and the perimeter. $(A = \frac{1}{2}ap)$

9-9 For all circles the ratio of the circumference to the diameter is a constant.

COROLLARY The circumference of a circle is the product of 2π and the radius. $(C = 2\pi r)$

9-10 The area of a circle is equal to the product of π and the square of the radius of the circle. $(A = \pi r^2)$

The Coordinate Plane

11-1 The distance d between two points (x_1, y_1) and (x_2, y_2) is:
$$d = \sqrt{(x_2 - x_1)^2 + (y_2 - y_1)^2}$$

11-2 The coordinates of the midpoint of the segment joining the points (x_1, y_1) and (x_2, y_2) are $\left(\dfrac{x_1 + x_2}{2}, \dfrac{y_1 + y_2}{2}\right)$.

11-3 Two nonvertical lines are parallel if and only if they have equal slopes.

11-4 Two nonvertical lines are perpendicular if and only if the slope of one line is the negative reciprocal of the slope of the other line.
$$m_1 = -\frac{1}{m_2}, \text{ or } m_1 \cdot m_2 = -1$$

11-5 The graph of any equation that can be written in the form $ax + by = c$, a and b not both 0, is a line.

11-6 An equation of the line passing through the point (x_1, y_1) and having slope m is $y - y_1 = m(x - x_1)$.

COROLLARY An equation of the line containing points (x_1, y_1) and (x_2, y_2) is $y - y_1 = m(x - x_1)$, where $m = \dfrac{y_2 - y_1}{x_2 - x_1}$ and $x_2 \neq x_1$.

ANSWERS FOR SELF-TESTS

CHAPTER 1

PAGES 8–9

1–4, 6. Answers may vary.   **1.** R; $\overleftrightarrow{RS}$ **2.** $\overleftrightarrow{TZ}$; M **3.** M; X
4. $\overrightarrow{RX}$; $\overrightarrow{TX}$ **5.** X **6.** T; Y; X; Z
7. No   **8.** Yes   **9.** Through any two points there is exactly one line. (Postulate 2)   **10.** Through any three points not on one line there is exactly one plane. (Postulate 3)   **11.** If two points lie in a plane, then the line joining the points lies in that plane. (Postulate 4)   **12.** If two planes intersect, then their intersection is a line. (Postulate 5)   **13.** plane contains the line and the point (Theorem 1-2)   **14.** plane contains both lines (Theorem 1-3)

PAGE 16

1. d   **2.** b   **3.** a   **4.** c
5. 8   **6.** 2   **7.** 1   **8.** $\overline{ABK}$
9. with equal lengths
10. one midpoint

PAGE 28

1. Deductive   **2.** Inductive
3. X is the midpoint of $\overline{JK}$.
4. $\overline{JX} \cong \overline{XK}$ **5.** If $\overline{JX} \cong \overline{XK}$, then X is the midpoint of $\overline{JK}$.   **6.** Yes; no
7. Given information; definitions; postulates; theorems that have already been proved   **8.** Given
9. Definition of between   **10.** Given
11. Substitution principle   **12.** Given
13. Substitution principle
14. Definition of congruent segments

CHAPTER 2

PAGE 50

1.
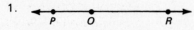

2.
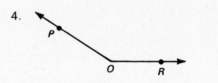

3.
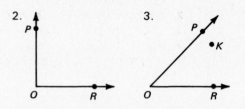

4.

5. $\angle POR$ (or $\angle ROP$)
6. See Exercise 3.   **7.** 20
8. $90 - j$; $180 - j$ **9.** Two pairs
10. Nine pairs   **11.** If the exterior sides of two adjacent angles lie in a line, then the angles are supplementary.
(Theorem 2-1)   **12.** Angle Addition Postulate

PAGE 68

1. In a half-plane, through the endpoint of a ray that lies in the edge of the half-plane, there is exactly one other ray such that the angle formed by the two rays has a given measure.
(Theorem 2-2)   **2.** An angle has exactly one bisector. (Theorem 2-3)
3. Vertical angles are congruent.
(Theorem 2-13)   **4.** If two lines form congruent adjacent angles, the lines are perpendicular. (Theorem 2-6)   **5.** If the exterior sides of two adjacent acute angles lie in perpendicular lines, the angles are complementary.
(Theorem 2-7)   **6.** If two angles are supplementary to the same angle, they are congruent to each other.
(Theorem 2-11)   **7.** lines that form right angles   **8.** Statement; Figure; Given (Hypothesis); To Prove (Conclusion); Proof   **9.** reflexive   **10.** transitive

CHAPTER 3

PAGE 87
1. Parallel; intersecting; skew
2. Parallel; intersecting   3. parallel
4. False   5. True   6. True
7. True   8. True   9. True
10. negation   11. contradiction

PAGE 96
1. If two lines are skew, then they do not
intersect; no; yes   2. If two parallel
lines are cut by a transversal, alternate
interior angles are congruent.
(Theorem 3-1)   3. If two lines are cut
by a transversal so that corresponding
angles are congruent, the lines are
parallel. (Postulate 12)   4. No. (See
Exercise 5.)   5. In a plane, if two lines
are perpendicular to a third line, they are
parallel to each other. (Theorem 3-4)
6. Through a point outside a line, exactly
one perpendicular can be drawn to that
line. (Theorem 3-6)   7. Through a point
outside a line, exactly one parallel can be
drawn to the line. (Theorem 3-5)

PAGE 107
1. $\overline{AB}$; $\overline{BC}$; $\overline{AC}$ 2. $\angle ABC$; $\angle BCA$;
$\angle CAB$ 3. $\angle ABC$; $\angle BCA$
4. $\angle DAE$ 5. 125   6. Isosceles
7. Equiangular   8. 1620   9. A
regular polygon is a convex polygon with
all sides congruent and all angles
congruent.   10. Let n = the number of
sides. Then $22n = 360$; $n = 16\frac{4}{11}$. But n
must be an integer, so the measure of
each exterior angle cannot be 22.

CHAPTER 4

PAGE 130
1. J 2. T; $\overline{TN}$ 3. If three sides of
one triangle are congruent to the
corresponding parts of another triangle,
the triangles are congruent.   4. If the
hypotenuse and a leg of one right triangle

are congruent to the corresponding parts
of another right triangle, the triangles are
congruent.

5. 1. $m\angle KBA = 90$; $m\angle CBA = 90$
(Given)
   2. $\angle KBA$ and $\angle CBA$ are rt. $\angle$.
   (Definition of rt. $\angle$)
   3. $\triangle KBA$ and $\triangle CBA$ are rt. $\triangle$.
   (Definition of rt. $\triangle$)
   4. $\overline{KB} \cong \overline{CB}$ (Given)
   5. $\overline{AB} \cong \overline{AB}$ (Congruence of segments
   is reflexive.)
   6. $\triangle KBA \cong \triangle CBA$ (LL Theorem)

6. 1. $m\angle KBA = 90$; $m\angle CBA = 90$
(Given)
   2. $m\angle KBA = m\angle CBA$ (Substitution
   principle)
   3. $\angle KBA \cong \angle CBA$ (Definition of
   $\cong \angle$)
   4. $\overline{KB} \cong \overline{CB}$ (Given)
   5. $\overline{AB} \cong \overline{AB}$ (Congruence of segments
   is reflexive.)
   6. $\triangle KBA \cong \triangle CBA$ (SAS Postulate)

PAGE 138
1. Yes   2. Yes   3. No   4. Yes

5. 1. $\overline{ZX} \perp \overline{XY}$; $\overline{WY} \perp \overline{XY}$ (Given)
   2. $\angle ZXM$ and $\angle WYM$ are rt. $\angle$.
   (Definition of $\perp$ lines)
   3. $\triangle ZXM$ and $\triangle WYM$ are rt. $\triangle$.
   (Definition of rt. $\triangle$)
   4. M is the midpoint of $\overline{XY}$. (Given)
   5. $\overline{XM} \cong \overline{YM}$ (Definition of midpoint)
   6. $\angle XMZ \cong \angle YMW$ (Vert. $\angle$ are $\cong$.)
   7. $\triangle ZXM \cong \triangle WYM$ (LA Theorem)

6. 1. $\overline{ZX} \perp \overline{XY}$; $\overline{WY} \perp \overline{XY}$ (Given)
   2. $\angle ZXM$ and $\angle WYM$ are rt. $\angle$.
   (Definition of $\perp$ lines)
   3. $\angle ZXM \cong \angle WYM$ (All rt. $\angle$
   are $\cong$.)
   4. M is the midpoint of $\overline{XY}$. (Given)
   5. $\overline{XM} \cong \overline{YM}$ (Definition of midpoint)
   6. $\angle XMZ \cong \angle YMW$ (Vert. $\angle$ are $\cong$.)
   7. $\triangle ZXM \cong \triangle WYM$ (ASA Postulate)

PAGE 148
1. **a.** No   **b.** Yes
2. $\triangle KAB \cong \triangle KDC$ 3. 6   4. 30
5. Corresponding parts of congruent triangles are congruent.

6. 1. M is the midpoint of $\overline{PT}$ and $\overline{RS}$. (Given)
   2. $\overline{PM} \cong \overline{TM}$; $\overline{RM} \cong \overline{SM}$ (Definition of midpoint)
   3. $\angle PMR \cong \angle TMS$ (Vert. ⊿ are $\cong$.)
   4. $\triangle PMR \cong \triangle TMS$ (SAS Postulate)
   5. $\angle R \cong \angle S$ (Corr. parts of $\cong$ ⧄ are $\cong$.)

CHAPTER 5

PAGE 162
1. parallel   2. congruent
3. parallelogram   4. can   5. Yes
6. Yes   7. Yes   8. No   9. Yes
10. No

PAGE 170
1. always   2. sometimes
3. sometimes   4. never
5. never   6. always
7. sometimes   8. always
9. never   10. sometimes

PAGE 182
1. D 2. DF 3. 11   4. 1
5. $<$ 6. $>$ 7. $=$ 8. 18

CHAPTER 6

PAGE 202
1. $\frac{3}{4}$ 2. No   3. Yes   4. $\frac{5}{x}$
5. $\frac{20}{3}$ (or $6\frac{2}{3}$)   6. True   7. False
8. True   9. True   10. True

PAGE 214
1. AA Postulate   2. BC 3. AD
4. EC; DB 5. sometimes
6. always   7. sometimes   8. always

CHAPTER 7

PAGE 249
1. $4\sqrt{2}$ 2. $7\sqrt{2}$ 3. 12
4. 10   5. $6\sqrt{2}$ 6. RX
7. $(ST)^2$ 8. $\sqrt{55}$

PAGE 261
1. $\frac{7}{15}$ 2. $\frac{7}{\sqrt{274}}$ $\left(\text{or } \frac{7\sqrt{274}}{274}\right)$

3. $\frac{15}{7}$ 4. $\frac{7}{\sqrt{274}}$ $\left(\text{or } \frac{7\sqrt{274}}{274}\right)$

5. 25   6. 5.1   7. 13   8. 18
9. 26   10. 23 cm

CHAPTER 8

PAGE 288
1. **a.** A circle is the set of points in a plane that are a given distance from a given point in the plane.   **b.** A secant of a circle is a line that contains a chord of the circle.   **c.** A chord of a circle is a segment whose endpoints lie on the circle.   **d.** A line tangent to a circle is a line that lies in the plane of the circle and intersects the circle in exactly one point.

2.

3. k 4. tangent to $\odot O$ 5. No
6. 330   7. A tangent to a circle is perpendicular to the radius drawn to the point of tangency. (Theorem 8-2)
8. In the same circle or in congruent circles, if two minor arcs are congruent, their central angles are congruent. (Theorem 8-5)   9. 8 cm

10. 1. $\overline{ZW} \perp \overline{XY}$ (Given)
    2. $\overline{ZW}$ bisects $\overline{XY}$. (A diameter that is ⊥ to a chord bisects the chord and its two arcs.)
    3. $\overline{XT} \cong \overline{YT}$ (Definition of bisect)
    4. $\angle XTW$ and $\angle YTW$ are rt. ∡. (Definition of ⊥ lines)
    5. $\triangle XTW$ and $\triangle YTW$ are rt. ▲. (Definition of rt. △)
    6. $\overline{TW} \cong \overline{TW}$ (Congruence of segments is reflexive.)
    7. $\triangle XTW \cong \triangle YTW$ (LL Theorem)
    8. $\overline{XW} \cong \overline{YW}$ (Corr. parts of ≅ ▲ are ≅.)

PAGE 302
1. 25   2. 60   3. 90   4. 65
5. 4   6. 5; 8   7. 30   8. 70
9. 12   10. 4

11. Given: A circle with inscribed ∡ BAC and BDC
    Prove: $\angle BAC \cong \angle BDC$

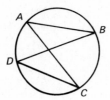

Proof:
1. $m\angle BAC = \frac{1}{2}m \widehat{BC}$;
   $m\angle BDC = \frac{1}{2}m \widehat{BC}$ (The measure of an inscribed $\angle$ = half the measure of the intercepted arc.)
2. $m\angle BAC = m \angle BDC$ (Substitution principle)
3. $\angle BAC \cong \angle BDC$ (Definition of ≅ ∡)

12. 1. $m \widehat{RX} = 100$ (Given)
    2. $m \angle RSX = \frac{1}{2}m \widehat{RX}$ (The measure of an inscribed $\angle$ = half the measure of the intercepted arc.)

3. $m \angle RSX = 50$ (Substitution principle)
4. $m \angle T = 50$ (Given)
5. $m \angle T = m \angle RSX$ (Substitution principle)
6. $\angle T \cong \angle RSX$ (Definition of ≅ ∡)
7. $\overline{RT}$ is a tangent segment. (Given)
8. $m \angle TRS = \frac{1}{2}m \widehat{RS}$ (When a secant ray and a tangent ray are drawn from a point on a ⊙, the measure of the $\angle$ formed = half the measure of the intercepted arc.)
9. $m \angle SXR = \frac{1}{2}m \widehat{RS}$ (Same as Step 2)
10. $m \angle TRS = m \angle SXR$ (Substitution principle)
11. $\angle TRS \cong \angle SXR$ (Definition of ≅ ∡)
12. $\triangle RST \sim \triangle XRS$ (AA Postulate)

CHAPTER 9

PAGE 321
1. False   2. True   3. True
4. True   5. False   6. False
7. 40   8. $17\frac{1}{2}$ 9. 108
10. 22   11. $9\sqrt{3}$ 12. $24\sqrt{3}$
13. 24 cm²   14. $\frac{27}{2}\sqrt{3}$ cm²

PAGE 328
1. 12π 2. 36π 3. 2π
4. 10π 5. 6π 6. 30π
7. 25π 8. 14π 9. 9:25
10. 200

PAGE 338
1. 4   2. altitude   3. slant height
4. base   5. lateral   6. 1:2
7. 144 cm²; 216 cm²; 216 cm³
8. 128π cm³   9. 80π cm²
10. $8\sqrt{13}\pi$ cm²

PAGE 372

1.

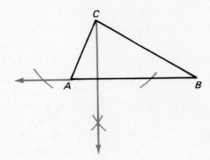

5.

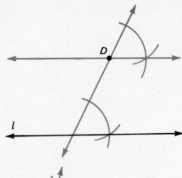

6.

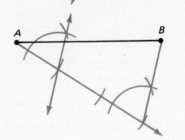

2.

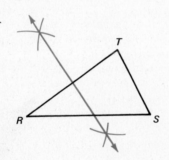

3.

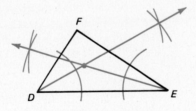

4.

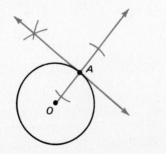

PAGE 384

1. The locus is a circle with center A and radius d units. 2. The locus is a sphere with center E and radius 5 cm. 3. The locus is a plane parallel to and midway between the given planes. 4. The locus is the pair of lines which bisect the vertical angles formed by the intersecting lines. 5. The locus is a cylindrical surface with radius k units and line l as axis. 6. The locus is the line which is the perpendicular bisector of $\overline{RS}$. 7. The locus is a line which contains the center of the circumscribed circle, and is perpendicular to the plane of the triangle. 8. The locus is a line which contains the center of the inscribed circle, and is perpendicular to the plane of the triangle. 9. The locus of points 2 cm from X is a circle with center X and radius 2 cm. The locus of points 5 cm from Y is a circle with center Y and radius 5 cm. *Possibility 1:* If $3 < XY < 7$ the locus is the pair of points in which $\odot X$ and $\odot Y$ intersect. *Possibility 2:* If $XY = 7$, the locus is the point of tangency for $\odot X$ and $\odot Y$. *Possibility 3:* If $XY < 2$ or $XY > 7$, the locus is $\varnothing$. 10. Yes

CHAPTER 11

PAGE 397
1. $(-3, 4)$ 2. $(0, 0)$
3. $(1, -2)$ 4. $(3, 2)$
5. $x = -3$ 6. $y = 4$ 7. $y = 0$
8. $x = 0$ 9. $2\sqrt{5}$ 10. No

11.

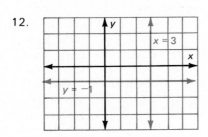

12.

In Exercises 10 and 11, answers may vary. 10. $x - 2y = 15$
11. $y - 2 = \frac{1}{8}(x - 1)$ 12. $(-2, 6)$

PAGE 419
1. b 2. $(-a, 0)$ and $(-a, b)$
3. $(2a, 0)$ and $(a, a\sqrt{3})$, or $(2a, 0)$ and $(a, -a\sqrt{3})$ 4. $(b, a + c)$ 5. The slope of $\overline{EF}$ = the slope of $\overline{GH} = \frac{1}{2}$; the slope of $\overline{FG}$ = the slope of $\overline{EH} = -2$. Since $\overline{EF} \parallel \overline{GH}$ and $\overline{FG} \parallel \overline{EH}$, quad. $EFGH$ is a parallelogram. $\overline{EF} \perp \overline{FG}$ and $\overline{EF} \perp \overline{EH}$; also $\overline{GH} \perp \overline{FG}$, and $\overline{GH} \perp \overline{EH}$, so $\square EFGH$ is a parallelogram with four rt. $\angle$. Then by definition $\square EFGH$ is a rect. 6. Let three consecutive vertices of the parallelogram be $A(b, c)$, $B(0, 0)$ and $C(a, 0)$ with a, b, and $c > 0$. Then the fourth vertex is $D(a + b, c)$. By the distance formula, $AB = CD = \sqrt{b^2 + c^2}$, $BC = AD = a$, $AC = \sqrt{(b - a)^2 + c^2}$, and $BD = \sqrt{(a + b)^2 + c^2}$. Then $(AB)^2 + (BC)^2 + (CD)^2 + (AD)^2 = (b^2 + c^2) + a^2 + (b^2 + c^2) + a^2 = 2(a^2 + b^2 + c^2)$. $(AC)^2 + (BD)^2 = [(b - a)^2 + c^2] + [(a + b)^2 + c^2] = 2(a^2 + b^2 + c^2)$. Hence $(AB)^2 + (BC)^2 + (CD)^2 + (AD)^2 = (AC)^2 + (BD)^2$.

PAGE 410
1. $(-3, 3)$ 2. $\left(\dfrac{a + 3}{2}, \dfrac{b - 3}{2}\right)$
3. $(-12, 7)$ 4. $(2s + 1, 2s + 1)$
5. $\frac{9}{2}$ 6. 0 7. $\overline{AB} \parallel \overline{CD}$; $\overline{AD} \parallel \overline{BC}$; $\overline{AB} \perp \overline{BC}$; $\overline{AB} \perp \overline{AD}$; $\overline{CD} \perp \overline{BC}$; $\overline{CD} \perp \overline{AD}$

8.

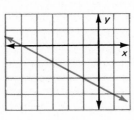

9.

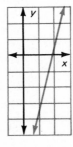

CHAPTER 12

PAGE 441
1. R' 2. $\overline{RT}$ 3. $\angle R'T'S'$
4. Yes 5. Yes
6. image; preimage 7. Q 8. S
9. P 10. $\overline{QP}$ 11. $\overline{SQ}$ 12. O

PAGES 462–463
1. DXF 2. FXD 3. X
4. $(2, 2)$ 5. $(4, 8)$ 6. $(-2, 3)$
7. $(2, 2)$ 8. $(1, -2)$
9. $(-2, 4)$ 10. $(2, -4)$
11. $(-3, -9)$ 12. $(3, 6)$
13. $(2, 1)$ 14. reflections; reflections

GLOSSARY

acute angle: An angle whose measure is less than 90. (p. 45)

acute triangle: A triangle with three acute angles (p. 97)

adjacent angles: Two angles in a plane that have a common side but have no interior points in common. (p. 38)

alternate exterior angles: One pair in the diagram below is ∠1 and ∠8; the other pair is ∠2 and ∠7. (p. 78)

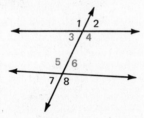

alternate interior angles: One pair in the diagram above is ∠3 and ∠6; the other pair is ∠4 and ∠5. (p. 78)

altitude to a base of a rectangle or a parallelogram: Any perpendicular segment whose endpoints lie on the lines containing the base and the side opposite the base. (p. 310)

altitude of a circular cylinder: *See* circular cylinder.

altitude of a prism: A segment perpendicular to the planes of the bases and having an endpoint in each plane. (p. 330)

altitude of a pyramid: *See* pyramid.

altitude of a right circular cone: *See* right circular cone.

altitude of a trapezoid: A perpendicular segment from any point in one base to a point in the line containing the other base. (p. 316)

altitude of a triangle: The segment drawn from any vertex of a triangle perpendicular to the line that contains the opposite side. (p. 144)

angle: The union of two noncollinear rays that have the same endpoint. (p. 37)

angle of a triangle: *See* triangle.

angle of depression: The acute angle through which a telescope must be depressed from the horizontal to sight on an object. (p. 258)

angle of elevation: The acute angle through which a telescope must be elevated from the horizontal to sight on an object. (p. 258)

apothem of a regular polygon: The distance from the center of the polygon to a side. (p. 319)

arc of a chord: The minor arc cut off by the chord. (p. 283)

area of a circle: The limit of the areas of the inscribed regular polygons. (p. 322)

auxiliary line: A line added to a figure in order to prove a theorem. (p. 92)

axiom: A basic assumption in mathematics. (p. 5)

axis of a circular cylinder: *See* circular cylinder.

axis of a right circular cone: *See* right circular cone.

base angles of an isosceles triangle: The two angles that include the base of an isosceles triangle. (p. 143)

base of a circular cylinder: *See* circular cylinder.

base of a prism: *See* prism.

base of a pyramid: *See* pyramid.

base of a rectangle or parallelogram: Any side of a rectangle or parallelogram can be considered as a base. (p. 310)

base of a right circular cone: *See* right circular cone.

base of an isosceles triangle: The side of an isosceles triangle other than the legs. (p. 143)

bases of a trapezoid: The parallel sides of a trapezoid. (p. 167)

between: Point B, on $\overleftrightarrow{AC}$, is said to lie between points A and C if and only if $AB + BC = AC$. We express this: $\overline{ABC}$. (p. 10)

bisector of a segment: A line, segment, ray, or plane that intersects a segment at its midpoint bisects the segment and is a bisector of the segment. (p. 10)

bisector of an angle: $\overrightarrow{AX}$ is the bisector of $\angle BAC$ if X lies in the interior of $\angle BAC$ and $\angle BAX \cong \angle XAC$. (p. 47)

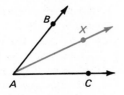

bisector of an arc: Any line or segment that contains the midpoint of the arc. (p. 284)

center of a circle: *See* circle.

center of a regular polygon: The common center of its inscribed and circumscribed circles. (p. 319)

center of an arc: The center of the circle that includes the arc as a subset. (p. 284)

central angle of a circle: An angle whose vertex is the center of the circle. (p. 280)

central angle of a regular polygon: An angle formed by two radii drawn to consecutive vertices. (p. 319)

chord of a circle: A segment whose endpoints lie on the circle. (p. 272)

circle: The set of points in a plane that are a given distance from a given point in the plane. The given point is called the *center*. (p. 271)

circular cylinder: The cylinders shown are *circular cylinders*. The circular regions are *bases* and the segment $\overline{OO'}$ is the *axis* of each cylinder. An *altitude* is any perpendicular segment from a point in one base to a point in the plane of the other base. The length of an altitude is the *height* of the cylinder. A cylinder such as B, in which the axis is also an altitude, is a *right circular cylinder*. (p. 335)

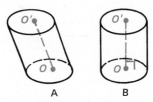

circumference of a circle: The limit of the perimeters of the inscribed regular polygons. (p. 322)

circumscribed circle: *See* inscribed polygon.

circumscribed polygon: A polygon is *circumscribed about a circle* and the circle is *inscribed in the polygon* when each side of the polygon is tangent to the circle. (p. 276)

collinear points: A set of points that lie on one line. (p. 2)

common tangent: A line that is tangent to each of two coplanar circles. A common *internal* tangent intersects the segment that joins the centers of the circles. A common *external* tangent does not intersect the segment that joins the centers. (p. 276)

complementary angles: Two angles whose measures have the sum 90. (p. 46)

concentric circles: Two or more coplanar circles with the same center. (p. 272)

conclusion: *See* conditional.

conditional: A compound statement that can be written in the form *If p, then q,* where *p* and *q* represent statements. *p* is the *hypothesis;* it states what is given. *q* is the *conclusion;* it states what we are to prove. (p. 22)

cone: *See* right circular cone.

congruence mapping: When a mapping is such that a figure and its image are congruent, we call the mapping a *congruence mapping,* or an *isometry.* (p. 429)

congruent angles: Angles that have equal measures. (p. 41)

congruent arcs: Arcs that have equal measures. (p. 281)

congruent circles: Circles that have congruent radii. (p. 281)

congruent segments: Segments with equal lengths. (p. 10)

congruent triangles: When the following six statements are true for $\triangle ABC$ and $\triangle DEF$, the triangles are said to be congruent: (p. 118)

$$\angle A \cong \angle D \qquad \overline{AB} \cong \overline{DE}$$
$$\angle B \cong \angle E \qquad \overline{BC} \cong \overline{EF}$$
$$\angle C \cong \angle F \qquad \overline{AC} \cong \overline{DF}$$

consecutive sides of a polygon: Two sides of a polygon that intersect. (p. 103)

consecutive vertices of a polygon: The endpoints of one side of a polygon. (p. 103)

constructing a geometric figure: In the construction of a geometric figure, the straightedge is used only to draw lines, rays, or segments, and the compass is used only to draw circles or arcs of circles. (p. 349)

contraction: *See* dilation.

converse of a conditional: The *converse* of the conditional *If p, then q* is the conditional *If q, then p.* (p. 22)

convex polygon: A polygon such that no line containing a side of the polygon will contain a point in the interior of the polygon. (p. 102)

coordinate of a point: On the number line, the number paired with a point. (p. 13)

coordinate system: A one-to-one correspondence between the set of points in a plane and the set of ordered pairs of real numbers. (p. 393)

coplanar points: A set of points that lie in one plane. (p. 2)

corollary: A statement which can be proved easily by applying a theorem. (p. 98)

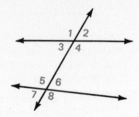

corresponding angles: There are four pairs of corresponding angles in the figure. The pairs are $\angle 1$ and $\angle 5$, $\angle 2$ and $\angle 6$, $\angle 4$ and $\angle 8$, $\angle 3$ and $\angle 7$. (p. 78)

corresponding angles of two triangles: In the correspondence $\triangle ABC \leftrightarrow \triangle DEF$, the corresponding angles are $\angle A$ and $\angle D$, $\angle B$ and $\angle E$, $\angle C$ and $\angle F$. (p. 118)

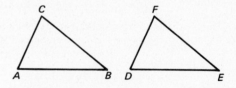

corresponding sides of two triangles: In the correspondence $\triangle ABC \leftrightarrow \triangle DEF$, the corresponding sides are $\overline{AB}$ and $\overline{DE}$, $\overline{BC}$ and $\overline{EF}$, $\overline{AC}$ and $\overline{DF}$. (p. 118)

cosine of an acute angle of a right triangle: In a right triangle, the ratio of the length of the leg adjacent to the acute angle to the length of the hypotenuse. (p. 254)

cube: A rectangular solid in which all edges are congruent. (p. 330)

deductive reasoning: The process of reasoning from accepted facts to a conclusion. (p. 18)

demonstration of a theorem: A demonstration of a theorem consists of five parts: *Statement, Figure, Given* or *Hypothesis, Prove* or *Conclusion,* and *Proof.* (p. 63)

diagonal of a polygon: A segment joining two nonconsecutive vertices of a polygon. (p. 103)

diagonal of a rectangular solid: *See* rectangular solid.

diameter: A chord that contains the center of a circle; also, the length of that chord. (p. 272)

dihedral angle: The union of a line and two noncoplanar half-planes that have the line as edge. Each of the half-planes is a *face* of the dihedral angle. (p. 47)

dilation: A *dilation* with center O and scale factor k $(k > 0)$ is a mapping such that:
(1) If P is different from O, then P' lies on $\overrightarrow{OP}$ and $OP' = k(OP)$.
(2) If P is the point O, then P' is the same point as P.
If $k > 1$, the dilation is called an *expansion*. If $0 < k < 1$, the dilation is a *contraction*. If $k = 1$, the dilation is the identity mapping. (p. 460)

distance from a point to a line: The length of the segment drawn perpendicular to the line from the point. (p. 285)

edge of a rectangular solid: *See* rectangular solid.

endpoint of a ray: *See* ray.

endpoint of a segment: *See* segment.

equiangular triangle: A triangle with all angles congruent. (p. 97)

equilateral triangle: A triangle with all sides congruent. (p. 97)

expansion: *See* dilation.

extended proportion: An extended proportion is used to show that three or more ratios are equal. For example:

$$\frac{a}{b} = \frac{c}{d} = \frac{3}{5} \qquad \text{(p. 190)}$$

exterior angle of a triangle: If $\overrightarrow{BD}$ is opposite to $\overrightarrow{BA}$, then $\angle CBD$ is called an exterior angle of $\triangle ABC$. The two angles of the triangle not adjacent to $\angle CBD$, $\angle A$ and $\angle C$, are called *remote interior angles*. (p. 97)

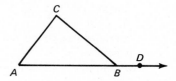

exterior angles formed by two lines and a transversal: *See* interior angles formed by two lines and a transversal.

exterior of a circle: The exterior of a circle with center P and radius r is the set of all coplanar points whose distance from P is greater than r. (p. 271)

exterior of a triangle: *See* triangle.

exterior of an angle: *See* interior of an angle.

exterior sides of two adjacent angles: The sides not common to the angles. (p. 38)

face of a dihedral angle: *See* dihedral angle.

face of a prism: *See* prism.

face of a rectangular solid: *See* rectangular solid.

geometric mean: If a, b, and x are positive numbers and $\dfrac{a}{x} = \dfrac{x}{b}$, then x is called the *geometric mean* between a and b. (p. 233)

graph of a number: On the number line, the point paired with the number. (p. 13)

half-plane: In the diagram, line j separates plane M into three subsets. One subset is line j. Another subset, shown in gray, contains point A. That subset is called a half-plane. The third subset, shown in color, is also a half-plane. Points A and B lie on opposite sides of line j and lie in opposite half-planes. Line j is the edge of each half-plane, but does not lie in either half-plane. (p. 38)

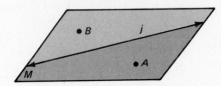

half-turn: A *half-turn* about point O maps every point P into a point P' such that:
(1) If P is different from O, then O is the midpoint of $\overline{PP'}$.
(2) If P is the point O, then P' is the same point as P. (p. 438)

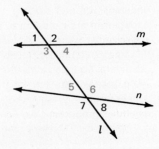

hypotenuse of a right triangle: The side opposite the right angle. (p. 125)

hypothesis: *See* conditional.

identity mapping: A mapping under which every point is mapped into itself. (p. 443)

identity self-congruence: *See* self-congruence.

if-then statement: A conditional stated in the form *If p, then q*, where p and q represent statements. (p. 22)

image: Under the mapping $ABC \rightarrow MXD$, $\triangle MXD$ is called the image of $\triangle ABC$. $\triangle ABC$ is the *preimage* of $\triangle MXD$. (p. 428)

indirect proof: A form of proof in which you suppose that the negation of what you wish to prove is true, and then reason logically until you encounter a contradiction of a known fact. (p. 84)

inductive thinking: *Induction* is the process of observing individual cases and then stating a general principle suggested by them. (p. 18)

inscribed angle: An angle whose vertex lies on a circle and whose sides contain chords of the circle. (p. 289)

inscribed circle: *See* circumscribed polygon.

inscribed polygon: A polygon is said to be *inscribed in a circle*, and the circle is *circumscribed about the polygon*, when each vertex of the polygon lies on the circle. (p. 272)

intercepted arc: In each figure below, the angles intercept the arcs shown in red. Note that some angles intercept two arcs. (p. 289)

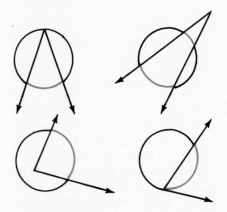

interior angles formed by two lines and a transversal: With respect to lines m and n, cut by transversal l, angles 3, 4, 5, and 6 are *interior angles*. Angles 1, 2, 7, and 8 are *exterior angles*. (p. 78)

interior of a circle: The interior of a circle with center *P* and radius *r* is the set of all coplanar points whose distance from *P* is less than *r*. (p. 271)

interior of a triangle: *See* triangle.

interior of an angle: The *interior* of ∠*RST* is the intersection of the half-plane that contains *R* and has edge $\overleftrightarrow{ST}$ with the half-plane that contains *T* and has edge $\overleftrightarrow{SR}$. Points *P* and *V*, which lie neither on the angle nor in the interior, lie in the *exterior* of ∠*RST*. (p. 38)

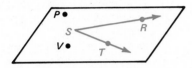

intersecting planes: When the intersection of two planes contains points, we say that the planes *intersect*. (p. 2)

isometry: *See* congruence mapping.

isosceles trapezoid: A trapezoid with congruent legs. (p. 167)

isosceles triangle: A triangle with at least two sides congruent. (p. 97)

lateral area of a prism: The sum of the areas of its lateral faces. (p. 330)

legs of a right triangle: The two sides other than the hypotenuse. (p. 125)

legs of a trapezoid: The nonparallel sides of a trapezoid. (p. 167)

legs of an isosceles triangle: The two congruent sides of an isosceles triangle. (p. 143)

line of symmetry: When reflection of a figure in some line leads to a self-congruence, the line is called a *line of symmetry* for the figure. (p. 443)

line parallel to a plane: If a line and a plane have no point in common, we say the line is parallel to the plane. (p. 78)

line perpendicular to a plane: A line is perpendicular to a plane if it is perpendicular to every line that lies in the plane and intersects the line. (p. 56)

locus: The set of all points, and only those points, that satisfy a given condition. (p. 374)

major arc of a circle: *See* minor arc of a circle.

measure of a major arc: The difference between 360 and the measure of the minor arc. (p. 280)

measure of a minor arc: The measure of the central angle that intercepts the arc. (p. 280)

measure of an angle: A unique number between 0 and 180 paired with the angle. (p. 42)

median of a trapezoid: The segment joining the midpoints of the legs of the trapezoid. (p. 167)

median of a triangle: The segment that joins a vertex of the triangle and the midpoint of the opposite side. (p. 144)

midpoint of a segment: Point *M* is the midpoint of $\overline{RS}$ if *M* lies on $\overline{RS}$ and *RM* = *MS*. (p. 10)

midpoint of an arc: If $\overarc{AM} \cong \overarc{MB}$, point *M* is called the midpoint of $\overarc{AB}$. (p. 284)

minor arc of a circle: The union of two points on the circle and all the points of the circle that lie in the interior of the central angle whose sides contain the two points. The part of ⊙*O* shown in red is *minor arc AB* ($\overarc{AB}$ or $\overarc{AXB}$). The part of ⊙*O* shown in black is *major arc AYB* ($\overarc{AYB}$). To name a major arc, three letters must be used. (p. 280)

oblique prism: *See* prism.

obtuse angle: An angle whose measure is greater than 90. (p. 46)

obtuse triangle: A triangle with an obtuse angle. (p. 97)

one and only one: A phrase meaning "exactly one." (p. 6)

opposite rays: $\overrightarrow{SR}$ and $\overrightarrow{ST}$ are called opposite rays if S lies on $\overleftrightarrow{RT}$ between R and T. (p. 10)

ordered pair of numbers: A pair of numbers is an ordered pair when the order in which they are named has significance. (p. 391)

origin: On the number line, the point that is matched with zero. (p. 13)

parallel lines: Lines that lie in the same plane and have no point in common. (p. 77)

parallel planes: When the intersection of two planes is the empty set, we say that the planes are parallel. (p. 2)

parallelogram: A quadrilateral in which both pairs of opposite sides are parallel. (p. 155)

perimeter of a polygon: The sum of the lengths of the sides of the polygon. (p. 198)

perpendicular bisector: A line that is perpendicular to a segment and bisects the segment. (p. 56)

perpendicular lines: Two lines that form right angles. (p. 54)

point of symmetry: Whenever a figure is mapped, under a half-turn about some point O, into itself, then O is called a *point of symmetry* for the figure. (p. 444)

point of tangency: The point where a circle and a line tangent to the circle intersect. (p. 275)

polygon: The union of three or more coplanar segments called sides such that:
1. No two segments with a common endpoint are collinear.
2. Each segment intersects exactly two other segments, but only in endpoints. (p. 101)

polygonal region: The union of a polygon and its interior. (p. 309)

postulate: A basic assumption in mathematics. (p. 5)

preimage: *See* image.

prism: The solids pictured are *prisms*. In each, the bounding plane surfaces are called *faces*. The shaded faces are *bases* and the remaining faces are *lateral faces*. Bases lie in parallel planes and are congruent polygons. Lateral faces are parallelograms intersecting in parallel segments called *lateral edges*. Prism A, in which all lateral faces are rectangles, is a right *prism*. Prism B is an *oblique prism*. (p. 330)

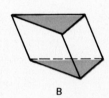

A   B

proportion: A sentence of the form $\dfrac{a}{b} = \dfrac{c}{d}$. (p. 190)

pyramid: The *pyramid* shown has polygon *ABCDE* as *base* and *vertex V*. The five triangular faces having *V* in common are *lateral faces*. The segments in which lateral faces intersect are *lateral edges*. The segment from *V* perpendicular to the base is the *altitude* and its length is the *height* of the pyramid. In a *regular pyramid*, the base is a regular polygon and all lateral edges are congruent.

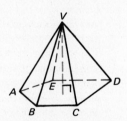

A regular pyramid has these properties:
1) the altitude meets the base at the center of the bounding polygon; 2) all lateral faces are congruent isosceles triangles. In each isosceles triangle, the altitude from the vertex is a *slant height*. (p. 333)

Diagonal: A segment whose endpoints are two vertices which do not lie in the same face. $\overline{AG}$ is a diagonal. (p. 246)

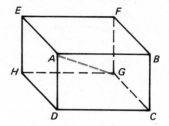

radical: An indicated root of a number. The symbol $\sqrt{}$ means the positive square root. The number appearing under the radical sign is called the *radicand*. (p. 234)

radicand: *See* radical.

radius of a circle: A segment that joins the center of a circle to a point on the circle; also, the length of that segment. (p. 272)

radius of a regular polygon: The distance from the center of the polygon to a vertex. (p. 319)

ratio: The *ratio* of k to l ($l \neq 0$) is the number $\dfrac{k}{l}$. (p. 189)

ray: Ray *AB,* denoted by $\overrightarrow{AB}$, is the union of $\overline{AB}$ and the set of points X for which it is true that B lies between A and X. Notice that the endpoint of $\overrightarrow{AB}$, point A, is the point named first. (p. 10)

rectangle: A parallelogram with four right angles. (p. 163)

rectangular solid: The figure pictured below is a rectangular solid. The following vocabulary is used when we speak of a rectangular solid.

Face: A rectangular solid has six faces. Each face is bounded by a rectangle. Rectangle *ABCD* bounds one face.
Edge: The segment formed by the intersection of two faces. $\overline{AB}$ is an edge.
Vertex: The intersection of two edges. Point *E* is a vertex.

reflection in a line: A *reflection* in the line *j* maps every point *P* into a point *P'* such that:
(1) If *P* does not lie on *j*, then *j* is the perpendicular bisector of $\overline{PP'}$.
(2) If *P* lies on *j*, then *P'* is the same point as *P*. (p. 432)

regular polygon: A convex polygon with all sides congruent and all angles congruent. (p. 103)

regular pyramid: *See* pyramid.

remote interior angles of a triangle: *See* exterior angle of a triangle.

rhombus: A parallelogram with four congruent sides. (p. 163)

right angle: An angle whose measure is 90. (p. 46)

right circular cone: In the diagram the *right circular cone* has *axis* $\overline{TO}$ perpendicular to the circular *base* at its center *O*. The axis is also the *altitude*. All segments that join the vertex *T* to a point on the circle that bounds the base are *slant heights* and are congruent. (p. 336)

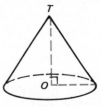

right circular cylinder: *See* circular cylinder.

right prism: *See* prism.

right triangle: A triangle with a right angle. (p. 97)

rotation: A *rotation* about point O through $\alpha°$ maps every point P into an image point P' such that:
  (1) If P is different from O, then $OP' = OP$ and $m \angle P'OP = \alpha$.
  (2) If P is the point O, then P' is the same point as P. (p. 452)

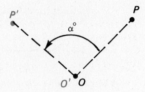

scalene triangle: A triangle with no two sides congruent. (p. 97)

secant of a circle: A line that contains a chord. (p. 272)

secant ray: *See* tangent ray.

secant segment: If point P lies in the exterior of $\odot O$, and $\overleftrightarrow{PD}$ intersects the circle at C and D, $\overline{PD}$ is a secant segment and $\overline{PC}$ is the *external segment* of $\overline{PD}$. (p. 298)

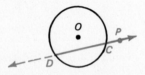

sector of a circle: A region bounded by two radii and an arc of the circle. (p. 326)

segment of a circle: A region bounded by an arc of a circle and the chord of that arc. (p. 326)

segment: Given any two points R and S, segment RS is the set of points consisting of R and S and all points that lie between R and S. Segment RS is denoted by $\overline{RS}$. Points R and S are the endpoints of $\overline{RS}$. (p. 10).

segments divided proportionally: Two segments $\overline{AB}$ and $\overline{CD}$ are said to be *divided proportionally* if points Y and Z are on $\overline{AB}$ and $\overline{CD}$, respectively, so that $\dfrac{AY}{YB} = \dfrac{CZ}{ZD}$. (p. 209)

self-congruence: A congruence in which a figure is congruent to itself. A self-congruence of the following type is called an *identity self-congruence:* For any triangle ABC, $\triangle ABC \cong \triangle ABC$. If $\overline{AB} \cong \overline{BC}$, $\triangle ABC$ has a second *self-congruence* in addition to the identity self-congruence: $\triangle ABC \cong \triangle CBA$. (p. 443)

semicircle: The union of the endpoints of a diameter and all points of the circle lying on one side of the diameter. (p. 280)

side of a triangle: *See* triangle.

sides of an angle: The two rays that make up an angle. (p. 37)

similar polygons: Two polygons are said to be similar if and only if there is a one-to-one correspondence between their vertices such that:

  1. Corresponding angles are congruent.
  2. Lengths of corresponding sides are in proportion. (p. 196)

sine of an acute angle of a right triangle: In a right triangle, the ratio of the length of the leg opposite the acute angle to the length of the hypotenuse. (p. 254)

skew lines: Lines that do not lie in any one plane. (p. 77)

slant height of a right circular cone: *See* right circular cone.

slant height of a pyramid: *See* pyramid.

slope of a line: The slope m of a line passing through any two points (x_1, y_1) and (x_2, y_2) where $x_1 \neq x_2$ is defined as follows:

$$m = \frac{y_2 - y_1}{x_2 - x_1} \qquad \text{(p. 401)}$$

space: The set of all points. (p. 2)

sphere: The set of points a given distance from a given point. (p. 272)

square: A rectangle with four congruent sides. (p. 164)

supplementary angles: Two angles whose measures have the sum 180. (p. 46)

tangent circles: When two coplanar circles are tangent to one line at one point, the circles are tangent to each other. They are *externally* tangent if each circle, except for the point of tangency, lies in the exterior of the other, and *internally* tangent if one circle, except for the point of tangency, lies in the interior of the other. (p. 276)

tangent of an acute angle of a right triangle: In a right triangle, the ratio of the length of the leg opposite the acute angle to the length of the leg adjacent to the acute angle. (p. 250)

tangent ray: In the figure, $\overrightarrow{RS}$ is called a *tangent ray*. $\overrightarrow{TW}$ and $\overrightarrow{UV}$ are called *secant rays*. (p. 291)

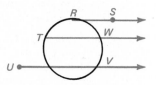

tangent segment: If $\overleftrightarrow{AB}$ is tangent to $\odot O$ at point B, then $\overline{AB}$ is a *tangent segment* from A to $\odot O$. (p. 298)

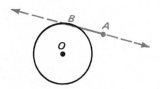

tangent to a circle: A line that lies in the plane of the circle and intersects the circle in exactly one point. (p. 275)

term of a proportion: Each of the numbers in a proportion. In the proportion $\dfrac{a}{b} = \dfrac{c}{d}$, a is the first term, b is the second term, c is the third term, and d is the fourth term. (p. 190)

theorem: A statement that is proved. (p. 5)

total area of a prism: The sum of the areas of all faces. (p. 330)

transformation: A *transformation* of the plane is a mapping such that:
(1) Each point of the plane has exactly one image.
(2) For each point of the plane there is exactly one preimage. (p. 429)

translation: A translation that maps point X into point X' maps every point P into a point P' such that:
(1) If P does not lie on $\overleftrightarrow{XX'}$, then $PXX'P'$ is a parallelogram.
(2) If P lies on $\overleftrightarrow{XX'}$, then there is a segment $\overline{YY'}$ such that both $XYY'X'$ and $PYY'P'$ are parallelograms. (p. 455)

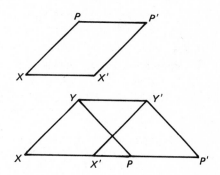

transversal: A line that intersects two or more coplanar lines in different points. (p. 78)

trapezoid: A quadrilateral with exactly one pair of parallel sides. (p. 167)

triangle: The union of three segments determined by three noncollinear points.
Each of the points R, S, and T, is a
vertex of the triangle. $\overline{RS}$, $\overline{ST}$, and $\overline{RT}$
are the *sides* of the triangle. $\angle R$, $\angle S$,
and $\angle T$ are the *angles* of the triangle.

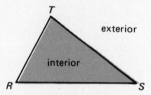

A triangle divides the plane into three
sets of points: (1) the triangle, (2) the
interior of the triangle, (3) the exterior
of the triangle. (p. 96)

vertex angle of an isosceles triangle: The
angle included by the legs of an isosceles triangle. (p. 143)

vertex of a pyramid: *See* pyramid.

vertex of a rectangular solid: *See* rectangular solid.

vertex of a triangle: *See* triangle.

vertex of an angle: The common endpoint
of the two rays that make up an angle.
(p. 37)

vertical angles: Two angles whose sides
form two pairs of opposite rays.

INDEX

Exterior angle(s)
    of a polygon, 104, 105
    of a triangle, 97, 99
    of two lines cut by a transversal, 78
Exterior sides of adjacent angles, 38
Extra for Experts, 35, 74–75,
        153, 186, 220–221,
        306–307, 343–345,
        388–389, 469–470

Face(s) of a prism, 330
Flow chart, 111–112
FOR-NEXT loop, 73

Geometric mean, 233, 235
Glide reflection, 469–470
Graph of a number, 13
Graph of an ordered pair, 391

HA Theorem, 135
Half-plane(s), 38
    edge of, 38
    opposite, 38
Half-turn, 437–438, 448
Height of cylinder, 335
HL Postulate, 127
Hypotenuse, 125, 127, 135, 153
Hypothesis, 22, 63

Identity mapping, 443
Identity self-congruence, 443
If-then statement, 22
Image, 428
Indirect proof, 84–85
Induction, 18
Inequalities, 170–179
    for one triangle, 170–173
    the triangle inequality, 176
    for two triangles, 178, 179
Inscribed angle, 289, 290
Inscribed circle, 276, 318, 319
Inscribed polygon, 272, 318
Intercepted arc, 289, 290
Interior
    of an angle, 38

    of a circle, 271
    of a triangle, 97
Interior angles
    of a polygon, 104
    of two lines cut by a transversal, 78
Intersecting secants, 294
Intersection
    of lines, 5, 6
    of loci, 378–379
    of planes, 5
Isometry, 429
Isosceles trapezoid, 167
Isosceles triangle, 97, 143–145, 206
    base, 143
    base angles, 143
    legs, 143
    vertex angle, 143

LA Theorem, 136
Lateral area
    of a prism, 330, 331
    of a regular pyramid, 333
    of a right circular cone, 336–337
    of a right circular cylinder, 335–336
    similar solids, 343–345
Lateral edge(s)
    of a prism, 330
    of a regular pyramid, 333
Lateral face(s)
    of a prism, 330
    of a regular pyramid, 333
Legs
    of an isosceles triangle, 143
    of a right triangle, 125–127, 136,
        153
    of a trapezoid, 167
Line(s), 1, 5
    auxiliary, 92
    determined by two points, 5
    intersecting, 5, 6
    parallel, 77, 80, 81, 89, 90, 92,
        160, 211, 403–404
    perpendicular, 54–56, 81, 90, 93
    perpendicular to a plane, 56
    skew, 77
Line of symmetry, 443–444
Line perpendicular to a plane, 56
LL Theorem, 126

PHOTO CREDITS

FGHIJ-RM-7987